NON-AQUEOUS
SOLVENT SYSTEMS

NON-AQUEOUS SOLVENT SYSTEMS

Edited by

T. C. WADDINGTON

School of Molecular Sciences,
University of Warwick,
Coventry, England

1965

ACADEMIC PRESS

London and New York

ACADEMIC PRESS INC. (LONDON) LTD
Berkeley Square House
Berkeley Square
London, W.1.

U.S. Edition published by
ACADEMIC PRESS INC.
111 Fifth Avenue
New York, New York 10003

Copyright © 1965 by Academic Press Inc. (London) Ltd

Library of Congress Catalog Number: 65–14294

PRINTED IN GREAT BRITAIN AT
THE UNIVERSITY PRESS
ABERDEEN

List of Contributors

H. BLOOM, *Chemistry Department, University of Tasmania, Hobart, Tasmania, Australia* (p. 353)

R. S. DRAGO, *Chemistry Department, University of Illinois, Urbana, Illinois, U.S.A.* (p. 211)

R. J. GILLESPIE, *Department of Chemistry, McMaster University, Hamilton, Ontario, Canada* (p. 117)

C. J. HALLADA, *Department of Chemistry, and Inorganic Materials Research Division of the Lawrence Radiation Laboratory, University of California, Berkeley, California, U.S.A.* (p. 1)

J. W. HASTIE, *Chemistry Department, University of Tasmania, Hobart, Tasmania, Australia* (p. 353)

H. H. HYMAN, *Chemistry Division, Argonne National Laboratory, Argonne, Illinois, U.S.A.* (p. 47)

W. L. JOLLY, *Department of Chemistry, and Inorganic Materials Research Division of the Lawrence Radiation Laboratory, University of California, Berkeley, California, U.S.A.* (p. 1)

J. J. KATZ, *Chemistry Division, Argonne National Laboratory, Argonne, Illinois, U.S.A.* (p. 47)

D. S. PAYNE, *Chemistry Department, The University, Glasgow, Scotland* (p. 301)

M. E. PEACH, *Anorganisch-Chemisches Institut der Universität, Göttingen, West Germany* (p. 83)

K. F. PURCELL, *Chemistry Department, University of Illinois, Urbana, Illinois, U.S.A.* (p. 211)

E. O. ROBINSON, *Department of Chemistry, University of Toronto, Toronto, Ontario, Canada* (p. 117)

A. G. SHARPE, *University Chemical Laboratory, Cambridge, England* (p. 285)

T. C. WADDINGTON, *School of Molecular Sciences, University of Warwick, Coventry, England* (pp. 83, 253)

Preface

The subject of non-aqueous solvent systems is now so large and the number of different solvents that have been investigated, at least partially, is so great that to give complete coverage to all the topics in the field would require a multivolumed work. In giving an account of non-aqueous solvents in one volume, the choice must be made between a superficial discussion of a wide variety of solvents, many of them differing only slightly, or a treatment in depth of a limited number. The latter course has been chosen here. Each of the chapters in the book contains an up-to-date account of a particular solvent or group of solvents by specialists in the relevant fields, who have usually had research experience in the topics they discuss.

The choice of solvent systems covered reflects both the importance of the solvent discussed and also the type of behaviour it exhibits. There are chapters on the three important non-aqueous protonic solvents, liquid ammonia, liquid hydrogen fluoride, and sulphuric acid. These solvents are of great importance, not only because of their constant utilization by chemists of all types for preparative work and physical measurements, but also because, like water they are "good" solvents, dissolving a wide range of materials both organic and inorganic. It is with these solvents too that we probably have the most detailed accumulation of quantitative physical measurements. Even here we see the effect of the overwhelming preponderance of physical measurements on aqueous systems; we have very little information about even so simple a set of thermodynamic quantities as the heats of solution of the alkali halides in systems other than water and hence no entry to the fascinating field of comparative solvation energies of simple ions in differing solvents. A chapter on the higher hydrogen halides has been included, to give examples of the behaviour of extremely acidic solvents of low dielectric constant. Here one has much less quantitative physical data than for the more well-known protonic solvents, but one has the opportunity of studying ions the generation of which would be difficult in any other solvents.

The remaining chapters of the book are devoted to a discussion of solvents and classes of solvents of the type usually referred to as aprotic. Liquid sulphur dioxide is a typical aprotic solvent. It has been extensively used by organic chemists and metallo-organic chemists as a reaction medium. However, it is only now, thanks to the work of Norris and his co-workers on the isotope exchange reactions in the solvent and to the extremely detailed and accurate measurements of Lichtin and his co-workers on conductances in the solvent, that we are beginning to understand the role this solvent plays in chemical reactions. The two chapters on the halides and oxyhalides of group V and on the halogens as solvents deal with those systems where the role of the solvent may involve halide ion donation and exchange and the evidence for this is critically discussed.

A good deal of evidence has accumulated that indicates that many solvents, particularly those with lone pairs on oxygen and nitrogen atoms, function as co-ordinating solvents without themselves undergoing autosolvolysis or without the autosolvolytic reaction being of any importance. An account of a selection of such solvents is presented in the chapter on co-ordinating solvents. Finally, there is a chapter on molten salts as solvents. Such systems, which are in themselves highly ionized and highly conducting, before the addition of solutes, require methods of investigation rather different from those employed in the study of most room-temperature solvents.

School of Molecular Sciences   T. C. WADDINGTON
University of Warwick
Coventry
England
March 1965

Contents

		Page
LIST OF CONTRIBUTORS		v
PREFACE		vii

CHAPTER 1

Liquid Ammonia

W. J. JOLLY AND C. J. HALLADA

I. Introduction	1
II. Physical Properties of Ammonia	2
A. Vapour Pressure of Solid Ammonia	2
B. Vapour Pressure of Liquid Ammonia	3
C. Heat of Fusion of Ammonia	3
D. Heat of Vapourization of Ammonia at Boiling Point	3
E. Heat Capacity of Ammonia	3
F. Thermodynamic Functions for Ammonia Gas at 25°C	4
G. Density of Liquid Ammonia	4
H. Viscosity of Liquid Ammonia	4
I. Dielectric Constant of Liquid Ammonia	5
J. Surface Tension of Liquid Ammonia	5
K. Crystal Structure	5
L. Electrical Conductivity of Liquid Ammonia	5
M. Refractive Index of Liquid Ammonia	5
N. Some Derived Constants	5
III. Physical Properties of Liquid Ammonia Solutions	6
A. Non-electrolytes	6
B. Electrolytes	6
C. Metals	10
IV. Reactions in Liquid Ammonia	19
A. Comparison of Ammonia with Other Solvents	19
B. Ionic Solvation	26
C. Acid–Base Reactions	28
D. Reactions of Metal Solutions	34
References	41

CHAPTER 2

Liquid Hydrogen Fluoride

H. H. HYMAN AND J. J. KATZ

I. Introduction	47
A. Equipment for Studying Liquid Hydrogen Fluoride	50

Page

II. Properties of Pure Liquid Hydrogen Fluoride..............   52
   A. Physical Properties......................................   52
   B. Vibronic Absorption Spectra...........................   55
   C. Structure of the Liquid................................   57
   D. Acidity...   62
III. Solutes in Liquid Hydrogen Fluoride.......................   64
   A. Metal Fluorides...   65
   B. Non-metallic, Non-acidic, Ionizing Fluorides.............   67
   C. Proton Acceptors.......................................   68
   D. Acid Solutes: Fluoride Ion Acceptors....................   72
   E. Salts in the Hydrogen Fluoride System as Solutes.........   74
   F. Solution in Hydrogen Fluoride without Ionization.........   75
IV. Solution in Anhydrous Hydrogen Fluoride of Compounds of
    Biological Importance................................   76

CHAPTER 3

The Higher Hydrogen Halides as Ionizing Solvents

M. E. Peach and T. C. Waddington

I. Introduction..   83
   A. Some Physical Properties of the Liquid Hydrogen Halides...   84
   B. Self-ionization   86
   C. Experimental Methods...................................   88
II. Solutions in the Hydrogen Halides.........................   97
   A. Acids and Bases......................................   97
   B. Solvolysis Reactions..................................   111
   C. Redox Reactions.....................................   112

CHAPTER 4

Sulphuric Acid

R. J. Gillespie and E. A. Robinson

I. Introduction...   117
   A. Bases..   118
   B. Acids..   121
   C. Non-electrolytes   122
   D. Sulphates and Hydrogen Sulphates......................   122
II. The Physical Properties of Sulphuric Acid and Its Solutions, In-
    cluding Experimental Methods of Investigation........   123
   A. Properties of Sulphuric Acid...........................   123
   B. Properties of Solutions...............................   131

Page

III. Inorganic Solutes... 162
   A. The Solutes Water and Sulphur Trioxide 162
   B. Boron.. 164
   C. Silicon.. 167
   D. Tin and Lead.. 170
   E. Nitrogen and Phosphorus............................... 172
   F. Arsenic, Antimony and Bismuth......................... 174
   G. Vanadium, Chromium and Manganese 177
   H. Sulphur, Selenium and Tellurium....................... 179
   I. Halogens.. 180
   J. Transition Metal Complexes............................ 184
   K. Chelation by the Sulphate Group....................... 186
IV. Organic Solutes.. 187
   A. Simple Bases.. 187
   B. Polybasic Compounds.................................. 188
   C. Amides and Ureas..................................... 190
   D. Esters.. 192
   E. Carboxylic Anhydrides................................. 193
   F. Ethers.. 194
   G. Nitriles... 195
   H. Carboxylic Acids...................................... 196
   I. Carbonium Ions....................................... 198
   J. Aromatic Sulphonation................................ 204
   References.. 205

CHAPTER 5

Co-ordinating Solvents

R. S. DRAGO AND K. F. PURCELL

I. Introduction.. 211
II. Criteria for Establishing Co-ordination...................... 215
   A. Ultra-violet and Visible Spectroscopy................... 215
   B. Infra-red Spectroscopy................................. 216
   C. Nuclear Magnetic Resonance Spectroscopy............... 217
   D. Cryoscopy.. 219
   E. Conductivity.. 219
III. Energetics of the Co-ordination Process..................... 220
   A. Statement of the Problem.............................. 220
   B. Evaluation of the Energy Terms........................ 222
IV. Solute Behaviour in Selected Solvents....................... 226
   A. NN-Dimethylacetamide (DMA).......................... 228
   B. N-Methylacetamide (NMA)............................. 230
   C. Dimethyl Sulphoxide (DMSO).......................... 230

Page

D. Nitromethane and Nitrobenzene (NM, NB).............. 234
E. Acetone (Ac)...................................... 237
F. Methanol and Ethanol (MeOH, EtOH) 239
G. Pyridine (Py)..................................... 241
H. Acetronitrile (Me CN)............................. 243
I. Tetramethylene Sulphone........................... 245
V. Some Generalizations (Sulpholane–TMSO$_2$).............. 247
References... 249

CHAPTER 6

Liquid Sulphur Dioxide

T. C. WADDINGTON

I. Introduction....................................... 253
II. Solubilities in Liquid Sulphur Dioxide.................. 254
III. Solvate Formation with Sulphur Dioxide................ 256
IV. Electrical Conductivity and Ionization in Liquid Sulphur Dioxide Solutions.................................... 260
V. Electrochemical Studies in Solutions in Liquid Sulphur Dioxide 264
A. Electrolysis..................................... 264
B. Electrode Potentials............................. 264
VI. Chemical Reactions in Liquid Sulphur Dioxide........... 266
A. Solvolysis...................................... 266
B. Metathetical Reactions........................... 267
C. Amphoteric Reactions............................ 268
D. Oxidation–Reduction Reactions 271
E. Complex Formation.............................. 272
VII. Isotopic Exchange Reactions in Liquid Sulphur Dioxide....... 273
VIII. Conclusion and Summary.............................. 280
References... 282

CHAPTER 7

The Halogens and Interhalogens as Solvents

A. G. SHARPE

I. The Halogens...................................... 286
A. Chlorine....................................... 287
B. Bromine.. 287
C. Iodine... 288
II. The Interhalogens.................................. 290
A. Compounds of Formula AB........................ 290
B. Compounds of Formula AB$_3$...................... 292

Page

C. Compounds of Formula AB_5.......................... 295
D. Compounds of Formula AB_7.......................... 297
References... 298

CHAPTER 8

Halides and Oxyhalides of Group V Elements as Solvents

D. S. PAYNE

I. Introduction.. 301
II. Experimental Methods................................... 306
   A. Qualitative Solubility Considerations................. 306
   B. The Examination of Solid Phases.................... 307
   C. The Products of Electron Transfer.................... 307
   D. Conductance Measurements........................... 307
   E. Transport Number Measurements..................... 308
   F. Potentiometric Measurements........................ 308
   G. Titrations Using Indicators......................... 309
   H. Spectrometric Measurements........................ 309
   I. Viscosity Measurements.............................. 310
   J. Thermodynamic Measurements....................... 310
   K. Isotopic Exchange Reaction......................... 310
   L. Ebullioscopic and Cryoscopic Measurements.......... 310
III. Halides as Solvents.................................... 311
IV. Oxyhalides as Solvents................................ 327
V. Phosphoryl Chloride................................... 332
VI. Uses of Group V Halide and Oxyhalides as Solvents......... 348
References... 349

CHAPTER 9

Molten Salts as Solvents

H. BLOOM AND J. W. HASTIE

I. Summary... 353
II. Introduction... 354
III. The Nature of Molten Salts............................. 354
   A. Type of Entities Present............................ 355
   B. Holes and Free Volume in Ionic Melts............... 356
   C. Distribution Functions.............................. 357
   D. Nature of the Interionic Forces (Bonding) in Simple Melts.. 357
IV. Solutions of Salt and Water............................ 357
V. Solutions of Salt and Organic Compounds................ 358
   A. Solutions in an Organic Solvent..................... 358

Page

    B. Solutions of Organic Compounds in Molten Salts........... 360
  VI. Solutions of Non-metallic Elements in Molten Salts.......... 361
    A. Sulphur... 361
    B. Iodine.. 361
 VII. Solutions of Gases in Molten Salts......................... 361
    A. Simple Solutions of Gas and Salt........................ 362
    B. Complex Solutions of Gases in Molten Salts.............. 362
VIII. Solutions of Metals in Molten Salts......................... 364
    A. Introduction... 364
    B. Solutions Without Significant Interaction................. 365
    C. Solutions With Strong Solute–Solvent Interaction (i.e. Non-
       metallic Solutions)................................. 369
    D. Solutions of Metals in Salts of Another Metal—Displacement
       Solubility... 373
  IX. Solutions of Salt in Molten Salt............................. 374
    A. Molten Salt Systems with Incomplete Miscibility........... 375
    B. Molten Salt Systems with Complete Miscibility............ 377
    C. The Structure of Molten Salt Solutions................... 377
    D. Solvation and Complex Ion Formation in Molten Salt
       Mixtures.. 382
    E. Complex Ions and Reaction Kinetics..................... 382
   X. Application of Molten Salts as Solvents...................... 383
    A. Reactions Involving Organic Substances or Volatile In-
       organic Liquids in Molten Salt Solvents.............. 383
    B. Other Reactions Involving Inorganic Substances in Molten
       Salt Solvents...................................... 385
    C. Future Developments.................................. 387
    References... 387
AUTHOR INDEX.. 391
SUBJECT INDEX... 405

CHAPTER 1

Liquid Ammonia

WILLIAM L. JOLLY AND CALVIN J. HALLADA

*Department of Chemistry, and Inorganic Materials Research Division of the Lawrence
Radiation Laboratory, University of California, Berkeley, California, U.S.A.*

I. Introduction	1
II. Physical Properties of Ammonia	2
A. Vapour Pressure of Solid Ammonia	2
B. Vapour Pressure of Liquid Ammonia	3
C. Heat of Fusion of Ammonia	3
D. Heat of Vapourization of Ammonia at Boiling Point	3
E. Heat Capacity of Ammonia	3
F. Thermodynamic Functions for Ammonia Gas at 25°C	4
G. Density of Liquid Ammonia	4
H. Viscosity of Liquid Ammonia	4
I. Dielectric Constant of Liquid Ammonia	5
J. Surface Tension of Liquid Ammonia	5
K. Crystal Structure	5
L. Electrical Conductivity of Liquid Ammonia	5
M. Refractive Index of Liquid Ammonia	5
N. Some Derived Constants	5
III. Physical Properties of Liquid Ammonia Solutions	6
A. Non-electrolytes	6
B. Electrolytes	6
C. Metals	10
IV. Reactions in Liquid Ammonia	19
A. Comparison of Ammonia with Other Solvents	19
B. Ionic Solvation	26
C. Acid–Base Reactions	28
D. Reactions of Metal Solutions	34
References	41

I. INTRODUCTION

The chemistry of liquid ammonia has been studied so extensively that it cannot be adequately discussed in less than a book. In writing this chapter, we have decided not to attempt to cover all aspects of the solvent, but rather to discuss those aspects which are susceptible to quantitative treatment. We have emphasized the application of thermodynamics and kinetics to liquid ammonia chemistry. It should be recognized that this type of treatment is possible only as a result of many physical-chemical studies carried out in recent years. We hope, however, that it will be apparent that much remains to be done in the systematization of liquid ammonia chemistry.

In other books and review articles, liquid ammonia has normally been discussed in rather qualitative terms. The principal device for systematizing the chemistry has usually been analogy with aqueous chemistry. Some important literature sources are listed below. These chapters and articles are recommended as sources of information on topics not covered, or only touched on, in this chapter:

General

Chapters 3–6 in "Non-Aqueous Solvents" by Audrieth and Kleinberg (1953).

Chapter 4 in "Systematic Inorganic Chemistry" by Yost and Russell (1944).

"The Nitrogen System of Compounds" by Franklin (1935).

Chapter 2 in "Chemistry in Non-Aqueous Solvents" by Sisler (1961).

Chapter 3 in "Die Chemie in Wasserähnlichen Lösungsmitteln" by Jander (1949).

Review article: "Inorganic Reactions in Liquid Ammonia" by Fowles and Nicholls (1962).

Specific

Ammonolysis: Fernelius and Bowman (1940).

Alkali amides: Bergstrom and Fernelius (1933, 1937); Levine and Fernelius (1954).

Metal–ammonia solutions: Kraus (1953); Jolly (1959); Symons (1959); Lepoutre and Sienko (1964).

Reactions of metal–ammonia solutions: Birch (1950); Watt (1950); Birch and Smith (1958).

Chemical thermodynamics: Jolly (1956).

II. Physical Properties of Ammonia

In this section, we tabulate the important physical properties of ammonia.

A. Vapour Pressure of Solid Ammonia (Armstrong, 1953)

(Based on 0°C = 273·16°K)

T(°K)	θ(°C)	P(mm)
175	−98·16	4·85
180	−93·16	8·78
185	−88·16	15·42
190	−83·16	26·27
195	−78·16	43·57
195·46	−77·70	45·58 (triple point)

$$\log_{10}P = 9 \cdot 98379 - \frac{1627 \cdot 22}{T}$$

B. VAPOUR PRESSURE OF LIQUID AMMONIA (Armstrong, 1953)

(Based on 0°C = 273·16°K)

$T(°K)$	$θ(°C)$	$P(mm)$
195·46	−77·70	45·58 (triple point)
200	−73·16	64·92
210	−63·16	133·21
220	−53·16	253·97
230	−43·16	454·28
239·78	−33·38	760 (boiling point)
240	−33·16	768·43
250	−23·16	1237·5
260	−13·16	1914·8
270	−3·16	2857·1
280	6·84	4130·0
290	16·84	5804·2
298·16	25·00	7520·5
300	26·84	7956·6
320	46·84	14,028
340	66·84	23,089
360	86·84	35,973
380	106·84	53,597
400	126·84	77,334
405·6	132·4	85,400 (critical point)

$$\log_{10}P = 9·95028 - \frac{1473·17}{T} - 0·0038603T \text{ (for } T < 250°K)$$

C. HEAT OF FUSION OF AMMONIA (Overstreet and Giauque, 1937)

$$ΔH = 1351·6 \text{ cal mole}^{-1}.$$

D. HEAT OF VAPOURIZATION OF AMMONIA AT BOILING POINT (Overstreet and Giauque, 1937)

$$ΔH = 5581 \text{ cal mole}^{-1}.$$

E. HEAT CAPACITY OF AMMONIA (Overstreet and Giauque, 1937)

(Based on 0°C = 273·10°K and a temperature scale appreciably different from the International Temperature Scale)

$T(°K)$	C_p	$T(°K)$	C_p	$T(°K)$	C_p
20	0·368	110	6·877	200	17·58 (liq.)
30	1·033	120	7·497	210	17·75
40	1·841	130	8·102	220	17·90

$T(°\mathrm{K})$	C_p	$T(°\mathrm{K})$	C_p	$T(°\mathrm{K})$	C_p
50	2·663	140	8·699	230	18·03
60	3·474	150	9·272	240	18·12
70	4·232	160	9·846		
80	4·954	170	10·42		
90	5·612	180	11·03		
100	6·246	190	11·71 (sol.)		

F. THERMODYNAMIC FUNCTIONS FOR AMMONIA GAS AT 25°C (Rossini *et al.*, 1952)

ΔH_f°	−11·04 kcal mole^{-1}
ΔF_f°	−3·976 kcal mole^{-1}
S°	46·01 e.u.
C_p°	8·523 cal mole^{-1} deg^{-1}

G. DENSITY OF LIQUID AMMONIA (Cragoe and Harper, 1921)

$\theta(°\mathrm{C})$	Density (g/ml)	$\theta(°\mathrm{C})$	Density (g/ml)
−70	0·7253	−20	0·6650
−60	0·7138	−10	0·6520
−50	0·7020	0	0·6386
−40	0·6900	10	0·6247
−34	0·6826	20	0·6103
−33	0·6814	25	0·6028
−30	0·6776	30	0·5952

H. VISCOSITY OF LIQUID AMMONIA

$\theta(°\mathrm{C})$	Viscosity (centipoises)	$\theta(°\mathrm{C})$	Viscosity (centipoises)
−33·5	0·2543 [a]	15	0·1457, 0·1479 [c,d]
−26	0·230 [b]	20	0·1411 [d]
−10	0·183 [b]	25	0·1350, 0·1345 [c,d]
−4	0·170 [b]	30	0·138 [b]
5	0·1618 [c]	50	0·125 [b]
10	0·152 [b]		

[a] Elsey (1920)   [b] Pinevich (1948a,b)
[c] Plank and Hunt (1939)   [d] Shatenshtein *et al.* (1949a,b)

I. DIELECTRIC CONSTANT OF LIQUID AMMONIA (Grubb *et al.*, 1936)

$\theta(°C)$	Dielectric constant
-60 ± 10	26·7
-33	(23) interpolated
5	18·94
15	17·82
25	16·90
35	16·26

J. SURFACE TENSION OF LIQUID AMMONIA (Berthoud, 1918a,b; Stairs and Sienko, 1956)

$\theta(°C)$	$\gamma(erg\ cm^{-2})$
11·10	23·38
34·05	18·05
58·98	12·95

where $\theta = °C$, $\gamma = 23\cdot41 - 0\cdot3371\theta - 0\cdot000943\theta^2 (-75° < \theta < -39°)$

K. CRYSTAL STRUCTURE (Vegard and Hillesund, 1942)

Cubic, 4 molecules per unit cell.
at $-185°$, $a_o = 5\cdot2253\ kX$
$= 5\cdot2358\ Å.$
Calculated density $= 0\cdot7881\ g\ cm^{-3}.$

L. ELECTRICAL CONDUCTIVITY OF LIQUID AMMONIA (Hnizda and Kraus, 1949)

$L_o \sim 1 \times 10^{-11}\ ohm^{-1}\ cm^{-1}$ (very pure NH_3).

M. REFRACTIVE INDEX OF LIQUID AMMONIA (Franklin, 1935)

$\eta = 1\cdot325$ at $16°$ for $\lambda = 5899\ Å.$

N. SOME DERIVED CONSTANTS

Freezing point constant, $K_f = \dfrac{RT_f^2}{1000\ \Delta H_f} = 0\cdot9567.$

Boiling point constant, $K_b = \dfrac{RT_b^2}{1000\ \Delta H_v} = 0\cdot3487.$

III. PHYSICAL PROPERTIES OF LIQUID AMMONIA SOLUTIONS

A. NON-ELECTROLYTES

Liquid ammonia is an excellent solvent for many non-electrolytes that are relatively insoluble in water (see Section IVA, 1). Most research on these solutions has centred on practical problems such as the separation by extraction and crystallization of materials which are difficultly separable. We shall mention here only a few basic studies in the area of non-electrolytic solutions.

Phase studies have been performed on several hydrocarbon–liquid ammonia systems by Ishida (1957, 1958, 1959, 1960a,b) and Fenske *et al.* (1955). It was found that the experimental data for both the critical composition and the activity coefficients are best interpreted by the solubility parameter theory if it is assumed that ammonia is associated nearly to a dimer as a liquid.

Some data are available on the heats of solution for non-electrolytes in liquid ammonia. It has been observed by Schmidt *et al.* (1941) that the molar heats of solution of normal alcohols in liquid ammonia decrease from 1960 cal for methanol to -100 cal for normal butanol. Gunn and Green (1960) found that the molar heats of solution for water and methylamine are independent of concentration.

It is interesting that nitrogen (Wiebe and Tremearne, 1933), hydrogen (Ipat'ev and Teodorovich, 1932), helium and argon (Cseko and Cornides, 1960) all obey Henry's Law up to pressures of about 100 atm when dissolved in liquid ammonia. The temperature dependence of the solubility of the mixture $N_2 + 3H_2$ in liquid ammonia was studied by Lefrancois and Vaniscotte (1960). They observed that the solubility follows a third order function of the temperature (°C).

The spectra, from 2500 to 6000 Å, of solutions of several nitrophenols and nitronaphthols in liquid ammonia have been interpreted by Dykhno and Shatenshtein (1948, 1951). Comparison was made with the spectra of these same molecules in 0·005 M NaOH solutions in water. General similarities were found in the spectra of both solvent systems; however the peaks were shifted to higher wavelengths in liquid ammonia. These shifts were attributed to the formation of acid–base complexes.

B. ELECTROLYTES

Solutions of electrolytes in liquid ammonia have been subjected to extensive research. Nearly all the types of measurements which have been made with aqueous solutions of electrolytes have also been made with liquid ammonia solutions even though the handling of liquid ammonia is more difficult than that of water. It is not possible to present the results of all the work which has been carried out in determining the nature of electrolyte–liquid ammonia solutions. However, some of the more important data and conclusions will be covered.

1. *Molar Volumes*

The densities of the solutions of several alkali metal halides and ammonium halides have been measured at various temperatures and concentrations (Johnson and Martens, 1936; Kikuchi and Kudo, 1944, 1948). It was found (Johnson and Martens, 1936) that the densities vary linearly with the temperature and that the apparent molar volumes, V, are a linear function of $c^{\frac{1}{2}}$ (in moles/litre). This behaviour is entirely similar to that found in aqueous solutions.

In more recent work, Gunn and Green (1962a) have determined the apparent molar volumes of several electrolytes in liquid ammonia at 0°C. They find that plots of V against $c^{\frac{1}{2}}$ (in equivalents/litre) have almost the same shapes for several alkali metal halides, ammonium halides, and barium nitrate. Even at concentrations where considerable ion pairing would be expected, the ion additivity rule is obeyed. Using estimated association constants, Gunn and Green extrapolate their data to infinite dilution to obtain the volumes given in Table I. The table includes the volumes of the same salts in water at 25°C (Harned and Owen, 1958).

TABLE I

Some Molar Volumes at Infinite Dilution in Ammonia and Water

Salt	V^0 in NH$_3$ at 0°C (cm^3)	V^0 in H$_2$O at 25°C (cm^3)
NaCl	−38	16·4
NaI	−55	35·1
KI	−6	45·4

From the data it may be noted that

$$V^0_{\text{NaI}}(\text{NH}_3,\ 0°) - V^0_{\text{NaCl}}(\text{NH}_3,\ 0°) = 23\ \text{cm}^3$$
$$V^0_{\text{NaI}}(\text{H}_2\text{O},\ 25°) - V^0_{\text{NaCl}}(\text{H}_2\text{O},\ 25°) = 18\cdot7\ \text{cm}^3$$

thus
$$V^0_{\text{I}^-}(\text{NH}_3) - V^0_{\text{Cl}^-}(\text{NH}_3) \approx V^0_{\text{I}^-}(\text{H}_2\text{O}) - V^0_{\text{Cl}^-}(\text{H}_2\text{O})$$

and
$$V^0_{\text{KI}}(\text{NH}_3,\ 0°) - V^0_{\text{NaI}}(\text{NH}_3,\ 0°) = 9\ \text{cm}^3$$
$$V^0_{\text{KI}}(\text{H}_2\text{O},\ 25°) - V^0_{\text{NaI}}(\text{H}_2\text{O},\ 25°) = 10\cdot3\ \text{cm}^3$$

thus
$$V^0_{\text{K}^+}(\text{NH}_3) - V^0_{\text{Na}^+}(\text{NH}_3) \approx V^0_{\text{K}^+}(\text{H}_2\text{O}) - V^0_{\text{Na}^+}(\text{H}_2\text{O}).$$

Since there is no "absolute" way of finding the V^0 for any single ion, the ionic V^0 values still remain unknown. Ionic volumes obtained by assuming that $V^0_{K^+} = V^0_{Cl^-}$ have been given elsewhere (Jolly, 1959); a more detailed calculation will be given here. Using an expression similar to Hepler's (1957), one calculates a $V^0_{Na^+}$ (in ammonia at 0°C) of $-41 \cdot 5$ cm³. The expression of Couture and Laidler (1956) yields the value -34 cm³. If we take the average of these two, we calculate

$$V^0_{Na^+} = -37 \text{ cm}^3$$
$$V^0_{K^+} = -28 \text{ cm}^3$$
$$V^0_{Cl^-} = -1 \text{ cm}^3$$
$$V^0_{I^-} = +22 \text{ cm}^3.$$

2. Thermochemistry

The heats of solution of several electrolytes in liquid ammonia have been measured at 25°C and -33°C by Gunn and Green (1960). Table II gives the heats of solution of several salts in ammonia at 25°C and -33°C and in water at 25°C. The heats of solution are all for a mole ratio of solvent to solute of 500. It will be noted that the heats of solution are more negative in ammonia than in water, and are likewise more negative at 25°C than at -33°C.

TABLE II

Some Heats of Solution in Water and Ammonia (ΔH^0 in kcal/mole)

	$H_2O(25°C)$ [a]	$NH_3(25°C)$ [b]	$NH_3(-33°C)$ [b]
H_2O(liq.)	0	$-3 \cdot 32$	$-2 \cdot 81$
CH_3NH_2(liq.)	$-5 \cdot 0$	$+0 \cdot 50$	—
HgI_2	—	$(-20 \cdot 8)$	$(-20 \cdot 15)$
NaCl	$+1 \cdot 02$	$-6 \cdot 75$	$-1 \cdot 57$
KI	$+4 \cdot 95$	$-9 \cdot 44$	$-7 \cdot 89$
CsI	$+7 \cdot 9$	$-5 \cdot 27$	—
NH_4Cl	$+3 \cdot 71$	$-8 \cdot 23$	$-6 \cdot 95$
NH_4I	$+3 \cdot 3$	$-16 \cdot 10$	$-13 \cdot 37$
$Ba(NO_3)_2$	$+9 \cdot 96$	$-15 \cdot 31$	—

[a] Rossini et al. (1952)   [b] Gunn and Green (1960).

The slope obtained from a plot of the heat of solution versus $c^{\frac{1}{2}}$ for KI solutions of low concentrations is 27 kcal mole$^{-3/2}$ litre$^{1/2}$. This is almost twelve times the calculated Debye-Hückel slope and undoubtedly is the result of a high degree of ionic association in liquid ammonia. Therefore the thermal effects accompanying dilution are principally due to dissociation of the ion pairs and solvation of the resulting ions; that is, KI in liquid ammonia is analogous to most "strong" 2–2 salts in water.

3. Electrochemistry

(a) Conductance. The conductances of several salts and acids in liquid ammonia have been determined. Unfortunately, the agreement between equivalent conductances measured by different experimenters has seldom been as good as that found for aqueous solutions. Some of the better conductance data are presented in Table III. The data are not exactly self-consistent. Thus, using the data of Hnizda and Kraus (1949) at $-34°$,

$$\Lambda^0_{KBr} - \Lambda^0_{NaBr} = 32.5 = \lambda^0_{K^+} - \lambda^0_{Na^+}$$

while from the data of Monoszon and Pleskov (1931) at $-33.5°$,

$$\Lambda^0_{KNO_3} - \Lambda^0_{NaNO_3} = 39 = \lambda^0_{K^+} - \lambda^0_{Na^+}.$$

TABLE III

Conductances of Salt Solutions in Ammonia and Water

Electrolyte	$\theta(°C)$	Λ^0 in NH_3	$10^8 \, \mathring{a}$	K_{assoc}	Λ^0 in H_2O at 25°
KCl [a]	−34	348.0	6.7	1060	149.9
KBr [a]	−34	346.98	7.8	453	151.9
KI [a]	−34	345.1	6.6	183	150.4
NaBr [b]	−34	314.3	5.9	263	128.3
LiNO₃ [b]	−33.5	299			110.1
LiNO₃ [b]	−40	290			110.1
NaNO₃ [b]	−33.5	315			121.6
NaNO₃ [b]	−40	300			121.6
KNO₃ [b]	−33.5	354			145.0
KNO₃ [b]	−40	338			145.0
RbNO₃ [b]	−40	344			149.2
CsNO₃ [b]	−40	345			148.7
KNH₂ [c]	−33	343		13,700	

[a] Data are those of Hnizda and Kraus (1949). These data were recently treated by Kay (1960), using the extended form of the Onsager-Fuoss conductance theory (Fuoss and Accascina, 1959).

[b] Monoszon and Pleskov (1931).

[c] Hawes (1933).

Monoszon and Pleskov have used the transference data of Franklin and Cady (1904) to assign λ_+^0 to the alkali metal ions and λ_-^0 to the nitrate ion, but due to the lack of agreement in the nitrate and halide data, there is no advantage gained by assigning λ_-^0 values to the halide ions.

It will be noted that the association constants of the potassium halides follow the order expected from the relative sizes of the halide ions. However, it is surprising that the values for the closest distance of approach, $\mathring{a}$, of the potassium and halide ions which best fit the extended Onsager-Fuoss conductance theory are larger than they are in either water or methanol (Kay, 1960). The $\mathring{a}$ values for aqueous solutions often agree closely with the sum of the ionic radii (Fuoss and Accascina, 1959). However, this is apparently not true for the alkali metal halides in liquid ammonia.

(b) Polarography. Polarographic studies using the dropping mercury electrode have contributed much to our understanding of the nature of solutions of electrolytes in liquid ammonia, in spite of the fact that the freezing point of mercury ($-38\cdot9°C$) is very close to the boiling point of liquid ammonia ($-33\cdot4°C$). Polarograms, can indicate whether the reduction occurs in one or more steps and thereby also indicate the nature of intermediate species that are involved.

Thus Laitinen and Shoemaker (1950a) showed that the oxidation product of the Hg pool anode during polarographic measurements in liquid ammonia is Hg^{2+}, and that the $Hg-Hg^{2+}$ electrode behaves reversibly in liquid ammonia.

Table IV presents the half-wave potentials for several reduction processes in liquid ammonia at $-36°$. The half-wave potentials given are versus a $Pb/0\cdot1N\,Pb(NO_3)_2$ electrode.

When the cation of the indifferent electrolyte is non-reducible, platinum and mercury electrodes act as electron electrodes in liquid ammonia. The standard potential of the electron electrode relative to the standard hydrogen electrode at $-36°C$ is $-1\cdot9$ V.

Schaap et al. (1961) have used a high-pressure polarographic cell for measurements at room temperature.

C. METALS

In spite of the large amount of work done on metal–ammonia solutions since they were first studied by Weyl (1864), there is still some uncertainty concerning the nature of the solutions. All metal–ammonia solutions are metastable and decompose to give hydrogen and the metal amide. Since this reaction is catalysed by certain impurities, the need for extreme care and cleanliness when working with these solutions cannot be over emphasized.

TABLE IV

Polarographic Half-Wave Potentials in Ammonia at $-36°$

Species reduced	$E_{\frac{1}{2}}$ (V)	Reversibility
Li$^+$	$-1·67$	Rev.[a]
Na$^+$	$-1·31$	Rev.[a]
K$^+$	$-1·24$	Rev.[a]
Rb$^+$	$-1·21$	Rev.[a]
Cs$^+$	$-1·15$	Rev.[a]
Tl$^+$	$+0·15$	Rev.[b]
Cu^{2+}→Cu$^+$	$+0·16$	Rev.[b]
Cu$^+$→amalgam	$-0·21$	Irrev.[b]
NH$_4^+$	$-1·37$	Rev.[b]
Pb^{2+}→Pb amalgam	$-0·01$	Rev.[c]
Cd^{2+}→Cd	$-0·45$	Rev.[c]
Ni^{2+}→Ni	$-0·79$	Irrev.[c]
Zn^{2+}	$-0·89$	Irrev.[c]
Ca^{2+}→Ca	$-1·96$	—[d]
Sr^{2+}→Sr	$-1·68$	—[d]
Ba^{2+}→Ba	$-1·59$	—[d]

[a] Laitinen and Nyman (1948a, 1948b).
[b] Laitinen and Shoemaker (1950b).
[c] McElroy and Laitinen (1953).
[d] Nyman (1949).

This could well be the source of much of the disagreement found in the results obtained by various workers in these systems. It is generally agreed, however, that when a metal is dissolved in liquid ammonia, it dissociates into a metal ion and electron(s), at least in very dilute solutions.

1. *Phase Diagrams*

The metals which dissolve in liquid ammonia are those with low ionization potentials and high solvation energies. Thus the alkali metals, the alkaline earth metals heavier than beryllium, and those rare earths which exhibit the $+2$ oxidation state are soluble.

The solubilities of the alkali metals are given in Table V. The alkaline earth metals, europium and ytterbium do not exist in equilibrium with their solutions. These metals form solid hexammoniates. The hexammoniate of calcium separates out at a concentration of 10 mole per cent calcium at $-64°C$ and 11 mole per cent calcium at $0°C$. The ratio of ammonia to hexammoniate is about 4 to 5, which is about the same as the ratio of ammonia to metal for the alkali metals.

A portion of the phase diagram for the sodium–ammonia system is shown in Fig. 1. The significant features of this diagram (which are general for metal–ammonia systems) are: (1) a steep solubility curve for the metal or its hexammoniate, (2) a low temperature eutectic point, and (3) a miscibility gap in the liquid region corresponding to the co-existence of two different metal solutions. In the region of the miscibility gap, the more concentrated

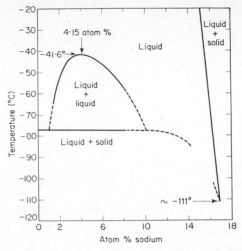

Fig. 1. Sodium–ammonia phase diagram (reproduced with permission from Jolly, 1959).

phase is bronze coloured and less dense than the blue phase, which is of considerably lower concentration at the lower temperatures. The alkali metals, except caesium, and the alkaline earth metals all show this behaviour. Sienko (1964) has reviewed the subject of metal–ammonia systems, and has proposed an electron model which predicts consolute concentrations of 3·9 atom per cent metal in ammonia, in remarkable agreement with observed values.

TABLE V

Solubilities of Metals in Liquid Ammonia

Metal	θ(°C)	Gram-atoms of metal per 1000 g NH_3	Moles NH_3 per gram-atom of metal
Lithium [a,b]	0	16·31	3·60
	−33·2	15·66	3·75
	−39·4	16·25	3·61
	−63·5	15·41	3·81
Sodium [c,d,e]	22	9·56	6·14
	0	10·00	5·87
	−30	10·63	5·52
	−33·8	10·72	5·48

Metal	$\theta(°C)$	Gram-atoms of metal per 1000 g NH_3	Moles NH_3 per gram-atom of metal
Sodium [c,d,e]	−33·5	10·93	5·37
	−50	10·89	5·39
	−70	11·29	5·20
	−105	11·79	4·98
Potassium [c,d,e,f]	0	12·4	4·68, 4·74
	−33·2	11·86	4·95
	−50	12·3	5·05, 4·79
	−100	12·2	4·82
	−33·5	12·05	4·87
Caesium [g]	−50	25·1	2·34

[a] Johnson and Piskur (1933).   [c] Johnson and Meyer (1932).   [e] Ruff and Geisel (1906).
[b] Kraus and Johnson (1925).   [d] Kraus and Lucasse (1921).   [f] Johnson and Meyer (1929).
[g] Hodgins (1949.)

There are other differences between the alkali metal– and alkaline earth metal–ammonia systems besides the difference in the solid species that exist in equilibrium with saturated solutions. Whereas the upper consolute temperature for the sodium–ammonia two-liquid equilibrium is − 41·6°, the upper consolute temperature for calcium–ammonia solutions is not yet reached at 50° (Jolly *et al.*, 1964). The concentration at which the second phase first begins to appear is much lower for calcium solutions than for sodium solutions (Hallada and Jolly, 1963). The eutectic temperatures are much lower for alkali metal–ammonia systems than for the alkaline earth metal–ammonia systems. The eutectic points of several systems are given in Table VI.

TABLE VI

Metal–Ammonia Eutectics (Birch and MacDonald, 1947, 1948)

Metal	$\theta(°C)$	Mole percentage metal
Li	−185	22
K	−157	15
Cs	−118	—
Ca	−87	12
Sr	−89	7
Ba	−89	7·7

2. *Molar Volumes*

When a metal is dissolved in liquid ammonia, there is a large net increase in volume. Table VII presents the densities of saturated solutions of lithium, sodium and potassium at several temperatures.

TABLE VII

Densities of Saturated Solutions of Alkali Metals in Ammonia

Lithium [a]		Sodium [b]		Potassium [b]	
$\theta(°C)$	Density	$\theta(°C)$	Density	$\theta(°C)$	Density
19	0·477	−31·6	0·576	−33·3	0·625
−80	0·495	−33·3	0·578	−39·0	0·627
		−40·7	0·581	−41·0	0·629
		−47·0	0·585	−46·4	0·636
		−51·0	0·587	−49·6	0·638

[a] Jaffe (1935).   [b] Johnson *et al.* (1950).

Gunn and Green (1962a) found that the apparent molar volumes at 0°C of alkali metals change only slightly over the concentration range 0·01–1·0 molar. They assign the following partial molar volumes at infinite dilution:

$$V_{Li}^0 = 49 \text{ cm}^3$$
$$V_{Na}^0 = 57 \text{ cm}^3$$
$$V_{K}^0 = 65 \text{ cm}^3.$$

Using the values of the partial molar volumes at infinite dilution that were given earlier (Section IIIB,1) for KI and NaI, one obtains the molar volume of the solvated electron at infinite dilution:

$$V_{K}^0 - V_{KI}^0 = 65 - (-6) = 71 \text{ cm}^3 = V_{e^-}^0 - V_{I^-}^0$$
$$V_{Na}^0 - V_{NaI}^0 = 57 - (-15) = 72 \text{ cm}^3 = V_{e^-}^0 - V_{I^-}^0.$$

Since
$$V_{I^-}^0 = 22 \text{ cm}^3,$$
$$V_{e^-}^0 = 94 \text{ cm}^3 \text{ mole}^{-1}.$$

This volume corresponds to a sphere of radius 3·34 Å. Other calculations have also led to values around 3 Å for the electron cavity radius (Jolly, 1959; Hutchison and O'Reilly, 1962a).

3. Thermochemistry

The alkali metals, except lithium, have very low heats of solution, but the metals that form solid ammoniates evolve large amounts of heat when they are dissolved in liquid ammonia. The heats of solution of several metals are given in Table VIII.

The heat of dilution of sodium is endothermic, and when NaI is present, the heat of dilution is greater (Gunn and Green, 1962b).

The heat of ammonation of the electron (that is, the heat of transfer from the gas phase to ammonia) is of considerable interest. Coulter (1953) calculated an ammonation heat of -11 kcal mole^{-1}. This seems to be too positive compared to the experimental photoelectric threshold energy, 33 kcal mole^{-1} (Hasing 1940); a value for the heat of ammonation of the electron of about -40 kcal mole^{-1} seems more reasonable (Jolly, 1959). Jortner (1959) theoretically calculated a heat solution of -39 kcal mole^{-1} for the electron in a cavity of radius 3·2–3·4 Å.

TABLE VIII

Heats of Solution of Metals in Ammonia at $-33°C$

Metal	Concentration (mole/litre)	ΔH^0 (kcal mole^{-1})
Li	0·067	$-9·65$ [a]
Na	0·4	$+1·4$ [b]
K	0·07	$0·0$ [b,c]
Rb	0·13	$0·0$ [c]
Cs	0·19	$0·0$ [c]
Ca	0·023	$-19·7$ [d]
Sr	—	$-20·7$ [e,f]
Ba	—	$-19·0$ [e,f]

[a] Coulter and Monchick (1951).
[b] Kraus and Schmidt (1934).
[c] Schmidt et al. (1938).
[d] Wolsky et al. (1952).
[e] Coulter (1953).
[f] Wolsky (1952).

4. Electrical Conductance

The equivalent conductances of metal solutions in liquid ammonia are greater than those for any other type of electrolyte in any known solvent. The specific conductivities of concentrated solutions are of the same order of magnitude as the conductivities of metals, and the equivalent conductances of dilute solutions approach values near 1000, i.e. some five to ten times the values for salts in water (Kraus and Lucasse, 1921). The equivalent conductances of lithium, sodium and potassium are given in Fig. 2. It will be noticed that as the concentration increases from infinite dilution the equivalent conductance decreases to a minimum near 0·04 molar, and then increases very abruptly with increasing concentration.

Transference studies of sodium solutions have shown that the conductance of the electron, λ_-, has a minimum value at about 0·04 molar, whereas the conductance of the sodium ion, λ_+, decreases continuously as concentration

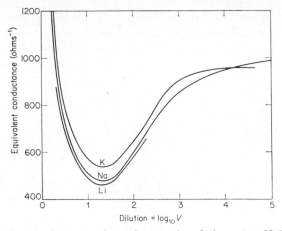

Fig. 2. Equivalent conductance of metal–ammonia solutions at $-33\cdot5°$. $V =$ litres of ammonia of density 0·674 in which one gram-atom of metal is dissolved (reproduced with permission from Jolly, 1959).

increases (Dye *et al.*, 1960). The ratio T_-/T_+ varies from seven in dilute solutions to 280 at $\sim 0·9$ molar (Kraus, 1914). These transference data show that the behaviour of the conductance curves is determined primarily by the mobility of the electron.

The temperature coefficient of specific conductivity for sodium,

$$\frac{\Delta K}{\Delta \theta} \cdot \frac{100}{K_{-33\cdot5°C}},$$

is 1·9% per degree for dilute solutions, reaches a maximum of about 4% per degree at ~ 1 molar, and falls almost to zero at higher concentrations (Kraus and Lucasse, 1922 and 1923). These data are not explicable by changes in viscosity, and must be due to quite different conduction mechanisms in the various concentration regions. A review of the many mechanisms that have been proposed for the low field conductance has been given elsewhere (Jolly, 1959).

In measurements of the Wien effect, fields of magnitude 15,000 V/cm gave a 4% increase in the conductivity of alkali metal solutions (Lepoutre and Patterson, 1955). Comparable increases in aqueous solutions of electrolytes require fields of magnitude 100,000 V/cm.

5. *Magnetic Properties*

The molar magnetic susceptibility of an alkali metal solution approaches that of a mole of free electron spins, $N\mu_0^2/kT$, at infinite dilution. As the concentration is increased, however, the molar susceptibility decreases rapidly (Freed and Sugarman, 1943). Comparison of static susceptibilities of sodium and potassium, and susceptibilities obtained from paramagnetic resonance measurements, has been interpreted to indicate that the radius of the cavity in which the electron resides is 3·0 Å (Hutchison and Pastor, 1953). This agrees well with the value calculated earlier from partial molar volumes. The paramagnetic resonance line width for potassium solutions is only about 0·03 gauss. The line width varies directly with viscosity (Levy, 1956) and has been interpreted as due to motionally narrowed hyperfine interactions between unpaired electrons and the protons bordering the electron cavity (Kaplan and Kittel, 1953).

The spin-spin relaxation times, T_1, and spin-lattice relaxation times, T_2, are about equal in dilute solutions, and again in concentrated solutions, of potassium; in the middle concentration range, T_1 is larger than T_2 (Hutchison and O'Reilly, 1961b). Within a limited concentration range, T_1 and T_2 are almost equal for solutions of lithium, sodium and calcium (Cutler and Powles, 1962). The equality of T_1 and T_2 is interpreted as meaning that the electron interaction is with the nitrogen nucleus of the ammonia, not with the protons. The relaxation times vary from 1 to 3 μsec depending on concentration and temperature (Pollak, 1961; Cutler and Powles, 1962).

It is now well known that the nuclear magnetic resonance absorption for a given species in metallic systems occurs at higher fields than normal (Knight, 1949). McConnell and Holm (1957) measured the Knight shifts of ^{14}N and ^{23}Na in sodium–ammonia solutions. They found that the average hyperfine contact density of ^{23}Na and an unpaired electron is 3×10^{-3} to 5×10^{-3} as large as the contact density in an isolated sodium atom when the NH_3/Na ratio of the solutions is 50 to 400. At NH_3/Na ratios less than 50, the contact density increases markedly. On the other hand, the average hyperfine contact density of ^{14}N and an unpaired electron is almost 0·1 that on a nitrogen atom at all solution concentrations. This supports the suggestion that the electron interaction is with the nitrogen nucleus (Pollak, 1961). The temperature dependence of the Knight shift for sodium solutions over a hundred-fold range of concentrations was measured by Acrivos and Pitzer (1962).

6. *Absorption Spectra*

The blue colour of dilute metal solutions is due to the short wavelength tail of a broad absorption band that peaks at approximately 15,000 Å. The spectra of the alkali metals, and at least calcium of the alkaline earth metals, are essentially the same (Gold and Jolly, 1962; Hallada and Jolly, 1963).

Furthermore, the alkali metals obey Beer's law at the lower wavelengths up to concentrations as high as 0·2 molar. At wavelengths beyond 20,000 Å, there may be a positive deviation from Beer's Law at the higher concentrations.

Up to concentrations at which phase separation occurs, calcium solutions also obey Beer's Law at all but the highest wavelengths. The molar extinction coefficients of the calcium solutions are very nearly twice the molar extinction coefficients of the alkali metal solutions at all wavelengths.

It has been reported that addition of NaI to sodium solutions produces a new band at 8000 Å (Clark *et al.*, 1959); however, this peak was not observed in independent experiments (Gold and Jolly, 1962). It is entirely possible that the 8000 Å peak is due to a short-lived species which disappears after a few minutes.

Reflection spectra on sodium solutions with NH_3/Na ratios of 5 to 168 were measured at 1–20 μ (Beckman and Pitzer, 1961). Dilute solutions show a strong peak near 1·5 μ. The concentrated solutions show high reflectivity over broad wavelength ranges.

7. *Models*

In the preceding paragraphs on the physical properties of metal–ammonia solutions, we have occasionally interpreted the data in terms of particular models. Now, in conclusion, it will be instructive to briefly review some of the microscopic models that have been proposed for metal–ammonia solutions, especially those for low and intermediate concentrations.

The early conductivity work of Kraus led him to the conclusion that, in very dilute solutions, metals dissociate to give ammoniated cations and electrons.

$$M = M^+ + e^-. \tag{1}$$

As the concentration is increased these species associate and the conductivity decreases. Eventually, incipient metallic behaviour occurs and the equivalent conductance increases rapidly.

When magnetic data became available it was obvious that the model Kraus proposed from conductivity data was not adequate, since it did not account for the pairing of electrons. The magnetic data were explained by Huster (1930), and Freed and Sugarman (1943) in terms of an equilibrium between the ionic species and diamagnetic metal atom dimers:

$$2M^+ + 2e^- = M_2. \tag{2}$$

Becker *et al.* (1956) showed that both the conductivity data and the susceptibility data can be approximately accounted for by considering both of the above equilibria. However, Arnold and Patterson (1964) have shown that the equilibrium constants for these reactions obtained from electrochemical data do not agree with those obtained from magnetic data. They resolve the discrepancy by postulating another diamagnetic species, M^-, and give the following equilibrium constants:

$$M = M^+ + e^- \qquad k = 9\cdot9 \times 10^{-3} \qquad (3)$$

$$M^- = M + e^- \qquad k = 9\cdot7 \times 10^{-4} \qquad (4)$$

$$M_2 = 2M \qquad k = 1\cdot9 \times 10^{-4}. \qquad (5)$$

Detailed models of the species involved in these equilibria have continually evolved.

All the data are fairly well explained by assuming that the electron-in-a-cavity retains its identity even when species such as M, M^- and M_2 are being formed. The M species may be described as an ion pair in which an ammoniated metal ion and an ammoniated electron are held together by coulombic forces with little distortion of the ammoniated electron, and the M^- and M_2 species may be pictured as quadrupolar ionic assemblies of either one or two ammoniated cations and two ammoniated electrons. The wave functions for the two electrons in the latter species overlap sufficiently so that the singlet state is lower in energy than the triplet by more than kT. The highly concentrated metal solutions are like molten metals in which the metal cations are ammoniated (Gold *et al.*, 1962).

IV. REACTIONS IN LIQUID AMMONIA

A. COMPARISON OF AMMONIA WITH OTHER SOLVENTS

1. *Solubilities*

The most important function of a solvent is to dissolve other substances. Thus a knowledge of the kinds of substances which a solvent is capable of dissolving is of great importance. Hildebrand (1948) has discussed the properties of liquid ammonia which are significant in comparing solubilities in ammonia with solubilities in other solvents, and, in the following paragraphs, we shall cite solubility data to illustrate the effects of these properties.

The dielectric constant of ammonia (about 23 at the boiling point) is considerably lower than that of water (78·5), and yet significantly greater than that of acetic acid (6·4). As one might expect, the solubilities of ionic salts in ammonia lie, in general, between the values for the same salts in water and acetic acid. This generalization does not hold for salts whose anions are highly polarizable, because of London forces which are discussed in a later paragraph. Some typical solubilities for these three solvents are presented in Table IX. Salts with polynegative anions, such as sulphates, carbonates, and phosphates, are practically insoluble in liquid ammonia. In such salts, the solvation energy of the ions in ammonia is insufficient to compensate for the high lattice energy.

The abnormally high boiling point of ammonia is evidence of the tendency for ammonia to form hydrogen bonds. Substances which are capable of forming hydrogen bonds with ammonia have high solubilities in ammonia, just as they have in other hydrogen-bonding solvents such as water and hydrogen fluoride. Thus sugars, esters, amines, and phenols are very soluble in liquid ammonia.

TABLE IX

Solubilities of some Ionic Salts in Water, Ammonia, and Acetic Acid [a]
(g/100 g of solvent at 25°)

	Water	Ammonia	Acetic Acid
$LiNO_3$	52·2	243·7	10·3 (30°)
$NaNO_3$	91·8	97·6	0·17
KNO_3	37·8	10·4	0·18
NH_4OAc	148 (4°)	253·2	39·3
NaCl	37	3·02	0·073 (30°)

[a] Solubilities taken largely from Jander (1949) and Audrieth and Kleinberg (1953).

The basic character of ammonia is largely responsible for the high solubility of carboxylic acids, alcohols, and phenols in ammonia. In many cases, it may be difficult to distinguish the effects of ammonia's basicity from the effects of its tendency to hydrogen bond. A characteristic closely related to the basicity of ammonia is its tendency to co-ordinate to transition metal ions

TABLE X

Comparison of the Dispersion and Orientation Potentials for Water and Ammonia

	Dispersion potential	Orientation potential
H_2O	47	190
NH_3	93	84

such as Ni^{2+}, Cu^{2+}, Zn^{2+}, Ag^+, etc. Salts of such metal ions usually have high solubilities in ammonia. This co-ordinating characteristic of ammonia is clearly shown by the high solubilities of the silver halides in ammonia. At 25°, the solubilities (in g/100 g of ammonia) are 0·83, 5·92 and 206·8 for AgCl, AgBr, and AgI, respectively (Jander, 1949).

Molecules which do not react chemically with one another nevertheless are attracted by London, or Van der Waals, forces which arise from a coupling of the motion of the electrons in the separate atoms. The London interaction energy between two molecules may be approximated by the relation

$$E_{AB} = -\frac{3\alpha_A\alpha_B}{2R^6}\frac{I_A I_B}{I_A+I_B}$$

where α_A and α_B denote the polarizabilities of the molecules, R their distance apart, and I_A and I_B their ionization potentials. In the case of molecules which not only have high dipole moments, but also have enough electrons to be highly polarizable, the London forces may outweigh the dipole orientation effect. In Table X, the London and orientation potentials for water and ammonia are compared. It will be noted that the attractive potential for water depends mainly on its dipole moment, whereas that for ammonia depends almost equally on its dipole moment and its polarizability. Thus, although ammonia is generally a poorer solvent than water for ionic salts

TABLE XI

Solubility Parameters and Solubilities in Ammonia [a]

	$(\Delta E_v/V)^{\frac{1}{2}}$	Solubility in liquid NH_3
n-Hexane	7·3	5·1% at 20° [b] (compare with 0·014% at 15·5° for H_2O)
Carbon tetrachloride	8·6	soluble
Benzene	9·2	moderately soluble
Yellow phosphorus	13·1	soluble
Ammonia	13·1	
Water	23·8	infinitely miscible because of hydrogen-bonding, etc.
Mercury	30·7	practically insoluble

[a] Solubility parameters from Hildebrand and Scott (1962).   [b] Ishida (1958).

and highly polar molecules, it is a better solvent for non-polar molecules, particularly those with many electrons. The higher polarizability of the thiosulphate ion as compared with that of the sulphate ion is probably why sodium thiosulphate dissolves to the extent of 0·17 g/100 g of ammonia, whereas sodium sulphate has no detectable solubility in ammonia.

Similarly, the increase in anionic polarizability on going from chloride to iodide is probably the main cause of the increase in solubility on going from AgCl to AgI, for which the data are quoted above.

The "solubility parameter", or the square root of the energy of vapourization per cc, is a useful criterion of solubility. In the absence of strong dipole and acid–base effects, substances are most soluble in one another when their solubility parameters are of the same order of magnitude. The solubility parameters for several substances, and their solubilities in ammonia, are presented in Table XI.

2. *Available Oxidation Potential Range**

If all reactions in liquid ammonia were thermodynamically controlled (as opposed to kinetically controlled), no oxidizing agent more powerful than nitrogen, and no reducing agent more powerful than hydrogen, would be capable of existence in liquid ammonia. The NH_3—N_2 and H_2—NH_3 couples, and their potentials in volts at 25°, in both acid and basic solutions are given below.

Acid Solutions $(1 \text{ M } NH_4^+)$:

$$\tfrac{1}{2}H_2 + NH_3 = NH_4^+ + e^- \qquad\qquad E^0 = 0 \qquad\qquad (6)$$

$$4NH_3 = \tfrac{1}{2}N_2 + 3NH_4^+ + 3e^- \qquad\qquad E^0 = -0.04. \qquad (7)$$

Basic Solutions $(1 \text{ M } NH_2^-)$:

$$\tfrac{1}{2}H_2 + NH_2^- = NH_3 + e^- \qquad\qquad E^0 = 1.59 \qquad\qquad (8)$$

$$3NH_2^- = \tfrac{1}{2}N_2 + 2NH_3 + 3e^- \qquad\qquad E^0 = 1.55. \qquad\qquad (9)$$

Obviously with only a 0.04 V range available, hardly any species are thermodynamically stable in ammonia. Fortunately, however, both the hydrogen couple and the nitrogen couple usually exhibit "overvoltages" of about 1 V. So in acid solutions, the practical range of potentials for dissolved species is from 1.0 to −1.0 V. In basic solutions, where the hydrogen and nitrogen couples have potentials of about 1.6 V, the practical range extends from 2.6 to 0.6 V. Thus it is possible to work in liquid ammonia with species which are extremely strong reducing agents (such as the alkali metals) and with species which are extremely strong oxidizing agents (such as permanganates, ozonides, and superoxides).

In Fig. 3, the oxidation potentials for several couples are plotted against pH (pH = 0 corresponds to $1 \text{ M } NH_4^+$, and pH = 27 corresponds to $1 \text{ M } NH_2^-$). The dotted lines in Fig. 1 correspond to the approximate boundaries of the stability zones for redox couples. Thus we see that the ammoniacal electron is thermodynamically unstable with respect to hydrogen evolution at all pH values; however, in alkaline solutions and in the absence of catalysts, the

---

* A table of oxidation potentials in ammonia and a discussion of their application to liquid ammonia chemistry is given by Jolly (1956).

decomposition reaction is slow. In general, solid metals show negligible overvoltage effects in the reduction of ammonia. Thus, although the zinc couple falls within the dotted line boundaries, metallic zinc causes hydrogen

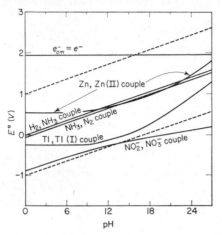

FIG. 3. Oxidation potentials in ammonia at 25° as a function of pH.

evolution both in acid solutions and in alkaline solutions (Bergstrom and Fernelius, 1933). The probable net reaction in alkaline solutions is

$$Zn + 2NH_2^- + 2NH_3 = Zn(NH_2)_4^{2-} + H_2. \tag{10}$$

Metallic thallium is, of course, inert toward ammonia at all pH values, and it happens that neither Tl^+ nor $Tl(NH_2)_2^-$ reacts with ammonia (Bergstrom and Fernelius, 1933). The nitrate ion is essentially inert toward ammonia in acid solutions, but in alkaline solutions nitrogen evolution slowly occurs (Bergstrom, 1940):

$$3K^+ + 3NH_2^- + 3NO_3^- = 3KOH + N_2 + 3NO_2^- + NH_3. \tag{11}$$

3. *Available Acid–Base Range*

The basicity of ammonia is about 10^{12} times greater than that of water, and the acidity of ammonia is about 10^{-25} times smaller than that of water. Consequently acids for which pK is less than $\sim$12 in aqueous solutions are "strong" acids in liquid ammonia, and acids for which pK is greater than $\sim$39 in aqueous solutions have practically no acidity in liquid ammonia. Acids of intermediate strength are weak acids in ammonia, and they may be differentiated according to their acid strengths. In Fig. 4, the pK ranges in which differentiation of acid strength is possible are indicated for the solvents acetic acid, water, ammonia, and benzene. On the same graph the aqueous pK values of several acids are indicated. It will be noted that, because of the smaller ionization constant of ammonia, a wider range of acid strengths may be studied in ammonia than in the other protonic solvents. In addition, because ammonia is more basic than either acetic acid or water, the pK values of the acids which can be differentiated are higher for ammonia than for acetic acid and water. Finally it may be

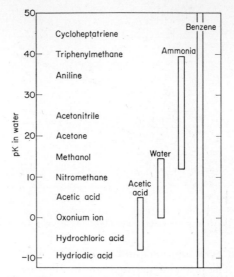

Fig. 4. Ranges of acidity differentiation for several solvents. Most of the pK values were taken from Cram (1963). (The values for HCl and HI are taken from Pauling, 1960.)

noted that inasmuch as benzene is an aprotic solvent, it is possible in principle to study any acid in benzene. In practice, however, difficulty is often encountered in dissolving ionic species in benzene.

Acids for which aqueous pK <12 react completely with ammonia to form the corresponding ammonium salts. However, it must not be thought that these acids (or ammonium salts) are strong in the sense that they are completely dissociated to independent ions in liquid ammonia. All salts, ammonium salts included, are weakly dissociated in ammonia. The "strength" of an acid is best measured in terms of the equilibrium constant of the reaction

$$HX + NH_3 = (NH_4^+)(X^-). \tag{12}$$

However, rather than always indicate the formation of ion-pairs when these are the principal species, it is customary to write the ions as independent species, keeping in mind that considerable ionic aggregation takes place in moderately concentrated solutions. Thus we write

$$HOAc + NH_3 = NH_4^+ + OAc^- \tag{13}$$

even though the ion-pair dissociation constant for ammonium acetate is $7 \cdot 7 \times 10^{-5}$ (Gur'yanova and Pleskov, 1936).

Bases whose conjugate acids have aqueous pK values greater than $\sim$39 undergo essentially complete ammonolysis in liquid ammonia to form the amide ion. Two examples of such ammonolysis are given below.

$$KH + NH_3 = K^+ + NH_2^- + H_2 \tag{14}$$

$$Na_2O + NH_3 = NaNH_2 + NaOH. \tag{15}$$

The aqueous ionization constants of H_2 and OH^- have been estimated to be 10^{-38} and $<10^{-36}$, respectively (Latimer, 1952). Thus the criterion for basic ammonolysis is just barely satisfied in these cases.

Some oxidizing agents react with liquid ammonia to form nitrogen-containing products which can be looked upon either as oxidation-reduction products or as ammonolysis products. Consider, for example, the reactions of chlorine, bromine, and iodine:

$$X_2 + 2NH_3 = NH_4^+ + X^- + NH_2X. \tag{16}$$

(The halamine NH_2X reacts further at a lower rate to form species such as hydrazine and nitrogen.) The initial reaction can be looked upon as a self-oxidation-reduction of the halogen to the $+1$ and -2 oxidation states, but it is equally valid to consider the reaction as the ammonolytic cleavage of the X—X bond. Similarly, consider the following reaction (Franklin, 1934):

$$3K^+ + 3NH_2^- + NO_3^- = N_3^- + 3KOH + NH_3. \tag{17}$$

This reaction corresponds to the oxidation of amide to azide by nitrate, but it may be looked upon as the basic ammonolysis of the nitrate ion. (The $O{=}\overset{+}{N}\overset{\diagup O^-}{\diagdown O^-}$ ion is converted to the $\overset{-}{N}{=}\overset{+}{N}{=}\overset{-}{N}$ ion by replacing the $O{=}\overset{+}{N}$ bond by an $\overset{-}{N}{=}\overset{+}{N}$ bond and by replacing the $\overset{+}{N}\overset{\diagup O^-}{\diagdown O^-}$ bonds by an $\overset{+}{N}{=}\overset{-}{N}$ bond.)

4. *Ease of Handling*

The low boiling point of ammonia ($-33 \cdot 4°$) is an obvious disadvantage when working with this solvent. However, in many types of work it is not necessary to use any refrigeration when handling liquid ammonia. Because of the high heat of vapourization, the liquid may be kept at its boiling point in open containers such as beakers, flasks etc., without too rapid boiling of the ammonia. The rate of evaporation of ammonia in dewar flasks (even when unsilvered for ease in observation) is practically negligible. The vapour pressure of the liquid at room temperature (8–10 atm) is low enough so that it may be handled in sealed glass ampoules without much danger of explosion. Techniques for handling liquid ammonia are discussed by Audrieth and Kleinberg (1953), Franklin (1935), Jolly (1960) and Sanderson (1948).

The viscosity of ammonia at its boiling point is only one-quarter that of water at room temperature. The low viscosity of ammonia is a definite

advantage when filtering ammonia solutions and when carrying out heterogeneous reactions which require the diffusion of solutes through the liquid.

B. IONIC SOLVATION

1. *Thermodynamic Functions for Ammonation and Hydration Processes*

The free energies of formation of pairs of oppositely-charged ions are found
to be of approximately the same magnitude in ammonia as they are in
water, if one restricts the comparison to ions which do not form abnormally
strong ammonia complexes (Jolly, 1953, 1956). The data for a few pairs of
ions of this type are presented in Table XII. We shall claim as a reasonable

TABLE XII

Free Energies of Formation in Water and Ammonia

| Ion pair | ΔF_f^0(kcal mole^{-1})(25°) | |
	in water	in ammonia
$Na^+ + F^-$	$-128 \cdot 7$	$-124 \cdot 4$
$Li^+ + I^-$	$-82 \cdot 6$	-83
$Rb^+ + NO_3^-$	$-93 \cdot 9$	$-90 \cdot 3$
$NH_4^+ + Br^-$	$-43 \cdot 6$	$-42 \cdot 6$
$Na^+ + ClO_3^-$	$-63 \cdot 2$	$-61 \cdot 3$

approximation for ions of the type given in Table XII, that the free energy
of transfer of an individual ion from water to ammonia is zero. We shall
therefore assume that the free energy of transfer of an ion which forms
strong ammonia complexes can be equated to the sum of the free energies of
transfer of that ion and an equivalent number of non-ammonia-complexing
counter-ions. We shall call such ionic free energies of transfer "experimental"
free energies of transfer. It is interesting to compare such "experimental"
free energies of transfer with the free energies of the aqueous reactions of
type

$$M(H_2O)_x^{Z+} + xHN_3 = M(NH_3)_x^{Z+} + xH_2O. \tag{18}$$

The free energy (in kcal mole^{-1}) of such a reaction, using the 1 M solution as
the standard state for both water and ammonia, is given by the expression

$$\Delta F_K^\circ = -1 \cdot 36 (\log K + x \log 55) \tag{19}$$

where K is the usual equilibrium constant for aqueous solutions. In Table
XIII, values for ΔF_K^0 may be compared with the corresponding "experimental" free energies of transfer, ΔF_t^0. It can be seen that the correspondence

is very close. Hence we may estimate the standard free energy of formation of an ion in liquid ammonia from the relation:

$$\Delta F_f^0(NH_3) = \Delta F_f^0(H_2O) + 16Z - 1\cdot 36 (\log K + x \log 55)$$

where $\Delta F_f^0(NH_3)$ and $\Delta F_f^0(H_2O)$ are the standard free energies of formation in ammonia and water, respectively, and Z is the charge (taking account

TABLE XIII

Calculated and "Experimental" Free Energies of Transfer from Water to Ammonia
(kcal mole^{-1} at 25°)

Ion	x	$-\Delta F_K^0$	$-\Delta F_t^0$
Hg^{2+}	4	36	40
Cu^{2+}	5	29	29
Zn^{2+}	4	22	22
Cu^+	2	20	20
H^+	1	15	16
Ag^+	2	14	17

of sign) of the ion. The term $16Z$ arises from the fact that $\Delta F_f^0 = 0$ for the hydrogen ion in both solvents, and $\Delta F_t^0 = -16$ kcal mole^{-1} for the hydrogen ion. Similar equations have been given for estimating ionic entropies and heats of formation in ammonia (Jolly, 1956).

2. *Kinetics of Ammonia Exchange Reactions*

The ammoniated hydrogen ion, or ammonium ion, is the simplest ion one can have in liquid ammonia. The rate at which protons move from ammonium ions to ammonia molecules (or the rate at which solvent ammonia molecules displace ammonia molecules from ammonium ions) is much too great to measure by classical chemical techniques (Nyman *et al.*, 1950). However Ogg (1954) has shown that it is possible to measure this rate by n.m.r. techniques. The proton magnetic resonance spectrum of pure liquid ammonia consists of three peaks, due to the spin-spin coupling of the protons with the ^{14}N nucleus. A trace of ammonium salt causes the signal to change to a single line. The change is attributed to the reaction

$$NH_3 + NH_4^+ \rightleftharpoons NH_4^+ + NH_3 , \tag{19}$$

and from a rough estimate of the ammonium ion concentration required to cause collapse of the triplet, Ogg calculated a rate constant of about 5×10^8 litre mole^{-1} sec^{-1}. He estimated rate constants of the same order of magnitude for the reactions

$$NH_3 + NH_2^- \rightleftharpoons NH_2^- + NH_3 \qquad (20)$$

and

$$NH_3 + H_2O \rightleftharpoons NH_4^+ + OH^-. \qquad (21)$$

Wiesendanger et al. (1957) have shown, using ^{15}N, that the exchange of ammonia molecules between the solvent and the ions $Ag(NH_3)_2^+$, $Cu(NH_3)_4^{2+}$, and $Ni(NH_3)_6^{2+}$ is too fast to measure by classical methods, but they were able to show that the ions $Cr(NH_3)_6^{3+}$ and $Co(NH_3)_6^{3+}$ exchange their ammonia molecules relatively slowly with the solvent. In the case of $Cr(NH_3)_6^{3+}$, a bimolecular rate constant $1\cdot3 \times 10^{-6}$ litre mole^{-1} sec^{-1} was measured. Hunt et al. (1963) measured the rate of exchange of ^{14}N between $Ni(NH_3)_6^{2+}$ and the solvent ammonia molecules by n.m.r. line broadening measurements. Because the rate of the corresponding exchange reaction in water was found to be independent of the ammonia concentration and to be of practically the same magnitude as that for the exchange in anhydrous ammonia, they proposed that the reaction is unimolecular and reported the rate constant $k = 4\cdot7 \times 10^4$ sec^{-1} at 25°.

C. ACID–BASE REACTIONS

1. *The Nature of the Ammonium and Amide Ions*

The ammonium ion and amide ion are analogs of the oxonium ion and hydroxide ion, respectively. Thus the neutralization of a strong acid with a strong base in ammonia is represented by the equation

$$NH_4^+ + NH_2^- \rightarrow 2\,NH_3 \qquad (22)$$

whereas the analogous reaction in water is usually written as

$$H^+ + OH^- \rightarrow H_2O. \qquad (23)$$

The analogy breaks down, however, when one considers the mobilities of the ions. The aqueous oxonium ion and aqueous hydroxide ion have ionic

TABLE XIV

Ionic Conductances in Ammonia and Water

Ion	Equivalent ionic conductance (cm^2 ohm^{-1} eq.$^{-1}$)	
	Liquid NH$_3$, $-33\cdot5°$	Water,[c] 25°
Na$^+$	158 [a]	50·1
NH$_4^+$	142 [a]	73·4
H$^+$		349·8
NO$_3^-$	177 [a]	71·4
NH$_2^-$	166 [b]	
OH$^-$		198·0

[a] Laitinen and Shoemaker (1950).   [b] Hawes (1933).   [c] MacInnes (1939).

conductances which are several times as large as the conductances of ordinary $+1$ and -1 ions (see Table XIV). These abnormally high conductances are explained in terms of a mechanism, the essentials of which were first described by de Grotthuss (1806). Oxonium ion migration is accomplished when the proton of an oxonium ion moves the small distance necessary to partially break its bond to the oxygen atom and to form a bond to the oxygen atom of the adjacent hydrogen-bonded water molecule:

$$
\begin{array}{cccc}
\text{H} & \text{H} & \text{H} & \text{H} \\
| & | & | & | \\
\text{H—O—H} \cdots \text{O—H} & \rightarrow & \text{H—O} \cdots \text{H—O—H} \\
+ & & & +
\end{array}
$$

Hydroxide ion migration is quite similar:

$$
\begin{array}{cccc}
\text{H} & \text{H} \ \ \text{H} & & \text{H} \\
| & |\ \ \ | & & | \\
\text{O} \cdots \text{H—O} & \rightarrow & \text{O—H} \cdots \text{O} \\
- & & & -
\end{array}
$$

Analogous processes do not contribute appreciably to the mobilities of the NH_4^+ and NH_2^- ions in ammonia because of the much weaker hydrogen bonds in this solvent. (The weaker a hydrogen bond, the higher the barrier between the two equilibrium positions for the proton.) It is clear from the data in Table XIV that the mobilities of the ammonium and amide ions in ammonia are similar to the mobilities of ordinary univalent ions in the same solvent. We have noted above that the rate constants for the reactions

$$NH_4^+ + NH_3 \rightarrow NH_3 + NH_4^+ \tag{24}$$

$$NH_2^- + NH_3 \rightarrow NH_3 + NH_2^- \tag{25}$$

are of the order of magnitude 5×10^8 litre mole^{-1} sec^{-1}. The rate constants for the corresponding aqueous reactions

$$H_3O^+ + H_2O \rightarrow H_2O + H_3O^+ \tag{26}$$

$$OH^- + H_2O \rightarrow H_2O + OH^- \tag{27}$$

are $1 \cdot 1 \times 10^{10}$ and 5×10^9 litre mole^{-1} sec^{-1}, respectively (Loewenstein and Szöke, 1962).

2. *Determination of Ammonium Ion Concentration*

Platinum black electrodes show very little hydrogen overvoltage in liquid ammonia and, when equilibrated with hydrogen, may be used as reversible hydrogen electrodes. Pleskov and Monozson (1935) used the hydrogen electrode in ammonia at $-50°$ to determine the activity coefficients for NH_4NO_3 and NH_4Cl. By studying the cell

$$\text{Pt, H}_2 \mid 0 \cdot 1 \ \text{m} \ NH_4NO_3 \mid \text{saturated KNO}_3 \mid KNH_2(C) \mid \text{Pt, H}_2,$$

they determined the self-ionization constant for liquid ammonia:

$$2NH_3 = NH_4^+ + NH_2^- \qquad K = 1 \cdot 9 \times 10^{-33} \text{ at } -50°.$$

Using the heat of reaction, $\Delta H° = 26·1$ kcal/mole (Mulder and Schmidt, 1951), one calculates $K = 5·1 \times 10^{-27}$ at 25°. This is to be compared with the value $2·2 \times 10^{-28}$ calculated from the free energy of solution of sodium amide (Coulter *et al.*, 1959). For most purposes, the value $K = 10^{-27}$ is sufficiently accurate. If we set up a pH scale using the relation pH $= -\log [NH_4^+]$, we calculate that pure liquid ammonia has a pH of 13·5 at 25°.

Zintl and Neumayr (1930) were unsuccessful with the hydrogen electrode, but they did find the quinhydrone electrode to be reproducible. They obtained self-consistent results with the concentration cell

Pt | quinhydrone (C_1), NH$_4$Cl (c_1) | | quinhydrone (C_2), NH$_4$Cl (c_2) | Pt

at $-50°$.

Heyn and Bergin (1953) attempted the use of glass electrodes in liquid ammonia solutions. Their cells were of the type

Pb | 0·1 M_1Pb(NO$_3$)$_2$, NH$_4$NO$_3$ (C) | glass membrane |

$$0·1 \text{ M} \, \text{Pb(NO}_3)_2, \, 0·1 \text{ M} \, \text{NH}_4\text{NO}_3 \mid \text{Pb.}$$

Each of the several glasses tried failed to show glass-electrode response. It appears that the ammonium ions in liquid ammonia are not in equilibrium with ions on the surface of the glass electrode. Perhaps the ammonia dehydrates the glass to such an extent that protons are no longer mobile in the glass. It would be interesting to try a sheet of cation exchange resin in the ammonium form as a pH-sensitive membrane.

A number of acid–base indicators, including some that are used in aqueous solutions, have been studied in liquid ammonia (Shatenshtein, 1939, and Franklin and Kraus, 1900). Some of these are listed in Table XV with their

TABLE XV

Acid–Base Indicators in Liquid Ammonia

Indicator	Colour of solution in pure NH$_3$	Basic solution	Acidic solution
Phenolphthalein	pale red	deep red	colourless
Carmine	dirty red	blue	red
Saffranine	crimson	blue	crimson
m-Nitroaniline	yellow	green	yellow
p-Nitroaniline	yellow	orange	yellow
o-Nitroaniline	yellow	red	yellow

colours in acid and basic solutions. Cuthrell *et al.* (1963) have determined the ionization constants and dissociation constants for the weak acids *o*- and *p*-nitroacetanilide by a spectrophotometric method. These compounds are colourless in acidic solutions and yellow-brown in alkaline solutions. The ionization, to form an ion pair, may be represented by the general equation

$$HX + NH_3 = NH_4^+X^-; \qquad K_i = [NH_4^+X^-]/[HX]$$

and the dissociation by the equation

$$NH_4^+X^- = NH_4^+ + X^-; \qquad K_d = [NH_4^+][X^-]/[NH_4^+X^-].$$

The equilibrium constants, corrected to infinite dilution, are:

o-nitroacetanilide: $K_i = 2 \cdot 2 \times 10^{-2}$; $\qquad K_d = 2 \cdot 2 \times 10^{-4}$

p-nitroacetanilide: $K_i = 9 \cdot 3 \times 10^{-2}$; $\qquad K_d = 0 \cdot 89 \times 10^{-4}$.

In solutions of very high pH, the concentration of amide ion may be determined spectrophotometrically. The amide ion absorbs at 3410 Å (Ogg et al., 1933).

Watt et al. (1955) have potentiometrically titrated several acids in liquid ammonia with potassium amide. A "difference indicator" electrode system was used, in which one electrode is immersed in the solution being titrated, and the other is immersed in a solution having a composition the same as the initial composition of the titrated solution but separated from the bulk of the solution by a capillary tube (Zintl et al., 1931; Watt and Sowards, 1955). From the positions of the inflection points in the titration of mixtures of acids, the following order of acid strength was determined:

$$NH_4^+ > H_2NC(NH)NH_3^+ > H_2NC(S)NH_2 > H_2NC(O)NH_2 > H_2NC(NH)NH_2 >$$
$$H_2NC(S)NH^- > H_2NC(O)NH^- > H_2NC(NH)NH^- > NH_3.$$

Unfortunately this method is not suitable for the quantitative measurement of acid strength.

3. Base-Catalysed Exchange Reactions

Weak acids exchange their hydrogen for deuterium when they are dissolved in liquid ND_3. The exchange rate constants for several hydrocarbons

TABLE XVI

Comparison of Deuterium Exchange Rate Constants at 120° with Aqueous pK Values
(No Amide Catalyst Added)

Hydrocarbon	Rate constant [a] (sec^{-1})	Aqueous pK [b]
Indene	4×10^1	~21
Fluorene	2×10^{-2}	~31
Triphenylmethane	2×10^{-7}	~40
Diphenylmethane	7×10^{-9}	~42

[a] Shatenshtein (1962).   [b] Cram (1963).

are given in Table XVI. It will be noted that the more acidic a hydrocarbon, the more rapidly it exchanges its hydrogen with ammonia. Probably these rate constants correspond to the rate constants for the ionization of the hydrocarbons.

Extremely weak acids such as benzene do not undergo exchange in deuteroammonia in the absence of a catalyst. However, in the presence of a strong base such as potassium amide, exchange takes place. The mechanism for exchange is probably of the following type:

$$RH + ND_2^- \rightarrow R^- + NHD_2 \tag{28}$$

$$R^- + ND_3 \rightarrow RD + ND_2^-. \tag{29}$$

Some experimental rate constants for benzene are presented in Table XVII. These constants are pseudo first-order rate constants, calculated assuming (for convenience) that the rate is independent of the potassium amide concentration. It can be seen that in dilute solution the rate is approximately proportional to the potassium amide concentration, and that at higher concentrations the apparent rate constant falls off. This fall in catalyst activity is probably attributable to the formation of ion pairs.

TABLE XVII

Deuterium Exchange Rate Constants for Benzene in Potassium Amide Solutions
(Shatenshtein, 1962)

(Constants, in sec⁻¹, calculated assuming rate = k[benzene].)

$\theta(°C)$	Molarity of potassium amide					
	0·010	0·014	0·021	0·059	0·19	0·43
−30				4×10^{-7}		
0	4×10^{-6}		$7 \cdot 3 \times 10^{-6}$			$8 \cdot 9 \times 10^{-5}$
25	$4 \cdot 4 \times 10^{-5}$	$5 \cdot 7 \times 10^{-5}$	$8 \cdot 6 \times 10^{-5}$	$1 \cdot 8 \times 10^{-4}$	$4 \cdot 2 \times 10^{-4}$	
40	$1 \cdot 6 \times 10^{-4}$	$3 \cdot 1 \times 10^{-4}$				

It has been found that the rate of exchange of a deuterium atom in the *ortho* position of a substituted benzene is highly sensitive to the electronegativity of the substituent group. Thus the rate constant for fluorobenzene is more than 10^7 times greater than the rate constant for toluene. If we plot the logarithm of the relative exchange rate constants for substituted benzenes against the aqueous pK values for the corresponding substituted acetic acids, a straight line is obtained, as shown in Fig. 5. This is further evidence that the rate of exchange parallels the acidity of the hydrocarbon.

The exchange of hydrogen between organic compounds and ammonia can be used for the preparation of deuterated compounds. Some compounds which have been fully deuterated in this way are benzene, naphthalene,

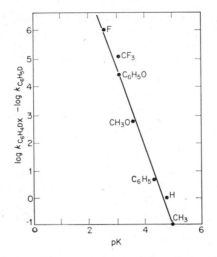

FIG. 5. Correlation between exchange rate constants for substituted benzenes and aqueous pK values for the corresponding substituted acetic acids.

phenanthrene, biphenyl, triphenylmethane, diphenylmethane, bibenzyl, and pyridine (Shatenshtein, 1962).

Wilmarth and Dayton (1953) observed that the conversion of *para*-hydrogen to *ortho*-hydrogen is catalysed by liquid ammonia solutions of potassium amide. The exchange of deuterium gas was found to proceed at approximately the same rate in these solutions, and the initial product was found to be HD. In each case, the rate was found to be proportional to the concentrations of amide ion and hydrogen (*para*-hydrogen or deuterium). They reported a rate constant at $-50°$ of 130 litre mole^{-1} sec^{-1}. The data are consistent with the following type of mechanism:

$$D_2 + NH_2^- \rightarrow D^- + NH_2D \tag{30}$$
$$D^- + NH_3 \rightarrow HD + NH_2^-. \tag{31}$$

A study of the deuterium exchange reaction over a wide concentration range at various temperatures indicated that the reaction is catalysed both by the free amide ion and by the undissociated potassium amide (Bar-Eli and Klein, 1962). The calculated rate constants at $-61°$ are $k_{NH_2^-} = 36$ litre mole^{-1} sec^{-1} and $k_{KNH_2} = 1.7$ litre mole^{-1} sec^{-1}. The activation energy for the amide ion reaction was found to be 7·5 kcal mole^{-1}. From the exchange rates for D_2, HD, and HT, and from the *para*-hydrogen conversion rate, the following isotope effects were calculated:

$$2k_{\mathrm{HD}}/k_{\mathrm{D_2}} = 1{\cdot}28 \pm 0{\cdot}03$$
$$k_{\mathrm{HD}}/k_{\mathrm{HT}} = 1{\cdot}64 \pm 0{\cdot}07$$
$$2k_{\mathrm{H_2}}/k_{\mathrm{D_2}} = 2{\cdot}36 \pm 0{\cdot}30.$$

The amide-catalysed exchange of hydrogen with ammonia is under serious consideration as the basis of a method for concentrating deuterium in ammonia (Haul *et al.*, 1961; Dirian and Grandcollot, 1961; Bourke and Lee, 1961a,b; Brown and Roberts, 1961; Rebora, 1962).

4. *Acid-Catalysed Reactions*

Many esters undergo ammonolysis when treated with liquid ammonia.

$$RCO_2R + NH_3 \rightarrow RCONH_2 + ROH. \tag{32}$$

Ammonium salts catalyse such ammonolyses, just as aqueous acids catalyse the corresponding hydrolyses. The order of catalytic activity for ammonium salts is, however, the reverse of the order of acid strengths based on conductance studies. For example, in the ammonolysis of ethyl benzoate, Fellinger and Audrieth (1938) found the catalytic effect to decrease in the following order: ammonium benzoate$>NH_4Cl>NH_4Br>NH_4ClO_4$. It was later observed that sodium salts are also capable of catalysing ester ammonolysis. Such electrolytes are not as effective as the ammonium salts, but it seems clear that all these catalysed ester ammonolyses are best looked upon as examples of electrolyte catalysis (Audrieth and Kleinberg, 1953).

The exchange of nitrogen between carboxylic acid amides and liquid ammonia has been studied by the use of ^{15}N-labelled ammonia (Heyns *et al.*, 1958). The exchange is catalysed by ammonium chloride, and the following mechanism has been proposed:

$$RCONH_2 + {}^{15}NH_4^+ \rightleftharpoons R - \overset{\overset{\displaystyle +}{\underset{\displaystyle |}{OH_2}}}{\underset{\underset{\displaystyle NH_2}{\displaystyle |}}{C}} - {}^{15}NH_2 \tag{33}$$

$$\downarrow$$

$$RCO^{15}NH_2 + NH_4^+$$

D. REACTIONS OF METAL SOLUTIONS

1. *Systematics*

An enormous number of synthetic reactions involving metal–ammonia solutions have been carried out. These reactions have been reviewed by Birch (1950), Birch and Smith (1958), Watt (1950 and 1957), and Fowles and Nicholls (1962). Practically nothing is known of the mechanisms of these reactions; nevertheless some systematization is possible by considering the products of the reactions. Most reactions involving metal–ammonia solutions may be considered as being initiated by one of the following three steps:

(1) simple electron addition without bond cleavage,

$$e_{am}^- + X \to X^- \tag{34}$$

(2) bond cleavage by the addition of one electron,

$$e_{am}^- + X{-}Y \to X\cdot + Y^- \tag{35}$$

or (3) bond cleavage by the addition of two electrons,

$$2e_{am}^- + X{-}Y \to X^- + Y^-. \tag{36}$$

Electron addition without bond cleavage. The reactions of the electron with molecular oxygen and the nitrite ion involve the formation of products which have reasonable kinetic stabilities in liquid ammonia:

$$e_{am}^- + O_2 \to O_2^- \tag{37}$$

$$e_{am}^- + NO_2^- \to NO_2^{2-}. \tag{38}$$

The rates of these reactions in liquid ammonia are unknown. Thus it is interesting that, even though the electron and the O_2^- and NO_2^{2-} ions are extremely short-lived species in water, the rates of these reactions in water have been measured (Czapski and Schwarz, 1962; Dorfman, 1963).

Some very interesting reductions of transition metal ions appear to involve the simple addition of one or more electrons:

$$e_{am}^- + MnO_4^- \to MnO_4^{2-} \tag{39}$$

$$2e_{am}^- + Ni(CN)_4^{2-} \to Ni(CN)_4^{4-} \tag{40}$$

$$2e_{am}^- + Pd(CN)_4^{2-} \to Pd(CN)_4^{4-} \tag{41}$$

$$2e^- + Pt(NH_3)_4^{2+} \to Pt(NH_3)_4 \tag{42}$$

$$2e^- + Pt(en)_2^{2+} \to Pt(en)_2. \tag{43}$$

Bond cleavage by the addition of one electron. The reactions of the electron with protonic acids fall in this category. The kinetics and mechanisms of the following three examples are discussed in the following sections.

$$e_{am}^- + NH_3 \to NH_2^- + \tfrac{1}{2}H_2 \tag{44}$$

$$e_{am}^- + NH_4^+ \to NH_3 + \tfrac{1}{2}H_2 \tag{45}$$

$$e_{am}^- + EtOH \to EtO^- + \tfrac{1}{2}H_2. \tag{46}$$

The reaction of the electron with organic sulphides may be interpreted in terms of the intermediate formation of R· radicals:

$$e_{am}^- + R_2S \to RS^- + \tfrac{1}{2}R_2. \tag{47}$$

The following reaction is an unusual case in which a stable radical is formed:

$$e_{am}^- + (C_2H_5)_3SnBr \to (C_2H_5)_3Sn\cdot + Br^-. \tag{48}$$

Bond cleavage by the addition of two electrons. When a bond is broken by the addition of two electrons, either two anions or a "di-anion" form:

$$2e_{am}^- + Ge_2H_6 \rightarrow 2GeH_3^- \tag{49}$$

$$2e_{am}^- + C_6H_5NHNH_2 \rightarrow C_6H_5NH^- + NH_2^- \tag{50}$$

$$2e_{am}^- + C_6H_5-N{=}O \rightarrow C_6H_5-N^--O^-. \tag{51}$$

However, one of the anions usually undergoes ammonolysis, as in the following examples:

$$2e_{am}^- + N{\equiv}N^+-O^- \rightarrow N{\equiv}N + O^{2-}$$

$$\downarrow NH_3$$

$$OH^- + NH_2^- \tag{52}$$

$$2e_{am}^- + N{\equiv}C-O^- \rightarrow N{\equiv}C^- + O^{2-}$$

$$\downarrow NH_3$$

$$OH^- + NH_2^- \tag{53}$$

$$2e_{am}^- + Br-C_2H_5 \rightarrow Br^- + C_2H_5^-$$

$$\downarrow NH_3$$

$$C_2H_6 + NH_2^- \tag{54}$$

$$2e_{am}^- + RCH{=}CH_2 \rightarrow RCH-CH_2^{2-}$$

$$\downarrow 2NH$$

$$RCH_2CH_3 + 2NH_2^-. \tag{55}$$

It has been observed that many reductions which take place in liquid ammonia solutions containing both an alkali metal and a protonic acid such as an alcohol or water do not occur at all in the absence of the protonic acid (Birch, 1950; Birch and Smith, 1958). Thus benzene does not appreciably react with sodium in ammonia. However, in the presence of alcohol, reduction to 1,4-dihydrobenzene takes place. Behaviour of this type is probably best explained in terms of the buffering action of the alcohol or other protonic acid. The reduction of a species X to H_2X may be considered to proceed by the following type of mechanism:

$$X \underset{-e^-}{\overset{e^-}{\rightleftharpoons}} X^- \underset{-e^-}{\overset{e^-}{\rightleftharpoons}} X^{2-}$$

In most cases, the intermediate X^{2-} is thermodynamically very unstable; consequently practically no reaction proceeds via this intermediate. The ratio between the concentrations of HX and X^- depends on the pH of the solution. In the absence of any added protonic acid, the pH will soon reach quite high values as a consequence of the reaction proceeding to a slight extent; hence, unless HX is an exceedingly weak acid, the HX concentration will drop, and the reaction will essentially stop. In the presence of an added protonic acid, the solution will be buffered at a pH depending on the strength of the acid. If the added acid is sufficiently strong, the [HX]/[X$^-$] ratio will be high, and the reduction will proceed steadily.

2. *The Reaction of Metals with Ammonia*

All metal-ammonia solutions are metastable. If they are allowed to stand for long periods, or if suitable catalysts are present, decomposition to hydrogen and the metal amide occurs:

$$M + xNH_3 \rightarrow \frac{x}{2}H_2 + M(NH_2)_x. \tag{56}$$

In dilute solutions of sodium or potassium (the amides of which are soluble), the net reaction is

$$e_{am}^- + NH_3 \rightarrow NH_2^- + \tfrac{1}{2}H_2. \tag{57}$$

If pure reagents and clean apparatus are used, and if the solutions are kept cold, decomposition may be held to 0·1% per day (Dewald and Lepoutre, 1954). Warshawsky (1963) has pointed out that an initial hydrogen evolution from metal–ammonia solutions in glassware is attributable to reaction of the metal with a strongly adsorbed layer of water on the glass surface. This water may be removed from a Pyrex surface by baking at 400° for 200 hours *in vacuo*.

The reaction of potassium with liquid ammonia at room temperature has been followed spectrophotometrically by Chou *et al.* (1963). These investigators found that the reaction was first order in metal for the first 75% of reaction and reported half-times of 9-13 hours for initial concentrations in the range 2×10^{-4}—$1·13 \times 10^{-3}$ M. Because the reaction was observed to take place at different rates in different reaction vessels, and because other investigators have observed entirely different rates, it is believed that the reaction is wall-catalysed. I. Warshawsky (unpublished results) has observed that the decomposition of dilute ($< 10^{-4}$ M) solutions of sodium in ammonia at $-78°$ in the presence of platinum foil is zero order in sodium. A rate constant of $1·5 \times 10^{-9}$ moles of H_2 cm^{-2} h^{-1} was reported. The first-order and zero-order behaviours observed in the above studies indicate that the rates are independent of the ammonium ion concentration and the amide ion concentration (in the concentration ranges under study).

A reaction of more fundamental interest than the surface-catalysed reactions described above is the homogeneous reaction of the electron with ammonia. It may be that this reaction is too slow to observe directly. If we assume that the rate of the homogeneous reaction is less than that of the presumably heterogeneous reaction observed by Chou *et al.*, we calculate, for the first-order rate constant, $k < 1.5 \times 10^{-5}$ sec^{-1}. This may be compared with the rate constant $k < 4.4 \times 10^4$ sec^{-1} for the relatively fast reaction of the aqueous electron with water (Dorfman and Taub, 1963):

$$e_{aq}^- + H_2O \rightarrow H + OH^-. \tag{58}$$

The large difference in the reactivity of the electron in water and ammonia is not unexpected. A higher activation energy for the liquid ammonia process,

$$e_{am}^- + NH_3 \rightarrow H + NH_2^- \tag{59}$$

than for the aqueous process is consistent with the estimated heats of reaction, $+33$ kcal mole^{-1} for the liquid ammonia process, and -10 kcal mole^{-1} for the aqueous process.

The mechanism of the homogeneous reaction is, of course, unknown. One can postulate that the atomic hydrogen formed in the initial step dimerizes,

$$2H \rightarrow H_2, \tag{60}$$

or that it reacts further with electrons to form the hydride ion,

$$H + e_{am}^- \rightarrow H^- \tag{61}$$

$$H^- + NH_3 \rightarrow H_2 + NH_2^-. \tag{62}$$

3. *The Reaction of Metals with the Ammonium Ion*

The ammonium ion reacts very rapidly with the electron in ammonia.

$$NH_4^+ + e_{am}^- \rightarrow NH_3 + \tfrac{1}{2}H_2 \tag{63}$$

The half-time for the reaction of 10^{-4} M electrons with 10^{-4} M ammonium ions is less than 1 second. This observation places a lower limit of 10^4 litre mole^{-1} sec^{-1} on the second-order rate constant. We believe that the rate constant for the $NH_4^+ + e_{am}^-$ reaction cannot be greater than the rate constant of the exchange of protons between NH_4^+ and NH_3, for which the value 5×10^8 litre mole^{-1} sec^{-1} has been reported. Therefore we place the $(NH_4^+ + e^-)$ rate constant between the limits of 10^4 and 5×10^8 litre mole^{-1} sec^{-1}.

The rate constant for the corresponding reaction of the aqueous electron and the aqueous proton is 2.3×10^{10} litre mole^{-1} sec^{-1} (Dorfman and Taub, 1963):

$$e_{aq}^- + H_{aq}^+ \rightarrow H. \tag{64}$$

There are at least two ways in which it should be possible to determine the rate of reaction of the electron with the ammonium ion in liquid ammonia. First, it should be possible to utilize the same techniques of pulse radiolysis (Dorfman, 1963) and photolysis (Swenson *et al.*, 1963) which have been used to study reactions of the aqueous electron. Second, it should be possible to study the decomposition of metals in solutions which are buffered at an ammonium ion concentration such that the reaction proceeds at a conveniently measurable rate. We have interpreted data on the reaction of sodium in ethanol–ethoxide solutions in this way in the following section.

4. The Reaction of Sodium with Ethanol

Kelly et al. (1962) followed the reaction of sodium with ethanol in liquid ammonia at $-33\cdot4°$ by measuring the evolved hydrogen as a function of time

$$e_{am}^- + \text{EtOH} \rightarrow \text{EtO}^- + \tfrac{1}{2}\text{H}_2. \tag{65}$$

They obtained data over a remarkably wide time interval. The data for a run in which the sodium was in excess are presented in Table XVIII in the form of the fraction of the alcohol reacted as a function of time. The investigators noted that, during the first 25% of reaction, the reaction was first-order in alcohol and essentially zero-order in sodium. During the second 25% of reaction, the reaction did not appear to be of definite kinetic order, but for the last half of the reaction, the reaction was first-order in both alcohol and sodium, or second-order overall. We believe that the data are most easily explained in terms of the following mechanism:

$$\text{EtOH} + \text{NH}_3 \underset{k_2}{\overset{k_1}{\rightleftharpoons}} \text{NH}_4^+ + \text{EtO}^- \tag{66}$$

$$\text{NH}_4^+ + e_{am}^- \overset{k_3}{\rightarrow} \text{NH}_3 + \tfrac{1}{2}\text{H}_2. \tag{67}$$

If we assume a low, steady-state concentration for the ammonium ion, we calculate the rate law:

$$-\frac{d[\text{EtOH}]}{dt} = \frac{k_1[\text{EtOH}][e_{am}^-]}{(k_2/k_3)[\text{EtO}^-] + [e_{am}^-]}.$$

Qualitatively the data fit this rate law. At the beginning of the reaction, when the EtO$^-$ concentration is very low, the rate law reduces to

$$-\frac{d[\text{EtOH}]}{dt} = k_1[\text{EtOH}].$$

Under these conditions, the rate-determining step is the ionization of the ethanol. During the last stages of the reaction, when $(k_2/k_3)[\text{EtO}^-] \gg [e_{am}^-]$, the rate law reduces to

$$-\frac{d[\text{EtOH}]}{dt} = \frac{k_1[\text{EtOH}][e_{am}^-]}{(k_2/k_3)[\text{EtO}^-]}.$$

Under these conditions, the rate-determining step is the reaction of the ammonium ion with the electron. The accuracy with which the data may be quantitatively represented by the complete rate law can be seen from the "Powell plot" in Fig. 6 (Frost and Pearson, 1961). Here we have plotted the

W. L. JOLLY AND C. J. HALLADA

fraction of reaction, f, against the logarithm of time, t. The circles correspond to the experimental points, and the solid curve has been calculated from the complete rate law, using the constants $k_1 = 0.0303$ sec^{-1} and $k_2/k_3 = 460$. The discrepancy between the experimental points and the calculated

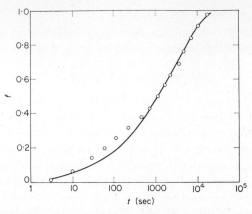

FIG. 6. Plot of fraction reaction *vs* logarithm, of time for sodium–ethanol reaction (Kelly *et al.*, 1962).

curve in the region $f = 0.10$ to $f = 0.40$ is not understood. It does not appear that the discrepancy may be accounted for by ion-pairing, by assuming an initial reaction of the sodium with the ammonia, or by a rate-law term first order in ethanol and first order in sodium.

TABLE XVIII

The Reaction of Sodium with Ethanol (from data of Kelly *et al.*, 1962)

Initial sodium: 0·96 M
Initial ethanol: 0·34 M

t (sec)	f (fraction reaction)	t (sec)	f (fraction reaction)
∼3	0·012	1200	0·495
10	0·065	1680	0·565
30	0·141	2400	0·620
60	0·198	3600	0·687
120	0·254	4800	0·760
240	0·315	7200	0·840
480	0·377	10,800	0·910
720	0·425	18,000	0·975
		28,800	1·000

The pK_a of ethanol in water is ~ 17 (Cram, 1963). If we use the rule that pK values in ammonia are 12 units lower than those in water, and estimate an ion-pair dissociation constant of 10^{-4} for NH_4OEt in ammonia, we may calculate an overall ionization and dissociation constant for ethanol (k_1/k_2) in ammonia of 10^{-9}. From our values for k_1 and k_2/k_3 we may then calculate the rate constant for the reaction of the electron with the ammonium ion, $k_3 \sim 10^5$ litre mole^{-1} sec^{-1}. It will be noted that this value lies within the limits which was imposed above.

5. Comparison with Other Metal Solutions

Solutions of alkali metals in aliphatic amines are extensively used by organic chemists as reducing agents (Birch, 1950; Birch and Smith, 1958). The advantages of amines over ammonia include higher boiling points, higher solubilities for organic compounds, and stronger reducing power in their metal solutions. The metal–amine solutions, however, are much more unstable with respect to decomposition to amide and hydrogen.

Down *et al.* (1959) found that potassium and NaK dissolve slightly (or the order of 10^{-4} M) in certain ethers to give unstable blue solutions. The ethers which show the highest solubilities are the "glyme" solvents (dimethyl ethers of ethylene glycols), 1-methoxymethyltetrahydrofuran, and the cyclic tetramer of propylene oxide. The solubility of potassium in such ethers accounts for the successful use of these solvents in various reactions of potassium, such as the reactions with transition metal carbonyls to form potassium "carbonylates".

$$2K + Mn_2(CO)_{10} \rightarrow 2Mn(CO)_5^- + 2K^+. \tag{68}$$

Aromatic hydrocarbons such as naphthalene react with potassium and sodium in glyme ethers to form green solutions of electron addition compounds (Scott *et al.*, 1936):

$$K + C_{10}H_8 \rightarrow K^+ + C_{10}H_8^-. \tag{69}$$

These relatively stable solutions are very useful as strong reducing agents in circumstances in which it is necessary to avoid solvolysis by protonic solvents. Thus Chatt and Watson (1962) have prepared zero-oxidation-state transition-metal complexes of the type $M[(CH_3)_2PCH_2CH_2P(CH_3)_2]_3$ by the reduction of higher-valent complexes with sodium naphthalenide in tetrahydrofuran.

This work was supported in part by the United States Atomic Energy Commission.

References

Acrivos, J. V. and Pitzer, K. S. (1962) *J. Phys Chem.* **66**, 1693.

Armstrong, G. T. (1953) U.S. National Bureau of Standards Report 2626, "A Critical Review of theLiterature Relating to the Vapor Pressure of Ammonia and Trideutero-ammonia", Washington, D.C.

Arnold, E. and Patterson, A., Jr. (1964) Chapter in "Solutions Metal-Ammoniac", (Lepoutre, G. and Sienko, M. J., eds.). W. A. Benjamin, New York.

Audrieth, L. F. and Kleinberg, J. (1953) "Non-Aqueous Solvents". Wiley, New York.

Bar-Eli, K. and Klein, F. S. (1962) *J. chem. Soc.* 1378.

Becker, E., Lindquist, R. H. and Alder, B. J. (1956) *J. chem. Phys.* **25**, 971

Beckman, T. A. and Pitzer, K. S. (1961) *J. phys. Chem.* **65**, 1527.

Bergstrom, F. W. (1940) *J. Amer. chem. Soc.* **62**, 2381.

Bergstrom, F. W. and Fernelius, W. C. (1933) *Chem. Rev.* **12**, 43.

Bergstrom, F. W. and Fernelius, W. C. (1937) *Chem. Rev.* **20**, 413.

Berthoud, A. (1918a) *Helv. chim. acta* **1**, 84.

Berthoud, A. (1918b) *Chem. Abstr.* **12**, 1849.

Birch, A. J. and MacDonald, D. K. C. (1947) *Nature, Lond.* **159**, 811.

Birch, A. J. and MacDonald, D. K. C. (1948) *Trans. Faraday Soc.* **44**, 735.

Birch, A. J. (1950) *Quart. Rev.* **4**, 69.

Birch, A. J. and Smith, H. (1958) *Quart. Rev.* **12**, 17.

Bourke, P. J. and Lee, J. C. (1961a) *Trans. Inst. chem. Engrs.* (*Lond.*) **39**, 280.

Bourke, P. J. and Lee, J. C. (1961b) *Chem. Abstr.* **55**, 26615i.

Brown, J. and Roberts, N. W. (1951) Brit. Pat. 867, 848.

Brown, J. and Roberts, N. W. (1962) *Chem. Abstr.* **56**, Pl 48c.

Chatt, J. and Watson, H. R. (1962) *J. chem. Soc.* 2545.

Chou, D. Y. P., Pribble, M. J., Jackman, D. C. and Keenan, C. W. (1963) *J. Amer. chem. Soc.* **85**, 3530.

Clark, H. O., Horsfield, A. and Symons, M. C. R. (1959) *J. chem. Soc.* 2478.

Coulter, L. V. and Monchick, L. (1951) *J. Amer. chem. Soc.* **73**, 5867.

Coulter, L. V. (1953) *J. phys. Chem.* **57**, 553.

Coulter, L. V., Sinclair, J. R., Cole, A. G. and Roper, G. C. (1959) *J. Amer. chem. Soc.* **81**, 2986.

Couture, A. M. and Laidler, K. J. (1956) *Canad. J. Chem.* **34**, 1209.

Cragoe, C. and Harper, D. (1921) *Bur. Stds. Sc. Pp.* **420**, 313.

Cram, D. J. (1963) *Chem. Engng News* **93**, 92.

Cseko, G. and Cornides, I. (1960) *J. inorg. nucl. Chem.* **14**, 139.

Cuthrell, R. E., Fohn, E. C. and Lagowski, J. J. (1963) Paper 30 presented before the Division of Inorganic Chemistry, American Chemical Society Meeting, New York, pp. 13N–14N.

Cutler, D., and Powles, J. G. (1962) *Proc. Phys. Soc.* (*Lond.*) **80**, 130.

Czapski, G. and Schwarz, H. A. (1962) *J. phys. Chem.* **66**, 471.

De Grotthuss, C. J. T. (1806) *Annls Chim.* **58**, 54.

Dewald, J. F. and Lepoutre, G. (1954) *J. Amer. chem. Soc.* **76**, 3369.

Dirian, G. and Grandcollot, P. (1961a) *Comm. energie at.* (*France*), *Rappt.* No. 1981.

Dirian, G. and Grandcallot, P. (1961b) *Chem. Abstr.* **55**, 26623d.

Dorfman, L. M. (1963) *Science* **141**, 493.

Dorfman, L. M. and Taub, I. A. (1963) *J. Amer. chem Soc.* **85**, 2370.

Down, J. L., Lewis, J., Moore, B. and Wilkinson, G. (1959) *J. chem. Soc.* 3767.

Dye, J. L., Sankuer, R. F. and Smith, G. E. (1960) *J. Amer. chem. Soc.* **82**, 4797.

Dykhno, N. and Shatenshtein, A. (1948) *J. phys. chem.* (*U.S.S.R.*) **22**, 461.

Dykhno, N. and Shatenshtein, A. (1951) *Zh. fiz. khim.* **25**, 670.

Elsey, H. M. (1920) *J. Amer. chem. Soc.* **42**, 2454.

Fellinger, L. L. and Audrieth, L. F. (1938) *J. Amer. chem. Soc.* **60**, 579.

Fenske, M. R., McCormick, R. H., Lawroski, H. and Geier, R. G. (1955) *A. I. Ch. E. Journal* **1**, 335.

Fenske, M. R., McCormick, R. H., Lawroski, H. and Geier, R. G. (1956) *Chem. Abstr.* **50**, 2154b.

Fernelius, W. C. and Bowman, G. B. (1940) *Chem. Rev.* **26**, 3.

Fowles, G. W. A. and Nicholls, D. (1962) *Quart. Rev.* **16**, 19.

Franklin, E. C. (1934) *J. Amer. chem. Soc.* **56**, 568.

Franklin, E. C. (1935) "The Nitrogen System of Compounds". Reinhold Publishing Corp., New York.

Franklin, E. C. and Kraus, C. A. (1900) *Amer. chem. J.* **23**, 227.

Franklin, E. C. and Cady, H. P. (1904) *J. Amer. chem. Soc.* **26**, 499.

Freed, S. and Sugarman, N. (1943) *J. chem. Phys.* **11**, 354.

Frost, A. A. and Pearson, R. G. (1961) "Kinetics and Mechanism", 2nd edition. Wiley, New York.

Fuoss, R. M. and Accascina, F. (1959) "Electrolytic Conductance". Interscience, New York.

Gold, M. and Jolly, W. L. (1962) *Inorg. Chem.* **1**, 818.

Gold, M., Jolly, W. L. and Pitzer, K. S. (1962) *J. Amer. chem. Soc.* **84**, 2264.

Grubb, H. M., Chittum, J. F. and Hunt, H. (1963) *J. Amer. chem. Soc.* **58**, 776.

Gunn, S. R. and Green, L. R. (1960) *J. phys. Chem.* **64**, 1066.

Gunn, S. R. and Green, L. R. (1962a) *J. chem. Phys.* **36**, 363.

Gunn, S. R. and Green, L. R. (1962b) *J. chem. Phys.* **36**, 368.

Gur'yanova, E. N. and Pleskov, V. A. (1936) *J. phys. Chem. (U.S.S.R.)* **8**, 345.

Hallada, C. J. and Jolly, W. L. (1963) *Inorg. Chem.* **2**, 1076.

Harned, H. S. and Owen, B. B. (1958) "The Physical Chemistry of Electrolytic Solutions", 3rd edition. Reinhold Publishing Corp., New York.

Hasing, J. (1940) *Annln Phys.* **37**, 509.

Haul, R., Ihle, H., Schierholz, H. and Blennemann, D. (1961) *Chemie-Ingr.-Tech.* **33**, 713.

Hawes, W. W. (1933) *J. Amer. chem. Soc.* **55**, 4422.

Hepler, L. G. (1957) *J. phys. Chem.* **61**, 1426.

Heyn, A. H. A. and Bergin, M. J. (1953) *J. Amer. chem. Soc.* **75**, 5120.

Heyns, K., Brockmann, R. and Roggenbuck, A. (1958) *Liebigs Ann.* **614**, 97.

Hildebrand, J. H. (1948) *J. chem. Educ.* **25**, 74.

Hildebrand, J. H. and Scott, R. L. (1962) "Regular Solutions". Prentice-Hall, Englewood Cliffs, N.J.

Hnizda, V. F. and Kraus, C. A. (1949) *J. Amer. chem. Soc.* **71**, 1565.

Hodgins, J. W. (1949) *Canad. J. Res.* **27**, 861.

Hunt, J. P., Dodgen, H. W. and Klanberg, F. (1963) *Inorg. Chem.* **2**, 478.

Huster, E. (1938) *Annln Phys.* **33**, 477.

Hutchison, C. A., Jr. and O'Reilly, D. E. (1961a) *J. chem. Phys.* **34**, 163.

Hutchison, C. A., Jr. and O'Reilly, D. E. (1961b) *J. chem. Phys.* **34**, 1279.

Hutchison, C. A., Jr. and Pastor, R. C. (1953) *J. chem. Phys.* **21**, 1959.

Ipat'ev, V. V. and Teodorovich, V. P. (1932) *J. gen. Chem., Moscow* **2**, 305.

Ishida, K. (1957) *Kogyo Kagaku Zasshi* **60**, 864.

Ishida, K. (1958) *Bull. chem. Soc. Japan* **31**, 143.

Ishida, K. (1959) *Chem. Abstr.* **53**, 980lh.

Ishida, K. (1960a) *Bull. chem. Soc. Japan* **33**, 693.

Ishida, K. (1960b) *Chem. Abstr.* **54**, 23687f.

Jaffe, H. (1935) *Z. Phys.* **93**, 741.

Jander, G. (1949) "Die Chemie in Wasserähnlichen Lösungsmitteln", Springer-Verlag, Berlin.

Johnson, W. C. and Martens, R. I. (1936) *J. Amer. chem. Soc.* **58**, 15.

Johnson, W. C. and Meyer, A. W. (1929) *J. phys. Chem.* **33**, 1922.

Johnson, W. C. and Meyer, A. W. (1932) *J. Amer. chem. Soc.* **54**, 3621.

Johnson, W. C., Meyer, A. W. and Martens, R. D. (1950) *J. Amer. chem. Soc.* **72**, 1842.

Johnson, W. C. and Piskur, M. M. (1933) *J. phys. Chem.* **37**, 93.

Jolly, W. L. (1953) *J. phys. Chem.* **58**, 250.

Jolly, W. L. (1956) *J. chem. Educ.* **33**, 512.

Jolly, W. L. (1959) *Prog. inorg. Chem.* **1**, 235.

Jolly, W. L. (1960) "Synthetic Inorganic Chemistry". Prentice-Hall, Englewood Cliffs, N.J.

Jolly, W. L., Hallada, C. J. and Gold, M. (1964) Chapter in "Solutions Metal-Ammoniac" (edited by Lepoutre, G. and Sienko, M. J.), W. A. Benjamin, New York.

Jortner, J. (1959) *J. chem. Phys.* **30**, 839.

Kaplan, J. and Kittel, C. (1953) *J. chem. Phys.* **21**, 1429.

Kay, R. L. (1960) *J. Amer. chem. Soc.* **82**, 2099.

Kelly, E. J., Secor, H. Y., Keenan, C. W. and Eastham, J. F. (1962) *J. Amer. chem. Soc.* **84**, 3611.

Kikuchi, S. and Kudo, S. (1944) *J. Soc. chem. Ind. Japan* **47**, 302.

Kikuchi, S. and Kudo, S. (1948) *Chem. Abstr.* **42**, 6208i.

Knight, W. D. (1949) *Phys. Rev.* **76**, 1259.

Kraus, C. A. (1914) *J. Amer. Chem. Soc.* **36**, 864.

Kraus, C. A. and Johnson, W. C. (1925) *J. Amer. chem. Soc.* **47**, 725.

Kraus, C. A. and Lucasse, W. W. (1921) *J. Amer. chem. Soc.* **43**, 2529.

Kraus, C. A. and Lucasse, W. W. (1922) *J. Amer. chem. Soc.* **44**, 1941.

Kraus, C. A. and Lucasse, W. W. (1923) *J. Amer. chem. Soc.* **45**, 2551.

Kraus, C. A. and Schmidt, F. C. (1934) *J. Amer. chem. Soc.* **56**, 2297.

Kraus, C. A. (1953) *J. chem. Educ.* **30**, 83.

Laitinen, H. A. and Nyman, C. J. (1948a) *J. Amer. chem. Soc.* **70**, 2241.

Laitinen, H. A. and Nyman, C. J. (1948b) *J. Amer. chem. Soc.* **70**, 3002.

Laitinen, H. A. and Shoemaker, C. E. (1950a) *J. Amer. chem. Soc.* **72**, 663.

Laitinen, H. A. and Shoemaker, C. E. (1950b) *J. Amer. chem. Soc.* **72**, 4975.

Latimer, W. M. (1952). "Oxidation Potentials", 2nd edition, pp. 34–36. Prentice-Hall, Englewood Cliffs, N.J.

Lefrancois, B. and Vaniscotte, C. (1960) *Chal. et Industr.* **41**, 183.

Lepoutre, G. and Patterson, A., Jr. (1955) *C.R. Acad. Sci., Paris* **240**, 1644.

Lepoutre, G. and Sienko, M. J., Editors (1964) "Solutions Metal-Ammoniac". W. A. Benjamin, New York.

Levine, R. and Fernelius, W. C. (1954) *Chem. Rev.* **54**, 449.

Levy, R. A. (1956) *Phys. Rev.* **102**, 31.

Loewenstein, A. and Szöke, A. (1962) *J. Amer. chem. Soc.* **84**, 1151.

MacInnes, D. A. (1939) "The Principles of Electrochemistry". Reinhold Publishing Corp., New York.

McConnell, H. M. and Holm, C. H. (1957) *J. chem. Phys.* **26**, 1517.

McElroy, A. D. and Laitinen, H. A. (1953) *J. phys. Chem.* **57**, 564.

Monoszon, A. M. and Pleskov, V. A. (1931) *Z. phys. Chem.*, Abt. A. **156**, 176.

Mulder, H. D. and Schmidt, F. C. (1951) *J. Amer. chem. Soc.* **73**, 5575.

Nyman, C. J. (1949) *J. Amer. chem. Soc.* **71**, 3914.

Nyman, C. J., Si Chang Fung and Dodger, H. W. (1950) *J. Amer. chem. Soc.* **72**, 1033.

Ogg, R. A., Jr. (1954) *Disc. Faraday Soc.* No. 17, 215.

Ogg, R. A., Jr., Leighton, P. A. and Bergstrom, F. W. (1933) *J. Amer. chem. Soc.* **55**, 1754.

Overstreet, R. and Giauque, W. F. (1937) *J. Amer. chem. Soc.* **59**, 254.

Pauling, L. (1960) "The Nature of the Chemical Bond", 3rd edition, p. 621. Cornell University Press, Ithaca, N.Y.

Pinevich, G. (1948a) *Kholod. Tekh.* **20**, No. 3, 30.
Pinevich, G. (1948b) *Chem. Abstr.* **43**, 8813e.
Plank, C. J. and Hunt, H. (1939) *J. Amer. chem. Soc.* **61**, 3590.
Pleskov, V. A. and Monoszon, A. M. (1935a) *Acta Phys.-chim. URSS* **1**, 713.
Pleskov, V. A. and Monoszon, A. M. (1935b) *Acta Phys-chim. URSS* **2**, 615.
Pollak, V. L. (1961) *J. chem. Phys.* **34**, 864.
Rebora, P. L. (1962a) *Energia nucl.* **9**, 338.
Rebora, P. L. (1962b) *Chem. Abstr.* **57**, 16078a.
Rossini, F. D., Wagman, D. D., Evans, W. H., Levine, S. and Jaffe, I. (1952). National Bureau of Standards Circular 500, "Selected Values of Chemical Thermodynamic Properties". Washington, D.C.
Ruff, O. and Geisel, E. (1906) *Ber. dtsch. chem. Ges.* **39**, 828.
Sanderson, R. T. (1948) "Vacuum Manipulation of Volatile Compounds". Wiley, New York.
Schaap, W. B., Conley, R. F. and Schmidt, F. C. (1961) *Analyt. chem.* **33**, 498.
Schmidt, F. C., Sottysiak, J., Tajkowski, E. and Denison, W. A. (1941) *J. Amer. chem. Soc.* **63**, 2669.
Schmidt, F. C., Studer, F. J. and Sottysiak, J. (1938) *J. Amer. chem. Soc.* **60**, 2780.
Scott, N. D. Walker, J. F. and Hansley, V. L. (1936) *J. Amer. chem. Soc.* **58**, 2442.
Shatenshtein, A. I. (1939) *Acta Phys.-chem. URSS* **10**, 121.
Shatenshtein, A. I. (1962) "Isotopic Exchange and the Replacement of Hydrogen in Organic Compounds". Consultants Bureau, New York.
Shatenshtein, A. I., Izrailevich, E. A. and Ladyshnikova, N. I. (1949a) *Zh. fiz. khim.* **23**, 497.
Shatenshtein, A. I., Izrailevich, E. A. and Ladyshnikova, N. I. (1949b) *Chem. Abstr.* **43**, 6024c.
Sisler, H. H. (1961) "Chemistry in Non-Aqueous Solvents". Reinhold Publishing Corp., New York.
Stairs, R. A. and Sienko, M. J. (1956) *J. Amer. chem. Soc.* **78**, 920.
Swenson, G. W., Zwicker, E. F. and Grossweiner, L. I. (1963) *Science* **141**, 1042.
Symons, M. C. R. (1959) *Quart. Rev.* **13**, 99.
Vegard, L. and Hillesund, S. (1942) Avhandl. Norske Videnskaps-Akad. Oslo I. Mat.-Naturv. Klasse, No. 8; Wyckoff, R. W. G. (1948, 1951) "Crystal Structures", Vol. I. Interscience, New York.
Warshawsky, I. (1963) *J. inorg. nucl. Chem.* **25**, 601.
Watt, G. W. (1950) *Chem. Rev.* **46**, 289, 317.
Watt, G. W. (1957) *J. chem. Educ.* **34**, 533.
Watt, G. W. and Sowards, D. M. (1955) *J. electrochem. Soc.* **102**, 46.
Watt, G. W., Sowards, D. M. and McBride, W. R. (1955) *J. Amer. chem. Soc.* **77**, 5835.
Weyl, W. (1864) *Annln Phys.* **121**, 601.
Wiebe, R. and Tremearne, T. H. (1933) *J. Amer. chem. Soc.* **55**, 975.
Wiesendanger, H. U. D., Jones, W. H., and Garnet, C. S. (1937) *J. chem. Phys.* **27**, 668.
Wilmarth, W. K. and Dayton, J. C. (1953) *J. Amer. chem. Soc.* **75**, 4553.
Wolsky, S. P. (1952) Thesis, Boston University, Boston, Massachusetts.
Wolsky, S. P., Zdanuk, E. J. and Coulter, L. V. (1952) *J. Amer. chem. Soc.* **74**, 6196.
Yost, D. M. and Russell, H., Jr. (1944). "Systematic Inorganic Chemistry". Prentice-Hall, Englewood Cliffs, N.J.
Zintl, E., Goubeau, J. and Dullenkopf, W. (1931) *Z. phys. Chem.* A**154**, 1.
Zintl, E. and Neumayr, S. (1930) *Ber. dtsch. chem. Ges.* **63**B, 237.

CHAPTER 2

Liquid Hydrogen Fluoride

H. H. HYMAN AND J. J. KATZ

Chemistry Division, Argonne National Laboratory, Argonne, Illinois, U.S.A.

I. Introduction.. 47
    A. Equipment for Studying Liquid Hydrogen Fluoride...................... 50
II. Properties of Pure Liquid Hydrogen Fluoride................................ 52
    A. Physical Properties.. 52
    B. Vibronic Absorption Spectra... 55
    C. Structure of the Liquid... 57
    D. Acidity.. 62
III. Solutes in Liquid Hydrogen Fluoride....................................... 64
    A. Metal Fluorides... 65
    B. Non-metallic, Non-acidic, Ionizing Fluorides.......................... 67
    C. Proton Acceptors... 68
    D. Acid Solutes: Fluoride Ion Acceptors.................................. 72
    E. Salts in the Hydrogen Fluoride System as Solutes...................... 74
    F. Solution in Hydrogen Fluoride without Ionization...................... 75
IV. Solution in Anhydrous Hydrogen Fluoride of Compounds of Biological Importance   76

I. INTRODUCTION

Hydrogen fluoride is an interesting and important member of the class of non-aqueous ionizing solvents. It is a simple binary compound, and the anion and cation species formed by self-ionization are the smallest and most mobile ionic species found in any solution. Investigations of this powerful solvent have been severely handicapped in the past by the reactivity of glass and quartz with hydrogen fluoride. Ordinary laboratory equipment thus cannot be used, and this circumstance, together with the extraordinarily unpleasant physiological properties of the compound, prevented until very recently any systematic investigation of the solvent behaviour of hydrogen fluoride.

The advent of nuclear energy has changed all this. The urgent necessity for the manipulation of uranium hexafluoride for the separation of the uranium isotopes generated a keen interest in hydrogen fluoride and in fluorine chemistry generally, and resulted ultimately in a wide variety of laboratory tools that make the study of hydrogen fluoride a practical undertaking. It is not surprising, therefore, that many recent developments have occcurred in laboratories supported by Atomic Energy authorities. Particularly noteworthy is the development of fluorine-containing plastics that are completely inert to hydrogen fluoride. Polytetrafluoroethylene and polychlorotrifluoroethylene are available on a large scale as sheets, rods, or tubes, are easily worked, and, in the case of polychlorotrifluoroethylene, are

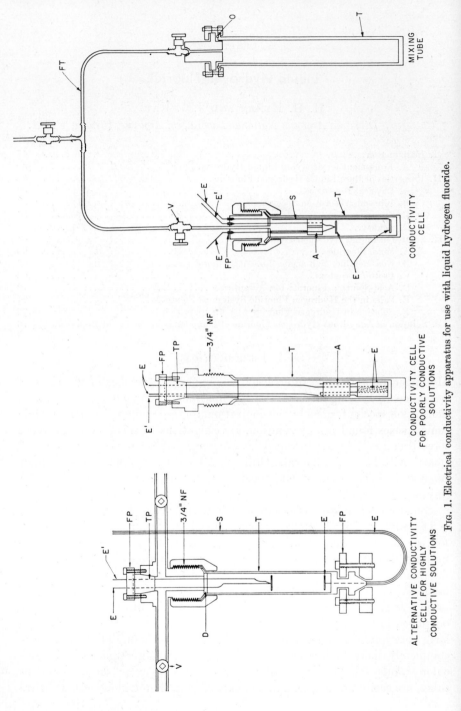

FIG. 1. Electrical conductivity apparatus for use with liquid hydrogen fluoride.

transparent. Apparatus fabricated from these resistant plastics have indeed revolutionized research with hydrogen fluoride, and have converted hydrogen fluoride to a tractable and useful substance.

Hydrogen fluoride is of interest from many points of view. It is important in the preparation of elemental fluorine, in the synthesis of inorganic and

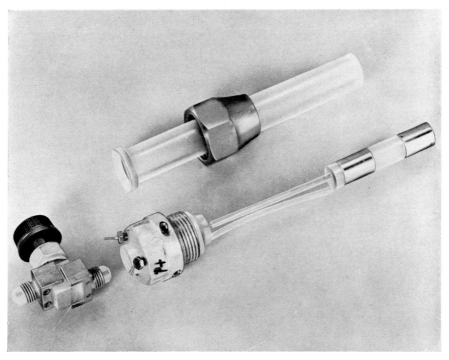

Fig. 2. A cell for electrical conductivity measurements in liquid hydrogen fluoride. For this cell the geometry of the electrodes is fixed, and results are reproducible, though the design is somewhat different from that found in ordinary conductivity cells.

Fig. 1. (*Facing page.*)

A	An aligning block, polytetrafluoroethylene.
D	A polychlorotrifluoroethylene porous disc.
E	Electrodes and leads of platinum.
E'	Platinum–rhodium alloy lead used to make thermocouple.
FP	A forcing plate used to squeeze a wedge-shaped polytetrafluoroethylene seal around the fine lead.
FT	Flexible polychlorotrifluoroethylene tubing.
O	An o-ring type flanged seal. Major parts are polychlorotrifluoroethylene, o-rings are polytetrafluoroethylene. Metal bolts and flanges are used.
NF	A nickel or nickel alloy flare fitting. (A threader hollow ring of any metal with a polychlorotrifluoroethylene centre may be substituted.)
S	A sheath of polychlorotrifluoroethylene tubing.
T	The polychlorotrifluoroethylene tube may be injection molded, machined, or fabricated from extruded tubing.
TP	A polytetrafluoroethylene plug forced around the electrical leads.
V	Valves (a variety of plastic and metal valves have been used).

organic fluorine compounds, and as a solvent. Emphasis here will be focused on its solvent properties. Extensive reviews on other important aspects of hydrogen fluoride are given by Simons (1950, 1964) and Mellor (1956).

A. EQUIPMENT FOR STUDYING LIQUID HYDROGEN FLUORIDE

Modern techniques make it possible to carry out on hydrogen fluoride solutions all the physical chemical observations that can be made on aqueous solutions. Such measurements include, by way of example, electrical conductivity; vapour pressure; absorption spectrophotometry in the ultra-violet, visible, and infra-red; Raman spectroscopy; proton magnetic resonance; polarimetry; and refractometry.

FIG. 3. A 1 mm cell for spectrophotometry with liquid hydrogen fluoride solutions.

Electrical conductivity measurements can be conveniently made in all polychlorotrifluoroethylene (Kel-F) systems (Quarterman et al., 1957, 1961). Hydrogen fluoride can be prepared in very pure form by distillation in all polychlorotrifluoroethylene apparatus (Runner et al., 1956). Hydrogen fluoride prepared in this way has the lowest electrical conductivity of any hydrogen fluoride routinely prepared and is eminently suitable as a solvent for electrical conductivity measurements (Figs. 1 and 2).

Absorption spectrophotometry in the visible and ultra-violet has become a simple process by the use of absorption cells fitted with synthetic sapphire (Al_2O_3) windows that are highly transparent and completely resistant to hydrogen fluoride (Fig. 3). In the infra-red region silver chloride windows are quite resistant to almost all hydrogen fluoride solutions, and measurements can be made in this region with little difficulty. Alternative windows may often be substituted in a single cell (Fig. 4) (Quarterman *et al.*, 1957). Raman spectra can be observed with sapphire tubes, but many recent investigations have depended on polychlorotrifluoroethylene tubing. Such tubing, in smaller sizes, has also been successfully used for nuclear magnetic resonance studies.

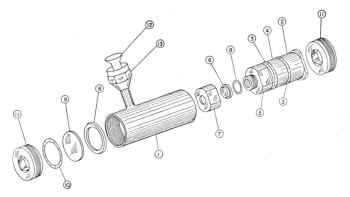

FIG. 4. A variable light path cell for spectrophotometry with liquid hydrogen fluoride solutions. 1. Body. 2. Polychlorotrifluoroethylene barrel. 3. Polytetrafluoroethylene o-rings for sliding seal. 4. Kel-F spacer. 5. Kel-F adjustment nut for sliding seal. 6. Inner window sapphire or silver chloride. 7. Kel-F end piece for inner assembly. 8. Teflon gasket. 9. Outer window sapphire or silver chloride. 10. Teflon o-ring. 11. Brass plug. 12. Flared lip. 13. Brass flare nut.

The availability of extruded polychlorotrifluoroethylene tubing and solid forms suitable for machining has greatly facilitated the construction of vacuum lines for the preparation and manipulation of hydrogen fluoride solutions. Valves, tees, elbows, unions, and similar fittings can be easily fabricated from this transparent thermoplastic. Threads may be machined directly in the plastic, but metal threads are generally more satisfactory, and a variety of fittings have been fabricated employing plastic to plastic seals between threaded or flanged metal connections, as in the connections shown in Figs. 1 and 2. Split rings of threaded metal are assembled around flanged plastic tubes. This type of connection or closure has been found to be widely applicable (cf. Katz and Hyman, 1953; Adams and Katz, 1956, 1957; Hyman *et al.*, 1957, 1961).

Polytetrafluoroethylene (Teflon) is softer than Kel-F, opaque, and not readily fusible. However, it is also completely resistant to hydrogen fluoride solutions, and so finds considerable use. It can be employed at much higher temperature than can the chlorine-containing plastic. Ordinarily, however, hydrogen fluoride is used at near ambient temperatures, and under such conditions lower-melting plastics are more readily fabricated and equally satisfactory in use. Other fluorine-containing elastomers (e.g. Viton A) are also useful for hydrogen fluoride resistant equipment. The moral of this very brief description is that practical means exist for fabricating practically any kind of apparatus for experimenting with hydrogen fluoride. The problems encountered in the past have for the most part been solved, and the experimental problems associated with hydrogen fluoride are now less severe than for many substances commonly encountered in the laboratory.

II. Properties of Pure Liquid Hydrogen Fluoride

A. physical properties

Table I describes the melting and boiling points, density, refractive index, viscosity, surface tension, dielectric constant, and electrical conductivity of hydrogen fluoride. Some of these data have not been checked recently and may have been determined on impure material. Small amounts of water or other impurities can seriously affect many of the values quoted.

However, the data given in Table I provide an entirely adequate basis for qualitative conclusions about the solvent properties of liquid hydrogen fluoride.

These physical properties indicate at once that it is an unusual solvent. The high boiling point, long liquid range, and high dielectric constant suggest that, like water, hydrogen fluoride is an associated liquid, that hydrogen bonding and proton transfer reaction will be important in hydrogen fluoride solution, and that ionization will frequently accompany solution.

The relatively low surface tension and viscosity of liquid hydrogen fluoride are very different from those of water and rule out the presence of three-dimensional networks such as those found in water or sulphuric acid. The structure of liquid hydrogen fluoride will thus be markedly different from these other high dielectric solvents. The molecular processes taking place in pure liquid hydrogen fluoride are important and will be discussed in detail below.

The heat of formation of hydrogen fluoride has recently been reinvestigated. Feder et al. (1963) combine results based on precision fluorine bomb calorimetry, e.g. for the heat of formation of SiF_4, with data on the heat of hydrolysis, e.g. $SiF_4 + 2H_2O \rightarrow SiO_2 + 4HF$. The results suggest a value of -64.9 kcal mole^{-1} for the heat of formation of gaseous monomeric hydrogen fluoride at 25°C.

The vapour pressure p of liquid hydrogen fluoride was measured by Jarry and Davis (1953). Their data is represented by either of two equations:*

$$\log p(\text{torr}) = 8.38036 - 1952.55/(335.52 + t) \tag{1}$$

$$\log p(\text{torr}) = -1.91173 - 918.24/T + 3.21542 \log T. \tag{2}$$

Table II gives the vapour pressure at selected temperatures as calculated from each of these equations. Jarry and Davis arrive at a boiling point,

* t refers to °C, T to °K.

19·51°C, which is close to that found by many other workers, but the heat of vapourization determined from their vapour pressure curve, 1·608 kcal mole^{-1} at this boiling point, does not agree with the value found by earlier workers

TABLE I

Some Properties of Liquid Hydrogen Fluoride

Property	Value*
Melting point	$-89 \cdot 37°C$[a]
Boiling point	$19 \cdot 51°C$[b]
Density (g/ml)	$1 \cdot 0020 - (2 \cdot 2625 \times 10^{-3}t)$
	$+ (3 \cdot 125 \times 10^{-6}t^2)$[c]
	$1 \cdot 1231$ at $-50°C$[c]
	$1 \cdot 0606$ at $-25°C$[c]
	$1 \cdot 002$ at $0°C$[c]
	$0 \cdot 9546$ at $25°C$[d]
	$0 \cdot 908$ at $50°C$[e]
	$0 \cdot 796$ at $100°C$[e]
	$0 \cdot 646$ at $150°C$[e]
Critical density	$0 \cdot 29$ ($\pm 0 \cdot 03$) at $188°C$[e]
Refractive index	
$n^{25°C}$	$1 \cdot 15436 + 0 \cdot 001025/\gamma(A)$[f]
$n_D^{25°C}$	$1 \cdot 1574$[f]
$\Delta n_D / \Delta t$	$-0 \cdot 0004$[f]
Viscosity	
(at $-50°C$)	$0 \cdot 570$ centipoise
	$0 \cdot 507$ centistoke[g]
(at $-25°C$)	$0 \cdot 350$ centipoise
	($= 0 \cdot 330$ centistoke)[g]
(at $0°C$)	$0 \cdot 256$ centipoise
	($= 0 \cdot 256$ centistoke)[g]
Surface tension	$40 \cdot 7 \ (1 - T/503 \cdot 2)^{1 \cdot 78}$[c]
(dynes/cm)	$17 \cdot 7$ at $-81 \cdot 8°C$[c]
	$12 \cdot 0$ at $-23 \cdot 2°C$[c]
	$10 \cdot 1$ at $0°C$[c]
	$8 \cdot 62$ at $18 \cdot 2°C$[c]
Dielectric constant	175 at $-73°C$[h]
	134 at $-42°C$[h]
	111 at $-27°C$[h]
	84 at $0°C$[h]
Electrical conductivity	$1 \cdot 4 \times 10^{-5}$ at $-15°C$[i]
(ohm^{-1} cm^{-1})	$\sim \times 10^{-6}$ at $0°C$[k]

[a] Hu et al., 1953.
[b] Jarry and Davis, 1953.
[c] Simons and Bouknight, 1932.
[d] Hyman et al., 1963.
[e] Franck and Spalthoff, 1957.
[f] Perkins, 1965.
[g] Simons and Dresdner, 1944.
[h] Fredenhagen and Dahmlos, 1929.
[i] Fredenhagen and Cadenbach, 1929.
[k] Runner et al., 1956.

* In equations, t is used for °C, T for °K.

(cf. Mellor, 1956) or by Hu *et al.* (1953). The thermochemical data determined by this latter group are summarized in Table III. The discrepancy between the two values for the heat of vapourization has not been satisfactorily resolved.

TABLE II

Vapour Pressure of Liquid Hydrogen Fluoride

Temperature °C	Vapour pressure (torr)	
	Equation 1[a]	Equation 2[b]
−80	5·55	4·84
−50	34·82	33·52
−25	123·7	122·5
0	363·8	363·8
10	536·2	536·7
20	773·2	774·1
25	921·4	922·5
50	2069·0	2069·0
100	7891·0	7894·0
150	23,460[b]	
188[c]	48,690[b]	

[a] According to Jarry and Davis, 1953 (see text).
[b] Franck and Spalthoff, 1957.
[c] Critical temperature (188 ± 3°C), and pressure (48,700 ± 2500 torr).

TABLE III

Fusion and Vapourization of Hydrogen Fluoride[a]

Melting point	189·79 ± 0·02°K
Heat of Fusion	46·93 ± 0·04 cal/g at the melting point
	= 0·939 kcal mole⁻¹ [b]
Entropy of fusion	4·942 e.u.
Boiling point	292·61 ± 0·1°K at 741·4 mm
Heat of vapourization	89·45 ± 0·20 cal/g at the above boiling point
	= 1·789 kcal mole⁻¹ [b]
Entropy of vapourization	= 6·117 e.u.
Molar entropy of gaseous hydrogen fluoride at 741 mm and 292·61°K	= 23·9 e.u.
Molar entropy of monomeric gaseous hydrogen fluoride (spectroscopic)	41·5 e.u. at 298·16°K

[a] According to Hu *et al.*, 1953. See text.
[b] The formula molecular weight is taken as 20·006 g/mole.

B. VIBRONIC ABSORPTION SPECTRA

The absorption spectrum of hydrogen fluoride has been employed to investigate the molecular properties of four different states of aggregation, gaseous monomer and polymer, liquid, and solid.

To observe the vibration and rotation spectrum of gaseous monomeric hydrogen fluoride, measurement must be carried out at low pressure and moderately elevated temperature to assure complete disaggregation.

Calcium fluoride, silver chloride, and polyethylene are suitably inert window materials. The fundamental HF stretching vibration is found in the 3μ region, the rotation bands in the far infra-red. Highly precise observations are available (Kuipers *et al.*, 1956; Kuipers, 1958; Rothschild, 1964) on the gas and need not concern us directly in our discussion of liquid hydrogen fluoride. Some of the pertinent data on the monomeric gas are summarized in Table IV.

TABLE IV

Some Spectroscopic Data for Monomeric HF Gas

Constant[a]	Value (cm^{-1})
ν_0 $(0\leftarrow1)$	3961·64
$(0\leftarrow2)$	7751·24
$(0\leftarrow3)$	11372·7
$(0\leftarrow4)$	14831·6
B_0	20·56
D_0	0·00211
ω_e	4137·25
$x_e\omega_e$	88·73
$y_e\omega_e$	0·533
B_e	20·95
D_e	0·00213
α_e	0·789
γ_e	0·0087

[a] Standard spectroscopic notation, cf. e.g. Herzberg, 1950.

At lower temperatures and higher pressures hydrogen fluoride associates into polymers. This association is discussed in detail in a later section. The infra-red absorption spectrum has been invaluable in ascertaining the nature of the polymer species in the gas (Smith, 1958).

The nature of the absorption bands in the 3μ region is the most significant in the study of gas polymers, since these absorptions arise from the hydrogen stretching fundamentals in the HF polymers.

Liquid hydrogen fluoride likewise has a number of infra-red absorption bands, and Figs. 5 and 6 summarize the situation in two regions of the spectrum. These absorption bands appear to be primarily due to h.f. vibrations in polymer molecules (Maybury *et al.*, 1955; Hyman *et al.*, 1957).

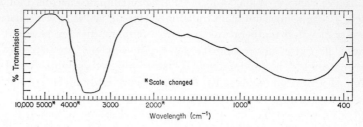

Fig. 5. Infra-red spectrum of liquid hydrogen fluoride (according to Maybury *et al.*, 1955) (cell thickness, 6μ).

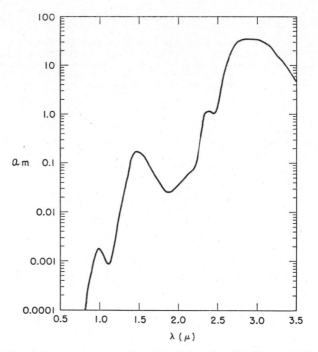

Fig. 6. Near infra-red spectrum of liquid hydrogen fluoride (Hyman *et al.*, 1957).

For infra-red studies with liquid hydrogen fluoride, silver chloride appears to be the most suitable window material. Since, as is also the case with liquid water, hydrogen fluoride absorbs intensely in the infra-red, very short light paths are needed. A typical infra-red cell with a very short and variable light path is shown in Fig. 7. The intense and broad absorption band in the

3μ region exhibited by liquid hydrogen fluoride reduces the utility of infra-red analysis for the study of dilute solutions, but infra-red studies have been applied effectively to more concentrated solutions (Adams and Katz, 1957).

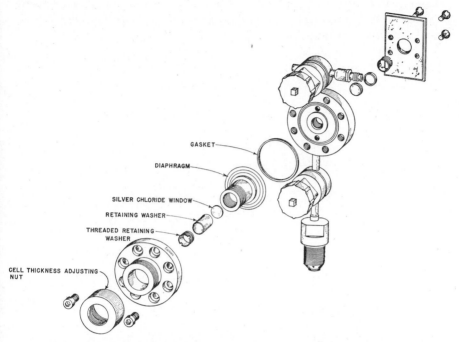

FIG. 7. A cell for infra-red absorption spectrophotometry with liquid hydrogen fluoride solutions. The flexible diaphragm permits variation in light path.

Finally, the infra-red absorption spectrum of solid hydrogen fluoride has been studied (Table V). The interpretation involves some speculation as to the structure of the solid and thus is briefly discussed in connection with association.

C. STRUCTURE OF THE LIQUID

It is obvious from its physical properties that liquid hydrogen fluoride has a complex structure. At least two types of molecular interaction appear to play an important role in liquid hydrogen fluoride. These are self-ionization and intermolecular association.

1. *Self-ionization*

As in most protonic ionizing solvents, the ionic species formed by self-ionization are probably part of a hydrogen-bonded network; individual molecules cannot readily be distinguished. A naked, unsolvated proton is clearly unrealistic, and the formal self-ionization equation in its simplest form must approximate:

$$2HF \rightleftharpoons H_2F^+ + F^-. \tag{3}$$

It is highly likely that the proton is in fact attached not to monomeric hydrogen fluoride but to hydrogen fluoride polymers. The fluoride ion must also be heavily solvated.

The extent to which self-ionization takes place in pure liquid hydrogen fluoride is not yet completely established. The most useful criterion for determining the extent of self-ionization is the electrical conductivity, but

TABLE V

Absorption Bands in the Spectra of Pure HF and DF Crystals

DF[a] (cm^{-1})	HF (cm^{-1})	
	a	b
	3581 w	3590 w
2527	3414 s	3420 s
	3270 w	3270 w
2284	3060 s	3060 s
855	1200	1204
715	971	(955–1010)
570	790	
405	555	547
	515	
	370	366

[a] Sastri and Hornig, 1963.
[b] Giguère and Zengin, 1958.

the true minimum value for this parameter is still uncertain. The impurity contributing most to enhanced conductivity is water, which must be rigorously removed in order to assess the extent of self-ionization of pure hydrogen fluoride. Commercial hydrogen fluoride drawn directly from cylinders shows high electrical conductivity. To purify hydrogen fluoride, not only must adventitious water itself be rigorously excluded, but virtually all other metal oxides as well. Hydrogen fluoride reacts with oxides to yield water, and even the usual protective oxide film on nickel metal equipment reacts in this way. Fredenhagen and Cadenbach (1929) were able to prepare very dry hydrogen fluoride with a conductivity of 1.4×10^{-5} ohm^{-1} cm^{-1} at 0°C in platinum equipment. Such a conductivity is now known to correspond to a water content of less than 0·0002% H_2O. More recently, hydrogen fluoride with a conductivity as low as 10^{-6} ohm^{-1} cm^{-1} has been obtained by distillation in a polychlorotrifluoroethylene fractionating column (Runner et al., 1956), but only a few measurements have been made on hydrogen fluoride of this purity.

If the equivalent conductivity of the ionic species present in pure HF at 0°C is assumed to have a value of 700, a specific conductivity of 10^{-6} ohm^{-1} cm^{-1} corresponds to an H^+ or F^- concentration of 1.4×10^{-6} mole/litre, or an equilibrium constant for self-ionization K_{HF} of 2×10^{-12}. The true equilibrium constant for self-ionization will probably be lower, and may even approach that of water itself in the rigorous absence of all impurities.

Both the proton and the fluoride ion show high equivalent conductances in liquid hydrogen fluoride. The high equivalent conductance is undoubtedly due to a chain conductivity mechanism, quite comparable to that observed in water or anhydrous sulphuric acid. Chain conductivity for the fluoride ion and especially for the proton was only established many years after such a mechanism was first suspected to play a role in conductivity. The low viscosity of hydrogen fluoride reduces differences between chain conductivity and ordinary ionic mobility. Experimental difficulties have also been encountered in obtaining solutions free enough from basic impurities to measure accurately the conductivity of low concentrations of strong acids. It has now become clear, however, that a chain conductivity mechanism is operative in the migration of ions in hydrogen fluoride (Kilpatrick and Lewis, 1956; Hyman et al., 1963).

2. Polymerization

The association or polymerization of hydrogen fluoride has been studied most directly in the gas phase. The average molecular weight as a function of temperature and pressure is now reasonably well known (Table VI). The data indicate that HF in the gas phase is extensively associated. Indeed, gaseous hydrogen fluoride is probably the most imperfect gas known.

The infra-red absorption studies of Smith (1958) have helped resolve the debate as to the nature of the high molecular weight species present in the gas. Smith's observations confirm the early suggestion of Simons and Hildebrand (1924) that at elevated pressures aggregates of the type $(HF)_6$ are the predominant form. Dielectric polarization measurements strongly support the ring hypothesis for the structure of the hexamer. At lower pressures the tetramer, dimer, and monomer become increasingly important species. Smith notes, however, that the cyclic hexamer is present in higher concentration than the tetramer even at rather low pressures where both become minor constituents, and rejects the existence of linear zig-zag chains of $(HF)_n$

units (where n is statistically distributed around a mean value which grows with increasing pressure) (cf. Fig. 8) (Briegleb, 1953; Strohmeier, 1953). Franck and Meyer (1959) accept the ring form as dominant, but give equilibrium constants allowing for both chain and ring polymers.

X-Ray diffraction of solid hydrogen fluoride shows the solid to possess a linear zig-zag arrangement (Atoji and Lipscomb, 1954) (Fig. 8). The infrared absorption spectrum of solid hydrogen fluoride is consistent with linear

TABLE VI

Association Factor for Gaseous Hydrogen Fluoride

Temperature 0°C	Pressure (torr)	Z (molecules HF/polymer)
0·0	363·8	4·717[a]
	244·5	3·118[b]
	200·2	2·597[b]
19·5	760·0	3·76[a]
25·0	921·4	3·553[a]
26·0	488·5	1·708[b]
	401·0	1·422[b]
	342·5	1·279[b]
38·0	639·0	1·354[b]
	501·0	1·184[b]
	407·0	1·118[b]
50·0	2069·0	3·015[a]
100·0	7891·0	2·453[a]
160·0	26,500·0	1·70[a]
200·0	37,600·0	1·32[c]
	58,800·0	2·05[c]
300·0	57,500·0	1·09[c]
	173,000·0	1·43[c]

[a] Jarry and Davis, 1953.
[b] Long et al., 1943.
[c] Franck and Spalthoff, 1957; Spalthoff and Franck, 1957.

zig-zag chains (Sastri and Hornig, 1963). The extra absorption peaks attributed to lattice combinations in HF (and not found in DF) suggest unusually strong interactions between the chains in solid hydrogen fluoride. The differences in molecular configuration between solid and gaseous HF have not been adequately explained.

There is no direct evidence of the extent of association or the configuration of the polymeric molecules that exist in the liquid state. The heat of vapourization of the liquid is low for a highly associated liquid. Since the heat of dissociation of the polymer is substantial, it can tentatively be concluded that not much change occurs in the average number of polymer units in the transition from liquid to gas. From vapour density measurements of saturated vapour in equilibrium with the liquid, it appears that the average number of hydrogen fluoride units in gas aggregates is about 3·5, and this probably is close to the average size of the molecular aggregates in the liquid.

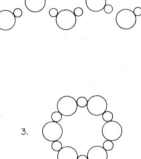

FIG. 8. Some possible structural arrangements in hydrogen fluoride.

The nature and extent of molecular association in liquid hydrogen fluoride are greatly influenced by the presence of ionizing impurities. For example, the density, acidity, and proton nuclear magnetic resonance behaviour of liquid hydrogen fluoride vary as a function of added water in a way that can best be explained by assuming drastic changes in the size and arrangement of $(HF)_n$ polymers. Thus, the density of aqueous hydrogen fluoride solutions shows a maximum value (1·25 g/ml at 0°C) at about 75% HF. This is a remarkable increase of 25% over the density of either pure component. As water is added to liquid hydrogen fluoride, the concentration of hydrogen fluoride molecules per litre actually increases and attains a maximum value at about 88% hydrogen fluoride. In this connection the density of the solid (1·653 g/ml at −93·8°C (Le Boucher et al., 1932)) is noteworthy. The change in volume on melting is exceptionally large.

The variation in density can be explained in terms of a transition from a high concentration of the ring polymer in pure liquid HF to linear chains in the solid, or in the liquid phase under conditions of substantial ionization (Fig. 9). The electrical conductivity approaches the very high value of 1 ohm^{-1} cm^{-1} in these maximum density HF–H$_2$O solutions, and more than 2% of the fluorine atoms present are calculated to exist as fluoride ions. The displacement of ring-chain equilibria can also be used to interpret the behaviour of other proton acceptors in liquid hydrogen fluoride solutions.

D. ACIDITY

Liquid anhydrous HF has long been recognized to be a very acidic substance. Many organic compounds with a variety of functional groups dissolve readily in liquid HF. Such solutions usually exhibit substantial ionic conductivity even though ordinary ionic dissociation is highly improbable. The

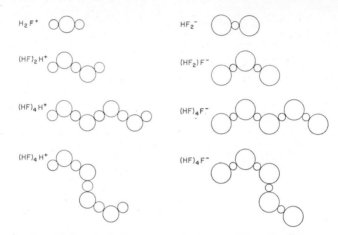

FIG. 9. Hypothetical arrangement of H^+ and F^- in liquid HF.

available data are best interpreted in terms of substantial proton transfer from the solvent to the solute in question (Simons, 1950):

$$R + HF \rightleftharpoons RH^+ + F^-. \tag{4}$$

In dilute aqueous solution, however, HF is a rather weak acid. The weak acid character of dilute aqueous hydrofluoric acid is at first sight surprising, and must be accounted for by any explanation that pretends to interpret acid–base interactions between molecules. Pauling (1956) suggests that the solvation stabilizing the ions increases in the sequence $I^- < Br^- < Cl^- < F^-$ as a linear function of the electronegativity of the halogen. The stability of the hydrogen halide molecule, in aqueous solution as in the gas phase, however, follows a quadratic function of the electronegativity difference between the halogen and hydrogen. Therefore, it is not surprising that the order of acid strength of the hydrogen halides in water is $HI > HBr > HCl > HF$. Indeed the differences in acid ionization constants are roughly in agreement with simple calculations based on the electronegativity differences tabulated by Pauling. He further points out that it is similarly true that water is a much weaker acid than the other hydrides of the sixth group elements, hydrogen sulphide, selenide, and telluride. The difference in acid strength between H_2O and H_2Te is very comparable to that between HF and HI. These relationships may be accepted without much argument, but it is nevertheless surprising that the equilibrium

$$H_2O + HF \rightleftharpoons H_3O^+ + F^- \tag{5}$$

proceeds in dilute aqueous solution only to the extent indicated by an ionization constant

$$K = \frac{[H_3O^+][F^-]}{[HF]} \tag{6}$$

of about $3\text{-}7 \times 10^{-4*}$ (Roth, 1959). The surprise is occasioned by the observation that proton transfer by anhydrous HF to an indicator is no less than 10^{17} times as great as it is in pure H_2O.

We have noted that no significant concentration of HF molecules exists as such in liquid hydrogen fluoride, and the same is true of individual H_2O molecules in liquid H_2O. Proton transfer from the aggregated molecules making up the HF matrix to an isolated H_2O molecule is very different from proton transfer from an isolated HF molecule to the group of molecules associated in the H_2O matrix. In the former case the fluoride ion remaining after proton transfer is part of a relatively stable zig-zag hydrogen fluoride chain (Fig. 9). In the latter case the fluoride ion is solvated only by water molecules. Therefore, the ease with which the HF unit loses a proton increases steadily as the concentration of hydrogen fluoride in the system is increased. The attempt to describe this in terms of a single addition of F^- to HF to yield an HF_2^- ion is a crude approximation, and we should not be surprised at the failure to find a satisfactory equilibrium constant.

While a number of acidity scales have been advanced, the H_0 function first proposed by Hammett (1935, 1940) (Hammett and Deyrup, 1932) appears to be the most useful for strong proton acids. H_0 is defined as

$$H_0 = pK_{In} - \frac{\log C_{InH^+}}{\log C_{In}}.$$

To measure H_0 a series of neutral indicators is employed. The indicators are selected to be of decreasing basicity, and to have uncharged and protonated species of markedly different absorption spectra

$$In + HA \rightarrow InH^+ + A^-.$$

---

* Unfortunately, there is no agreement on an accurate value for this constant. The ionization has usually been treated as a two-step process:

$$H_2O + HF \rightleftharpoons H_3O^+ + F^- \quad K_1 = \frac{(H_3O^+)(F^-)}{HF}$$

$$HF + F^- \rightleftharpoons HF_2^- \quad K_2 = \frac{(HF_2^-)}{(HF)(F^-)}.$$

Literature values of K_1 range from $2 \cdot 4 - 7 \cdot 2 \times 10^{-4}$ and K_2 from $5-25$ (Mellor, 1956), but the experimental data usually show K's that are far from constant.

The method has been reviewed by Paul and Long (1957) and indicator constants (K_{In}) are given there for a number of useful reagents. The H_0 values for some hydrogen fluoride solutions are given in Table VII.

TABLE VII

Acidity Constant (H_0) for Liquid Hydrogen Fluoride

H_0	Impurity concentration (moles/litre)	Electrical conductivity (ohm^{-1} cm^{-1} at 0°C)
$-10 \cdot 98$ ⎤	$< 10^{-4}$	3×10^{-5}
$-10 \cdot 65$ ⎬ a		5×10^{-5}
$-9 \cdot 72$ ⎦	$\sim 2 \cdot 5 \times 10^{-4}$	10^{-4}
$-10 \cdot 2$ ⎤	$< 10^{-3}$	
$-9 \cdot 6$ ⎬ b	$0 \cdot 1$	
$-8 \cdot 86$ ⎢	$1 \cdot 0$ (H_2O)	
$-8 \cdot 4$ ⎦	$1 \cdot 0$ (NaF)	

a Hyman et al., 1963. b Hyman et al., 1957.

The H_0 value for anhydrous sulphuric acid is -11, about the same value found for hydrogen fluoride. Since the H_0 scale is related to pH and is intended to represent a continuous set of acidity values on a logarithmic scale, these H_0 values show hydrogen fluoride and sulphuric acid to be exceptionally strong acids.

The acid strength of anhydrous hydrogen fluoride, as well as dilute solutions, must be influenced by ring-chain equilibrium. It has been suggested (Hyman et al., 1963) that the fluoride ion and solvated proton are stabilized by chain structures, and that the neutral HF molecule is stabilized by ring structures. The detailed shape of the acid strength versus impurity content curve is affected by this transformation. A much more detailed analysis of the structure of liquid hydrogen fluoride than is yet available will be necessary for the validity of this hypothesis to be established.

III. SOLUTES IN LIQUID HYDROGEN FLUORIDE

As technical difficulties are overcome, hydrogen fluoride becomes an increasingly interesting solvent, and more of its potentialities are being realized. A vast array of solutes dissolve freely in liquid hydrogen fluoride. As previously described, hydrogen fluoride is a low molecular weight solvent of high volatility, an ionizing solvent of exceptionally high dielectric constant, and a very strong acid. Hydrogen fluoride has essentially neither oxidizing nor reducing powers. While it can be reduced with evolution of hydrogen by most of the reagents that reduce water, it cannot be oxidized to elemental fluorine by any chemical oxidant. It thus becomes of interest in the study of extremely powerful oxidizing agents in solution.

Solutes in liquid hydrogen fluoride may be classified in a number of ways. The binary fluorides have been studied most extensively as solutes and may well be considered as a separate class. As the most electronegative element, fluorine forms binary fluorides with every element except helium, neon, and argon. Fluorides can be further classified with respect to the ionic species they yield in hydrogen fluoride solution. The metal fluorides, where the metal oxidation number is four or less, behave as simple bases to yield a metal-containing cation and the fluoride ion:

$$HF + MF_x \rightleftharpoons MF_{x-1} + HF_2^-. \tag{9}$$

Non-metal fluorides are usually volatile and often are liquids. When they dissolve in hydrogen fluoride, they may remain unionized, or they may react with hydrogen fluoride with the gain or loss of a fluoride ion:

$$HF + MF_x \rightleftharpoons MF_{x-1}^+ + HF_2^- \tag{10}$$

$$HF + MF_x \rightleftharpoons H_2F^+ + MF_{x+1}^-. \tag{11}$$

Which reaction occurs and its extent depends on a number of factors, but the geometry of the original fluoride and the product ions plays an important and often a dominant role.

Fluorides that increase the concentration of the HF_2^- ion are bases in the hydrogen fluoride system, although the solutions may be very acidic indeed by the usual standards. Solutes that increase the concentration of H_2F^+ ion are classified as acids.

A. METAL FLUORIDES

The simplest solutes in hydrogen fluoride are the metal fluorides. On dissolution, metal fluorides yield a new cation (e.g. Na^+), while the concentration of fluoride anion is increased. The simple alkali metal fluorides thus are bases in liquid hydrogen fluoride and correspond to metal hydroxides in the water system. The solubilities of some metallic fluorides, derived mainly from the work of Jache and Cady (1952), are summarized in Table VIII. The alkali metal fluorides are highly soluble, as are the alkaline earths. Silver(I) fluoride is likewise very soluble, and mercury(I) fluoride is appreciably so. Silver and mercury sulphates are soluble in sulphuric acid, while the oxides are very insoluble in water. In this respect the water system may be distinguished from the strong acid systems.

Many sparingly soluble fluorides are more soluble in the presence of a variety of complexing agents such as acetic acid, citric acid, methyl cyanide, 7,10-phenanthroline, 8-hydroxyquinoline, dithizone and carbon monoxide (Clifford and Sargent, 1957).

Ionization of dilute solutions of the alkali metal fluorides in liquid hydrogen fluoride is essentially complete. The electrical conductivity of sodium and potassium fluoride dissolved in hydrogen fluoride is shown in Fig. 10 (Simons,

TABLE VIII

Solubility of Metal Fluorides in Hydrogen Fluoride

Fluoride	Solubility in HF (g/100 g)	Temperature °C
LiF	10·3	12
NaF	30·1	11
KF	36·5	8
RbF	110·0	20
CsF	199·0	10
NH_4F	32·6	17
AgF	83·2	19
Hg_2F_2	0·87	12
TlF	580·0	12
CuF_2	0·010	12
AgF_2	0·048	12
CaF_2	0·817	12
SrF_2	14·83	12
BaF_2	5·60	12
BeF_2	0·015	11
MgF_2	0·025	12
ZnF_2	0·024	14
CdF_2	0·201	14
HgF_2	0·54	12
PbF_2	2·62	12
FeF_2	0·006	12
CrF_2	0·036	14
NiF_2	0·037	12
AlF_3	<0·002	11
CeF_3	0·043	12
TlF_3	0·081	12
SbF_3	0·536	12
BiF_3	0·010	12
MnF_3	0·164	12
FeF_3	0·008	12
CoF_3	0·257	12
ZrF_4	0·009	12
CeF_4	0·10	12
ThF_4	<0·006	18
NbF_5	6·8	25
TaF_5	15·2	25
SbF_5	∞	25

1950 ; Kilpatrick and Lewis, 1956). The data are far from precise by the standard of aqueous conductivity measurements, but the equivalent conductivities of these solutes at 0°C seem to be about 400. Transference measurements (Kilpatrick and Lewis, 1956) suggest that approximately 70% of the current is carried by the fluoride ion. Taking into account the low viscosity of liquid hydrogen fluoride, this transference number, while less than that found for KOH in water, has been explained in terms of a chain mechanism for fluoride ion conduction.

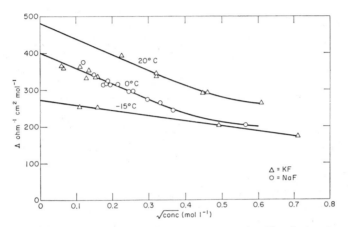

FIG. 10. Electrical conductivity of sodium and potassium fluoride solutions in anhydrous hydrogen fluoride.

As noted above, it seems likely that the fluoride ion is substantially solvated in liquid hydrogen fluoride, at least to the extent of forming HF_2^-, and finite concentrations of the higher species $H_2F_3^-$ and even $H_4F_5^-$ probably exist as well. The infra-red absorption spectra of hydrogen fluoride solutions is best interpreted in terms of the formation of a hydrogen bonded solvate of the fluoride ion (Adams and Katz, 1957). It is of course well-known that many metal fluorides have been isolated from hydrogen fluoride as salts of the HF_2^- anion.

B. NON-METALLIC, NON-ACIDIC, IONIZING FLUORIDES

The halogen fluorides constitute the most interesting members of this category. Chlorine trifluoride and bromine trifluoride are completely miscible with hydrogen fluoride and are appreciably ionized (Rogers et al., 1956a,b, 1957):

$$ClF_3 + HF \rightleftharpoons ClF_2^+ + HF_2^- \qquad (12)$$

$$BrF_3 + HF \rightleftharpoons BrF_2^+ + HF_2^-. \qquad (13)$$

Although the halogen fluorides are bases in the hydrogen fluoride system, hydrogen fluoride is itself an acid in the halogen fluoride system.

Halogen fluoride–hydrogen fluoride solutions may be neutralized from either direction in the appropriate solvent system. Neutralization can be followed by conductivity measurements, and the salt formed can be isolated by evaporation of excess solvent.

$$(BrF_2^+ + HF_2^-) + (H_2F^+ + SbF_6^-)^* \to BrF_2SbF_6 + HF \uparrow \qquad (14)$$

* (Acidic hydrogen fluoride solution)

$$(BrF_2^+ + HF_2^-) + (K^+ + BrF_4^-)^* \to KHF_2 + BrF_3 \uparrow \qquad (15)$$

* (Basic bromine trifluoride solution)

While much of the chemical behaviour of the halogen fluoride–hydrogen fluoride solutions can be explained in terms of the ionic species present, ionization need not take place to any great extent.

For most systems the maximum ionization observed is less than one per cent of complete ionization.

C. PROTON ACCEPTORS

The simple fluorides are the least interesting bases, in the sense that they present few anomalies. In liquid hydrogen fluoride, perhaps to an even greater extent than in anhydrous sulphuric acid, there are many materials, both organic and inorganic, that accept a proton from hydrogen fluoride and exist in solution as an ionized fluoride. Water is an obvious and interesting example. In anhydrous hydrogen fluoride, water behaves primarily as $H_3O^+HF_2^-$, a conclusion based on the sharp rise in conductivity as water is added:

$$H_2O + 2HF \to H_3O^+ + HF_2^-. \qquad (16)$$

If the electrical conductivity data of Fredenhagen is accepted at face value, water does not increase the conductivity of hydrogen fluoride as much as an equal concentration of sodium or potassium fluoride, or as much as a proton acceptor such as methyl alcohol or acetic acid. The best explanation for this observation is probably the incorporation of H_2O molecules into hydrogen-bonded polymers which carry a single proton $(H_2O)_n \cdot H_3O^+$, or $(H_2O)_n \cdot (HF)_n H_3O^+$:

$$nH_2O + 2HF \to (H_2O)_n H^+ + HF_2^- \qquad (17)$$

$$ROH + 2HF \to (ROH)H^+ + HF_2^-. \qquad (18)$$

Therefore, in terms of base strength,

$$1 \text{ mol ROH} \cong n \text{ mols } H_2O. \qquad (19)$$

A large number of organic compounds are bases in hydrogen fluoride. Most substances containing oxygen, nitrogen, or sulphur atoms that are not co-ordinatively saturated offer a lone electron pair capable of binding protons. A very large number of organic compounds fall into this category (Simons,

1950; Mellor, 1956). Alcohols, acids, aldehydes, ketones, ethers and amines are illustrative of classes of compounds that dissolve in hydrogen fluoride with extensive ionization. Saturated hydrocarbons are relatively insoluble.

Many soluble organic compounds seem to act as simple proton acceptors and may be recovered unchanged on removal of the hydrogen fluoride. Others, however, do undergo change as a result of solution in hydrogen fluoride. Butadiene and other unsaturated compounds polymerize and undergo rearrangement. Highly coloured solutions are frequently formed. Only on a few occasions has the behaviour of even a moderately complicated solute been studied in detail. The addition of a proton has usually, and justifiably, been assumed as the initial step.

A number of aromatic hydrocarbons are soluble in liquid hydrogen fluoride. The behaviour of the aromatic nucleus as a proton acceptor group is of some interest and has led to a number of studies in this solvent. For example, the question of the relative base strength of the methyl benzenes in solution in hydrogen fluoride has been explained using electrical conductivity measurements (Kilpatrick and Luborsky, 1953), thermochemical methods (Mackor $et\ al.$, 1958), and nuclear magnetic resonance measurements (MacLean and Mackor, 1962).

Some simple rules governing proton transfer in hydrogen fluoride are illustrated in Figs. 11 and 12. Acetic acid and trifluoroacetic acid, and ethanol and trifluoroethanol are each miscible with anhydrous hydrogen fluoride without any chemical reaction. Acetic acid ionizes essentially completely in dilute solution in anhydrous hydrogen fluoride to form the protonated acetic acid cation:

$$CH_3COOH + 2HF \rightleftharpoons CH_3CO_2H_2^+ + HF_2^-. \tag{20}$$

Trifluoroacetic acid is of course a much stronger acid than acetic acid, and it accordingly functions as a weaker base. It is no surprise, therefore, that trifluoroacetic acid has a much lower electrical conductivity in hydrogen fluoride solution than does acetic acid itself. It must be emphasized, however, that the lower extent of ionization results from the decrease in basicity occasioned by the substitution of fluorine for hydrogen in the methyl group of the acid. The acid strength of the molecule is thus not the determining factor. Ethanol is, as expected, essentially completely ionized in hydrogen fluoride solution, but trifluoroethanol solutions are like those of trifluoroacetic acid, and are only weakly ionized. This circumstance must be due to the decreased basicity of CF_3CH_2OH, for trifluoroethanol hardly qualifies as a strong acid.

Finally, attention is directed to the effect of dielectric constant on electrical conductivity of hydrogen fluoride solutions (Fig. 13). Nitrobenzene, a weak base with a high dielectric constant, and diethyl ether, a strong base with a low dielectric constant, are both miscible in all proportions with anhydrous

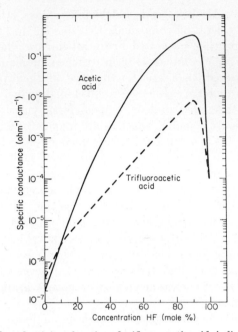

FIG. 11. Electrical conductivity of acetic and trifluoroacetic acids in liquid hydrogen fluoride.

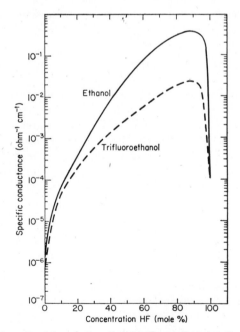

FIG. 12. Electrical conductivity of ethanol and trifluoroethanol in liquid hydrogen fluoride.

hydrogen fluoride. Concentrated solutions of diethyl ether exhibit essentially
no electrical conductivity, although diethyl ether is observed to be completely
ionized in dilute solution in hydrogen fluoride. Nitrobenzene on the other
hand shows appreciable conductivity in moderately concentrated solution,
but even in very dilute solution is only slightly ionized. In any acid–base
system, proton transfer depends on the relative strength of the two proton
acceptors, but ionization and extensive electric conductivity are found only
in solvents of high dielectric constant.

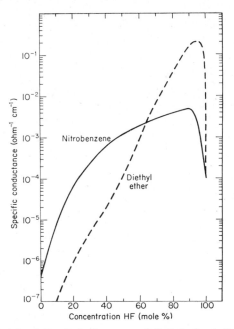

FIG. 13. Electrical conductivity of nitrobenzene and diethyl ether in liquid hydrogen fluoride.

The behaviour of nitrobenzene in hydrogen fluoride is easy to correlate
with its behaviour in fuming sulphuric acid. Nitrobenzene functions as an
acid-base indicator in both acids. It must be emphasized that solubility in
strong acids such as hydrogen fluoride and sulphuric acid, while often
associated with proton transfer and ionization, may take place even when the
solute is a weak base, and no proton transfer actually occurs. Solubility under
such circumstances has also been described as a weak acid-base interaction
while not involving atom transfer or the formation of bonds which can be
identified by absorption spectra or other simple observations (Hammett,
1940; Kilpatrick and Hyman, 1958).

Terms such as dipole–dipole interaction, acid–base interaction, and proton
transfer are used to describe solvent–solute interactions, often without great
precision, but usually with an adequate picture of the process taking place.

Infra-red absorption spectrophotometry has been applied to a number of hydrogen fluoride solutions studied over a range of concentrations (Adams and Katz, 1957). The solutes include most of those mentioned above, diethyl ether, ethanol, trifluoroethanol, nitrobenzene and others. Both the dipole alignment and the ionization processes affect the HF vibrations and the range of concentration in which each process dominated was noted in this study.

D. ACID SOLUTES: FLUORIDE ION ACCEPTORS

The extreme acidity of liquid hydrogen fluoride is the basis for both technological and scientific interest in the solvent. By the criterion of the Hammett acidity function, H_0, anhydrous hydrogen fluoride is an extremely strong acid with an H_0 value close to -11. This value is close to that of anhydrous sulphuric acid, and hydrogen fluoride is thus a member of the small class of super-acids. Some ambiguity exists in the exact value because the indicator must affect the concentration of anions and cations present, but H_0 values near -12 have been observed for hydrogen fluoride solutions which clearly contain an excess of acidic species (Hyman et al., 1963).

Because of the high acidity, only a limited number of solutes will act as acids in hydrogen fluoride. Only a few solutes increase the concentration of protonated solvent molecules. Perchloric and fluorosulphonic acids appear to be sufficiently strong and stable enough acids to fall into this category. The most important and interesting group of acids in liquid hydrogen fluoride solutions, however, are the fluoride ion acceptors. The majority of these compounds are Group V fluorides, of which antimony pentafluoride is the most frequently cited example. In hydrogen fluoride the net result of the addition of a fluoride ion acceptor is precisely the same as the addition of a proton donor, namely an increase in the concentration of solvated protons:

$$SbF_5 + 2HF \rightarrow H_2F^+ + SbF_6^-. \tag{21}$$

That antimony pentafluoride and arsenic pentafluoride can act as fluoride ion acceptors has been established in a number of ways (Clifford et al., 1957; Hyman et al., 1961, 1963). The electrical conductivity of $HF-SbF_5$ solutions is very high. When a base such as water is added to this system, the conductivity decreases, and the antimony pentafluoride can be titrated in this way. With further addition of water, the conductivity then increases (Hyman et al., 1963) (Fig. 14). The Raman spectrum of arsenic pentafluoride and antimony pentafluoride solutions in hydrogen fluoride provide most convincing evidence for the abilities of these solutions to act as acids in this solvent system. In dilute solution, the strong Raman line associated with the octahedral AsF_6^- ion or SbF_6^- ion is easily observed at the predicted frequency. Arsenic pentafluoride forms slightly less conductive solutions than SbF_5 and therefore is a weaker acid than is antimony pentafluoride. Niobium and tantalum pentafluorides have only limited solubility in anhydrous hydrogen fluoride. The solubility of NbF_5 and TaF_5 is sufficient, nevertheless, to show that these substances act as acids, although they are somewhat weaker acids than the more soluble arsenic and antimony compounds. Boron trifluoride appears to be the only fluoride ion acceptor other than the Group V fluorides that has definitely been shown to have acid properties in hydrogen fluoride. The low solubility of BF_3 (and low electrical conductivity of HF–BF_3 solutions) suggests that this solute is a rather weak acid (Kilpatrick and Luborsky, 1954). Group IV fluorides, i.e. titanium tetrafluoride and silicon

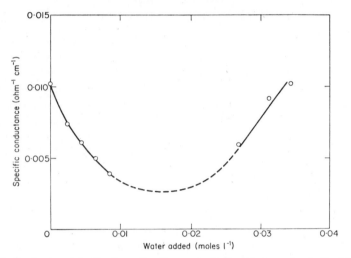

FIG. 14. Conductometric titration of antimony pentafluoride by water in liquid fluoride (SbF_5 0·02 M).

tetrafluoride, are essentially insoluble in anhydrous hydrogen fluoride, and have not been shown to increase the hydrogen ion concentration of the pure solvent. However, in multi-phase systems, titanium tetrafluoride appears to increase the solubility of some hydrocarbons and to function as a catalyst in hydrocarbon re-arrangement (McCauley et al., 1956; McCauley and Lien, 1951, 1957). This behaviour is very much like that of TaF_5 and MoF_5 in similar systems and is interpreted to involve acidic behaviour by TiF_4 and TaF_5. The solubility and acidity of sparingly soluble weak acid fluorides is significantly increased by the presence of a proton acceptor:

$$R + TaF_5 + HF \rightarrow RH^+ + TaF_6^-$$ \hfill (22)

$$R + 2TiF_4 + HF \rightarrow RH^+ + Ti_2F_9^-.$$ \hfill (23)

The fluorides may easily be ranked in terms of acid–base properties. The acid strength of fluorides increases regularly from the basic alkali metal fluorides to the pentafluorides, which are the most acidic.

In general, this order corresponds to the acid–base properties of the oxides in water:

strong bases:
$$NaF + HF \rightarrow Na^+ + HF_2^- \tag{24}$$
$$Na_2O + H_2O \rightarrow 2Na^+ + 2OH^- \tag{25}$$

weak acids:
$$AlF_3 + HF + NaF \rightarrow Na^+ + AlF_4^- + HF^* \tag{26}$$
$$Al_2O_3 + 3H_2O + 2NaOH \rightarrow 2Na^+ + 2Al(OH)_4^-* \tag{27}$$

strong acids:
$$SbF_5 + 2HF \rightarrow H_2F^+ + SbF_6^- \tag{28}$$
$$SO_3 + 3H_2O \rightarrow 2H_3O^+ + SO_4^{2-} \tag{29}$$
$$Cl_2O_7 + 3H_2O \rightarrow 2H_3O^+ + 2ClO_4^-. \tag{30}$$

Differences in the behaviour of oxides and fluorides are presumably due to specific geometrical stabilizing factors. The difference between the single electron charge associated with fluoride ion transfer and the electron pair associated with oxide ion transfer also renders the analogy less precise. In the hydrogen fluoride system octahedral symmetry stabilizes the monovalent hexafluoride anion MF_6^-. No strictly analogous species is possible with oxygen, and the pentoxide of antimony shows acid properties only with strong bases:

$$Sb_2O_5 + 2NaOH + 5H_2O \rightarrow Na^+ + 2Sb(OH)_6^-*. \tag{31}$$

On the other hand, the hydrogen acids of tetrahedral monovalent tetroxide anions, i.e. (ClO_4^-) of the Group VII elements are very strong acids in water. Acids derived from Group VI atoms (i.e. H_2SO_4) follow closely. Of the oxygen acids, only perchloric acid appears to be sufficiently acidic for the perchlorate anion to be stable as such in liquid hydrogen fluoride. The mixed fluorine-oxygen acid fluoro-sulphonic acid also appears to be in this category.

The solubility and ionization behaviour of hydrogen chloride or bromide in liquid hydrogen fluoride have not been adequately investigated. Fredenhagen (Fredenhagen and Cadenbach, 1930) originally suggested that the concentration of chloride or bromide in hydrogen fluoride solution is vanishingly small. However, it is possible to precipitate insoluble silver chloride from hydrogen fluoride solution, particularly at low temperatures near the melting point of hydrogen fluoride. This suggests a much higher solubility for the remaining halogen acids in hydrogen fluoride than has previously been suspected (Fredenhagen, 1939).

E. SALTS IN THE HYDROGEN FLUORIDE SYSTEM AS SOLUTES

So many solutes are protonated in liquid hydrogen fluoride that the number of true salts is limited. Solvolysis in hydrogen fluoride is the rule for many compounds which are salts in water. For example, potassium nitrate

---

* The anions containing aluminium or antimony which are actually present are more complicated, and their composition varies with concentration.

in anhydrous hydrogen fluoride is converted to KF, $H_3O^+F^-$, and $NO_2^+F^-$ (Del Greco and Gryder, 1961):

$$KNO_3 + 6HF \rightleftharpoons K^+ + NO_2^+ + H_3O^+ + 3HF_2^-. \tag{32}$$

Potassium perchlorate, on the other hand, does seem to be a true salt:

$$KClO_4 + HF \rightleftharpoons K^+ + ClO_4^- + HF. \tag{33}$$

Alkali metal sulphates are usually converted to fluorosulphonates, which then act as normal salts. Other oxygenated anions also usually yield the H_3O^+ cation and an oxide or oxyfluoride. The resulting oxygen compound may then react further to yield the free element. For example, chlorates appear to form chlorine dioxide, whereas bromates give free bromine.

The alkali metal salts of boron trifluoride and the Group V non-metal fluorides are typical salts in liquid hydrogen fluoride. A number of these have been identified by Clifford and Morris (1957). $AgPF_6$, $NaPF_6$, and $Ba(PF_6)_2$ are described as soluble in liquid hydrogen fluoride. $NaAsF_6$ and $NaSbF_6$ are sparingly soluble, $AgBF_4$ is rather insoluble (Clifford and Kongpricha, 1957), and KBF_4 is appreciably soluble.

Evaporation of hydrogen fluoride solutions of BaF_2 or NaF and weak volatile acids as TeF_6 or GeF_4 form solids to which the formulas $Ba(TeF_7)_2$ or $NaGeF_5$ have been assigned. No compelling evidence for the existence of ions such as TeF_7^- in hydrogen fluoride has been adduced. The identity of only a limited number of anions in liquid hydrogen fluoride has been established, and little is known of their behaviour or about the properties of the salts they may form.

F. SOLUTION IN HYDROGEN FLUORIDE WITHOUT IONIZATION

Solution in liquid hydrogen fluoride is not necessarily accompanied by ionic processes, even though proton transfer does occur in a very large number of instances. Weak bases, as noted above, dissolve in anhydrous hydrogen fluoride with only a slight increase in the electrical conductivity. Many such weak bases are organic compounds whose base strength has been lowered by substituents such as nitro or trifluoromethyl groups. In view of the high dielectric constant of hydrogen fluoride, hydrogen bonding usually leads to proton transfer and extensive ionization in dilute solution. Where no such process occurs, it may be inferred that the tendency toward hydrogen bond formation is very weak. Acid–base interactions and hydrogen bond formation play such important roles in understanding solution behaviour in acidic solvents like hydrogen fluoride that we are not quite sure how to treat solutions of weak bases that are miscible in all proportions with liquid hydrogen fluoride. However poorly understood, these solutes may in practice be useful diluents for hydrogen fluoride. Trifluoroacetic acid and liquid sulphur dioxide are miscible with anhydrous hydrogen fluoride in all proportions, do not seem to significantly reduce the acidity of the hydrogen fluoride, and are in fact useful diluents.

In addition, there are a substantial number of inert and rather insoluble compounds. Sparingly soluble and non-ionizing solutes include many simple inorganic molecules including binary fluorides.

The influence of geometrical stabilization in acidic solutes has been discussed. Most pentafluorides have acidic properties because formation of the octahedrally symmetrical hexafluoride anions is favoured. Stable hexafluorides can then be expected to dissolve in liquid hydrogen fluoride without fluoride ion transfer. To the extent that this has been investigated, this appears to be the situation. The uranium hexafluoride–hydrogen fluoride system shows a liquid miscibility gap, the solubility of solid uranium hexafluoride in hydrogen fluoride is rather slight, and there is no evidence for either ionization or compound formation (Rutledge et al., 1953). Investigation by nuclear magnetic resonance methods of a number of hexafluorides containing hydrogen fluoride confirm the absence of interaction (Muetterties and Phillips, 1959). No systematic studies of dilute solutions in hydrogen fluoride appear to have been carried out as yet.

The clear exception is xenon hexafluoride. The high solubility, rapid fluorine exchange, and extensive ionization found for this compound in hydrogen fluoride (Hyman and Quarterman, 1963; Hindman and Svirmickas, 1963) are in agreement with other observations that suggest a symmetry lower than octahedral for xenon hexafluoride (Gillespie, 1963; Smith, 1963).

While the octahedrally symmetrical compounds offer the best examples of non-interaction in solution in liquid hydrogen fluoride, other structures may also be important. Tetrahedral SiF_4 and CF_4 (Muetterties and Phillips, 1959) and the square planar XeF_4 (Hindman and Svirmickas, 1963; Brown et al., 1963) are examples.

IV. Solution in Anhydrous Hydrogen Fluoride of Compounds of Biological Importance

It might seem at first sight that a substance with as ferocious a reputation as anhydrous hydrogen fluoride would have little utility as a solvent for complex and labile organic compounds. Nevertheless, carbohydrates and proteins dissolve readily in anhydrous hydrogen fluoride, frequently with only minor chemical consequences. Despite the fact that anhydrous hydrogen fluoride is certainly one of the most hygroscopic substances known, complex organic compounds potentially capable of eliminating the elements of water often dissolve without dehydration. It is important that dissolution be carried out in such a way that the heat of solution, which is generally high, is dissipated without a concomitant rise in the temperature of the solution. If solutions are prepared at low temperatures, in vessels of good thermal conductivity, and with care taken to maintain a liquid phase at all times, then clear solutions of carbohydrates and proteins can be achieved without difficulty.

Fredenhagen and Cadenbach (1933) appear to have been the first to observe that cellulose is freely soluble in liquid hydrogen fluoride. Cellulose forms conducting solutions in hydrogen fluoride, and the material recovered from such solutions, designated by Fredenhagen as a glucosan, yields glucose on mild hydrolysis. This procedure was in fact suggested as a method for the saccharification of cellulose. Little has appeared in the literature subsequent to this early work that sheds light on the fate of carbohydrates in liquid hydrogen fluoride. Pedersen (1962, 1963) (Pedersen and Fletcher, 1960) has very recently examined the behaviour of a variety of sugar esters with hydrogen fluoride. Prolonged treatment of penta-O-acetyl-β-D-glucopyrannose with anhydrous hydrogen fluoride leads to the formation of derivatives of mannose and altrose; partial hydrolysis and isomerization result. It does not appear that any particular precautions were taken to render or maintain the solutions water-free. Even so, chemical attack on the sugar esters was slow. It would be interesting to study these solutes with strict exclusion of water.

Anhydrous hydrogen fluoride is a powerful solvent for proteins. Not only are the water-soluble proteins freely soluble in hydrogen fluoride, but many fibrous proteins normally insoluble in water, silk fibroin for instance, are also very soluble. Proteins found to dissolve freely are: ribonuclease, insulin, trypsin, serum albumin, serum globulin, edestin, haemoglobin and collagen. Although chemical reactions may ensue, these are not necessarily incompatible with retention of biological activity. Insulin can be recovered from hydrogen fluoride solution with essentially full retention of biological activity (Katz, 1954). The enzymes ribonuclease and lysozyme may be dissolved and re-covered from hydrogen fluoride or HF–SO_2 mixtures in a form indistinguish-able in enzymatic properties from the original, provided the temperature is kept low and the time of exposure is short (Koch *et al.*, 1958). At higher temperatures, inactivation occurs, but it appears that inactivation results from the splitting of a small number of peptide bonds, without causing a decrease in molecular weight but leading to an increase in hydrodynamic volume. Model experiments on compounds containing disulphide linkages strongly indicate that disulphide bonds in proteins are stable in hydrogen fluoride solution.

Anhydrous hydrogen fluoride swells collagen and disorients it, but probably does not break peptide bonds. Low molecular weight gelatins sometimes observed on recovery from hydrogen fluoride probably arise by hydrolysis with adventitious water (Veis and Katz, 1956). To further indicate the ability of hydrogen fluoride to function as a protein solvent, attention is directed to the polymerization of N-carboxy anhydrides in hydrogen fluoride to form poly-α-amino acids (Kopple and Katz, 1956). Polypeptides with chain lengths of 30 are readily obtained. An unexpected side-reaction, the elimination of carbon monoxide from the N-carboxy anhydride, probably accounts for the relatively short chain length (Kopple *et al.*, 1962).

Some possible chemical consequences for proteins dissolved in hydrogen fluoride have been the subject for recent investigations by Hess and co-workers (Lenard *et al.*, 1964; Shin *et al.*, 1962; Sakakibara *et al.*, 1962). These workers have shown that serine- and threonine-containing peptides undergo an N to O acyl shift in hydrogen fluoride. It has been known for a long time that under the influence of strong acids, such as concentrated sulphuric acid, that a reversible, pH-dependent rearrangement occurs at peptide links involving amino acids containing an aliphatic hydroxy group in the side chain. Migration occurs, and the peptide bond is converted to an ester group, with the peptide nitrogen now appearing as a free amino group. An hydroxy-oxazolidine is considered to be the intermediate in the N to O acyl migration:

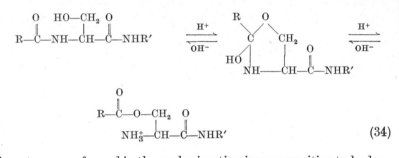

$$\tag{34}$$

Since the ester group formed in the acyl migration is very sensitive to hydrolysis, this furnishes the basis of a useful method for the chemical cleavage of peptide chains at peptide linkages adjacent to seryl or threonyl amino acid residues. Specific cleavage also appears to occur at C—methionyl peptide bonds. This work constitutes the most detailed analysis of the chemical consequences on proteins resulting from dissolution in hydrogen fluoride. The reactions that do occur are highly specific and may have value in protein structure determinations. Singer (1962) has recently reviewed the effects of non-aqueous solvents generally on protein conformation, and has directed particular attention to the effects of strong protonic solvents.

The observation that the iron-containing proteins cytochrome *c* and haemoglobin are soluble in liquid hydrogen fluoride to form solutions that have absorption spectra very similar to those in water has prompted examination of other metal co-ordination compounds in hydrogen fluoride. The ability of metal complex compounds to persist in hydrogen fluoride seems to be general, for metal phthalocyanines, cobalt(III) amines, and many other co-ordination compounds dissolve without destruction of the complex. Particularly interesting solutes are the biologically important metal co-ordination compounds chlorophyll and vitamin B_{12}. Chlorophyll yields solutions in hydrogen fluoride with absorption spectra characteristic of the more usual solvents. Vitamin B_{12} forms a deep olive-green solution in hydrogen fluoride as contrasted to its normal deep-red. This cobalt(III) co-ordination compound survives dissolution in hydrogen fluoride despite its very complicated structure and numerous functional groups. Vitamin B_{12} can be readily regenerated from the recovered solute and possesses full B_{12} activity.

REFERENCES

Adams, R. M. and Katz, J. J. (1956) *J. opt. Soc. Amer.* **46**, 895.
Adams, R. M. and Katz, J. J. (1957) *J. mol. Spectroscopy* **1**, 306.
Atoji, M. and Lipscomb, W. N. (1954) *Acta crystallogr.* **7**, 173.
Briegleb, G. and Strohmeier, W. (1953) *Z. Electrochem.* **57**, 668.
Brown, T. H., Whipple, E. B. and Verdier, P. H. (1963) "Noble Gas Compounds" (H. H. Hyman, ed.), pp. 263–9. University of Chicago Press, Chicago.
Clifford, A. F. and Kongpricha, S. (1957) *J. inorg. nucl. Chem.* **5**, 76.
Clifford, A. F. and Morris, A. G. (1957) *J. inorg. nucl. Chem.* **5**, 71.
Clifford, A. F. and Sargent, J. (1957) *J. Amer. chem. Soc.* **79**, 4041.
Clifford, A. F., Beachell, H. C. and Jack, W. M. (1957) *J. inorg. nucl. Chem.* **5**, 57.
Del Greco, F. P. and Gryder, J. W. (1961) *J. phys. Chem.* **65**, 922.
Feder, H. M., Hubbard, W. N., Wise, S. S. and Margrave, J. L. (1963) *J. phys. Chem.* **67**, 1148.
Franck, E. U. and Meyer, F. (1959) *Z. Elektrochem.* **63**, 571.
Franck, E. U. and Spalthoff, W. (1957) *Z. Elektrochem.* **61**, 348.
Fredenhagen, H. (1939) *Z. anorg. Chem.* **242**, 23.
Fredenhagen, K. and Cadenbach, G. (1929) *Z. anorg. Chem.* **178**, 289.
Fredenhagen, K. and Cadenbach, G. (1930) *Z. phys. Chem.* **146***A*, 245.
Fredenhagen, K. and Cadenbach, G. (1933) *Angew. Chem.* **46**, 113.
Fredenhagen, K. and Dahmlos, J. (1929) *Z. anorg. Chem.* **178**, 272.
Giguère, P. A. and Zengin, N. (1958) *Canad. J. Chem.* **36**, 1013.
Gillespie, R. J. (1963) "Noble Gas Compounds" (H. H. Hyman, ed.), pp. 333–9. University of Chicago Press, Chicago.
Hammett, L. P. (1935) *Chem. Rev.* **16**, 67.
Hammett, L. P. (1940) "Physical Organic Chemistry". McGraw-Hill Book Co., New York.
Hammett, L. P. and Deyrup, A. J. (1932) *J. Amer. Chem. Soc.* **54**, 2721.
Herzberg, G. (1950) "Molecular Spectra and Molecular Structure. I. Spectra of Diatomic Molecules," 2nd edition. D. van Nostrand Co., Inc., New York.
Hindman, J. C. and Svirmickas, A. (1963) *In* "Noble Gas Compounds" (H. H. Hyman, ed.), pp. 251–62. University of Chicago Press, Chicago.
Hu, J.-H., White, D. and Johnston, H. L. (1953) *J. Amer. chem. Soc.* **75**, 1232.
Hyman, H. H. and Quarterman, L. A. (1963) "Noble Gas Compounds" (H. H. Hyman, ed.), p. 275. University of Chicago Press, Chicago.
Hyman, H. H., Kilpatrick, M. and Katz, J. J. (1957) *J. Amer. chem. Soc.* **79**, 3668.
Hyman, H. H., Lane, T. I. and O'Donnell, T. A. (1963) 145th Meeting A. C. S. Abstracts, p. 63T.
Hyman, H. H., Quarterman, L. A., Kilpatrick, M. and Katz, J. J. (1961) *J. phys. Chem.* **65**, 123.
Jache, A. W. and Cady, G. H. (1952) *J. phys. Chem.* **56**, 1106.
Jarry, R. L. and Davis, W. J. (1953) *J. phys. Chem.* **57**, 600.

Katz, J. J. (1954) *Archs Biochem. Biophys.* **51**, 293.

Katz, J. J. and Hyman, H. H. (1953) *Rev. sci. Instrum.* **24**, 1066.

Kilpatrick, M. and Hyman, H. H. (1958) *J. Amer. chem. Soc.* **80**, 77.

Kilpatrick, M. and Lewis, J. I. (1956) *J. Amer. chem. Soc.* **78**, 5186.

Kilpatrick, M. and Luborsky, F. (1953) *J. Amer. chem. Soc.* **75**, 577.

Kilpatrick, M. and Luborsky, F. (1954) *J. Amer. chem. Soc.* **76**, 5863.

Koch, A. L., Lamont, W. A. and Katz, J. J. (1956) *Archs Biochem. Biophys.* **63**, 106.

Kopple, K. D. and Katz, J. J. (1956) *J. Amer. chem. Soc.* **78**, 6199.

Kopple, K. D., Quarterman, L. A. and Katz, J. J. (1962) *J. org. Chem.* **27**, 1062.

Kuipers, G. A. (1958) *J. mol. Spectroscopy* **2**, 75.

Kuipers, G. A., Smith, D. F. and Neilson, A. H. (1956) *J. chem. Phys.* **25**, 275.

Le Boucher, L., Fischer, W. and Biltz, W. (1932) *Z. anorg. Chem.* **206**, 61.

Lenard, J. I., Schally, A. V. and Hess, G. P. (1964) *Biochem. Biophys. Research Commun.* **14**, 498.

Long, R. W., Hildebrand, J. H. and Morell, W. E. (1943) *J. Amer. chem. Soc.* **65**, 182.

McCaulay, D. A. and Lien, A. P. (1951) *J. Amer. chem. Soc.* **75**, 2013.

McCaulay, D. A. and Lien, A. P. (1957) *J. Amer. chem. Soc.* **79**, 2495.

McCaulay, D. A., Higley, W. S. and Lien, A. P. (1956) *J. Amer. chem. Soc.* **78**, 3009.

Mackor, E. L., Hofstra, A. and Van de Waals, J. H. (1958) *Trans. Faraday Soc.* **54**, 186.

MacLean, C. and Mackor, E. L. (1961) *J. chem. Phys.* **34**, 2207.

MacLean, C. and Mackor, E. L. (1962) *Discuss. Faraday Soc.*, No. 34, 165.

Maybury, R. H., Gordon, S. and Katz, J. J. (1955) *J. Chem. Phys.* **23**, 1277.

Mellor's Comprehensive Treatise on Inorganic and Theoretical Chemistry. (1956) Supplement A, Part I. Longmans, Green and Co., London. Chapter I. Fluorine Section 3, 72–84. The preparation of hydrofluoric acid. Section 4, 85–146. The physical and chemical properties and uses of hydrogen fluoride and its aqueous solutions.

Muetterties, E. L. and Phillips, W. D. (1959) *J. Amer. chem. Soc.* **81**, 1084.

Paul, M. A. and Long, F. A. (1957) *Chem. Rev.* **57**, 1.

Pauling, L. (1956) *J. chem. Educ.* **33**, No. 1, 16–17.

Perkins, A. (1965) *J. phys. Chem.* (in the press).

Pedersen, C. (1962) *Acta chem. Scand.* **16**, 1831.

Pedersen, C. (1963) *Acta chem. Scand.* **17**, 673.

Pedersen, C. and Fletcher, H. G., Jr. (1960) *J. Amer. chem. Soc.* **82**, 941.

Quarterman, L. A., Hyman, H. H. and Katz, J. J. (1957) *J. phys. Chem.* **61**, 912.

Quaterman, L. A., Hyman, H. H. and Katz, J. J. (1961) *J. phys. Chem.* **65**, 90.

Rogers, M. T., Speirs, J. L. and Panish, M. B. (1956a) *J. Amer. chem. Soc.* **78**, 3288.

Rogers, M. T., Speirs, J. L. and Panish, M. B. (1956b) *J. phys. Chem.* **61**, 366.

Rogers, M. T., Speirs, J. L., Panish, M. B. and Thompson, H. B. (1956) *J. Amer. chem. Soc.* **78**, 936.

Roth, W. A. (1939) *Annls Chim. Phys.* **542**, 35.

Rothschild, W. G. (1964) *J. opt. Soc. Amer.* **54**, 20.

Runner, M. E., Balog, G. and Kilpatrick, M. (1956) *J. Amer. chem. Soc.*, 5183.

Rutledge, G. P., Jarry, R. L. and Davis, W., Jr. (1953) *J. phys. Chem.* **57**, 541.

Sakakibara, S., Shin, K. H. and Hess, G. P. (1962) *J. Amer. chem. Soc.* **84**, 4921.

Sastri, M. L. N. and Hornig, D. F. (1963) *J. chem. Phys.* **39**, 3497.

Shin, K. H., Sakakibara, S., Schneider, W. and Hess, G. P. (1962) *Biochem. Biophys. Res. Commun.* **8**, 288.

Simons, J. H. (1950) "Fluorine Chemistry" Vol. I, p. 225. Academic Press, New York.

Simons, J. H. (1964) "Fluorine Chemistry" Vol. V, p. 2–15, Academic Press, New York.

Simons, J. H. and Bouknight, J. W. (1932) *J. Amer. chem. Soc.* **54**, 129.

Simons, J. H. and Dresdner, R. D. (1944) *J. Amer. chem. Soc.* **66**, 1070.

Simons, J. H. and Hildebrand, J. H. (1924) *J. Amer. chem. Soc.* **46**, 2183.

Singer, S. J. (1962) *Adv. Protein Chem.* **17**, 1.

Smith, D. F. (1958) *J. chem. Phys.* **28**, 1040.

Smith, D. F. (1963) "Noble Gas Compounds" (H. H. Hyman, ed.), pp. 295–303. University of Chicago Press, Chicago.

Spalthoff, W. and Franck, E. U. (1957) *Z. Elektrochem.* **61**, 993.

Strohmeier, W. and Briegleb, G. (1953) *Z. Electrochem.* **57**, 662.

Veis, A. and Katz, J. J. (1956) *Biochim. biophys. Acta* **22**, 96.

CHAPTER 3

The Higher Hydrogen Halides as Ionizing Solvents

M. E. PEACH AND T. C. WADDINGTON

Anorganisch-Chemisches Institut der Universität, Göttingen, West Germany
School of Molecular Sciences, University of Warwick, Coventry, England

I. Introduction.. 83
   A. Some Physical Properties of the Liquid Hydrogen Halides............... 84
   B. Self-ionization.. 86
   C. Experimental Methods... 88
II. Solutions in the Hydrogen Halides.. 97
   A. Acids and Bases.. 97
   B. Solvolysis Reactions.. 111
   C. Redox Reactions... 112

I. INTRODUCTION

The higher hydrogen halides (HCl, HBr, HI) have interest as ionizing solvents both in their own right and also because of the comparison that can be made between their properties and those of liquid hydrogen fluoride, to which they are so similar and at the same time so different. Most of the work discussed in this paper will refer to liquid hydrogen chloride. It is interesting to note how much more important, in the past, the temperature factor has been than the extreme reactivity of hydrogen fluoride. Fremy was using platinum apparatus in his preparation of anhydrous hydrogen fluoride in 1856, whereas the work of Archibald, McIntosh and Steele at the beginning of this century was seriously handicapped by lack of high vacuum apparatus and a limited supply of solid carbon dioxide for producing low temperatures.

The first experiments using liquid hydrogen chloride as a solvent were performed about a century ago by Gore (1865). The experiments were rather hazardous, as he worked in an enclosed system, making hydrogen chloride from sulphuric acid and sal ammoniac. Only qualitative visual observations were made, but these did not augur well for the future: of the 66 compounds studied only 10 dissolved, and he concluded that "Liquid hydrogen chloride has but a feeble solvent power for solid bodies in general".

In spite of Gore's conclusions, the study of hydrogen chloride, bromide, and iodide as non-aqueous solvents was resumed for about a decade just after the turn of the century at McGill University, Canada. The vast majority of these results is collected together and discussed in a lengthy paper, published in English and German, divided into four sections, each of which is complete in itself, describing work impeccably performed under difficult experimental conditions (Steele, McIntosh and Archibald, 1905, 1906).

The first section describes the measurement of physical and thermodynamic constants of the hydrogen halides. The variation of vapour pressure and density were studied as a function of the temperature; the surface energy (by Ramsay and Shield's method) and viscosity (by rate of capillary flow) were also measured. The accuracy of this work can be judged from the fact that the latent heat of vapourization of liquid hydrogen chloride was calculated, from the vapour pressure curve, to be 3·54 kcal mole^{-1} the currently accepted value is 3·86 kcal mole^{-1} (Mellor). The main inaccuracy must have been the measurement of small volumes of the liquid hydrogen halides in graduated tubes. The second section describes solubility, conductivity and ebullioscopic measurements. The results obtained from the variation of conductivity with dilution and the ebullioscopic measurements were rather strange and very difficult to interpret. It is hoped to be able to present an explanation later in this review, based on the assumption that triple ions are formed in all but the most dilute solutions. The third section describes work that was very difficult experimentally, the measurement of transport numbers in liquid hydrogen bromide, and no attempt has yet been made to extend these observations. The validity of Faraday's Laws for these solutions was confirmed and the actual transport numbers were determined by Hittorf's method. In the last section there is a detailed discussion of the results, but little relationship was found between dissolving power, dielectric constant, conductivity and deviations in molecular weight determinations.

Direct study of some reactions in liquid hydrogen chloride was then resumed in the late 1950's in Cambridge (Waddington and Klanberg, 1960a) although a good deal of work bearing on the solvent properties, such as the study of phase diagrams, had been studied in the interim. Some further studies have also been made recently of the solvent properties of liquid hydrogen bromide and iodide by Waddington and White (1960a,b, 1963) and Klanberg and Kohlschutter (1961).

A. SOME PHYSICAL PROPERTIES OF THE LIQUID HYDROGEN HALIDES

Some of the physical properties of the liquid hydrogen halides and water, for comparative purposes, are listed in Table I.

From the table it can be seen that there are some quite marked similarities between water and hydrogen fluoride on the one hand, and the other hydrogen halides on the other hand, and some great differences between these two groups. Hydrogen chloride, bromide and iodide have a relatively narrow liquid range, thus increasing some of the experimental difficulties, and low dielectric constants. The consequences of these low dielectric constants can be seen experimentally when it is found that only salts with low lattice energies, such as the tetra-alkylammonium halides, are soluble, whereas "ordinary simple salts", such as ammonium chloride, with a high lattice energy, are insoluble. Another consequence of this low dielectric constant is the complex variation of the equivalent conductivity with concentration, discussed later in Section IC,2.

The Trouton's constants are high for water and hydrogen fluoride, indicating that some association, due to hydrogen bonding, must be occurring. In the other hydrogen halides, hydrogen bonding, although it can occur, is very much weaker than in hydrogen fluoride: this is reflected in the normal Trouton's constants, which indicate little association in the liquid.

TABLE I

Some Physical Constants of the Hydrogen Halides and Water

	H_2O	HF	HCl	HBr	HI
Mol. wt.	18·0	20·0	36·5	80·9	127·9
M.p. (°C)	0	−83·0	−114·6	−88·5	−50·9
B.p. (°C)	100	19·5	−84·1	−67·0	−35·0
Liquid range (°C)	100	102·5	30·5	21·5	15·9
Density of liquid	1·00	1·20	1·187	2·603	2·85
(g/ml near m.p.)	(0°)	(−80°)	(−114°)	(−84°)	(−47°)
Latent heats:					
Fusion	1440[a]	1094	476	600	686
Vapourization	9720[a]	7230[a]	3860	4210	4724
(cal/mol)					
Trouton's constant	26·0	24·7	20·4	20·4	19·8
Dielectric constant	84·2	175	9·28	7·0[a]	3·39[a]
of liquid	(0°)	(−73°)	(−95°)	(−85°)	(−50°)
Viscosity	1·00	0·24	0·51[f]	0·83[f]	1·35[f]
(centipoises)	(22°)	(0°)	(−95°)	(−67°)	(−35·4°)
Specific conduc-					
tivity	0·05[b]	0·1[d]	0·0035[g]	0·0014[h]	0·00085[i]
(μ mho cm^{-1})	(18°)	(−80°)	(−85°)	(−84°)	(−45°)
H.Hal stretching					
Frequency	3568*[c]	3961[e]	2886[e]	2558[e]	2230[e]
(gas, cm^{-1})					

* Value for the OH radical.

[a] "Handbook of Chemistry and Physics" Chemical Rubber Publishing Co.
[b] Glasstone: "Textbook of Physical Chemistry."
[c] Herzberg: "Infra-red and Raman Spectra of Polyatomic Molecules."
[d] Runner et al. (1956).
[e] Grange et al. (1960).
[f] Steele et al. (1905).
[g] Glockler and Peck (1936).
[h] Waddington and White (1963).
[i] Smyth and Hitchcock (1933).

All other values are quoted from Mellor's "Comprehensive Inorganic Chemistry".

B. SELF-IONIZATION

The self-conductances of the liquid hydrogen halides, except the fluoride, are somewhat less than that of water, but to account for these conductivities some form of self-ionization must be postulated. It is known that water ionizes into a proton and a hydroxide ion,

$$H_2O \rightleftharpoons H^+ + OH^- \tag{1}$$

and that this equation is more usually written with the proton solvated, as the hydroxonium ion, although further solvation of both ions must occur,

$$2H_2O \rightleftharpoons H_3O^+ + OH^-. \tag{2}$$

Similarly the hydrogen halides, HHal, can ionize,

$$HHal \rightleftharpoons H^+ + Hal^- \tag{3}$$

but in these systems solvation of both proton and the halide ion is known to occur :

$$3HHal \rightleftharpoons H_2Hal^+ + HHal_2^-. \tag{4}$$

The only well authenticated example of an H_2Hal^+ ion in solution is the hydrofluoronium ion, H_2F^+, which has been detected, together with the SbF_6^- ion, in the hydrogen fluoride—antimony pentafluoride system by conductivity measurements, Raman spectra and infra-red spectra (Hyman et $al.$, 1961). The H_2Cl^+ ion may exist in the compounds $HCl \cdot HClO_4$, which is explosive, $HCl \cdot H_2SO_4$, which it was not possible to isolate as a solid (Hantzsch, 1930) and in $HCl \cdot HBr$ (Klemenc and Kohl, 1927). This last compound has been claimed to have a structure $H_2Cl^+Br^-$ and not $H_2Br^+Cl^-$ by a dubious argument equating the H_2Cl^+ ion with the K^+ ion and the H_2Br^+ ion with the Rb^+ ion, as the nuclear charge and number of electrons are the same in both instances, and comparing the lattice energies of potassium bromide and rubidium chloride (del Fresno, 1928). There is, as yet, no evidence for the H_2Br^+ and H_2I^+ ions in solution, or in solids.

The existence of the hydrogen difluoride ion, HF_2^-, has long been known, and that of the hydrogen dichloride ion, HCl_2^-, is now well established. It was first postulated as an intermediate in some organic reactions in nitrobenzene (Herbrandson et $al.$, 1954), and was then prepared as tetramethylammonium hydrogen dichloride (Waddington, 1958a, b) and as some carbonium ion dichlorides (Sharp, 1958). Recently this ion has been encountered in several compounds. The reported preparation of caesium hydrogen dichloride by West (1957), has later proved to be false ; the compound was in fact $CsCl \cdot \frac{3}{4}HCl \cdot \frac{3}{4}H_2O$ (Valleé and McDaniel, 1963; Maki and West, 1963) with a structure $4Cs^+Cl^- \cdot 3H_3O^+Cl^-$. Caesium hydrogen dichloride has been prepared from hydrogen chloride and caesium chloride at $-78°$, and has a high dissociation pressure ($c.$ 4·4 atm, at room temperature)

(Valleé and McDaniel, 1962). The infra-red spectra of some of these compounds have been examined and frequencies assigned to the hydrogen dichloride ion (Waddington, 1958b; Sharp, 1958). The infra-red data is consistent with that of a linear ion $(Cl—H—Cl)^-$; the symmetric position of the proton has been confirmed by entropy measurements (Chang and Westrum, 1962). The heat of formation of the HF_2^- ion in the gas phase has been calculated to be 58—5 kcal mole^{-1} (Waddington, 1958a). The heats of formation for the HX_2^- ion with large cations are reported to approach limiting values of $+14.2$ kcal mole^{-1} for HCL_2^-, $+12.8$ kcal mole^{-1} for HBr_2^-, and $+12.4$ kcal mole^{-1} for the HI_2^- ion (Valleé and McDaniel, 1963). The hydrogen dichloride and dibromide ions have been found as their tropenium

TABLE II

The Infra-red Vibration Frequencies of the Hydrogen Dihalide Ions

Anion	ν_3 cm^{-1} (Assymetric stretch)	ν_2 cm^{-1} (Bending)	Salt
HF_2^-	1450	1223	KHF_2
HCl_2^-	1565	1180	Me_4NHCl_2[a]
	1565	1160	Me_4NHCl_2[b]
	1540	1150	n-Bu_4NHCl_2[b]
	1625	1150	$Si(acac)_3HCl_2$[b]
HBr_2^-	1670	1170	Et_4NHBr_2[b]
	1690	1170	n-Bu_4NHBr_2[b]
HI_2^-	1650	1165	n-Bu_4NHI_2[b]
$HBrCl^-$	1650	1100	n-$Bu_4NHBrCl$[c]
$HClI^-$	2000	990	n-Bu_4NHClI[c]

[a] Waddington (1958a, b).   [b] Valleé and McDaniel (1963).
[c] Salthouse and Waddington (1965).

salts, $C_7H_7^+HX_2^-$, which were prepared from the reaction of a solution of tropenyl methyl ether with a saturated ethereal solution of the hydrogen halide (Harmon and Davis, 1962). The hydrogen dibromide ion has also been prepared as the tetra-n-butylammonium and tetraphenylarsonium salts (Waddington and White, 1960a) and the hydrogen di-iodide ion as the tetra-n-butylammonium salt. Salts of mixed dihalide ions such as $HClBr^-$ and $HClI^-$, have also recently been prepared (Salthouse and Waddington, 1965).

A summary of the infra-red data on these ions is given in Table II.

If the self-ionization of the hydrogen halides can be represented by equation (4), two definitions of acids and bases are applicable, based upon a difference of emphasis, rather than of principle. This arises from the fact that either halide ion- or proton-transfer can be regarded as the primary step in the equilibrium. Acids can be defined as proton donors or halide ion acceptors, and bases as proton acceptors or halide ion donors: the halide ions in this concept must always be solvated as the hydrogen dihalide ions, similarly the protons are solvated as hydrohalonium ions H_2Hal^+. Thus hydrogen chloride shows some of the characteristics of a chloridotropic solvent such as arsenic trichloride (Gutmann, 1956), and some of an acidic solvent, such as sulphuric acid (Gillespie and Leisten, 1954; Gillespie and Robinson, 1959 and Chapter 4 of this book).

C. EXPERIMENTAL METHODS

1. *Preparation of the Pure Solvents, and Handling Techniques*

The main method used in the study of these solvents has been conductimetric measurements. Spectroscopic techniques have not been extensively used. The most sensitive test of the purity of the hydrogen halides is the specific conductivity of the liquid, although a rough guide can be obtained from vapour pressure measurements. The conductivity is very sensitive to traces of impurity, such as water, and very high purity solvent can only be obtained by repeated distillations. As the hydrogen halides, except the fluoride, are gases at room temperature, they must be handled in an enclosed vacuum system. The temperatures at which the solvents are usually studied are $-111 \cdot 6°$ (melting carbon disulphide) and $-95 \cdot 0°$ (melting toluene) for hydrogen chloride, $-83 \cdot 6°$ (melting ethyl acetate) for hydrogen bromide, and $-45 \cdot 2°$ (melting chlorobenzene) for hydrogen iodide.

2. *Conductimetric Measurements*

The conductivity of solutions in liquid hydrogen chloride and bromide, was studied by Steele *et al.* (1905, 1906) but not used as a means for following titrations of the acid–base type. This latter type of titration has been used extensively in recent work on these solvents. The conductivities of the pure solvents are shown in Table I, while a selection of conductivities of solutes in the various solvents are shown in Table III.

From this table it is seen that the conductivities of the solvobases are very much greater than those of the solvoacids. This is due to the highly acidic nature of these solvents, making it very difficult to find acids that are stronger than the solvents themselves. It is also seen that the conductivities in liquid hydrogen chloride are higher than in the bromide or iodide. The mechanism of the conduction is not known, but it can be postulated that it occurs by chloride ion transfer, in basic liquid hydrogen chloride solutions, viz:

$$Cl\text{——}H\text{——}Cl^- \, . \, . \, H\text{——}Cl$$
$$\downarrow$$
$$Cl\text{——}H \, . \, . \, . \, Cl\text{——}H\text{——}Cl^-$$

If this represents a true picture of the mode of conduction the molar conductances of all univalent bases should be approximately the same at infinite dilution: unfortunately it is not yet possible to measure these conductances with any degree of accuracy (Peach and Waddington, 1963a). Transport

TABLE III

Conductances of Some Solutions

Solvent	Solute	Concentration (mole/litre)	Specific conductivity (μ mho cm^{-1})	Molar conductances (cm^2 ohm^{-1} mole^{-1})	solution
HCl	PCl$_5$	0·36	9350	25·9	Basic[a]
HCl	Me$_4$NCl	0·32	6790	21·5	Basic[a]
HCl	BCl$_3$	0·32	0·13	$4·0 \times 10^{-4}$	Acidic[a]
HCl	BF$_3$	1·43	0·09	$0·6 \times 10^{-4}$	Acidic[a]
HCl	POF$_3$	0·25	3·6	$1·5 \times 10^{-2}$	Basic[b]
HBr	Me$_4$NBr	0·023	9·8	0·432	Basic[c]
HBr	SnBr$_4$	0·064	0·024	$3·8 \times 10^{-4}$	Acidic[c]
HI	Ph$_3$MeNI	0·10	243	2·55	Basic[d]
HI	Pyridine	0·38	125	0·32	Basic[d]

[a] Waddington and Klanberg (1960a).   [c] Waddington and White (1960a).
[b] Peach and Waddington (1962b).   [d] Klanberg and Kohlschütter (1961).

TABLE IV

Cation Transport Numbers in Liquid Hydrogen Bromide[a]

Substance	Concentration (mole/litre)	Mean value of t_+
Ether, (C$_2$H$_5$)$_2$O	1·0	0·82
Triethylamine, Et$_3$N	0·5	0·18
Triethylamine, Et$_3$N	0·62–0·75	0·22
Triethylamine, Et$_3$N	1·04	0·35
Acetone, Me$_2$CO	1·0	0·38
Acetone, Me$_2$CO	1·82	0·95
Methyl hexyl ketone	0·9	0·39
Methyl hexyl ketone	1·8	0·77

[a] Steele et al. (1905, 1906).

numbers have not yet been measured in liquid hydrogen chloride, but they have been measured for some hydrogen bromide solutions (Steele *et al.*, 1905, 1906). The results are summarized in Table IV. It will be seen from the table that the cation transport number is always increased by increase of concentration. This change probably indicates an increase in the complexity of the cation as the solution becomes stronger.

The hydrogen halides, except the fluoride, have low dielectric constants. Fuoss and Kraus studied the variation of conductivity with concentration in solvents of low dielectric constant (Krauss and Fuoss, 1933; Fuoss and Krauss, 1933). They found that plots of $\log \Lambda$ against $\log c$ (Λ = equivalent

TABLE V

Values of c_m, Λ_m and Λ_∞ in Hydrogen Chloride Solution[a]

Variable	Plot	Kraus and Fuoss[b, c]	Me$_2$S	Me$_3$N	Me$_3$NHBCl$_4$	MeCOCl
c_m	$\Lambda - c^{\frac{1}{2}}$	$\epsilon = 9 \cdot 0$	0·0196	0·0064	0·01538	0·0625
	$\Lambda c^{\frac{1}{2}} - c$	0·025	0·0197	0·0069	0·0133	0·114
	$\log \Lambda - \log c$		0·020	0·0072	0·01514	0·0603
Λ_m	$-c^{\frac{1}{2}}$	5·6	0·85	0·85	0·79	0·00485
	$\log \Lambda - \log c$		0·76	0·87	0·80	0·00516
Λ_∞	$\Lambda - c^{\frac{1}{2}}$	40	3·65	1·90	2·50	0·0151

[a] Peach and Waddington (1963a).   [b] Kraus and Fuoss (1933
[c] Fuoss and Kraus (1933).

conductance, c = concentration) showed a minimum and that this minimum moved to higher concentrations as the dielectric constant increased; with aqueous solutions this minimum was at concentrations too high to be observed. The variation of the conductances of hydrogen chloride, hydrogen bromide and hydrogen iodide solutions was studied by Steele *et al.* (1905, 1906), Peach and Waddington (1963a), and by Waddington and White (1963). In all these cases it was found that in plots of Λ and $\sqrt{c}$ the value of Λ tended to come to a minimum at low values of $\sqrt{c}$. The position of this minimum concentration, c_m, has been found for hydrogen chloride solutions of the bases dimethylsulphide and trimethylamine, the salt, trimethylammonium tetrachloroborate, and the weak electrolyte, (see Fig. 1) acetyl chloride; the values are shown in Table V (Peach and Waddington, 1963a). Extrapolation of these curves to infinite dilution is very difficult.

This variation of conductance with concentration in hydrogen chloride solutions is very much the same as that observed by Fuoss and Kraus with a

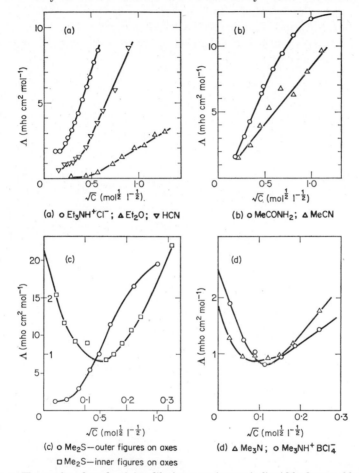

(a) o Et$_3$NH$^+$Cl$^-$; ▲ Et$_2$O; ▼ HCN

(b) o MeCONH$_2$; ▲ MeCN

(c) o Me$_2$S—outer figures on axes
□ Me$_2$S—inner figures on axes

(d) ▲ Me$_3$N; o Me$_3$NH$^+$BCl$_4^-$

FIG. 1. The results of conductivity dilution experiments in liquid hydrogen chloride.

solvent of about the same dielectric constant. To account for these results it is assumed that two modes of ionization for an ion pair, A$^+$B$^-$, are possible:

$$A^+B^- \overset{K_5}{\rightleftharpoons} A^+ + B^- \tag{5}$$

$$A^+B^- + A^+ \overset{K_6}{\rightleftharpoons} A_2B^+ \tag{6}$$

$$A^+B^- + B^- \overset{K_7}{\rightleftharpoons} AB_2^-. \tag{7}$$

Ionization of type (5) occurs in very dilute solutions, and of types (6) and (7) in more concentrated ones. Calculations from this basic operation, involving some drastic assumptions, show that the ionization of strong electrolytes in hydrogen chloride solutions can be represented by equations (5), (6), and (7) (Peach and Waddington, 1963a): similar reasoning must also apply to hydrogen bromide and iodide solutions. It is also possible to calculate the dissociation constants K_5, K_6 and K_7 (see Table V). The variation of the conductance of weak electrolytes with concentration is more complicated, and cannot easily be explained.

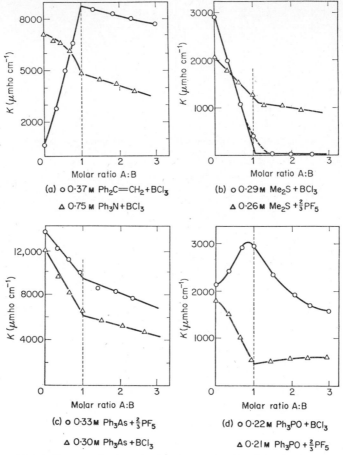

Fig. 2. Some conductimetric titrations in liquid hydrogen chloride.

For simplicity the ionization of all salts, when discussed further in the text, will be assumed to be of type (5), although ionization of types (6) and (7) must occur.

Reactions involving changes in the ionic species present in the solution can be followed conductimetrically, for example the acid–base reaction (Waddington and Klanberg, 1960a):

$$Me_4N^+HCl_2^- + BCl_3 \rightarrow Me_4N^+BCl_4^- + HCl \tag{8}$$

or an oxidation reaction where ions are formed (Salthouse and Waddington, 1965)

$$PCl_3 + Cl_2 + HCl \rightarrow PCl_4^+ \, HCl_2^-. \tag{9}$$

Several plots of conductimetric titrations are shown in Fig. 2 of bases against the solvoacids boron trichloride or phosphorus pentafluoride.

Phosphorus pentafluoride acts as a source of fluorophosphoric acid, HPF_6, one molecule of which is formed from one and a half molecules of phosphorus pentafluoride. Boron trichloride can react with bases to form either tetrachloroborates or a boron trichloride adduct; obviously it can only form tetrachloroborates with bases that readily lose a chloride ion, e.g. tetramethylammonium chloride. Phosphorus pentafluoride can only form hexafluorophosphates. There are four main types of conductimetric titrations. They are:

(1) salt formation, e.g. $Ph_3N + BCl_3$, $Me_2S + PF_5$, $Ph_3PO + PF_5$;
(2) adduct formation, e.g. $Me_2S + BCl_3$;
(3) ionization, e.g. $Ph_2C{=}CH_2 + BCl_3$;
(4) a mixture of two, or three, of the above, e.g. $Ph_3PO + BCl_3$.

TABLE VI

Conductances at Equivalence Points

Base	Acid	Λ_B	Λ_E	Λ_B/Λ_E	Product in solution
Ph_3N	BCl_3	12·6	7·8	1·62	Salt[a]
Ph_3As	BCl_3	39·5	20·4	1·94	Salt[a]
Ph_3As	PF_5	40·3	27·8	1·45	Salt[b]
Me_2S	BCl_3	10·05	0·033	304·6	Adduct[a]
Me_2S	PF_5	7·8	4·1	1·90	Salt[b]
$Ph_2C{=}CH_2$	BCl_3	1·77	23·8	0·074	Salt[c]
$PhC{\equiv}CH$	BCl_3	0·72	0·68	1·06	Salt[c]
Me_2O	BCl_3	0·43	0·012	25·8	Adduct[a]
$PhCN$	BCl_3	1·43	0·0052	27·5	Adduct[c]
Ph_2SO	BCl_3	6·65	1·60	4·15	Salt[d]

Λ_B = Conductance of free base ($cm^2 \, ohm^{-1} \, mole^{-1}$).
Λ_E = Conductance at equivalence point ($cm^2 \, ohm^{-1} \, mole^{-1}$).

[a] Peach and Waddington (1961).   [c] Peach and Waddington (1962a).
[b] Peach and Waddington (1963b).   [d] Peach and Waddington (1962b).

The shape of these curves is characteristic of the reactions occurring. In salt and adduct formation, the conductance per mole of base steadily decreases up to the equivalence point as the acid is added; it reaches a very low value when an adduct is formed in solution, but remains higher if a salt is formed. This is well illustrated by the figures show in Table VI for the conductances at the beginning and equivalence point in various titrations.

When the molar conductance at the equivalence point is low, below c. 0·1 cm² ohm⁻¹ mole⁻¹, it can be assumed that an adduct has been formed in solution, assuming, of course, that no precipitation has occurred during the titration. Using this technique it is possible to detect the formation of salts in solution, which are unstable at room temperature. For example boron trichloride undoubtedly reacts with triphenylarsine to form the salt $Ph_3AsH^+BCl_4^-$, but it was only possible to isolate the adduct, $Ph_3As . BCl_3$ at room temperature. It is noteworthy that the conductimetric curve is usually smooth in the equivalence point region when an adduct has been formed, but there is a sharp break associated with salt formation.

When ionization occurs during a titration the conductance increases as the acid is added, presumably due to the salt being more stable than the free base (see Fig. 2(a)). Sometimes it is impossible to assign a curve to one of the above categories, e.g. triphenylphosphine oxide and boron trichloride (see Fig. (2d)): the reaction is probably a mixture of at least two types, ionization and salt formation.

3. *Spectroscopic*

The spectra of solutions in hydrogen halides have been very little studied. One of the difficulties is the low temperatures involved, unless the experiments are performed at fairly high pressures. It has been possible to study some n.m.r. spectra of solutions in hydrogen chloride at room temperature, using tubes under pressure. Such spectra have confirmed the presence of $(C_6H_5)_2C . CH_3^+$ and $(C_6H_5)C(CH_3)^{2+}$ ions in solutions of unsymmetrical diphenyl ethylene and phenyl acetylene in liquid hydrogen chloride.

No experimental measurements have been made on solutions in the hydrogen halides, either at room temperature, or low temperature, of the Raman, infra-red, and ultra-violet spectra. In certain cases, such as the ultra-violet spectra of the aromatic olefins, this would provide valuable further evidence for the proposed mode of ionization (Peach and Waddington, 1962a).

$$Ph_2C\!\!=\!\!CH_2 + 2HCl \rightarrow Ph_2MeC^+ + HCl_2^-. \qquad (10)$$

Spectroscopic measurements have been extensively used for solutions in hydrogen fluoride, where measurements can be made at about room temperature: the presence of the ions H_2F^+ and SbF_6^- has been detected in solutions of antimony pentafluoride in hydrogen fluoride by Raman and infra-red spectra, as well as by conductivity measurements (Hyman et al., 1961).

Raman spectroscopy has been used in the study of some hydrogen chloride addition compounds. The spectra of the compounds $CH_3 . CO . NH_2 . HCl$ and $(CH_3 . CO . NH_2)_2HCl$, show that the hydrochloride is probably

$CH_3 . CO . NH_3^+ Cl^-$; the spectra of the hemihydrochloride was difficult to interpret (Kahovec and Knollmüller, 1941). The spectra of the compounds of dimethyl ether and hydrogen chloride, $Me_2O . HCl$, $Me_2O . 3HCl$, and $Me_2O . 4HCl$, reveal that the latter two compounds are ionic, whereas the monohydrochloride has a hydrogen-bonded structure. However the compounds $Me_2O . DCl$ and $Me_2O . HBr$ do have an ionic structure, the ether oxygen being protonated (Vidale and Taylor, 1956).

4. *Phase Diagrams*

Study of phase diagrams in which one of the hydrogen halides is one component, will not reveal very much about the nature of the solutions, but it does give indications of some of the compounds that can be formed in them. Study of the phase diagram of water and hydrogen chloride showed that three compounds are formed $HCl . 3H_2O$, m.p. $-24.4°$; $HCl . 2H_2O$, m.p. $-17.7°$; and $HCl . H_2O$, m.p. $-15.4°$ (Rupert, 1909). The last compound would be formed when some water is present in the liquid hydrogen chloride, but it is insoluble (Waddington and Klanberg, 1960a): the crystal structure of $H_2O . HCl$ shows that it is $H_3O^+Cl^-$, with every hydrogen atom joined by hydrogen bonds to the nearest chloride atom ion (Yoon and Carpenter, 1959).

The phase diagrams of solvoacids and solvobases can yield valuable information about the nature of the solvated protons and halide ions. The system, boron trichloride and hydrogen chloride does not show any compound formation (Graff, 1933): it can therefore be concluded that boron trichloride must be very weak solvoacid in hydrogen chloride. Although the phase diagram of the hydrogen chloride—chlorine system shows that the compounds formed are $2HCl . Cl_2$, m.p. $-121°$ and $HCl . Cl_2$, m.p. $-115°$ (Wheat and Browne, 1940), there is no evidence that chlorine solutions in hydrogen chloride are acidic (M. E. Peach and T. C. Waddington, unpublished results), although they can act as oxidizing agents (J. A. Salthouse and T. C. Waddington, unpublished results).

The diagrams of several compounds that are solvobases with hydrogen chloride or bromide have been studied. Some of the first observations were made by Maas and McIntosh (1913), although workers in Archibald's school had previously been able to isolate some hydrogen halide adducts with oxygen containing compounds. In the phase diagram of ethyl ether and hydrogen chloride the compounds detected were $Et_2O . HCl$, m.p. $-92°$; $Et_2O . 2HCl$, m.p. $-88°$; $Et_2O . 5HCl$, m.p. $-89°$ (Maas and McIntosh, 1913): from these results it seems reasonable to suppose that the ether is protonated, Et_2OH^+, and the chloride ion solvated $Cl(HCl)_x$ where $x = 0, 1,$ or 4.

More recently, phase diagrams of hydrogen chloride with π-orbital donor molecules have been studied. It was found that some aliphatic olefins and acetylenes formed very low melting point compounds of compositions 1 : 1, 2 : 1 and 4 : 1 (HCl: hydrocarbon): similar results showing 1 : 1 and 2 : 1 (HCL : hydrocarbon) adducts were obtained with aromatic hydrocarbons (Cook et al., 1956). The nitriles have also been studied as n-bond systems (Murray and Schneider, 1955): in the case of acetonitrile and hydrogen chloride the compounds detected were CH_3CN . HCL, m.p. $-63.2°$; $2CH_3CN$. $3HCl$, m.p. $-88°$; CH_3CN . $5HCl$, m.p. $-123.6°$; and CH_3CH . $7HCl$, m.p. $-125.0°$. These can again be interpreted as $CH_3CNH^+Cl(HCl)_x^-$. Infra-red study of a compound of composition, CH_3CN . $2HCl$ shows that it is ionic, $CH_3C{=}NH^+HCl_2^-$ (Janz and Danyluk, 1959). Although complete phase diagrams have not been studied the compounds n-$Bu_4NCl(HCl)_2$, n-Bu_4NBr $(HCl)_2$ and n-$Bu_4NI(HCl)_2$ have recently been isolated at low temperature (Salthouse and Waddington, 1965).

5. Cryoscopic and Ebullioscopic Measurements

Cryoscopic (Beckmann and Waentig, 1910) and ebullioscopic (Steele et al., 1905, 1906) measurements have been made on some solutions in hydrogen chloride, bromide and iodide. Experiments of this type are likely to lead to results which would be extremely difficult to interpret, due to the complex mode of ionization. This was in fact observed: Beckmann and Waentig (1910) concluded that some form of association was occurring in solution. Further interpretation of these results would be extremely difficult, but it ought to be possible to correlate them with the variation of conductivity with dilution for a particular solute.

6. Preparative Methods

Because of their low boiling points and consequent easy removal, the liquid hydrogen halides as solvents are good media for certain preparations. By using the hydrogen halide and the corresponding boron trihalide it is easy to prepare tetrahaloborates (Waddington and Klanberg, 1959, 1960; Waddington and White, 1960a,b): particularly easy are the tetra-chloroborates where the excess of solvent and boron trichloride can be removed by low temperature distillation at $c.$ $-80°$. Hexachlorodiborates can be prepared from diboron tetrachloride in the same way (Holliday et al., 1961). This method must be limited to reactions between two compounds, the excess of one of which can be removed either with the solvent, or by pumping on the compound under a high vacuum. If both of the reactants are involatile, care must be exercised in interpreting the results, as the product may be an equimolecular mixture of the reactants. Most of the compounds prepared in the liquid hydrogen halides have been isolated at the end of conductimetric titrations, where, although the amount recovered may only be of the order of a millimole there is sufficient for analysis and character-ization. By using a somewhat different reaction cell it is possible to study the products of a reaction by the increase in weight observed. Solvolysis reactions where one product is volatile can be studied similarly. However, if one of the products is insoluble and the other is soluble, the solute can be recovered by decantation in an inverted Y-shaped cell and evaporation of the solvent (Peach and Waddington, 1961). Solvolytic reactions are not very valuable preparative methods, as the chloro-, bromo-, and iodo-compounds which are formed can often be obtained more easily by other methods. A good method has been developed for the preparation of small quantities of high purity nitryl chloride by the solvolysis of dinitrogen pentoxide with liquid hydrogen chloride.

II. Solutions in the Hydrogen Halides

The experiments of Gore (1856) showed that a large variety of metals, non-metals and simple inorganic substances were insoluble in liquid hydrogen chloride. However he must have observed some solvolytic reactions, as he reported that materials such as cadmium sulphide turned white and the solid recovered contained no sulphide. The solubilities of a further large selection of inorganic materials were reported by Steele et al. (1905, 1906) who found that ionic halides, such as the alkali metal halides, were insoluble in hydrogen chloride. They did find that covalent chlorides, such as stannic chloride and phosphorus oxychloride were soluble. When the low dielectric constants and highly acidic nature of the solvents are borne in mind, later workers have been more successful in finding suitable solutes for hydrogen chloride, bromide, and iodide solutions.

A. ACIDS AND BASES

The hydrogen halides are highly acidic solvents, whose acidity increases in the order

$$HF < HCl < HBr < HI.$$

Consequently it is often very difficult to find any reasonably strong solvo-acids, particularly in hydrogen chloride, bromide and iodide which are appreciably more acidic solvents than hydrogen fluoride. Conversely there are very many solvo-bases, some of which act as very strong electrolytes.

1. Bases

It is possible for basic solutions to be formed by two distinct types of solute.

(a) Salts which ionize readily to give a free halide ion, solvated in the solution: the best examples of this type of compound are the tetra-alkylammonium halides, R_4NHal.

(b) Compounds containing atoms with a lone pair of electrons, or a π-bond system, which can easily be protonated, e.g. triphenylamine in liquid hydrogen chloride (Peach and Waddington, 1961).

A selection of conductances of basic solutions in hydrogen chloride are shown in Tables II and VII.

(a) *Salt type*. Bases of type (a) which can be found are rather few: if the compound exists as an ionic species in the solid state at room temperature, it must have a large cation, and consequent low lattice energy, as the solvent's dielectric constants are low. Generally salts of the Group V elements, $R_3^1MR^+Hal^-$, will act as solvo-bases (Waddington and Klanberg, 1960a;

TABLE VII

Conductances of Some Bases in Hydrogen Chloride at $-95°$[a]

Solute	Concentration (mole/litre)	Specific conductivity (μ mho cm^{-1})	Molar conductance (cm^2 ohm^{-1} mole^{-1})
Ph_3Cl	0·25	10640	42·9
Ph_3SiCl	Saturated	1·53	—
Ph_3As	0·20	7700	39·3
AsH_3	Saturated	26·3	—
H_2S	Saturated	2·8	—
Me_2O	0·26	114·4	0·43
Me_2S	0·35	3950	11·3
$Ph_2C=CH_2$	0·37	650	1·77
MeCN	0·42	1220	2·94
Me_2CO	0·41	4300	10·4
MeCOCl	0·30	2·9	0·0097
Ph_2SO	Saturated	1500	—
$COCl_2$	0·39	0·27	0·0007

[a] Peach and Waddington (1961, 1962a,b).

Waddington and White, 1960a, 1963; Klanberg and Kohlschütter, 1961), but when $R = H$ these salts can be formed *in situ* and are classified as bases of type (b). Bases are also formed when phosphorus pentachloride and bromide are dissolved in the corresponding solvent (Waddington and Klanberg, 1960a; Waddington and White, 1960a, 1963).

$$PCl_5(s) + 2HCl = PCl_4^+ + HCl_2^-. \tag{11}$$

Such solutions provide a ready source of $PHal_4^+$ ions, and further salts can be prepared after reaction with a solvo-acid. Although phosphorus pentachloride exists in the solid state as $PCl_4^+ PCl_6^-$, it has not been possible to detect the PCl_6^- ion in liquid hydrogen chloride (Waddington and Klanberg, 1960a), indeed there is surprisingly little evidence for the existence of the PCl_6^-

ion in any other salts containing "ordinary cations", although hexachloro-phosphates of the cations $EtCCl_2 . PCl_3^+$ (Kirsanov and Fedorova, 1960) and $(Cl_3P{=}N{-}(PCl_2N)_x{-}PCl_3)^+$ (Fluck, 1962) have been reported.

Carbon–halogen compounds, in which the carbon–halogen bond is easily broken with the formation of a stable carbonium ion, can act as solvo-bases. The triphenylmethyl carbonium ion, Ph_3C^+, can be readily formed from triphenylmethyl chloride in hydrogen chloride (Peach and Waddington, 1961), and is also probably formed from the chloride in hydrogen iodide (Klanberg and Kohlschütter, 1961). Detection of this ion in solution is easy as it is highly coloured; the colour must be caused by the presence of the triphenylmethyl carbonium ion, and not the hydrogen dichloride, as most other basic solutions are colourless. Attempts to prepare the ions Ph_3M^+ (M = Si, Ge, Sn, Pb) by dissolving the chlorides Ph_3MCl in hydrogen chloride failed (Peach and Waddington, 1961): with the tin and lead compounds partial replacement of the phenyl group by halogen was observed.

(b) *Protonation of Groups IV, V and VI elements.* Bases of type (b), involving protonation, have been studied with derivatives of Group IV, V and VI elements, various olefins, acetylenes, nitriles, azo compounds, and compounds containing doubly-bonded oxygen. Study of protonation reactions is easier in liquid hydrogen chloride than sulphuric acid, where similar reactions have been observed, as the undesirable side effects of sulphonation are avoided (Gillespie and Leisten, 1954). Triphenyl- and trimethylamine are both strong bases in liquid hydrogen chloride (Peach and Waddington, 1961, 1962a). A freshly purchased sample of triphenylamine gave a pale brown solution, but when the sample had been kept for six months and then vacuum sublimed the solution was blue: this colour change was not a function of the concentration, and might well have been due to the formation of the ion Ph_3N^+, as some ions of this type are reported as being blue (Peach and Waddington, 1961). It is possible to protonate the nitrogen in hydrazo-benzene in hydrogen chloride, but rearrangement occurs to give benzidine (Peach and Waddington, 1961). Pyridine acts as an excellent base in all three solvents (Waddington and Klanberg, 1960a; Waddington and White, 1960a,b) and it is easy to prepare pyridinium tetrahalogenborates.

The phosphorus atom in phosphine and triphenylphosphine is also easily protonated in hydrogen chloride, bromide, and iodide (Peach and Wadding-ton, 1961; Klanberg and Kohlschütter, 1961). If phosphine is used as a solvo-base in hydrogen chloride or bromide the phosphonium ion is formed and in this way phosphonium tetrachloroborate, chlorotrifluoroborate, and tetrabromoborate have been prepared (Waddington and Klanberg, 1960a; Waddington and White, 1960b). However, if diphosphine is employed, it is not possible to detect any diphosphonium ions as decomposition occurs (Peach and Waddington, 1961). Triphenylarsine can be readily protonated in hydrogen chloride, forming a strong base. It is not possible to isolate this protonated form at room temperature as a tetrachloroborate, after reaction with boron trichloride, since hydrogen chloride is lost and an adduct formed.

$$Ph_3As + 2HCl \rightarrow Ph_3AsH^+ \, HCl_2^- \tag{12}$$

$$Ph_3AsH^+ + BCl_3 + HCl_2 \rightarrow Ph_3AsH^+ \, BCl_4^- + HCl \tag{13}$$

$$\downarrow$$

$$Ph_3As \,.\, BCl_3$$

Attempts to use arsine to prepare arsonium salts were unsuccessful, as arsine reacts with the solvent. Triphenylstibine or triphenylbismuthane do not form stable protonated species in liquid hydrogen chloride; they react with the solvent and become partially chlorinated (Peach and Waddington, 1961).

The basic properties of various derivatives of oxygen and sulphur, ROR' and RSR', have been examined in liquid hydrogen chloride (Peach and Waddington, 1961). Early workers had shown that it is possible to detect protonated alcohols and ethers, derivatives of hydrogen chloride, bromide, or iodide (Maas and McIntosh, 1913; McIntosh, 1908) and that some alcohols and ethers form highly conducting solutions (Walker et al., 1904). Water and hydrogen sulphide are both insoluble in liquid hydrogen chloride (Waddington and Klanberg, 1960a; Peach and Waddington, 1961), but when one or both of the hydrogen atoms is replaced by a methyl or phenyl group, basic solutions are formed. Dimethyl sulphide is the strongest base, as is shown by its conductivity (see Tables VII and IX).

Conductimetric titrations of these bases against boron trichloride in hydrogen chloride do not reveal much useful information, except in the cases of dimethyl ether and sulphide where an adduct is formed in solution (see Fig. 2(b)). It is not possible to isolate any protonated oxygen or sulphur compounds from these solutions after reaction with boron trichloride. Adducts are formed and decomposition of these adducts produces oxygen and sulphur substituted boron chlorides (Peach and Waddington, 1961). An unstable protonated derivative of dimethyl sulphide could be isolated after its reaction in liquid hydrogen chloride with phosphorus pentafluoride (Peach and Waddington, 1963b).

(c) *Protonation of π-bond systems.* Aromatic olefins, such as 1,1-diphenyl-ethylene can easily be protonated, with the formation of a carbonium ion:

$$Ph_2C{=}CH_2 + H^+ \rightarrow Ph_2CMe^+. \tag{14}$$

Reactions such as this have been observed in sulphuric acid and hydrogen chloride (Gold and Tye, 1952; Peach and Waddington, 1962a). The conductimetric titration of 1,1-diphenylethylene against boron trichloride in liquid hydrogen chloride shows the interesting phenomena of ionization occurring as the acid is added (see Fig. 3): a sharp end-point was found at a mole ratio of $1:1::BCl_3:Ph_2C{=}C\,H$. In similar experiments using styrene and α-methylstyrene there is some evidence for the formation of carbonium ions in solution; this is based mainly on the colour of the solutions, as conductimetric titrations were inconclusive. This must reflect the stability of the carbonium ions which would have been formed:

$$Me_3C^+,\ PhMeHC^+,\ PhMe_2C^+ \ll Ph_2MeC^+ < Ph_3C^+.$$

A doubly charged carbonium ion $(C_6Me_5)ClC^{2+}$ has been detected in a solution of pentamethyltrichloromethylbenzene in sulphuric acid (Hart and Fish, 1958). Conductimetric study of the reaction of phenylacetylene with boron trichloride in hydrogen chloride indicated that the doubly charged carbonium ion $PhMeC^{2+}$ was formed (Peach and Waddington, 1962a), an end-point being found at a mole ratio of 2 : 1 (BCl_3 : PhC≡CH) (see Fig. 3)

$$PhC{\equiv}CH + 4HCl \rightarrow PhMeC^{2+} + 2HCl_2^- \qquad (15)$$

$$PhMeC^{2+} + 2HCl_2^- + 2BCl_3 \rightarrow PhMeC^{2+} + 2BCl_4^- + 2HCl. \qquad (16)$$

Diphenyl acetylene formed a much less basic solution and there was little evidence for the formation of the ion $PhC\,.\,CH_2Ph^{2+}$. The nitriles contain

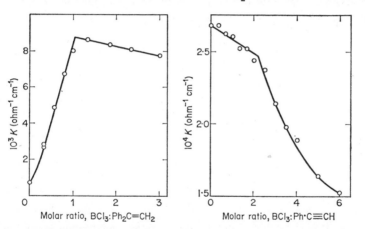

Fig. 3. Conductimetric titrations of $Ph_2C{=}CH_2$ and PhC≡CH with BCl_3 in liquid hydrogen chloride. (Reproduced by permission from the *Journal of the Chemical Society*.)

a triple bond which it is easy to protonate, and with hydrogen chloride, bromide, and iodide, it has been possible to prepare the compounds $MeCN\,.\,2HHal$. The infra-red spectra of these compounds indicate two distinct types of structure $MeC{\equiv}NH^+HCl_2^-$ and $MeBrC{=}NH_2^+\,Br^-$ (Janz and Danyluk, 1959). Both aceto- and benzonitriles have been found to be reasonably strong bases in liquid hydrogen chloride (Peach and Waddington, 1962a). In the reaction of all these basic solutions with boron trichloride it was not possible to isolate a tetrachloroborate, and hence examine further the structure of the cation. In the case of the nitriles an adduct was isolated, but with the ethylenes and acetylenes decomposition to tarry products occurred. It is impossible to say whether the acetonitrile adduct formed in solution, or as the product was warmed to room temperature, because precipitation occurred during the titration. After reaction of acetonitrile with phosphorus pentafluoride it was not possible to isolate a stable salt or adduct (Peach and Waddington, 1963b).

Azo compounds also contain a π-bond system, which it ought to be possible to protonate. Azobenzene and m-azotoluene both formed saturated basic solutions in liquid hydrogen chloride, from both of these solutions stable tetrachloroborates were isolated after reaction with boron trichloride (Peach and Waddington, 1962a). The position of the proton cannot be located from the infra-red spectra: other evidence, such as pKa measurements (Yeh and Jaffée, 1959) and the ultra-violet spectra of protonated azo compounds (Gerson and Heilbronner, 1962) suggests that the proton is located on the bond. Azoxybenzene and nitrobenzene are also reasonably strong bases in liquid hydrogen chloride. A boron trichloride adduct can be isolated from the reaction of an azoxybenzene solution and boron trichloride: the structure of this adduct is uncertain, as is the position of the original proton attachment. Nitrosobenzene in hydrogen chloride reacted with boron trichloride to form a compound which exploded just below room temperature, although a hydrochloride, of unknown structure, could be isolated from solution (Peach and Waddington, 1962a).

(d) *Protonation of doubly-bonded oxygen.* Carbonyl, nitro, phosphoryl, sulphonyl and sulphuryl groups all have at least one oxygen atom bonded to the central atom. The bonding is often considered to be polar, particularly in the carbonyl group,

$$\diagdown \atop C = O \leftrightarrow \overset{\diagdown}{C^+} - O^- \qquad (17)$$

and easy protonation of the oxygen atom would be expected. A fairly large variety of organic compounds containing these groups has been studied in liquid hydrogen chloride, the conductivities of which are shown in Table VIII.

Examination of this table reveals that most of the carbonyl compounds are strong bases, the exceptions being the aldehydes. In the case of the amides and esters, protonation may not have occurred at the carbonyl oxygen; acetamide hydrochloride is known to contain protonated nitrogen, $MeCONH_3^+Cl^-$ (Smyth and Hitchcock, 1933). The reactions of most of these carbonyl compounds with boron trichloride are complex, for instance with benzaldehyde the adduct $3PhCHO \cdot 2BCl_3$ is formed, which pyrolyses to benzylidene dichloride (Fraser et al., 1957). Compounds containing carbonyl groups always give, with boron trichloride in liquid hydrogen chloride, adducts and not tetrachloroborates (Peach and Waddington, 1962a). Trimethylamine oxide hydrochloride, $Me_3NOH^+Cl^-$ and triphenylphosphine oxide both act as strong solvo-bases. From the triphenylphosphine oxide solution a hydrochloride was isolated and, after reaction with phosphorus pentafluoride, a hexafluorophosphate, but with boron trichloride a mixture of the tetrachloroborate and adduct was formed. The protonated form of trimethylamine oxide was not retained on reaction with boron trichloride but

TABLE VIII

Conductances of Some Doubly-Bonded Oxygen Compounds in Liquid Hydrogen Chloride[a]

Compound	Concentration (mole/litre)	Specific conductivity (μmho cm^{-1})	Molar conductance (cm^2 ohm^{-1} mole^{-1})
MeCHO	Saturated	1·60	—
PhCHO	Saturated	1·81	—
Me$_2$CO	0·41	4300	10·4
Ph$_2$CO	0·25	1810	7·15
MeCONH$_2$	Saturated	1640	—
PhCONH$_2$	0·23	800	3·48
PhCO$_2$Et	0·33	3200	9·74
MeNO$_2$	Saturated	1·3	—
PhNO$_2$	0·31	490	0·16
Me$_2$SO	Saturated	1200	—
Ph$_2$SO	Saturated	1500	—
Me$_2$SO$_2$	0·23	47	0·20
Ph$_2$SO$_2$	0·21	110	0·51
Ph$_3$PO	0·22	2200	9·61

[a] Peach and Waddington (1962a,b).

an adduct was formed. Similar types of reaction were found with liquid hydrogen chloride solutions of dimethyl- and diphenylsulphoxide; the solution was fairly basic but after reaction with boron trichloride the adduct was recovered, although with phosphorus pentafluoride, dimethylsulphoxidium hexafluorophosphate was formed (Peach and Waddington, 1962b, 1963b).

The basic properties of the nitro compounds and sulphones were considerably less than that of the same type of compound containing only one doubly-bonded oxygen atom. This is probably due to resonance forms effectively reducing the charge on the oxygen atoms, as compared with that in a compound containing only one doubly-bonded oxygen, e.g. trimethylamine oxide and nitromethane

$$\text{Me}\diagdown \atop \text{Me}\!-\!\text{N}\!\rightarrow\!\text{O} \atop \text{Me}\diagup \leftrightarrow \text{Me}\diagdown \atop \text{Me}\!-\!\overset{+}{\text{N}}\!-\!\text{O}^- \atop \text{Me}\diagup \quad \text{cf.} \quad \text{Me}\!-\!\text{N}{\diagup^{\nearrow\text{O}} \atop \diagdown_{\text{O}}} \leftrightarrow \text{Me}\!-\!\overset{+}{\text{N}}{\diagup^{\diagup\text{O}^-} \atop \diagdown_{\text{O}}} \leftrightarrow \text{Me}\!-\!\overset{+}{\text{N}}{\diagup^{\diagup\text{O}} \atop \diagdown_{\text{O}^-}} \quad (18)$$

The basic properties of compounds such as benzoyl chloride in liquid hydrogen chloride can be due either to protonation of the carbonyl oxygen or loss of a chloride ion,

$$PhCOCl + 2HCl \rightleftharpoons PhCClOH^+ + HCl_2^- \qquad (19)$$

$$PhCOCl + HCl \rightleftharpoons PhCO^+ + HCl_2^-. \qquad (20)$$

The available evidence suggests that the compound ionizes as in equation (19): if ionization as in equation (20) occurs, solvolysis of benzoic acid would be expected, which is not observed (Reach and Waddington, 1962a).

$$PhCO_2H + 3HCl = PhCO^+HCl_2^- + H_3O^+Cl^-. \qquad (21)$$

Further evidence supporting this mechanism is found in the reactions of diphenylphosphoryl chloride, Ph_2POCl, in hydrogen chloride. If this compound ionizes by loss of a chloride ion, as equation (20), then the compound formed after reaction with boron trichloride ought to have the structure $Ph_2PO^+BCl_4^-$. All the available evidence suggests that this compound is in fact $Ph_2PClO–BCl_3$ (Peach and Waddington, 1962c), and that the tetrachloroborate is initially formed in the hydrogen chloride solution and then loses hydrogen chloride on removal of the solvent:

$$Ph_2PClOH^+HCl_2^- + BCl_3 {\rightarrow} Ph_2PClOH^+BCl_4^- + HCl$$
$$\downarrow \qquad\qquad (22)$$
$$Ph_2PClO–BCl_3 + HCl$$

Attempts to try and prepare the ion PCl_3OH^+ from the interaction of strong aquo-acids and phosphorus oxychloride in hydrogen chloride also failed (Peach and Waddington, 1962b). Most of the chloro compounds examined in liquid hydrogen chloride were weak bases, except diphenylphosphoryl chloride, and in most cases reaction with boron trichloride yielded an adduct, often unstable, or nothing (Peach and Waddington, 1962b). Some of the reactions of nitrosyl chloride observed in liquid hydrogen chloride (Waddington and Klanberg, 1960b) can be accounted for if no ionization of the solute is encountered.

When the molar conductances of solutions of the compounds in HCl described in this section and section (b) are examined, an interesting correlation is seen to exist between the conductance of the base and the negative inductive effect of the ligands attached to the atom which is protonated, as is seen in the Tables IX and X.

If the basicity, as measured by the molar conductance at comparable dilution, is controlled by the negative charge on the oxygen, or sulphur, then a direct relationship with the negative inductive effect as measured by the ionization in water of the corresponding substituted acetic acid is to be expected; this is observed. There are some exceptions as the figures in Tables IX and X show. Anomalies are ethyl benzoate, where protonation of

TABLE IX

K Classical for Substituted Acetic Acids, XCH_2CO_2H[a]

X	Me	H	Ph	OMe	I	Br	Cl	F
10^5K	1·34	2·1	5·6	33·5	75	138	155	217

[a] Peach and Waddington (1962b).

TABLE X

Variation of Molar Conductances with Ligands for Hydrogen Chloride Solutions[a]

XYO				XYS		
	Molar conductance $(cm^2\,ohm^{-1}\,mole^{-1})$				Molar conductance $(cm^2\,ohm^{-1}\,mole^{-1})$	
X	Y			X	Y	
	Me	H	Ph		Me	Ph
Me	0·43	0·13	0·021	Me	11·8	—
H	0·13	—	0·019	H	0·054	0·030
Ph	0·021	0·019	0·0017	Ph	—	0·15

X_2SO_2		X_3PO		PhCOX	
X	Molar conductance $(cm^2\,ohm^{-1}\,mole^{-1})$	X	Molar conductance $(cm^2\,ohm^{-1}\,mole^{-1})$	X	Molar conductance $(cm^2\,ohm^{-1}\,mole^{-1})$
Me	0·20	Ph	9·61	Ph	7·15
Ph	0·51	Cl	0·20	Cl	0·046
Cl	—	F	0·015	OEt	0·74

[a] Peach and Waddington (1962b).

the ethoxide oxygen can also occur, diphenyl sulphide, the sulphones and diphenylphosphoryl chloride; in all the latter cases protonation of the aromatic nucleus can also occur. Protonation of an aromatic nucleus causes highly coloured compounds to be formed: coloured liquid hydrogen chloride solutions were formed by anisole (pale pink) and diphenyl sulphide (purple) (Peach and Waddington, 1961), and by triphenylphosphine oxide (pale yellow) and diphenylphosphoryl chloride (yellow) (Peach and Waddington,

TABLE XI

Acid Conductances

Solvent	Solute	Concentration (mole/litre)	Specific conductivity (μmho cm^{-1})	Molar conductance (cm^2 ohm^{-1} mole^{-1})
HCl	MeSO$_3$H	Saturated	9·0	—[a]
HCl	CF$_3$SO$_3$H	Saturated	2·0	—[a]
HCl	ClSO$_3$H	0·38	2·7	$7·0 \times 10^{-3}$ [b]
HCl	SiF$_4$	0·13	0·98	$7·7 \times 10^{-3}$ [c]
HCl	PF$_5$	0·25	1·9	$7·5 \times 10^{-3}$ [c]
HCl	SO$_2$	Saturated	0·15	—[a]
HCl	P$_4$O$_{10}$	Saturated	0·82	—[a]
HCl	BCl$_3$	0·32	0·13	$4·0 \times 10^{-4}$ [b]
HCl	BF$_3$	1·43	0·09	$0·6 \times 10^{-4}$ [b]
HBr	Al$_2$Br$_6$	Saturated	0·073	—[d]
HBr	SnBr$_4$	0·064	0·024	$3·8 \times 10^{-4}$ [d]

[a] Peach and Waddington (1962b).   [c] Peach and Waddington (1963b).
[b] Waddington and Klanberg (1960a).   [d] Waddington and White (1960a).

1962b). In the series of phosphoryl compounds, X$_3$PO, it is seen that the molar conductance of phosphoryl chloride lies between that of triphenylphosphine oxide and phosphoryl fluoride, thus giving further support to the view that its mode of ionization probably involves protonation and not loss of a chloride ion.

2. Acids

There are two distinct possible types of acid in the hydrogen halide solvents, as is expected from the two different, but complementary, definitions of acids. They can either be halide ion acceptors, such as the boron halides, or proton donors, such as the strong aquo-acids. A selection of conductances is shown in Tables III and XI.

(a) *Group III Halide Ion Acceptors.* Boron compounds are well known acceptors and the trihalides function as solvo-acids in the corresponding hydrogen halide:

$$BHal_3 + 2HHal \rightleftharpoons H_2Hal^+ + BHal_4^-. \tag{23}$$

The extent of the ionization is small: the phase diagram of hydrogen chloride and boron trichloride shows that there is no compound formation (Graff, 1933). It is however very easy to prepare tetrahalogenoborates from a base and boron trihalide in the corresponding solvent (Waddington and Klanberg, 1959, 1960a; Waddington and White, 1960a,b). When boron trichloride is used as a solvo-acid in hydrogen chloride, some difficulty may be experienced because of adduct formation when the base is formed by protonation, e.g. with dimethylsulphoxide (Peach and Waddington, 1962b).

$$Me_2SOH^+HCl_2^- + BCl_3 \rightarrow Me_2SOH^+BCl_4^- + HCl \qquad (24)$$
$$\downarrow$$
$$Me_2SOBCl_3$$

However in many titrations sharp end-points are found (see Fig. 4). If diboron tetrachloride is employed as a solvo-acid in hydrogen chloride, salts of hexachlorodiboric acid, $H_2B_2Cl_6$ are formed (Holliday et $al.$, 1961)

$$2Me_4N^+HCl_2^- + B_2Cl_4 \rightarrow (Me_4N^+)_2B_2Cl_6^{2-} + 2HCl. \qquad (25)$$

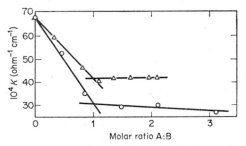

FIG. 4. Conductimetric titrations of boron halides against tetramethyl ammonium chloride in liquid hydrogen chloride; $\triangle$, $Me_4NCl + BCl_3$; O, $Me_4NCl + BF_3$. (Reproduced by permission from the $Journal$ of the $Chemical$ $Society$.)

Sharp end-points at 2 : 1 (Base: B_2Cl_4) are found. The acceptor properties of other boron compounds for chloride ions in liquid hydrogen chloride appear to be somewhat limited. When boron trifluoride is used as a solvo-acid in hydrogen chloride, salts of trifluorochloroboric acid, HBF_3Cl, can be isolated and several have been characterized (Waddington and Klanberg, 1959, 1960a): this is the only known method of making these salts. Conductimetric titrations with boron trifluoride show sharp 1 : 1 end-points (see Fig. 4). However diborane, triethylboron, triphenylboron, and dimethylboron chloride do not function as solvo-acids in hydrogen chloride, but there is some evidence that methylboron dichloride acts as a very weak solvo-acid (M. E. Peach and T. C. Waddington, unpublished results). In liquid hydrogen bromide, compounds of the type BR_3Br^- were not prepared: boron trifluoride showed no acidic properties and boron trichloride was completely solvolysed to the tribromide (Waddington and White, 1960a, 1963). However boron tribromide functions as a solvo-acid and in titrations with bromide ion donors, sharp 1 : 1 end points are found (see Fig. 5).

(b) *Group IV Halide Ion Acceptors.* Germanium tetrachloride showed no acidic properties in hydrogen chloride (see Fig. 6) (Waddington and Klanberg, 1959). Stannic halides are acidic in hydrogen chloride and bromide

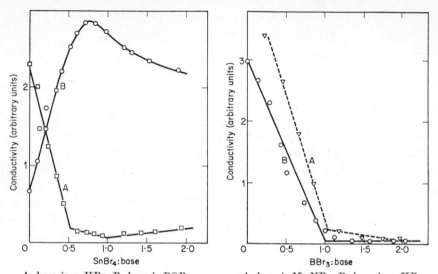

A, base is pyHBr; B, base is POBr$_3$ A, base is Me$_4$NBr; B, base is pyHBr

FIG. 5. Conductimetric titrations in liquid hydrogen bromide. (Reproduced by permission from the *Journal of the Chemical Society.*)

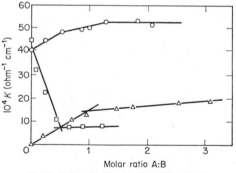

O, Me$_4$NCl+GeCl$_4$; □, Me$_4$NCl+SnCl$_4$

FIG. 6. Conductimetric titrations of Group IV chlorides against tetramethylammonium chloride. (Reproduced by permission from the *Journal of the Chemical Society.*)

(Waddington and Klanberg, 1960a; Waddington and White, 1960a, 1963) and it was possible to detect and isolate salts of hexachloro- and hexabromostanic acid in titrations (see Figs. 5 and 6). Attempts have been made to prepare the ions SiF$_4$Cl$_2^{2-}$ and GeF$_4$Cl$_2^{2-}$ by using the respective fluorides as acids in hydrogen chloride. Silicon tetrafluoride exhibited no tendency to accept a chloride ion: germanium tetrafluoride appeared to be acidic, but it was not possible to isolate a definite product, as solvolysis took place (Peach and Waddington, 1963b).

(c) *Group V Halide Ion Acceptors.* Phosphorus trichloride is neutral in liquid hydrogen chloride (Waddington and Klanberg, 1960a): the acidic properties of the other Group V tervalent chlorides have not been studied. Phosphorus trifluoride showed no acidic properties and was not solvolysed in hydrogen chloride, but, in contrast, arsenic trifluoride was totally solvolysed, so its acidic properties could not be studied (Peach and Waddington, 1963b).

Phosphorus pentachloride and pentabromide both act as solvo-bases in the respective hydrogen halides, and there is no evidence for the formation of the $PHal_6^-$ ion in solution (Waddington and Klanberg, 1960a; Waddington and White, 1960a, 1963). Antimony pentachloride is a very powerful electron acceptor, and as such, ought to be able to form the $SbCl_6^-$ ion with bases in hydrogen chloride: no such reactions have been reported. The properties of the Group V pentafluorides in hydrogen chloride have been more thoroughly studied. Phosphorus pentafluoride reacts with strong bases to form hexa-fluorophosphates: the stoichiometry of this reaction is shown in the equation

$$2Me_4NCl + 3PF_5 \rightarrow 2Me_4NPF_6 + PF_3Cl_2. \tag{26}$$

Conductimetric titration curves showed a break when the molar ratio of base : PF_5 was 2 : 3 (see Fig. 2): unfortunately in these experiments it was not possible to isolate any of the covalent form of phosphorus dichloro-trifluoride (m.p. $-125°$, b.p. $7 \cdot 1°$), as this constituted only c. 0·5% of the solvent removed at low temperature. When phosphorus pentachloride was used as a base in liquid hydrogen chloride, both the ionic and covalent forms of phosphorus dichlorotrifluoride were formed:

$$2PCl_5 + 3PF_5 \rightarrow PCl_4^+PF_6^- + PF_3Cl_2. \tag{27}$$

There was no indication that there is any interconversion of these two forms of phosphorus dichlorotrifluoride. Phosphorus pentafluoride has been em-ployed as a solvoacid in reactions with bases that form boron trichloride adducts in solution, e.g. dimethyl sulphoxide; in all cases a hexafluoro-phosphate was formed in the solution, but sometimes this decomposed on warming to room temperature. Phosphorus pentafluoride is, then, the strongest acid yet found in liquid hydrogen chloride that will not form adducts with protonated bases (Peach and Waddington, 1963b).

Arsenic pentafluoride was solvolysed to tetrachloroarsonium hexa-fluoroarsenate in liquid hydrogen chloride:

$$2AsF_5 + 4HCl \rightarrow AsCl_4AsF_6 + 4HF. \tag{28}$$

Similarly solvolysis, or partial solvolysis, was observed with antimony pentafluoride, but a definite product could not be isolated (Peach and Waddington, 1963b): from the reaction of nitrosyl chloride and antimony pentafluoride in liquid hydrogen chloride it had been possible to isolate nitrosyl chloropentafluorantimonate, but the role of the solvent in these reactions is not understood (Waddington and Klanberg, 1960b).

The mechanism for the superficially similar reactions of phosphorus pentafluoride and arsenic pentafluoride in liquid hydrogen chloride are not known. The difference between them is that the phosphorus pentafluoridedisproportionation will only occur in the presence of strong bases, and no free hydrogen fluoride is produced.

$$2MCl + 3PF_5 \rightarrow 2MPF_6 + PF_3Cl_2. \tag{29}$$

Neither reaction proceeds through the formation of a stable MF_5Cl^- ion, although this may be an intermediate, as in the scheme:

$$PF_5 + HCl_2^- \rightarrow PF_5Cl^- + HCl \tag{30}$$

$$PF_5Cl^- + PF_5 \rightarrow PF_6^- + PF_4Cl \tag{31}$$

$$PF_4Cl + HCl_2^- \rightarrow PF_4Cl_2^- + HCl \tag{32}$$

$$PF_4Cl_2^- + PF_5 \rightarrow PF_6^- + PF_3Cl_2. \tag{33}$$

A similar scheme involving free fluoride ions, which would react immediately with the solvent to form hydrofluoric acid, will explain the reaction of arsenic pentafluoride:

$$AsF_5 + HCl_2^- \rightarrow AsF_5Cl^- + HCl \tag{34}$$

$$AsF_5Cl^- + 2HCl \rightarrow AsF_4Cl + HF + HCl_2^- \tag{35}$$

$$AsF_4Cl + HCl_2^- \rightarrow AsF_4Cl_2^- + HCl \tag{36}$$

$$AsF_4Cl_2^- + 2HCl \rightarrow AsF_3Cl_2 + HF + HCl_2^-. \tag{37}$$

$$2AsF_3Cl_2 \rightarrow AsCl_4^+ AsF_6^-.$$

The compounds PF_4Cl, AsF_4Cl, AsF_3Cl_2 are unknown, but PF_3Cl_2, $PCl_4^+PF_6^-$ and $AsCl_4^+AsF_6^-$ are relatively stable (Holmes 1963; Holmes and Gallagher, 1963). It is interesting to note in this context that although the compound $SbCl_4^+SbF_6^-$ is known (Holmes, 1963) there is no indication of this being formed in the hydrogen chloride solution (Peach and Waddington, 1963b).

(d) *Group VII Halide Ion Acceptors.* The oxidation reactions of these compounds will be dealt with in a later section, but here we are concerned with their reactions as Lewis acids in the liquid hydrogen halides. Neither chlorine in liquid hydrogen chloride nor bromine in liquid hydrogen bromide function as halide ion acceptors. Iodine is fairly insoluble in hydrogen chloride and again does not function as an acceptor; there is no evidence for the formation of ions such as I_2Cl^- or I_3^-. However both bromine and iodine monochloride are acceptors in hydrogen chloride and in conductimetric titrations against tetra-alkylammonium chlorides in the solvents end-points were obtained at mole ratios of $1:1$ and the compounds R_4NBr_2Cl and R_4NICl_2 were isolated (J. A. Salthouse and T. C. Waddington, unpublished results).

(e) *Strong aquo-acids and anhydrides.* No strong oxy-acids appear to be sufficiently powerful to act as titratable solvo-acids in the hydrogen halides. Trifluoromethane, methane and chlorosulphuric acids, showed no acidic properties in liquid hydrogen chloride (Waddington and Klanberg, 1960a; Peach and Waddington, 1962b). It was possible to isolate some new chlorosulphonates from the solutions, but reaction may well have occurred after removal of the solvent. Other oxy-acids studied in liquid hydrogen chloride were nitric and phosphoric, which may have been weakly basic; here again no reaction was observed (Peach and Waddington, 1962b).

Hydrogen bromide and hydrogen iodide are both very strong acids in aqueous solutions and their properties were investigated in liquid hydrogen chloride. In titrations against tetramethylammonium chloride in the solvent neither gave an end-point thought there was a steady drop in conductivity during their addition (Salthouse and Waddington, unpublished results). On removal of the solvent tetramethylammonium bromide and iodide were left, respectively. When a larger cation, such as tetra-n-butylammonium, was used the mixed hydrogen dihalides, tetra-n-butylammonium hydrogen bromide chloride, $(n-Bu)_4NHBrCl$, and tetra-n-butylammonium hydrogen chloride iodide, $(n-Bu)_4NHClI$, were recovered (Salthouse and Waddington, 1965) (see Section IB and Table II). It thus appears that both hydrogen bromide and iodide can function as acids in liquid hydrogen chloride and that the reactions

$$HCl_2^- + HBr \rightarrow HClBr^- + HCl \tag{38}$$

$$HCl_2^- + HI \rightarrow HClI^- + HCl \tag{39}$$

do occur. Like some acids in water they are so weak that the end-points of titrations with them cannot be determined conductimetrically.

Various oxyacidan hydrides, such as sulphur dioxide, might also function as acid anhydrides in the hydrogen halides, but the acid anhydrides dinitrogen tetroxide, phosphorus pentoxide and sulphur dioxide all showed no acidic tendencies in liquid hydrogen chloride (Peach and Waddington, 1962b).

B. SOLVOLYSIS REACTIONS

A solvolysis reaction can be said to occur when a ligand is replaced by a halogen atom, viz.:

$$MX + HHal \rightarrow MHal + HX. \tag{40}$$

This type of reaction has been observed in solutions in hydrogen chloride when X is phenyl, hydroxyl, or fluorine. The only hydroxyl compound found to be solvolysed was triphenylcarbinol (Peach and Waddington, 1961):

$$Ph_3COH + 3HCl \rightarrow Ph_3C^+HCl_2^- + H_3O^+Cl^-. \tag{41}$$

The driving force in such a reaction may be the insolubility of the hydroxonium chloride, or the extreme stability of the triphenylmethyl carbonium ion, or more probably, a combination of both. It was not possible to solvolyse either benzoic acid or ethyl benzoate in hydrogen chloride solution (Peach and Waddington, 1962a): this was somewhat surprising as the latter compound is readily solvolysed in sulphuric acid solution (Gillespie and Leisten, 1954).

Triphenylstannyl chloride was found to be quantitatively solvolysed in solution in hydrogen chloride to diphenyldichlorostannane and benzene (Peach and Waddington, 1961):

$$Ph_3SnCl + HCl \rightarrow Ph_2SnCl_2 + PhH. \tag{42}$$

The mechanism for this reaction is obscure. A similar type of solvolysis was also observed in solutions of the higher triphenyl metal chlorides, Ph_3MCl, of Group IV and the higher triphenyl derivatives, Ph_3M, of the Group V elements in hydrogen chloride (Peach and Waddington, 1961).

The most commonly observed solvolysis reactions are the replacement of a lighter halogen atom by a heavier. Strong fluorinating agents, such as antimony trifluoride, react in solution in hydrogen chloride to form the chloride and hydrogen fluoride (Peach and Waddington, 1963b):

$$SbF_3 + 3HCl \rightarrow SbCl_3 + 3HF. \tag{43}$$

Boron trifluoride is not solvolysed in hydrogen chloride or bromide (Waddington and Klanberg, 1960a; Waddington and White, 1960a, 1963), but boron trichloride reacts in hydrogen bromide to form the tribromide (Waddington and White, 1960a, 1963) and both the trichloride and the tribromide are solvolysed in hydrogen iodide to the tri-iodide (Klanberg and Kohlschütter, 1961):

$$BCl_3 + 3HI \rightarrow BI_3 + 3HCl. \tag{44}$$

This difference presumably reflects the great stability of the B—F bond. Similar types of solvolysis have been observed with triphenylmethyl chloride and germanium tetrachloride in hydrogen iodide solution; in both cases the iodide was formed (Klanberg and Kohlschütter, 1961).

C. REDOX REACTIONS

The basic oxidation and reduction reactions in the hydrogen halide solvent systems can be represented by:

$$Hal^- \rightleftharpoons \tfrac{1}{2}Hal_2 + \epsilon, \quad E_{ox} \tag{45}$$

$$\tfrac{1}{2}H_2 \rightleftharpoons H^+ + \epsilon, \quad E_{red} \tag{46}$$

where E represents the standard oxidation potential. If as in water, $E_{red} > E_{ox}$, materials with $E < E_{red}$ will reduce the solvent and with $E > E_{ox}$ will oxidize the solvent. The strongest thermodynamically stable oxidizing agent in liquid hydrogen chloride must be chlorine, which shows no acidic properties.

Chlorine, bromine and iodine monochloride are all readily soluble in the solvent and it proved possible to study the oxidation reactions of these species conductimetrically. Iodine is relatively insoluble in liquid hydrogen chloride and in solutions of halides in the solvent. In all the reactions so far studied it does not appear to act as an oxidizing agent. The reactions of these oxidizing agents with simple halide ions are instructive. Chlorine oxidizes the iodide ion in two stages, to ICl_2^- and then to ICl_4^-, and both stages can be detected conductimetrically (see Fig. 7). Bromide ion is oxidized by chlorine to $BrCl_2^-$, and the end-point can again be detected conductimetrically (see Fig. 7). Bromine oxidizes the iodide ion to IBr_2^- and in a conductimetric titration a 1 : 1 end-point is found for the bromine and iodide ion (J. A. Salthouse and T. C. Waddington, unpublished results).

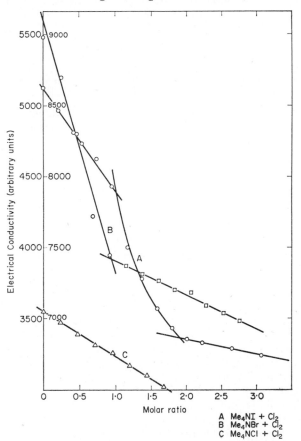

A Me$_4$NI + Cl$_2$
B Me$_4$NBr + Cl$_2$
C Me$_4$NCl + Cl$_2$

FIG. 7. The titrations of chlorine against tetra-alkylammonium halides in liquid hydrogen chloride. (Reproduced by permission from the *Journal of the Chemical Society*.)

The reactions of iodine monochloride are a little more complicated. In titrations of iodine monochloride against iodide ion, two end-points are found at 1 : 1 and 2 : 1 [ICl : I$^-$]. Iodine is first liberated:

$$I^- + ICl + HCl \rightarrow I_2 \downarrow + HCl_2^- \qquad (47)$$

and the ICl_2^- ion is then formed:

$$ICl + HCl_2^- \rightarrow HCl + ICl_2^-. \tag{48}$$

The second stage is not an oxidation reaction but the reaction of a Lewis acid in the solvent.

These reactions of halide ions with oxidizing agents in the solvent enable more complicated oxidation reactions in the solvent, such as the oxidation of phosphorus trichloride, to be interpreted. Phosphorus trichloride, itself a very poor conductor in liquid hydrogen chloride, is oxidized by chlorine to the pentachloride, a good conductor, and the reaction can be followed conductimetrically, a 1 : 1 end-point being found:

$$PCl_3 + Cl_2 + HCl \rightarrow PCl_4^+ + HCl_2^-. \tag{49}$$

Oxidation of phosphorus trichloride by bromine leads to the production of the ion PCl_3Br^+:

$$PCl_3 + Br_2 + HCl \rightarrow PCl_3Br^+ + HClBr^-. \tag{50}$$

On removal of the solvent the ion decomposes, but if boron trichloride is added the salt $PCl_3Br^+BCl_4^-$ can be isolated (J. A. Salthouse and T. C. Waddington, unpublished results).

REFERENCES

Beckmann, E. and Waentig, P. (1910) *Z. anorg. Chem.* **67**, 17.

Chang, S. and Westrum, E. F., Jr. (1962) *J. chem. Phys.* **36**, 2571.

Cook, D., Lupien, Y. and Schneider, W. G. (1956) *Canad. J. Chem.* **34**, 957, 964.

Del Fresno, C. (1928) *Z. anorg. Chem.* **170**, 222.

Fluck, E. (1962) *Z. anorg. Chem.* **315**, 191.

Fuoss, R. M. and Krauss, C. A. (1933) *J. Amer. chem. Soc.* **55**, 2387.

Fraser, M. J., Gerrard, W. and Lappert, M. F. (1957) *J. chem. Soc.* 639.

Gerson, F. and Heilbronner, E. (1962) *Helv. chim. acta* **45**, 51.

Gillespie, R. J. and Leisten, J. A. (1954) *Quart. Rev.* 8, 40.

Gillespie, R. J. and Robinson, E. A. (1959) *Adv. inorg. Chem. Radiochem.* **1**, 385.

Glasstone, S. (1960) "Textbook of Physical Chemistry", pp. 637, 647, 891, 2nd edition, Macmillan, London.

Glockler, G. and Peck, R. E. (1936) *J. chem. Phys.* **4**, 658.

Gold, V. and Tye, F. L. (1952) *J. chem. Soc.* 2172.

Gore, G. (1865) *Phil. Mag.* (4) **29**, 541.

Graff, W. (1933) *C.R. Acad. Sci., Paris,* **197**, 754.

Grange, P., Lascombe, J. and Josien, M. L. (1960) *Spectrochim. Acta,* **16**, 981.

Gutmann, V. (1956) *Quart. Rev.* **10**, 451.

"Handbook of Chemistry and Physics", (1957–8) 39th edition, Chemical Rubber Publishing Co.

Hantzsch, A. (1930) *Ber. dtsch. chem. Ges.* **63**B, 1789.

Harmon, K. M. and Davis, S. (1962) *J. Amer. chem. Soc.* **84**, 4359.

Hart, H. and Fish, R. W. (1958) *J. Amer. chem. Soc.* **80**, 5894.

Herbrandson, H. F., Dickerson, R. T. and Weinstein, J. (1954) *J. Amer. chem. Soc.* **76**, 4046.

Herzberg, G. (1945) "Infrared and Raman Spectra of Polyatomic Molecules", p. 280. Van Nostrand, New York.

Holliday, A. K., Peach, M. E. and Waddington, T. C. (1961) *Proc. chem. Soc., Lond.* 220.

Holmes, R. R. (1963) *J. chem. Educ.* **40**, 125.

Holmes, R. R. and Gallagher, W. P. (1963) *Inorg. Chem.* **2**, 433.

Hyman, H. H., Quarterman, L. A., Kilpatrick, M. and Katz, J. J. (1961) *J. phys. Chem.* **65**, 123.

Janz, G. J. and Danyluk, S. S. (1959) *J. Amer. chem. Soc.* **81**, 3846, 3850, 3854.

Kahovec, L. and Knollmüller, K. (1941) *Z. phys. Chem.* B**51**, 49.

Kirsanov, O. V. and Fedorova, G. K. (1960) *Dopov. Akad. Nauk ukr. R.S.R.* 1960, 1086 (*Chem. Abstr.* (1962) **56**, 15142).

Klanberg, F. and Kohlschütter, H. W. (1961) *Z. Naturf.* **16**b, 69.

Klemenc, A. and Kohl, O. (1927) *Z. anorg. Chem.* **168**, 163.

Krauss, C. A. and Fuoss, R. M. (1933) *J. Amer. chem. Soc.* **55**, 21.

Maas, O. and McIntosh, D. (1913). *J. Amer. chem. Soc.* **35**, 535.

McIntosh, D. (1908) *J. Amer. chem. Soc.* **30**, 1097.

Maki, A. G. and West, R. (1963) *Inorg. Chem.* **2**, 657.

Mellor, J. W. (1961). "Comprehensive Treatise on Inorganic and Theoretical Chemistry", p. 415, Supplement 2, Part I. Longmans, London.

Murray, F. E. and Schneider, W. G. (1955) *Canad. J. chem.* **33**, 797.

Peach, M. E. and Waddington, T. C. (1961) *J. chem. Soc.* 1238.

Peach, M. E. and Waddington, T. C. (1962a) *J. chem. Soc.* 600.

Peach, M. E. and Waddington, T. C. (1962b) *J. chem. Soc.* 2680.

Peach, M. E. and Waddington, T. C. (1962c) *J. chem. Soc.* 3450.

Peach, M. E. and Waddington, T. C. (1963a) *J. chem. Soc.* 69.

Peach, M. E. and Waddington, T. C. (1963b) *J. chem. Soc.* 799.

Runner, M. E., Balog, G. and Kilpatrick, M. (1956) *J. Amer. chem. Soc.* **78**, 5183.

Rupert, E. F. (1909) *J. chem. Soc.* **31**, 851.

Salthouse, J. A. and Waddington, T. C. (1965) *J. chem. Soc.* (in the press).

Sharp, D. W. A. (1958) *J. chem. Soc.* 2558.

Sharp, D. W. A. (1960) *Adv. Fluorine Chem.* **1**, 105.

Smyth, C. P. and Hitchcock, C. S. (1933) *J. Amer. chem. Soc.* **55**, 1830.

Steele, B. D., McIntosh, D. and Archibald, E. H. (1905) *Phil. Trans.* **205**, 99.

Steele, B. D., McIntosh, D. and Archibald, E. H. (1906) *Z. phys. Chem.* **55**, 129.

Valleé, R. E. and McDaniel, D. H. (1962) *J. Amer. chem. Soc.* **84**, 3412.

Valleé, R. E. and McDaniel, D. H. (1963) *Inorg. Chem.* **2**, 997.

Vidale, G. L. and Taylor, R. C. (1956) *J. Amer. chem. Soc.* **78**, 294.

Waddington, T. C. (1958a) *Trans Faraday Soc.* **54**, 25.

Waddington, T. C. (1958b) *J. chem. Soc.* 1708.

Waddington, T. C. and Klanberg, F. (1959) *Naturwissenshaften*, **46**, 578.

Waddington, T. C. and Klanberg, F. (1960a) *J. chem. Soc.* 2329, 2332.

Waddington, T. C. and Klanberg, F. (1960b) *Z. anorg. Chem.* **304**, 185.

Waddington, T. C. and White, J. A. (1960a) *Proc. chem. Soc., Lond.* 85.

Waddington, T. C. and White, J. A. (1960b) *Proc. chem. Soc., Lond.* 315.

Waddington, T. C. and White, J. A. (1963) *J. chem. Soc.* 2701.

Walker, J. W., McIntosh, D. and Archibald, E. (1904) *J. chem. Soc.* **85**, 1098 (1904).

West, R. (1957) *J. Amer. chem. Soc.* **79**, 4568.

Wheat, J. A. and Browne, A. W. (1940) *J. Amer. chem. Soc.* **62**, 1577.

Yeh, S.-J. and Jaffée, H. H. (1959) *J. Amer. chem. Soc.*, **81**, 3279.

Yoon, Y. K. and Carpenter, G. B. (1959) *Acta crystallogr.* **12**, 17.

CHAPTER 4

Sulphuric Acid

R. J. GILLESPIE AND E. A. ROBINSON

Department of Chemistry, McMaster University, Hamilton, Ontario, Canada
Department of Chemistry, University of Toronto, Toronto, Ontario, Canada

I. Introduction		117
	A. Bases	118
	B. Acids	121
	C. Non-Electrolytes	122
	D. Sulphates and Hydrogen Sulphates	122
II. The Physical Properties of Sulphuric Acid and Its Solutions, Including Experimental Methods of Investigation		123
	A. Properties of Sulphuric Acid	123
	B. Properties of Solutions	131
III. Inorganic Solutes		162
	A. The Solutes Water and Sulphur Trioxide	162
	B. Boron	164
	C. Silicon	167
	D. Tin and Lead	170
	E. Nitrogen and Phosphorus	172
	F. Arsenic, Antimony and Bismuth	174
	G. Vanadium, Chromium and Manganese	177
	H. Sulphur, Selenium and Tellurium	179
	I. Halogens	180
	J. Transition Metal Complexes	184
	K. Chelation by the Sulphate Group	186
IV. Organic Solutes		187
	A. Simple Bases	187
	B. Polybasic Compounds	188
	C. Amides and Ureas	190
	D. Esters	192
	E. Carboxylic Anhydrides	193
	F. Ethers	194
	G. Nitriles	195
	H. Carboxylic Acids	196
	I. Carbonium Ions	198
	J. Aromatic Sulphonation	204
References		205

I. INTRODUCTION

Sulphuric acid is a good solvent for compounds that ionize as electrolytes, as might be expected from its high dielectric constant, the polarity of its molecules, and their ability to form strong hydrogen bonds. Electrolytes may be classified in the usual way according to the solvo-system definition of acids and bases. Acids give the sulphuric acidium, $H_3SO_4^+$, ion

$$HA + H_2SO_4 = H_3SO_4^+ + A^-; \tag{1}$$

and bases give the hydrogen sulphate, HSO_4^-, ion

$$B + H_2SO_4 = BH^+ + HSO_4^-. \tag{2}$$

Because of the high acidity of sulphuric acid, bases are the largest class of electrolytes. Sulphuric acid has a levelling effect on the strengths of bases in the same way that water has a levelling effect on the strengths of acids. Acids of the sulphuric acid system are rarer but several examples are known. Many of the electrolytes of the sulphuric acid solvent system are unfamiliar as they are not known in aqueous solution; many compounds that do not have basic properties in water, including many that behave as acids in aqueous solution, are readily protonated in sulphuric acid, while many electrolytes that are encountered in water are not stable in sulphuric acid.

Sulphuric acid has proved a particularly valuable solvent in the study of the protonation of very weak bases such as ketones and nitro-compounds and in the preparation of stable solutions of reactive ions such as carbonium ions, NO_2^+ and I_3^+ that are unstable in more basic solvents such as water. Sulphuric acid resembles water as a solvent in many ways despite its greater acidity and a comparison of such properties as the conductivities, viscosities, densities and activities of electrolyte solutions in sulphuric acid with those of aqueous electrolyte solutions is proving valuable in aiding our understanding of electrolyte solutions in general.

There have been several previous reviews of the properties of sulphuric acid as a solvent (Gillespie and Leisten, 1954; Gillespie, 1959; Gillespie and Robinson, 1959). The purpose of this chapter is to provide a general introduction to the sulphuric acid solvent system and to cover in some detail recent work on the behaviour of solutes in this solvent.

A. BASES

1. *Metal Hydrogen Sulphates*

The alkali and some other metal hydrogen sulphates behave as fully ionized binary electrolytes. They are thus strong bases, analogous to hydroxides in water, e.g.

$$KHSO_4 = K^+ + HSO_4^- \tag{3a}$$
$$KOH = K^+ + OH^-. \tag{3b}$$

The corresponding normal sulphates are converted into the hydrogen sulphates and, formally, they are analogous to metal oxides in water,

$$K_2SO_4 + H_2SO_4 = 2K^+ + 2HSO_4^- \tag{4a}$$
$$K_2O + H_2O = 2K^+ + 2OH^-. \tag{4b}$$

Salts of other familiar inorganic acids are either insoluble, for example, AgCl, $CuBr_2$, $AlCl_3$, and $AlPO_4$, or undergo complete solvolysis as is illustrated in the following examples:

$$NH_4ClO_4 + H_2SO_4 = NH_4^+ + HSO_4^- + HClO_4 \qquad (5)$$
$$Na_3PO_4 + 3H_2SO_4 = 3Na^+ + 3HSO_4^- + H_3PO_4 \qquad (6)$$
$$KNO_3 + H_2SO_4 = K^+ + HSO_4^- + HNO_3. \qquad (7)$$

All such soluble salts thus give rise to strongly basic solutions. Solvolysis occurs because of the relatively high concentration of $H_3SO_4^+$ ions present in sulphuric acid as a result of its self-dissociation, and because the acids from which these salts are derived are either exceedingly weak or do not behave as acids at all in sulphuric acid. Thus perchloric acid is an exceedingly weak acid and both phosphoric acid and nitric acid react further as bases.

2. *Other Simple Bases*

A very large number of other substances behave as bases, forming their conjugate acids by the addition of a proton. Thus very many organic compounds, with the exception of aliphatic hydrocarbons, some aromatic hydrocarbons, and their halogen derivatives, are soluble in sulphuric acid. This can be attributed to their possessing atoms such as O, N, or P with lone pairs of electrons which can accept a proton from sulphuric acid.

Examples include ketones

$$R_2CO + H_2SO_4 = R_2COH^+ + HSO_4^- \qquad (8)$$

carboxylic acids

$$RCO_2H + H_2SO_4 = RCO_2H_2^+ + HSO_4^- \qquad (9)$$

esters

$$RCO_2R' + H_2SO_4 = RCO_2R'H^+ + HSO_4^- \qquad (10)$$

amines

$$RNH_2 + H_2SO_4 = RNH_3^+ + HSO_4^- \qquad (11)$$

amides

$$RCONH_2 + H_2SO_4 = R\overset{+}{C}(OH)NH_2 + HSO_4^- \qquad (12)$$

and phosphines

$$R_3P + H_2SO_4 = R_3PH^+ + HSO_4^-. \qquad (13)$$

Even triphenylamine and triphenylphosphine, which are normally regarded as exceedingly weak bases behave as strong bases in sulphuric acid. Some substances, such as nitro-compounds, dialkyl sulphones and nitriles, with only very weakly basic properties are incompletely protonated in sulphuric acid.

Molecules containing more than one basic group often form multi-charged cations. For example o-phenylenediamine is diprotonated, some amino acids are protonated on both the NH_2 and CO_2H groups, and hexamethylenetetramine accepts protons on all four nitrogen atoms.

Solutions of a very large number of organic compounds are quite stable at room temperature and the organic compound may be recovered unchanged by pouring the solution onto ice. Protonation often serves to deactivate the compound and thus prevent further reaction, such as aromatic sulphonation, which might otherwise occur.

Water and phosphoric acid provide examples of inorganic substances which behave as strong bases:

$$H_2O + H_2SO_4 \rightarrow H_3O^+ + HSO_4^- \tag{14}$$

$$H_3PO_4 + H_2SO_4 \rightarrow H_4PO_4^+ + HSO_4^-, \tag{15}$$

while selenium dioxide is a weak base:

$$SeO_2 + H_2SO_4 \rightleftharpoons HSeO_2^+ + HSO_4^-. \tag{16}$$

3. Complex Bases

A large number of oxy and hydroxy compounds behave as bases because they are dehydrated by the solvent. The simplest examples of this type of behaviour are given by a number of substances of the general formula XOH which are converted to the hydrogen sulphate XSO_4H:

$$XOH + 2H_2SO_4 = XSO_4H + H_3O^+ + HSO_4^-. \tag{17}$$

Ethyl alcohol is a base of this type, being converted into ethyl hydrogen sulphate

$$C_2H_5OH + 2H_2SO_4 = C_2H_5SO_4H + H_3O^+ + HSO_4^-. \tag{18}$$

Similarly iodic acid is converted to iodyl hydrogen sulphate

$$HIO_3 + H_2SO_4 = IO_2HSO_4 + H_3O^+ + HSO_4^-. \tag{19}$$

In addition the hydrogen sulphate itself sometimes acts as a base either by forming its conjugate acid

$$XSO_4H + H_2SO_4 = XSO_4H_2^+ + HSO_4^- \tag{20}$$

or by ionizing to X^+ and HSO_4^-.

Nitric acid, triphenyl carbinol, and mesitoic acid all provide examples of a hydrogen sulphate XSO_4H which is fully ionized to X^+ and HSO_4^- so that the overall ionizations of these compounds are:

$$HNO_3 + 2H_2SO_4 = NO_2^+ + H_3O^+ + 2HSO_4^- \tag{21}$$

$$Ph_3C.OH + 2H_2SO_4 = Ph_3C^+ + H_3O^+ + 2HSO_4^- \tag{22}$$

$$Me_3C_6H_2CO_2H + 2H_2SO_4 = Me_3C_6H_2CO^+ + H_3O^+ + 2HSO_4^-. \tag{23}$$

It has been shown recently that some interesting ions containing two carbonium ion centres can be obtained in sulphuric acid, e.g.

$$(C_6H_5)_2C\langle\!\!\!\langle\underline{}\rangle\!\!\!\rangle C\text{-}(C_6H_5)_2 + 4H_2SO_4 = (C_6H_5)_2\overset{+}{C}\langle\!\!\!\langle\underline{}\rangle\!\!\!\rangle\overset{+}{C}(C_6H_5)_2$$
$$\underset{OH}{|}\qquad\qquad\underset{OH}{|}\qquad\qquad\qquad\qquad + 2H_3O^+ + 4HSO_4^-. \tag{24}$$

Many of these cations are very strongly electrophilic and can only exist in very weakly basic solutions such as sulphuric acid, or in a suitable non-protonic solvent. Their formation in sulphuric acid is due not only to its high acidity but also to the very low activity of water in dilute solution in sulphuric acid. This low water activity is a consequence of its extensive conversion to H_3O^+. One advantage of sulphuric acid for the formation of such ions is that it is a good solvent for electrolytes whereas non-protonic solvents are often poor solvents for electrolytes. Thus relatively concentrated solutions of these reactive ions may be obtained in sulphuric acid.

Even some anhydrides react to give a hydrogen sulphate with the elimination of water

$$X_2O + 3H_2SO_4 = 2XSO_4H + H_3O^+ + HSO_4^-. \tag{25}$$

Hexamethyldisiloxane and arsenic (III) oxide behave in this way

$$[(CH_3)_3Si]_2O + 3H_2SO_4 = 2(CH_3)_3Si.SO_4H + H_3O^+ + HSO_4^- \tag{26}$$

$$As_2O_3 + 3H_2SO_4 = 2AsO.SO_4H + H_3O^+ + HSO_4^-. \tag{27}$$

Trimethylsilicon hydrogen sulphate is a non-electrolyte but $AsO.SO_4H$ is partially ionized. Dinitrogen pentoxide forms the fully ionized nitronium hydrogen sulphate:

$$N_2O_5 + 3H_2SO_4 = 2NO_2^+ + H_3O^+ + 3HSO_4^-. \tag{28}$$

B. ACIDS

The majority of substances that behave as acids in aqueous solution do not exhibit acidic properties in sulphuric acid but behave as bases of various types, as is shown by the following examples:

$$CH_3CO_2H + H_2SO_4 = CH_3CO_2H_2^+ + HSO_4^- \tag{29}$$

$$H_3PO_4 + H_2SO_4 = H_4PO_4^+ + HSO_4^- \tag{30}$$

$$HNO_3 + 2H_2SO_4 = NO_2^+ + H_3O^+ + 2HSO_4^- \tag{31}$$

$$H_3BO_3 + 6H_2SO_4 = B(HSO_4)_4^- + 3H_3O^+ + 2HSO_4^- \tag{32}$$

$$H_2SO_3 + H_2SO_4 = SO_2 + H_3O^+ + HSO_4^- \tag{33}$$

$$HF + 2H_2SO_4 = HSO_3F + H_3O^+ + HSO_4^-. \tag{34}$$

Even perchloric acid, which is often regarded as the strongest known mineral acid, is only very slightly ionized in sulphuric acid, and metal perchlorates undergo complete solvolysis

$$MClO_4 + H_2SO_4 = M^+ + HClO_4 + HSO_4^-. \tag{35}$$

The first acids of the sulphuric acid system to be recognized were disulphuric acid, $H_2S_2O_7$, and the higher polysulphuric acids, $H_2S_3O_{10}$ etc., which are present in oleums. These acids are weak acids of the sulphuric acid system. Another very weak acid is fluorosulphuric acid, HSO_3F.

Evidence has been obtained for the existence of a strong acid of the sulphuric acid solvent system, namely, the complex acid tetra(hydrogen sulphato)boric acid, $HB(HSO_4)_4$. Solutions of this acid can be obtained by dissolving boric acid in oleum

$$H_3BO_3 + 3H_2S_2O_7 = H_3SO_4^+ + B(HSO_4)_4^- + H_2SO_4. \qquad (36)$$

Solutions of some other complex sulphato acids such as hexa(hydrogen sulphato)stannic acid, $H_2Sn(HSO_4)_6$, and hexa(hydrogen sulphato)plumbic acid, $H_2Pb(HSO_4)_6$, have also been obtained.

C. NON-ELECTROLYTES

Rather few compounds that are soluble in sulphuric acid behave as non-electrolytes because the hydrogen-bonding interactions between the sulphuric acid molecules are sufficiently strong that unless a solute is strongly solvated, either because it is ionic, or because it can strongly hydrogen-bond with sulphuric acid, it is unlikely to be able to sufficiently disrupt the structure of the solvent to enable it to dissolve. Yet if a molecule is sufficiently basic to form strong hydrogen bonds with sulphuric acid it is likely that some proton transfer along the hydrogen bonds will occur, resulting in at least a small degree of ionization. Thus in order to behave as a non-electrolyte a solute must be sufficiently basic to form strong hydrogen bonds with the solvent but not basic enough to protonate. The only non-electrolytes that are known at present are alkyl sulphonyl fluorides and sulphonyl chlorides, sulphuryl chloride, picric acid, a few other polynitro-aromatic compounds and probably diphenyl sulphone and most of the sulphonic acids. Trichloroacetic acid and chlorosulphuric acid may also be non-electrolytes although the evidence is not conclusive (Gillespie et al., 1950; Brayford and Wyatt, 1955; Gillespie et al., 1956; Gillespie and Solomons, 1957; Hall and Robinson, 1964).

D. SULPHATES AND HYDROGEN SULPHATES

Because only a few anions are known that do not undergo extensive, if not complete, solvolysis in sulphuric acid, investigations have been mainly confined to the behaviour of sulphates and hydrogen sulphates, which are the analogues of the oxides and hydroxides in water. It should not be concluded, however, that the chemistry of solutions in sulphuric acid is therefore without any great interest, because many varieties of cations are known, a number of which cannot exist in aqueous solutions. When an oxide or hydroxide is dissolved in sulphuric acid there is a tendency for it to be converted to a sulphate or hydrogen sulphate with the elimination of water, although the extent to which this occurs varies widely from one element to another. Thus, for example, the oxides and hydroxides of the more electropositive metals are completely converted to the corresponding hydrogen sulphates, while phosphoric acid is merely protonated and undergoes no conversion to a sulphate derivative. In general a wide variety of compounds intermediate between the oxides and hydroxides of the aqueous system and the sulphates and hydrogen sulphates of the sulphuric acid system may be formed.

II. The Physical Properties of Sulphuric Acid and Its Solutions Including Experimental Methods of Investigation

A. PROPERTIES OF SULPHURIC ACID

1. *Structure*

The high viscosity, boiling point and surface tension (Table I), of sulphuric acid indicate that it is a highly associated liquid, doubtless because of strong hydrogen bonding between the molecules. It has been shown that the solid has a layer-type structure (Pascard, 1955) in which each sulphuric acid molecule is hydrogen bonded to four others. Unfortunately no great precision is claimed for the interatomic distances given in this X-ray determination. The structure of the liquid is likely to resemble that of the solid, just as the structure of liquid water is related to that of ice.

TABLE I

Some Physical Constants of Sulphuric Acid

H_2SO_4		
Freezing-point	$10 \cdot 371°$	
Boiling-point	$290–317°$	
Viscosity (centipoise)	$24 \cdot 54$	$25°$
Density (d_4^{25})	$1 \cdot 8269$	$25°$
Dielectric constant	100	$25°$
Specific conductivity (ohm^{-1} cm^{-1})	$1 \cdot 0439 \times 10^{-2}$	$25°$
Heat capacity (cal deg^{-1} g^{-1})	$0 \cdot 3373$	$25°$
Heat of fusion (cal mole^{-1})	2560	$10 \cdot 37°$
D_2SO_4		
Freezing-point	$14 \cdot 35°$	
Viscosity (centipoise)	$24 \cdot 88$	$25°$
Density (d_4^{25})	$1 \cdot 8573$	$25°$
Specific conductivity (ohm^{-1} cm^{-1})	$0 \cdot 2568 \times 10^{-2}$	$25°$

Extensive studies have been made of the vibrational spectrum of sulphuric acid, (Section IIA, 6). Symmetric and asymmetric stretching frequencies due to the SO_2 group and the $S(OH)_2$ group are readily identified and approximate stretching force constants derived from these frequencies (SO_2, $k = 10 \cdot 3 \times 10^5$ dynes cm^{-1}; $S(OH)_2$, $k = 5 \cdot 9 \times 10^5$ dynes cm^{-1}), indicate an S—O bond order of about $1 \cdot 8$ and an S—OH bond order near to $1 \cdot 3$ (Gillespie and Robinson, 1963b). The best single representation of the molecular structure is I in which the $d_{x^2-y^2}$ and d_{z^2} orbitals on sulphur are used in double bonds with oxygen.

I

2. Self-dissociation

The properties of 100% sulphuric acid are affected to an important extent by its rather extensive self-dissociation, and in order to understand the behaviour of solutes dissolved in sulphuric acid it is necessary to know the nature and extent of the self-dissociation processes.

Despite its high acidity, sulphuric acid is also appreciably basic, and belongs to the general group of solvents, like water, liquid ammonia, and liquid hydrogen fluoride, which are *amphoteric* or *amphiprotic*. This shows itself in the appreciable autoprotolysis of these solvents

$$2HA = H_2A^+ + A^- \tag{37}$$

in which one molecule behaves as an acid and the other as a base. The extent of autoprotolysis is determined by the acid and base strengths of the solvent and for sulphuric acid it is larger than for most protonic solvents (Table II).

TABLE II

Autoprotolysis Constants at 25°

Solvent	$-\text{Log } K_{ap}$	Solvent	$-\text{Log } K_{ap}$
NH_3	29·8	HF	9·7
C_2H_5OH	18·9	HCO_2H	6·2
D_2O	14·8	D_2SO_4	4·3
H_2O	14·0	H_2SO_4	3·6
CH_3CO_2H	12·6	H_3PO_4	~ 2
H_2O_2	12		

In addition to autoprotolysis

$$2H_2SO_4 = H_3SO_4^+ + HSO_4^- \tag{38}$$

sulphuric acid is also self-dissociated in other ways which are a consequence of a primary dissociation into water and sulphur trioxide.

$$H_2SO_4 = H_2O + SO_3. \tag{39}$$

Since water is extensively ionized according to the equation

$$H_2O + H_2SO_4 = H_3O^+ + HSO_4^- \tag{40}$$

and SO_3 forms disulphuric acid

$$SO_3 + H_2SO_4 = H_2S_2O_7 \qquad (41)$$

which is partially ionized as an acid,

$$H_2S_2O_7 + H_2SO_4 = H_3SO_4^+ + HS_2O_7^- \qquad (42)$$

and since the ions $H_3SO_4^+$ and HSO_4^- are in equilibrium as a result of the autoprotolysis reaction it follows that the ions H_3O^+ and $HS_2O_7^-$ must also be in equilibrium

$$2H_2SO_4 = H_3O^+ + HS_2O_7^-. \qquad (43)$$

This has been called the *ionic self-dehydration* reaction, with an equilibrium constant K_{id}. It has been found convenient to choose equations (38), (40), (42) and (43) to describe the complete self-dissociation of sulphuric acid. Values of the corresponding dissociation constants, K_{ap}, K_{H_2O}, $K_{H_2S_2O_7}$, and K_{id} for these reactions at 10°, 25° and 40° are given in Table III.

TABLE III

Equilibrium Constants for the Self-Dissociation Reactions of Sulphuric Acid.

	10°	25°	40°
$K_{ap} = [H_3SO_4^+][HSO_4^-]$	$1{\cdot}7 \times 10^{-4}$	$2{\cdot}7 \times 10^{-4}$	$4{\cdot}0 \times 10^{-4}$
$K_{id} = [H_3O^+][HS_2O_7^-]$	$3{\cdot}5 \times 10^{-5}$	$5{\cdot}1 \times 10^{-5}$	$8{\cdot}1 \times 10^{-4}$
$K_{H_2S_2O_7} = [H_3SO_4^+][HSO_4^-]/[H_2S_2O_7]$	$1{\cdot}4 \times 10^{-2}$	$1{\cdot}4 \times 10^{-2}$	$1{\cdot}4 \times 10^{-2}$
$K_{H_2O} = [H_3O^+][HSO_4^-]/[H_2O]$	1	1	1

The values at 10° were obtained from a detailed study of the freezing points of solutions of metal hydrogen sulphates, water and disulphuric acid, each of which represses the self-dissociation of sulphuric acid in a different way (Bass *et al.*, 1960). Values of K_{ap} and K_{id} at 25° and 40° were obtained from the values at 10° and the heats of autoprotolysis and ionic self-dehydration, which have been measured by Wyatt and his co-workers; $\Delta H_{ap} = 5{\cdot}0$ kcal mole^{-1}, $\Delta H_{id} = 6{\cdot}0$ kcal mole^{-1} (Kirkbride and Wyatt, 1957; Dacre and Wyatt, 1961; Gillespie and Robinson, 1963).

Table IV gives values for the self-dissociation equilibrium constants of dideuterosulphuric acid, D_2SO_4. These have been obtained in a similar way to those for H_2SO_4 but are rather less precise. It may be noted that the auto-deuterolysis constant of D_2SO_4 is smaller than the autoprotolysis constant of H_2SO_4. The frequencies of the stretching vibrations of the SO_2 group of D_2SO_4 are slightly lower than those of the SO_2 frequencies of H_2SO_4, implying that D_2SO_4 is a slightly stronger base than H_2SO_4 (Gillespie and Robinson, 1962a;

TABLE IV

Equilibrium Constants for the Self-Dissociation Reactions of Dideuterosulphuric Acid

	$14°$	$25°$	$40°$
$K_{ap} = [D_3SO_4^+][DSO_4^-]$	2.9×10^{-5}	4.6×10^{-5}	5.2×10^{-5}
$K_{1d} = [D_3O^+][DS_2O_7^-]$	5.0×10^{-5}	5.5×10^{-5}	6.0×10^{-5}
$K_{D_2S_2O_7} = [D_3SO_4^+][DS_2O_7^-]/[D_2S_2O_7]$	2.8×10^{-3}	2.8×10^{-3}	2.8×10^{-3}
$K_{D_2O} = [D_3O^+][DSO_4^-]/[D_2O]$	0.2	0.2	0.2

Gillespie and Robinson, 1963b). It would appear therefore that D_2SO_4 must be a weaker acid than H_2SO_4. It is interesting to note that the acid $D_2S_2O_7$ appears to be a weaker acid in D_2SO_4 than is the acid $H_2S_2O_7$ in H_2SO_4 (Gillespie et al., 1956).

TABLE V

Molal Concentrations of the Self-Dissociation Species

H_2SO_4		D_2SO_4	
HSO_4^-	0.0150	DSO_4^-	0.0112
$H_3SO_4^+$	0.0113	$D_3SO_4^+$	0.0041
H_3O^+	0.0080	D_3O^+	0.0112
$HS_2O_7^-$	0.0044	$DS_2O_7^-$	0.0049
$H_2S_2O_7$	0.0036	$D_2S_2O_7$	0.0071
H_2O	0.0001	D_2O	0.0006
Total	0.0424	Total	0.0391

Table V gives the molal concentrations of each of the products of self-dissociation of H_2SO_4 and D_2SO_4 at the freezing points of the respective acids.

3. Freezing Point

At atmospheric pressure 100% sulphuric acid has a freezing point of $10.371°$ (Kunzler and Giauque, 1952c; Bass and Gillespie, 1960). The 100% acid is conveniently prepared by adding dilute oleum to slightly aqueous sulphuric acid until the maximum freezing point of $10.371°$ is reached. The freezing point of the hypothetical completely undissociated acid can be computed from the concentration of self-dissociation species and the cryoscopic constant to be $10 \cdot 625°$ (Bass *et al.*, 1960). The freezing point curve of the H_2O–SO_3 system in the vicinity of the composition H_2SO_4 is shown in Fig. 1 together with the curve calculated on the basis of the equilibrium

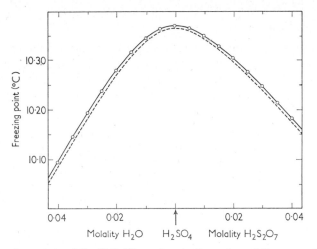

FIG. 1. Freezing points of the H_2O–SO_3 system in the region of the composition H_2SO_4. —O—O—, experimental curve; – – – –, calculated curve.

constants given in Table III. The small difference between the experimental and calculated curves may be attributed to the non-ideality of the solutions. The freezing point of D_2SO_4 is $14 \cdot 34°$ (Flowers *et al.*, 1956b).

4. *Density*

Values of the densities of H_2SO_4 and D_2SO_4 at $25°$ are given in Table I. The temperature variation of the densities may be represented by the equations

$$H_2SO_4 : d_4^t = 1 \cdot 8516 - 1 \cdot 000 \times 10^{-3} t \tag{44}$$

$$D_2SO_4 : d_4^t = 1 \cdot 8816 - 0 \cdot 980 \times 10^{-3} t. \tag{45}$$

The molar volumes are $53 \cdot 69$ for H_2SO_4 and $53 \cdot 89$ for D_2SO_4 at $25°$. It has been suggested that this rather large increase in molar volume on deuterium substitution might be due to the intermolecular deuterium bond being longer than the hydrogen bond (Greenwood and Thompson, 1959).

5. *Viscosity*

Values of the viscosity of H_2SO_4 and D_2SO_4 at $25°$ are given in Table I. The temperature dependence can be represented by the following equation (Greenwood and Thompson, 1959)

$$\eta = \eta_0 \exp (C_\eta / RT). \tag{46}$$

The energy of activation E_η is given by $E_\eta = 2C_\eta/T$ and decreases from 6·78 kcal mole^{-1} at 10° to 5·76 kcal mole^{-1} at 60° for H_2SO_4 and from 6·99 kcal mole^{-1} at 10° to 5·62 kcal mole^{-1} at 60° for D_2SO_4. This decrease in the activation energy is probably due to a progressive breaking of hydrogen bonds with increasing temperature.

6. *Dielectric Constant*

The dielectric constant of sulphuric acid has proved difficult to measure, mainly because of its high electrical conductivity. In 1953, Brand *et al.* using wave guide techniques made measurements in the frequency range 100–3000 Mc/s. They found that dielectric dispersion occurs at these fre-

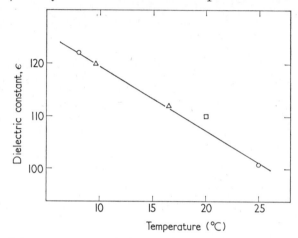

FIG. 2. The dielectric constant of sulphuric acid. □, Brand *et al.* (1953); ○, Gillespie and Cole (1956); △, Gillespie and White (1958).

quencies and they obtained the static dielectric constant by extrapolation. Two attempts have been made to obtain the static dielectric constant directly. Gillespie and Cole (1956) used a conventional bridge method for determining the capacity of a condenser containing sulphuric acid. The separation of the electrodes of the condenser could be varied and the large polarization capacity of the electrodes resulting from the high conductivity was thereby eliminated. An attempt has also been made (Gillespie and White, 1958) to use the force method first suggested by Furth in which the torque exerted by an electric field on a platinum ellipsoid suspended in the liquid is measured, although the high conductivity of the liquid caused considerable experimental difficulties. The values obtained are summarized in Fig. 2. They indicate a roughly linear dependence of the dielectric constant on the temperature in this range. Values of 120 at 10° and 100 at 25° are obtained by interpolation.

7. *Electrical Conductivity*

The relatively high concentration of ions in the pure liquid is responsible for the rather high conductivity of 100% sulphuric acid. The specific conductivities of both H_2SO_4 and D_2SO_4 at various temperatures are given in Table VI (Kunzler and Giauque, 1952a; Flowers *et al.*, 1956b; Gillespie *et al.*,

TABLE VI

Specific Conductivities of Sulphuric Acid and Dideuterosulphuric Acid at the 100% Composition and at the Composition of Minimum Conductance

Temperature	κ $(10^{-2} \text{ ohm}^{-1} \text{ cm}^{-1})$	κ $(10^{-2} \text{ ohm}^{-1} \text{ cm}^{-1})$	Composition at minimum conductance
	H_2SO_4	"Minimum"	(moles H_2O $kg^{-1}_{solution}$)
9·66°	0·570	0·5685	0·0023
25·00°	1·0439	1·0432	0·0019
40·00°	1·711	1·710	0·0015
	D_2SO_4	"Minimum"	(moles $D_2S_2O_7$ $kg^{-1}_{solution}$)
10·00°	0·133	—	—
25·00°	0·2568	0·2540	0·0045
40·00°	0·446	—	—

1956). Minima in the conductivities of the H_2O–SO_3 and D_2O–SO_3 systems occur almost, but not exactly, at the compositions H_2SO_4 and D_2SO_4. For the former the minimum occurs slightly on the aqueous side of the composition H_2SO_4, in the range 10–40°, and shifts towards the composition H_2SO_4 as the temperature increases. At 25° a minimum occurs slightly on the oleum side of the composition D_2SO_4. The position of the minimum depends on the concentrations and the mobilities of all the ions present, and it has been used in conjunction with other data to obtain important information concerning the values of these quantities. 100% Sulphuric acid can be conveniently prepared by first adjusting the composition to the minimum conductivity and then adding dilute oleum until the conductivity corresponding to 100% acid is obtained. The activation energy for the specific conductivity of sulphuric acid is very similar to that for the viscosity, but as Greenwood and Thompson (1959) pointed out this is almost certainly coincidental and has no implication for the mechanism of conduction in sulphuric acid. The conductivity of crystalline sulphuric acid is at least two powers of ten less than that of the liquid (Greenwood and Thompson, 1959).

8. *Heat Capacity and Heat of Fusion*

The specific heat of sulphuric acid is 0·3373 cal deg⁻¹ g⁻¹ (Kirkbride and Wyatt, 1957). The specific heat of the H_2O–SO_3 system has a small but sharp maximum at the composition H_2SO_4. This is due to the fact that a small part of the heat capacity of absolute sulphuric acid arises from the temperature coefficient of the heat of self-dissociation (Kunzler and Giauque, 1952b). The heat of fusion is 2560 cal mole⁻¹ (Kunzler and Giauque, 1952c).

TABLE VII

Assignment of the Fundamental Vibrational Frequencies of H_2SO_4 and D_2SO_4 (frequencies in cm⁻¹)

	H_2SO_4 liquid			H_2SO_4 Crystal	D_2SO_4 Liquid			D_2SO_4 Crystal	Approximate description
	(a)	(b)	(c)	(d)	(a)	(b)	(c)	(d)	
$\nu_2(a_1)$	1195	1170	1140	1170	1170	—	—	1190	SO₂ sym. stretch.
$\nu_4(a_1)$	910	907	905	907	907	—	—	910	S[OH(D)]₂ sym. stretch.
$\nu_5(a_1)$	563	549	741	548	522	—	—	550–566	SO₂ bend.
$\nu_6(a_1)$	392	332	381	386	356	—	—	363	S[OH(D)]₂ bend.
$\nu_8(a_2)$	392	—	417	—	356	—	—	—	Torsion.
$\nu_{11}(b_1)$	973	967	1370	967	980	—	—	980	S[OH(D)]₂ asym. stretch.
$\nu_{12}(b_1)$	563	420	1190	623	560	—	—	628	SO₂ rock.
$\nu_{13}(b_2)$	1368	1365	965	1365	1340	—	—	1350	SO₂ asym. stretch.
$\nu_{15}(b_2)$	422	372	564	412	395	—	—	371	S[OH(D)]₂ rock.
$\nu_1(a_1)$	2450	2450	2430	2450	—	1860	1820	1860	O–H(D) sym. stretch.
$\nu_3(a_1)$	1137	1170	1170–1240	1170	—	—	—	—	O–H(D) bend.
$\nu_7(a_2)$	—	740	420	—	—	—	305	518	O–H(D) sym. wag.
$\nu_9(b_1)$	2970	2970	3000	2970	—	2280	2230	2280	O–H(D) asym. stretch.
$\nu_1(b_1)$	—	1240	1800	1240	—	—	—	930	O–H(D) bend.
$\nu_{14}(b_2)$	—	675	675	650	—	—	475	478	O–H(D) asym. wag.

(a) Gillespie and Robinson (1962a).
(b) Giguere and Savoie (1960).
(c) Walrafen and Dodd (1961).
(d) Giguere and Savoie (1963).

9. Infra-red and Raman Spectra

The infra-red and Raman spectra of sulphuric acid, and D_2SO_4, have been investigated by several groups of workers. Much of the earlier work has been discussed by Gillespie and Robinson (1962a) by Giguere and Savoie (1960), and by Walrafen and Dodd (1961). Most of the measurements have been on the liquids but recently Giguere and Savoie (1963) have obtained the infra-red spectra of solid H_2SO_4 and D_2SO_4. They also attempted to measure the infra-red spectra in the gas phase but these measurements were apparently unsuccessful since the spectra obtained were identical with those obtained for the liquids. The generally agreed assignments of the frequencies of the fundamental vibrations of H_2SO_4 and D_2SO_4 are given in Table VII. Giguere and Savoie (1960) and Walrafen and Dodd (1961) have calculated thermodynamic data from the vibrational frequencies.

10. Sulphuric Acid as a Primary Analytical Standard

Kunzler (1953) has proposed the use of 100% sulphuric acid as a primary analytical standard. He concluded that it is much easier, and less time consuming to prepare a precisely accurate sulphuric acid standard than other common standards. He showed that:

(i) by following the change in the freezing point it is possible to adjust the composition to within 0·001% of 100% H_2SO_4;

(ii) constant boiling point sulphuric acid can be prepared with an accuracy of at least 0·01% and the effect of pressure on the composition of the constant boiling mixture is much smaller than it is for constant boiling hydrochloric acid;

(iii) minimum conducting sulphuric acid can be prepared with a composition is within 0·002% of 99·996% H_2SO_4;

(iv) the "water titration" or "fair and foggy" method developed by Brand (1946) in which water or aqueous sulphuric acid is added to oleum until the fuming ceases can be used to prepare acid that has a composition within 0·02% of 100%;

(v) that sulphuric acid solutions can be analysed to within 0·05% by Somiya's (1927) thermometric titration which utilizes the enormous difference between the partial molar heat content of water in oleum and in concentrated aqueous acid.

B. PROPERTIES OF SOLUTIONS

1. Cryoscopic Properties

(a) Freezing Point Depressions. Sulphuric acid has a relatively large molal freezing point depression or cryoscopic constant, k, of 6·12 g mole^{-1} kg (Wyatt, 1953; Gillespie, 1956). It has been shown that the contribution of the heat of self-dissociation to the cryoscopic constant is negligible (Gillespie, 1956), so that $k = 6·12$ for the hypothetical undissociated acid as well as for 100% H_2SO_4. The high value for the cryoscopic constant and the convenient freezing point of $10 \cdot 371°$ make sulphuric acid an ideal solvent for cryoscopy provided that adequate precautions are taken to prevent absorption of water from the atmosphere, and due allowance is made for the solvent self-dissociation. Usually the Beckmann method is used and then the techniques involved are straightforward. Suitable apparatus has been described by several workers (Hammett and Deyrup, 1933; Newman et al., 1949; Gillespie et al., 1950).

Cryoscopic measurements may be used to obtain the value of v, the number of moles of particles (molecules or ions), produced in solution by one mole of solute and hence to obtain information concerning the modes of ionization of solutes.

In general we have

$$\theta(1+0 \cdot 002\theta) = k\phi\Sigma m_i \qquad (47)$$

where θ is the freezing point depression measured from the freezing-point of hypothetical undissociated sulphuric acid $(10 \cdot 625°)$, k is the cryoscopic constant, Σm_i is the total concentration of all solute species (including the self-dissociation ions and molecules), and ϕ is the molal osmotic coefficient (Bass et al., 1960). In general ϕ is not known and it is necessary to set it equal to unity. Then if m_d is the total concentration of solvent self-dissociation species, if m is the stoichiometric molality of the added solute and if each mole of solute reacts with, and therefore uses up, s moles of solvent, i.e.

$$A + sH_2SO_4 = P+Q+R \qquad (48)$$

we have

$$\theta(1-0 \cdot 002\theta) = k\frac{vm}{1-0 \cdot 098\ ms} + m_d \qquad (49)$$

and therefore

$$v = \frac{\theta(1+0 \cdot 002\theta - 0 \cdot 098\ ms)}{6 \cdot 12\ m} - \frac{m_d}{m}. \qquad (50)$$

The total concentration of self-dissociation species m_d can be calculated for any concentration of added electrolyte using the equilibrium constants K_{ap}, K_{id}, $K_{H_2S_2O_7}$, and K_{H_2O} (Table III), and equations representing the composition and electrical neutrality of the solutions. Values of m_d have been tabulated (Bass et al., 1960) for solutions of a strong base B, a strong acid HA, water, disulphuric acid, and the complex base XOH ionizing according to

$$XOH + 2H_2SO_4 = X^+ + H_3O^+ + HSO_4^-. \qquad (51)$$

Similar calculations can be made for more complex electrolytes but it has been shown that for an electrolyte E ionizing according to the general equation

$$E = aH_3O^+ + bX^+ + (a+b)HSO_4^- + cY \qquad (52)$$

the concentration of self-dissociation species for a given stoichiometric concentration of added base may be calculated with sufficient accuracy by assuming that the autoprotolysis is independent of the other self-dissociation equilibria and that the concentration of autoprotolysis ions, m_α, is determined only by the concentration of HSO_4^-, while the concentration of ions and molecules resulting from the other self-dissociation processes, m_β, is determined only by the concentration of $H_3O.HSO_4$ (Bass *et al.*, 1960). Values for m_α can then be obtained from the tabulated values for a strong base, and for m_β from the tabulated values for water. These values are given in Table VIII. We then have $m_d = m_\alpha + m_\beta$.

TABLE VIII

Values of m_α and m_β

m_{HSO}^s	m_α	$m_{H_3O^+}^s$	m_β
0·00	0·0263	0·00	0·0160
0·01	0·0191	0·01	0·0081
0·02	0·0142	0·02	0·0041
0·03	0·0110	0·03	0·0030
0·04	0·0088	0·04	0·0020
0·06	0·0063	0·06	0·0014
0·08	0·0045	0·08	0·0009
0·10	0·0036	0·10	0·0009
0·12	0·0028	0·12	0·0006
0·14	0·0023	0·14	0·0006
0·16	0·0017	0·16	0·0004
0·18	0·0012	0·18	0·0004
0·20	0·0010	0·20	0·0003
0·24	0·0003	0·24	0·0002
0·28	0·0001	0·28	0·0000

Considerable controversy arose between early workers because of their lack of understanding of the self-dissociation equilibria of sulphuric acid. The importance of the solvent self-dissociation was first clearly appreciated by Hammett and Deyrup (1933) who established the rather general practice of using as solvent sulphuric acid containing sufficient water to lower the freezing point to about 9·8–10° in order to largely repress the solvent self-dissociation. Then $\Delta\theta$, the freezing point depression measured from the freezing point of the slightly aqueous solvent is given approximately by

$$\Delta\theta = \nu k m. \tag{53}$$

Small additions of other bases, e.g. $KHSO_4$ may also be used to depress the freezing point of the initial acid. The symbol i, the van't Hoff i-factor, is used by many workers for the approximate value of ν that is given by this equation.

This procedure is not completely satisfactory as the self-dissociation is by no means completely repressed, and some allowance for this should be made, and the presence of a third electrolyte, e.g. $H_3O.HSO_4$ or $KHSO_4$ has been shown to cause complications (Brayford and Wyatt, 1955; Gillespie and Robinson, 1957a). Another type of difficulty arises in the case of solutes that are capable of dehydrating sulphuric acid, e.g. carboxylic acid anhydrides. In slightly aqueous acid, acetic anhydride gives a freezing point depression corresponding to $\nu = 2$ and it might therefore be erroneously concluded that it is simply protonated, i.e.

$$(CH_3CO)_2O + H_2SO_4 = (CH_3CO)_2OH^+ + HSO_4^-. \tag{54}$$

However, in 100% H_2SO_4 the freezing point depression corresponds to $\nu = 4$. This result and the fact that conductivity measurements indicate the formation of one hydrogen sulphate ion show that acetic anhydride is capable of dehydrating sulphuric acid to give the carboxylic acidium ion according to the equation

$$(RCO)_2O + 3H_2SO_4 = 2RCO_2H_2^+ + HSO_4^- + HS_2O_7^-. \tag{55}$$

Leisten (1961, 1964a) has however pointed out how advantage may be taken of differences in the cryoscopic behaviour of a solute in sulphuric acid solvents containing small amounts of water or other electrolytes to obtain more detailed information concerning the ionization of the solute than is provided by measurements in any one of these solvents alone. He has proposed the use of the following cryoscopic mixtures

(i) sulphuric acid containing water, i.e. H_3O^+, HSO_4^-;
(ii) sulphuric acid containing $H_2S_2O_7$, $HS_2O_7^-$;
(iii) sulphuric acid containing $HS_2O_7^-$, HSO_4^-;
(iv) sulphuric acid containing $H_3SO_4^+$, H_3O^+;
(v) sulphuric acid containing $H_3SO_4^+$, $H_2S_2O_7$.

In general the reaction of any solute may be represented by the equation

$$S + nH_2SO_4 \rightarrow aS_1 + bHSO_4^- + cH_3SO_4^+ + dH_2O + eH_2S_2O_7. \tag{56}$$

The resultant increase or decrease in the total number of moles of particles in solution as a consequence of adding one mole of H_2O, $H_2S_2O_7$, HSO_4^- or $H_3SO_4^+$ is given in Table IX. A given solute will have a different cryoscopic behaviour in at least three of the cryoscopic mixtures and since either b or c and either d or e must be zero the determination of the cryoscopic behaviour of the solute in three appropriate solvents (cryoscopic mixtures) will enable a and either b or c and either d or e to be determined. Almost always this allows the mode of ionization of the solute to be unambiguously determined.

(b) *Osmotic Coefficients*. Treffers and Hammett (1937) first suggested that interionic forces are very small in sulphuric acid because solutions of electro-

TABLE IX

Number of Moles of Particles Resulting from Various Solutes in Some Cryoscopic Solvent Mixtures

Solute	(i)	(ii)	(iii)	(iv)	(v)
H_2O	2	−1	0	0	−1
HSO_4^-	1	0	1	−1	−1
$H_2S_2O_7$	−2	1	0	0	1
$H_3SO_4^+$	−1	0	−1	1	1

lytes appear to behave ideally. Gillespie *et al.* (1950) suggested that this might be due to a very high dielectric constant, and they showed that the apparent deviations from ideality that did occur could plausibly be attributed

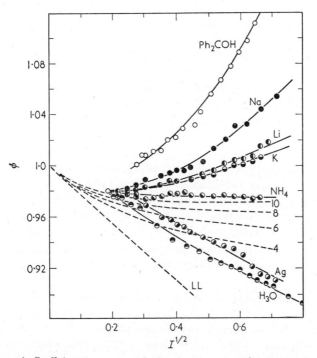

FIG. 3. Osmotic Coefficients. − − − −, calculated curves $(1+\phi^{el})$, with the values of $\overset{\circ}{a}$ indicated. LL = Debye-Hückel limiting law.

to ionic solvation. They attempted to make some allowance for this by a somewhat arbitrary assignment of solvation numbers. However, measurements of the dielectric constant of sulphuric acid (Section IIA, 6), showed that although it is high it is not so high that interionic forces may be completely ignored. Therefore in order to see if the effects of interionic forces could be detected, and to generally investigate deviations from ideal behaviour, some careful measurements of the freezing points of solutions of some completely ionized metal hydrogen sulphates were made by Bass and Gillespie (1960), using the method of equilibrium cryoscopy in which they determined the composition of the equilibrium solution by means of very accurate conductivity measurements. Molal osmotic coefficients ϕ were calculated from the results by means of equation (47). Figure 3 shows the osmotic coefficients plotted against the square root of the ionic strength of the solutions, $I^{\frac{1}{2}}$. The interpretation of these curves is not quite straightforward as they do not refer to solutions of single electrolytes but to mixtures of an electrolyte with the molecules and ions remaining from the solvent self-dissociation. The concentrations of the self-dissociation ions are negligibly small at the higher concentrations of electrolyte but become of increasing importance at lower concentrations until at infinite dilution the solution contains only the self-dissociation species. An ionic strength of less than that of 100% sulphuric acid cannot be obtained and all the osmotic coefficient curves terminate at $I^{\frac{1}{2}} = 0.0189$ and $\phi = 0.98$, which are the values for 100% H_2SO_4. For simplicity it is necessary to treat these solutions as if they contained a single electrolyte only, and agreement between the experimental and theoretical curves cannot be expected to be very good at low electrolyte concentrations. The variation of the osmotic coefficient with concentration may be accounted for by means of an equation of the form

$$\phi = 1 + \phi^{el} + b\Sigma m_i \tag{57}$$

where ϕ^{el} is the contribution of electrostatic interionic forces to the osmotic coefficient, which may be obtained from the Debye-Huckel theory, b is an arbitrary parameter, and Σm_i is the total concentration of ionic species in the solution. The electrostatic contribution was calculated using a dielectric constant of 120 and various values of the parameter $\mathring{a}$, the distance of closest approach of cation and anion. The values of $\mathring{a}$ and b that give the best fit to the observed osmotic coefficient curve for each electrolyte are given in Table X.

Except for $H_3O.HSO_4$ and $AgHSO_4$ the values of $\mathring{a}$ are all of the order of 10Å which is considerably larger than the values generally obtained for electrolytes in water. Such a value, however, is not unreasonable if it is assumed, following Wicke and Eigen (1953), that for non-associated electrolytes there is always at least one solvent molecule between oppositely charged ions when they collide. Values of approximately 10Å may indeed be calculated on this basis from crystal radii and estimated values of the radii of a sulphuric acid molecule and a hydrogen sulphate ion (Bass *et al.*, 1960).

The calculated osmotic coefficient curve for $\mathring{a} = 10$ and $b = 0$ is given in Fig. 3. For the concentrations that are accessible in sulphuric acid solutions the electrostatic contribution to the osmotic coefficient, although not negli-

TABLE X

$\mathring{a}$ and b Parameters and Solvation Numbers Calculated from
Cryoscopic Measurements

Cation	$\mathring{a}$	b	Solvation Numbers		
			(a)	(b)	(c)
Ba^{2+}	10	0·32	11·5	6·5	3·0
Na^+	10	0·14	3·8	3·0	2·0
Li^+	10	0·08	2·6	2·3	3·4
K^+	10	0·07	2·4	2·1	0·6
NH_4^+	0	0·015	1·2	1·2	0·2
Ag^+	2	0	—	—	—
H_3O^+	2	0	—	—	4·0
$Ag^+(K_b = 1)$	10	0·07	2·4	2·1	—
$H_3O^+(K_b = 1)$	10	0·06	2·1	1·8	4·0
Me_2COH^+	—	0·025	1·5	1·0	—
$MePhCOH^+$	—	0·14	3·8	1·4	—
Ph_2COH^+	—	0·31	7·2	1·3	—
$(p\text{-}MeC_6H_4)_2COH^+$	—	0·34	7·8	1·1	—
$(p\text{-}ClC_6H_4)_2COH^+$	—	0·15	4·0	0·5	—
$PhNH_3^+$	—	0·025	1·5	0·8	—
$Ph_2NH_2^+$	—	0·14	3·8	0·6	—
Ph_3NH^+	—	0·31	7·2	0·6	—

(a) Calculated from equation (58).
(b) Calculated from equation (59).
(c) Aqueous solutions (Gluekauf, 1955).

gible, is almost constant and therefore differences between different electrolytes result almost entirely from differences in their interaction with the solvent. This is a consequence of the rather high dielectric constant and of the relatively large sizes of the sulphuric acid molecule and of the hydrogen sulphate ion.

The interpretation of the low osmotic coefficients of solutions of AgHSO₄ and H₃O.HSO₄ is not quite certain. It is possible that AgHSO₄ and H₃O.HSO₄ are incompletely dissociated in dilute solution in sulphuric acid. In the former case there could be some covalent contribution to the bonding between the silver and the hydrogen sulphate and in the latter there could be strong hydrogen bonding between an H_3O^+ and an HSO_4^- ion, as appears to be indicated by detailed investigation of the vibrational spectra of solutions of water in sulphuric acid (E. A. Robinson, unpublished results). In fact if a dissociation constant of the order of unity is assumed for both of these electrolytes then their osmotic coefficient curves are found to closely resemble those of the other electrolytes studied (Fig. 3).

(c) *Ion Solvation.* Robinson and Stokes (1948) have given a quantitative treatment of the activity coefficients of aqueous electrolyte solutions which allows for ionic solvation and assumes that the solvated ions and solvent molecules form an ideal solution (i.e. obey Raoult's Law). By applying their theory to sulphuric acid solutions Bass *et al.* (1960) showed that the parameter b is related to the solvation number s of an electrolyte by the expression

$$b = (2s-v)/40\cdot8. \tag{58}$$

Values of s calculated from this equation are given in Table X.

Gluekauf (1955) has pointed out that this treatment ignores the entropy of mixing of the solvent molecules and the solvated ions, which may have very different sizes. He showed how this additional effect could be taken into account, and he obtained solvation numbers for aqueous electrolytes which were often smaller, and in general varied with ion size in a more reasonable manner than the values obtained by Robinson and Stokes. Following Gluekauf's treatment it may be shown that the parameter b for sulphuric acid solutions is given by the expression

$$b = \frac{(r+s)^2}{40\cdot8} - \frac{rv}{20\cdot4} \tag{59}$$

where r is the ratio of the apparent molar volume of the unsolvated electrolyte to the molar volume of solvent. The values of the solvation numbers given by this equation are also given in Table X.

Since all the solutes studied have the hydrogen sulphate ion as a common anion the solvation numbers reflect the relative solvation numbers of the cations, and if, in view of the large size of the hydrogen sulphate ion, it is assumed that it is not solvated, then these values may be regarded as the solvation numbers of the cations.

Equation (59) gives a smaller and more reasonable solvation number for the highly solvated, and therefore large, barium ion, and also for the large organic cations than does equation (58). On the whole the solvation numbers obtained by the Gluekauf treatment are of reasonable magnitude for primary solvation numbers and show roughly the expected variation with ion size. Lithium appears to be anomalous in that its solvation number is less than that of sodium. This has been attributed to the fact that the co-ordination number of lithium ion for sulphuric acid molecules is only three while that of sodium is four (Gillespie and Oubridge, 1956; Bass *et al.*, 1960). Solvation numbers in sulphuric acid appear to be rather larger than in aqueous solution (Table X) and this is consistent with the probable greater polarity of the sulphuric acid molecule as compared with the water molecule.

(d) *Non-electrolytes.* As 2,4,6-trinitrotoluene was found to give a freezing point depression in slightly aqueous sulphuric acid somewhat greater than that expected for a non-electrolyte it was originally concluded that it was a weak base (Gillespie, 1950b). However, Brand *et al.* (1952) could find no spectrophotometric evidence for the ionization of this compound. Brayford and Wyatt (1955) have subsequently shown that picric acid, trinitrobenzene and trinitrotoluene all give greater than expected freezing point depressions for a non-electrolyte in sulphuric acid containing a little water but in sulphuric acid containing a small amount of $KHSO_4$ or $H_2S_2O_7$ the observed depressions are somewhat smaller than expected for a non-electrolyte. These authors suggest that these solutes are in fact non-electrolytes and that water "salts-out" the non-electrolyte whereas $KHSO_4$ and $H_2S_2O_7$ "salt-in" the non-electrolyte. This would have the consequence that the solubility of the non-electrolyte would be increased in the presence of $KHSO_4$ or $H_2S_2O_7$ but decreased in the presence of water. This conclusion has been verified experimentally (Kirkbride and Wyatt, 1958) although the increase in solubility produced by $KHSO_4$ is very small.

The unionized portion of weak bases similarly give an anomalously high freezing point depression in slightly aqueous solution. Thus the basicity of nitrobenzene obtained from cryoscopic measurements in slightly aqueous acid (Gillespie, 1950b) was higher than that obtained by conductimetric measurements (Gillespie and Solomons, 1957) but if 100% acid is used for the cryoscopic measurements good agreement is obtained with the conductimetric data (Gillespie and Robinson, 1957a).

2. *Densities and Apparent Molar Volumes*

The densities of solutions of a large number of solutes have been measured at 25° (Flowers *et al.*, 1960a; Gillespie and Wasif, 1953b). Solutions of $NaHSO_4$ and $KHSO_4$ have also been studied at 10° and 40°. Some additional information on ion-solvent interactions in sulphuric acid can be obtained from the apparent molar volumes of electrolytes, ϕ_v, which may be calculated from the densities of their solutions. If it is assumed that the molar volume of the hydrogen sulphate ion is 54 cm³ (equal to that of sulphuric acid), this value may be subtracted from the apparent molar volume of a fully ionized hydrogen sulphate to give the apparent molar volume of the cation, ϕ_v^+. If this value is then compared with the volume of the cation calculated from its crystallographic radius, V^+, the difference, δV, indicates the contraction produced in the solvent by the cation. It is reasonable to assume that this contraction is proportional to the extent of ion–solvent interaction or solvation. Then taking the solvation number for a given ion, e.g. Na^+, from cryoscopic measurements, solvation numbers, s, for the other cations can be obtained by simple proportion. The solvation numbers obtained in this way agree surprisingly well with those obtained from cryoscopy; they are presumably therefore also a measure of primary solvation.

The apparent molar volumes of the cations may be compared with their partial molar volumes in aqueous solution (Couture and Laidler, 1956) which are also given in Table XI. The close similarity in the values for univalent ions in the two solvents is remarkable.

TABLE XI

Apparent Molar Volumes and Solvation Numbers of Cations in Solutions of Their Hydrogen Sulphates

Cation	ϕ_v (cm^3 mole^{-1})	ϕ_v^+ (cm^3 mole^{-1})	$\overline{V}_{H_2O}^+$ (cm^3 mole^{-1})	r (Å)	V^+ (cm^3 mole^{-1})	δV (cm^3 mole^{-1})	s	s_{cyros}
Li	47	-7	$-7\cdot0$	0·78	1·2	-8	2	2·3
Na	46	-8	$-7\cdot5$	0·98	2·4	-10	3	3·0
K	53	-1	1·7	1·33	5·9	-7	2	2·1
Rb	59	$+5$	7·7	1·49	8·3	-3	1	—
Cs	68	$+14$	15·1	1·65	11·3	$+3$	0	—
Ag	53	-1	$-7\cdot0$	1·13	3·6	-5	1·5	2·1
Tl	62	8	7·7	1·49	8·3	0	0	—
NH$_4$	59	5	—	1·48	8·2	-3	1	1·2
H$_3$O	61	7	12·0	1·48	8·2	-1	0·3	1·8
Ca	84	-24	$-29\cdot7$	1·06	3·0	-27	8	—
Sr	87	-21	$-30\cdot2$	1·27	5·8	-27	8	—
Ba	96	-12	$-24\cdot3$	1·43	7·4	-19	5	6·5

Couture and Laidler (1956) showed that the partial molar volumes of ions in aqueous solution are proportional to the charge, z, and the cube of the ionic radius, r^3. Their results fit the relationship

$$\overline{V}^+ = 14 + 5\cdot6r^3 - 26z. \tag{60}$$

A similar relationship, namely,

$$\phi_v^+ = 6 + 5\cdot6r^3 - 18z \tag{61}$$

appears to hold for the apparent molar volumes of cations in sulphuric acid. The physical significance of these empirical relationships is not clear.

3. Viscosities

Viscosities of some electrolyte solutions in sulphuric acid are shown in

Fig. 4. Although sulphuric acid itself has a very high viscosity some electrolytes further increase the viscosity and, in fact, have a considerably greater

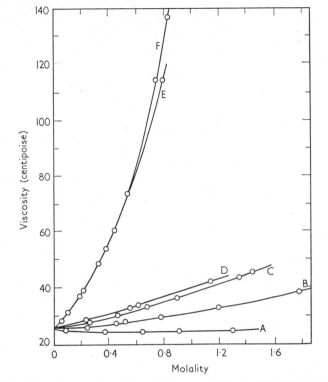

FIG. 4. Viscosities of some electrolyte solutions at 25°C: A, NH_4HSO_4; B, $KHSO_4$; C, $NaHSO_4$; D, $LiHSO_4$; E, $Ba(HSO_4)_2$; F, $Sr(HSO_4)_2$.

effect than do electrolytes in water. This again points to considerable ion–solvent interactions. The relative viscosities of electrolyte solutions may be described by an equation of the form (Jones and Dole, 1929)

$$\eta_r = \frac{\eta}{\eta_0} = 1 + Ac^{\frac{1}{2}} + Bc + Cc^2; \tag{62}$$

the term $Ac^{\frac{1}{2}}$ is almost negligible in sulphuric acid and the viscosities are a very nearly linear function of the molar concentration up to approximately 0·4 molar in the case of uni-univalent electrolytes and 0·2 molar in the case of uni-divalent electrolytes. Values of the parameter B are given in Table XII.

If it is assumed that the hydrogen sulphate ion has a negligible effect on the viscosity these values can be attributed to the cations. It is generally believed (Gurney, 1953) that viscosity B-values are a measure of ion–solvent interaction and the values given in Table XII are certainly in the order that would be expected on this basis. It is interesting that the ammonium ion causes a small lowering of the viscosity of sulphuric acid in the same way that it causes a small lowering of the viscosity of water (Gurney, 1953). The hydronium ion decreases the viscosity of sulphuric acid quite appreciably while it has the opposite effect on the viscosity of water. This decrease in the viscosity

TABLE XII

Viscosity B-Values

	H_2SO_4	H_2O
H_3O^+	-0.4	$+0.07$
NH_4^+	-0.1	-0.01
K^+	$+0.2$	-0.007
Na^+	$+0.8$	$+0.09$
Li^+	$+1.0$	$+0.15$
Ba^{++}	$+4.4$	$+0.22$

due to the H_3O^+ ion could be regarded as evidence that the hydronium ion is a "structure-breaking" ion in sulphuric acid. It is apparently not strongly solvated as it is in water.

4. *Electrical Conductivities*

(a) *Proton-transfer Conduction by $H_3SO_4^+$ and HSO_4^-.* Some measurements of the specific conductivities of solutions in sulphuric acid were made by early workers (Oddo and Scandola, 1908; Hantzsch, 1907; Bergius, 1910; Kendall *et al.*, 1921), but there were considerable differences between their results and between the conclusions drawn from them, partly because of lack of understanding of the solvent self-dissociation and the contribution that it makes to the conductivities of solutions. It is only relatively recently that a detailed and precise study of the conductivities of electrolyte solutions in sulphuric acid has been made. The specific conductivities of the alkali metal hydrogen sulphates and some other electrolytes are summarized in Table XIII (Bass *et al.*, 1960). At low concentrations all these hydrogen sulphates have very similar specific conductivities which suggests that in these solutions the HSO_4^- carries most of the current. This was confirmed by the measurement of the transport numbers of metal cations in solutions of their hydrogen sulphates in sulphuric acid (Gillespie and Wasif, 1953a). The results of these measurements are summarized in Table XIV; they show that in a solution of a metal hydrogen sulphate only a few percent of the current is carried by the cation. That the $H_3SO_4^+$ ion has an abnormally high mobility is confirmed by the results of conductimetric acid–base titrations in sulphuric acid

TABLE XIII

Specific Conductivities of Some Electrolytes at 25°C

c(moles litre^{-1})	0·01	0·02	0·04	0·06	0·10	0·20	0·30	0·40	0·50	0·60	0·70	0·80
$LiHSO_4$	1·050	1·068	1·145	1·252	1·520	2·23	2·86	3·39	3·85	4·23	4·56	4·84
$NaHSO_4$	1·051	1·068	1·147	1·258	1·536	2·26	2·92	3·49	3·99	4·77	4·79	5·12
$KHSO_4$	1·052	1·073	1·156	1·274	1·558	2·33	3·04	3·68	4·23	4·72	5·16	5·56
$RbHSO_4$	1·052	1·08	1·17	1·29	1·61	2·40	3·14	3·77	4·40	4·84	5·37	—
$CsHSO_4$	1·052	1·08	1·17	1·29	1·61	2·41	3·15	3·79	4·47	5·00	5·51	—
$AgHSO_4$	1·053	1·075	1·16	1·26	1·58	2·29	3·00	3·62	4·15	4·62	5·07	5·48
$TlHSO_4$	1·053	1·08	1·17	1·29	1·61	2·45	3·19	3·87	4·48	5·01	5·52	—
$NH_4.HSO_4$	1·053	1·075	1·161	1·278	1·590	2·38	3·11	3·79	4·39	4·94	5·44	—
$H_3O.HSO_4$	1·046	1·061	1·130	1·249	1·530	2·284	2·994	3·60	4·15	4·63	5·07	5·44
$H_2S_2O_7$	1·054	1·068	1·114	1·169	1·281	1·553	1·788	1·991	2·17	2·33	2·47	—
$HB(HSO_4)_4$	1·051	1·073	1·163	1·29	1·61	2·39	3·12	3·60	3·99	4·23	4·32	—
$[(CH_3)_2COH]HSO_4$	1·052	1·073	1·153	1·270	1·56	2·35	3·11	3·80	4·46	5·01	—	—
$[(CH_3.COH.C_6H_5)HSO_4$	1·052	1·073	1·153	1·270	1·56	2·35	3·11	3·75	4·32	4·79	—	—
$[(C_6H_5)_2COH]HSO_4$	1·052	1·073	1·153	1·270	1·56	2·34	3·01	3·58	4·04	4·42	4·72	—
$[(p\text{-}CH_3.C_6H_4)_2COH]HSO_4$	1·052	1·073	1·153	1·270	1·55	2·29	2·47	3·48	3·88	4·23	4·45	—
$[(p\text{-}Cl.C_6H_4)_2COH]HSO_4$	1·052	1·073	1·153	1·270	1·56	2·30	2·48	3·49	3·88	—	—	—

(Flowers *et al.*, 1960b; Hall and Robinson, 1964); addition of $KHSO_4$ to a solution of an acid, e.g. $HB(HSO_4)_4$ causes a marked decrease in the conductivity as the highly mobile $H_3SO_4^+$ ion is replaced by the relatively poorly conducting K^+ ion.

TABLE XIV

Apparent Transport Numbers of Some Ions in Sulphuric Acid (25°C)

Ion	m_{MHSO_4}	t_+	Ion	$m_{M(HSO_4)_2}$	t_+
Ag^+	0·2490	0·026	Ba^{2+}	0·17	0·009
	0·31	0·022		0·23	0·010
K^+	0·62	0·030		0·31	0·008
	1·23	0·025		0·80	0·004
Na^+	0·79	0·021	Sr^{2+}	0·21	0·007
Li^+	0·56	0·013		0·82	0·003

Ionic mobilities generally have rather small values in sulphuric acid because of its high viscosity. The $H_3SO_4^+$ and HSO_4^- ions, however, have mobilities that are greater than any other ions in sulphuric acid and most ions in water;

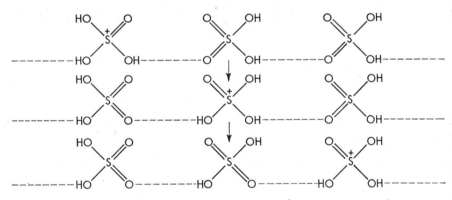

FIG. 5. Proton transfer conduction of the $H_3SO_4^+$ ion in sulphuric acid.

they are of the same order of magnitude as the abnormally conducting H_3O^+ and OH^- ions in water. The mobilities of the $H_3SO_4^+$ and HSO_4^- ions are unaffected by the high viscosity of the solvent because they conduct by a proton-transfer mechanism quite analogous to that which is generally accepted to account for the abnormally high mobilities of the H_3O^+ and OH^- ions in water. The mechanism is illustrated very diagrammatically for $H_3SO_4^+$ ions in Fig. 5. Successive transfers of protons along hydrogen bonds result in an effective movement of $H_3SO_4^+$ ions through the solution without the need for actual movement of individual ions. The details of this mechanism, and in particular the nature of the rate-determining step, are still under discussion (Greenwood and Thompson, 1959; Flowers *et al.*, 1960c). In general there must be a certain amount of molecular movement or re-orientation in order that suitable hydrogen-bonds may be formed to allow proton transfer to take place in the required direction. Thus hydrogen-bond

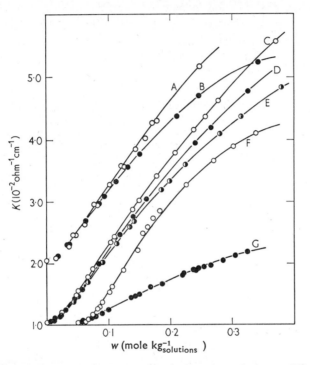

FIG. 6. Specific conductivities of some electrolyte solutions at 25°.

A, Acetone } displaced vertically by 1·0 (10^{-2} ohm^{-1} cm^{-1}) unit.
B, Di-*p*-tolyl ketone }
C, CsHSO$_4$.
D, KHSO$_4$.
E, NaHSO$_4$.
F, HB(HSO$_4$)$_4$ } displaced horizontally by 0·05 w unit.
G, H$_2$S$_2$O$_7$ }

formation rather than proton transfer could be the rate-determining stage of the process.

(b) *Effect of Ion-solvent Interaction on the Mobility of HSO_4^-.* Although all simple bases have very similar conductivities at low concentrations differences become increasingly apparent at higher concentrations. The specific conductivities of some univalent metal hydrogen sulphates are shown in Fig. 6. All the curves are of the same general shape, commencing convex to the concentration axis as a result of repression of the self-dissociation of the solvent and then becoming concave to the concentration axis at relatively high concentrations. This shows that the mobility of the hydrogen sulphate ion apparently decreases with increasing concentration. Moreover it decreases to different extents in different metal hydrogen sulphate solutions. These differences between the conductivities of different electrolytes are much too great to be attributed to the very small differences in the mobilities of the cations and it was therefore concluded that the cations can have specific effects on the mobility of the hydrogen sulphate ion (Gillespie and Wasif, 1953c; Flowers et al., 1960c).

After making allowance for the small contribution of the metal ions to the conductivity, values for the equivalent conductance or mobility of the hydrogen sulphate ion (λ_-) may be calculated from the specific conductivities of solutions of metal hydrogen sulphates and the values are given in Table XV.

TABLE XV

Values for the Mobility of the HSO_4^- Ion (λ_-) in Solutions of Hydrogen Sulphates

	λ_-					
	Cation					
m	Li^+	Na^+	K^+	Rb^+	Cs^+	NH_4^+
0·000	151·2	151·2	151·2	151·2	151·6	151·2
0·010	148·5	149·0	149·0	—	—	149·0
0·020	143·0	143·6	144·0	—	—	144·8
0·040	129·9	130·2	131·7	135·5	135·5	132·8
0·060	118·3	119·4	121·5	125·3	125·5	122·3
0·120	98·5	99·8	102·7	106·9	109·2	104·6
0·180	86·2	87·7	91·4	96·1	98·9	93·7
0·240	76·7	79·3	83·2	89·0	91·5	86·1

The order of decreasing conductance at any concentration is exactly the order that would be expected for increasing solvation of the cation (i.e. it is the order of decreasing ionic radius). It seems reasonable to suppose therefore that solvent molecules that are involved in solvating the cation cannot take part in the proton-transfer conduction process with the same ease as the "free" solvent molecules. Thus the mobility of the hydrogen sulphate ion decreases with increasing concentration of alkali metal hydrogen sulphate because of interaction of the cations with the solvent, and the magnitude of the decrease is related to the extent of this ion–solvent interaction. The lithium ion appears to have a greater interaction with the solvent than the sodium ion although cryoscopic measurements give a smaller solvation number for Li^+ than Na^+. This suggests that the ion–solvent interaction measured by conductivity measurements is not confined to the first solvation layer but is a more general interaction involving a number of layers of solvent around the ion, i.e. secondary solvation, whereas cryoscopic measurements give information on primary solvation. It may be noted that the conductivities of solutions of $H_3O.HSO_4$ and $Ag.HSO_4$ are normal and show no sign of the incomplete dissociation indicated by cryscopic measurements. There is at present no really satisfactory explanation for this. It is possible that water is fully ionized as $H_3O^+.HSO_4^-$ but that the ion-pairs are incompletely dissociated. Any incomplete dissociation would not affect the conductance of the solution if the life-time of the ion-pair were shorter than the average time between successive proton transfers.

(c) *Contribution of Asymmetric Autoprotolyses to the Conductance.* Wyatt (1961) has pointed out that the equivalent conductance of the hydrogen sulphate ion shows an unexpectedly large dependence on concentration, particularly for concentrations up to about 0·1 molal, since the equivalent conductance of HCl in water varies by only about 2% in the same concentration range. He therefore made the important suggestion that there may be a contribution to the conductance from asymmetric dissociation of the solvent in the applied field. He suggests that there is a slight bias towards the movement of protons from neutral molecules to their neutral neighbours (i.e. towards dissociation) in the direction of the field and that this contributes to the conductance. If a is the distance to which the autoprotolysis ions have to approach by a diffusion controlled process before neutralization can occur within a hydrogen-bonded complex, then in the self-dissociation or autoprotolysis it is the process of separating the charges by the distance a during the production of the autoprotolysis ions that gives the special contribution to the conductance. Wyatt derived the following expression for the contribution of asymmetric autoprotolysis to the conductance for a solvent HA

$$k_D = 3\cdot733 \times 10^{-11} k_R [H_2A^+][A^-] \left(\frac{\phi a^2}{T} \right) \qquad (63)$$

where k_R is the rate of recombination of the autoprotolysis ions, and ϕ is the effective internal field for an external applied field of 1 V cm^{-1}. It is seen that the magnitude of the effect depends on the autoprotolysis constant, which is relatively large for sulphuric acid, and although the internal field, ϕ, and k_R are not known with certainty Wyatt showed that asymmetric solvent dissociation might reasonably contribute as much as 30% of the conductance of the 100% acid. Because of the much smaller autoprotolysis constant of water asymmetric solvent dissociation could only contribute negligibly to its conductance. If κ' is the specific conductivity of a solution of a metal hydrogen sulphate from which the small contribution of ions other than $H_3SO_4^+$ and HSO_4^- has been subtracted then

$$10^3\kappa' = \rho\lambda_-(\mu m_+ + m_-) + 10^3\kappa_D \tag{64}$$

where m_+ and m_- are the molalities of $H_3SO_4^+$ and HSO_4^- respectively, λ_- is the mobility of HSO_4^-, μ is the ratio of the mobilities of the $H_3SO_4^+$ and HSO_4^- ions, ρ the density of the solution, and κ_D the contribution due to asymmetric autoprotolysis. If λ_- and μ are constant then a plot of $10^3\kappa'$ against $\mu m_+ + m_-$ should be a straight line with an intercept equal to κ_D.

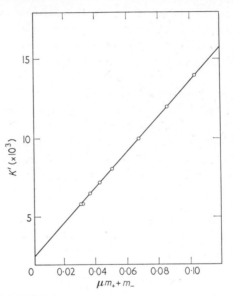

FIG. 7. Plot of $10^3\kappa'$ (KHSO$_4$) against $\mu m_+ + m_-$ for the determination of the contribution of asymmetric dissociation to the conductivity of sulphuric acid.

From the position of the minimum conductivity in the $H_2O–SO_3$ system in the vicinity of 100% H_2SO_4 it can be deduced that $\mu = 1.5$ (Gillespie and Robinson, 1964). Using this value and values of m_+ and m_- calculated from the solvent self-dissociation constants plots of $10^3\kappa$ against $\mu m_+ + m_-$ for various metal hydrogen sulphates were found to be straight lines with intercepts that gave $\kappa_D = 0.38 \times 10^{-2}$ and slopes that gave $\lambda_- = 166$ at 25° (Fig. 7). Thus the asymmetric dissociation does in fact contribute about 36% of the observed conductivity of the acid at 25° and λ_- remains satisfactorily constant at least up to 0.1 m.

(d) *Determination of γ.* That the mobilities of the $H_3SO_4^+$ and HSO_4^- ions are very much higher than those of other ions has the useful practical consequence that the conductivities of solutions of acids and bases in sulphuric acid are determined almost entirely by the concentrations of $H_3SO_4^+$ and/or HSO_4^- respectively. Consequently, γ, the number of moles of hydrogen sulphate ions, or the number of moles of sulphuric acidium ions, produced by one mole of an electrolyte can be obtained from the conductivities of solutions of any acid or base. It might be expected that at a given electrolyte

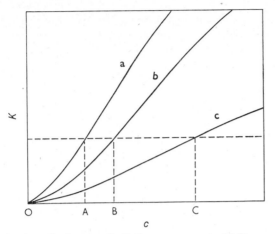

FIG. 8. Determination of γ from conductivity measurements. (a) Strong electrolyte, $\gamma > 1$; (b) standard strong electrolyte $\gamma = 1$ (e.g. KHSO$_4$); (c) weak electrolyte $\gamma < 1$.

concentration, the conductivity of a dihydrogen sulphate would be approximately twice that of a monohydrogen sulphate, but at low concentrations this is not the case because of the different extent to which the two

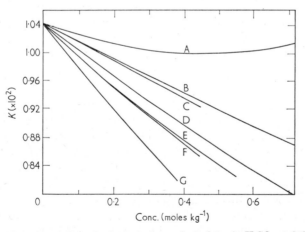

FIG. 9. Specific conductivities of solutions of non-electrolytes in H$_2$SO$_4$ at 25°: A, MeSO$_2$F; B, MeSO$_2$Cl; C, SO$_2$Cl$_2$; D, EtSO$_2$Cl; E, Ph$_2$SO$_2$; F, o-dinitrobenzene; G, 1 : 3 : 5 trinitrobenzene.

electrolytes repress the solvent autoprotolysis. However by comparing the concentration of a standard monohydrogen sulphate such as KHSO$_4$ needed to produce a given conductivity with the concentration of any other

6

electrolyte giving the *same* conductivity, the value of γ for the electrolyte may be obtained directly since the extent of repression of the autoprotolysis is the same for the two solutions that are compared. Figure 8 illustrates the application of this method for both a strong and a weak electrolyte. For the strong electrolyte $\gamma = OB/OA$ and for the weak electrolyte $\gamma = OB/OC$.

Recently Liler (1962) has attempted to allow for the effect on the conductivity of the unionized portion of a weak electrolyte since in general non-electrolytes reduce the conductivity of sulphuric acid. It is difficult to know how such a correction should be best made, however Liler was successful in obtaining values for the basic ionization constants of nitrocompounds which are in rather better agreement with those obtained from cryoscopy than were the earlier results of Gillespie and Solomons (1957).

(e) *Non-Electrolytes.* The conductivities of solutions of non-electrolytes are lower than that of the solvent itself (Fig. 9). This may be attributed to a decrease in the mobilities of the $H_3SO_4^+$ and HSO_4^- ions caused by the non-electrolyte and/or to a reduction in the concentrations of the autoprotolysis ions. A decrease in the mobilities of the characteristic solvent ions could be attributed to strong hydrogen bonding interactions between solute and solvent molecules which would hinder the orientation of the latter and hence decrease their effectiveness in the proton-transfer conduction process. A decrease in the concentrations of the autoprotolysis ions would result from a reduction in the concentration of "free" sulphuric acid as a consequence of solvent molecules removed into the solvation shell of solute molecules. For solutions of aromatic polynitro compounds it has been assumed that the decrease in conductivity is entirely due to the reduction in the concentration of the autoprotolysis ions and solvation numbers were thereby obtained. It was found, to a good approximation, that each nitro group is apparently solvated with one sulphuric acid molecule (Gillespie and Solomons, 1957). Recent measurements by Liler (1962) on the conductivities of $KHSO_4$ in H_2SO_4–SO_2Cl_2 mixtures have shown that sulphuryl chloride has a considerably greater effect on the conductivity of 100% H_2SO_4 than it does on solutions of $KHSO_4$ in H_2SO_4. It must be concluded therefore that the non-electrolyte sulphuryl chloride affects the concentrations of the autoprotolysis ions considerably more than it affects their mobilities, thus providing some support for the assumption used in interpreting the results for polynitro compounds. However this very simple approach does not appear to be entirely substantiated by recent measurements of the conductivities of solutions of some alkyl sulphonyl chlorides and fluorides. The conductivities of solutions of some sulphonyl compounds in sulphuric acid are given in Fig. 9. Despite the fact that $MeSO_2F$ is an intrinsically weaker base than $MeSO_2Cl$ (Hall and Robinson, 1964) it decreases the conductivity of sulphuric acid less than any other sulphonyl halide, at low concentrations, while at relatively high concentrations it actually increases the conductivity, which eventually rises

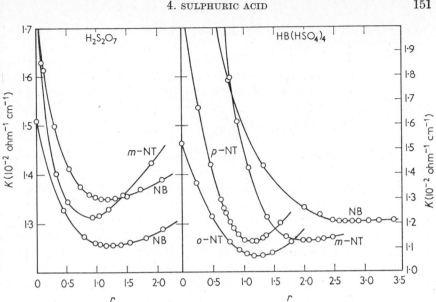

Fig. 10. Conductimetric titrations of weak bases with the acids $H_2S_2O_7$ and $HB(HSO_4)_4$. NB, nitrobenzene; o–NT, o-nitrotoluene; m–NT, m-nitrotoluene; p–NT, p-nitrotoluene.

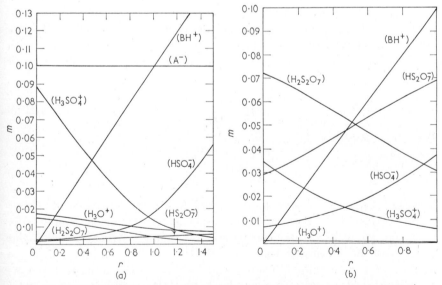

Fig. 11. (a) Concentrations of species in a strong acid–strong base reaction at 25° ($m_{HA}^i =$ 0.1). (b) Concentrations of species in a disulphuric acid–strong base reaction at 25° ($m_{H_2S_2O_7}^i =$ 0.1).

to a value greater than that for the solvent. These observations have not been satisfactorily explained.

(f) *Conductimetric Acid–Base Titrations:* (i) *Simple Bases.* Acid–base neutralization reactions can be carried out in sulphuric acid as in any other amphoteric solvent. The neutralization reaction is simply the reverse of the solvent autoprotolysis, i.e.

$$H_3SO_4^+ + HSO_4^- = 2H_2SO_4. \tag{65}$$

Since the ions $H_3SO_4^+$ and HSO_4^- have very much higher mobilities than any other ions neutralization reactions are conveniently followed by measuring the electrical conductivity of a solution. This decreases as base is added to acid and the highly conducting $H_3SO_4^+$ ion is removed by neutralization with HSO_4^-, passes through a minimum and then increases again as excess HSO_4^- ion is added to the solution (Fig. 10). The position of minimum conductivity depends on the dissociation constants of the acid and base, K_a and K_b, respectively, and if one dissociation constant is known it is possible to calculate the other from the experimentally determined position of minimum conductivity. A general treatment of the variation of the electrical conductivity during an acid–base reaction is possible and several special bases have been discussed (Flowers *et al.*, 1963). This treatment did not take into account asymmetric autoprotolysis of the solvent but this would affect only the magnitude and not the position of the conductivity minimum in an acid–base titration. The position of minimum conductivity may be described in terms of the ratio, $r = n_b/n_a^i$, of the number of moles of added base, n_b, to the initial number of moles of acid, n_a^i. Figure 11 shows how the concentrations of all the species in reactions of the strong acid HA and the acid $H_2S_2O_7$, respectively, with a strong base B vary with r for an initial concentration of acid m_{HA}^i or $m_{H_2S_2O_7}^i = 0.1$ molal. For a base–HA reaction:

$$r_{min} = \left(\frac{1+0.018}{K_b}\right)\left[\left(\frac{1+0.013}{K_a}\right)^{-1} + \frac{0.0007}{m_a^i}\right]. \tag{66}$$

For a base–$H_2S_2O_7$ reaction:

$$r_{min} = 0.56\left(1 + \frac{0.018}{K_b}\right). \tag{67}$$

Values of r_{min} for various values of K_a and K_b are given in Table XVI.

(ii) *Complex Bases.* For a simple base such as $KHSO_4$ added to an initially 0.1 M solution of $H_2S_2O_7$ the conductivity minimum occurs at $r = 0.56$, but in the case of a complex base, e.g. $Ph_3C.OH$ added to an initially 0.1 M solution of $H_2S_2O_7$ the minimum would be expected to occur at $r = 0.56/1+0.56) = 0.36$, since each molecule of $Ph_3C.OH$ ionizes to give a water molecule which reacts with a molecule of $H_2S_2O_7$ in addition to giving a triphenyl carbonium ion.

Nitric acid and mesitoic acid would be expected to behave similarly. In the case of N_2O_5 each molecule ionizes to give two nitronium ions as well as a molecule of water. In this case the conductivity minimum would be predicted at $r = \dfrac{0\cdot28}{1+0\cdot28} = 0\cdot22$.

TABLE XVI

Calculated Conductivity Minima for Acid–base Titrations

	Strong Acid ($K_a = \infty$)				
K_b	∞	$1\cdot0$	10^{-1}	10^{-2}	10^{-3}
r_{min}	$1\cdot01$	$1\cdot02$	$1\cdot19$	$2\cdot82$	$19\cdot1$
	Strong Base ($K_b = \infty$)				
K_a	∞	$1\cdot0$	10^{-1}	10^{-2}	10^{-3}
r_{min}	$1\cdot01$	$0\cdot98$	$0\cdot89$	$0\cdot44$	$0\cdot08$
	Disulphuric Acid				
K_b	∞	$1\cdot0$	10^{-1}	10^{-2}	10^{-3}
r_{min}	$0\cdot56$	$0\cdot57$	$0\cdot66$	$1\cdot58$	$11\cdot3$
	Water				
K_a	∞	$1\cdot0$	$0\cdot3$	10^{-1}	10^{-2}
r_{min}	$1\cdot00$	$1\cdot00$	$1\cdot00$	$0\cdot93$	$0\cdot42$

For the compound trichloromethylmesitylene which ionizes in sulphuric acid to give a carbonium ion and chlorosulphuric acid (R. J. Gillespie and E. A. Robinson, unpublished results) according to the equation

$$(CH_3)_3C_6H_2CCl_3 + 3H_2SO_4 = (CH_3)_3C_6H_2CCl_2^+ + HClSO_3 + H_3O^+ + 2HSO_4^-$$
(68)

titration in dilute oleum has been shown to give a conductivity minimum $r = 0\cdot37$. In this case disulphuric acid is used up both in neutralizing the base $(CH_3)_3C_6H_2CCl_2^+.HSO_4^-$ and in the formation of $HClSO_3$, according to the equation

$$(CH_3)_3C_6H_2CCl_3 + 2H_2S_2O_7 = (CH_3)_3C_6H_2CCl_2^+ + HS_2O_7^- + HClSO_3 + H_2SO_4.$$
(69)

Thus for an initially $0\cdot1$ M solution of $H_2S_2O_7$ the conductivity minimum would be predicted at

$$r = \frac{0\cdot56}{1+0\cdot56} = 0\cdot36,$$

which is close to the observed value of $0\cdot37$. Mesitoyl chloride behaves similarly. Thus conductimetric acid–base titrations of $H_2S_2O_7$ with a complex electrolyte provide information that supplements the results of cryoscopic and conductimetric measurements.

5. *Thermal Properties*

Kirkbride and Wyatt (1957) have measured the partial molar heat contents of potassium, ammonium, and barium hydrogen sulphates, acetic acid and water at 25°. Their results for water are in good agreement with the earlier and less detailed results of Kunzler and Giauque (1952a) and have also been confirmed by new measurements carried out very recently by Mountford and Wyatt (1964). The partial molar heat contents were found to depend markedly on the concentration because of the repression of the solvent self-dissociation at low concentrations. They also found that, on the addition of water to a solution containing a metal sulphate, the partial molar heat content of the water still varied markedly with concentration, confirming that a part of the solvent self-dissociation, namely the ionic self-dehydration, is not appreciably repressed by metal hydrogen sulphates. From the data they were able to obtain the values

$$K_{ap} = 3\cdot4 \times 10^{-4} \text{ mole}^2 \text{ kg}^{-2},$$
$$K_{id} = 1\cdot8 \times 10^{-4} \text{ mole}^2 \text{ kg}^{-2},$$
$$\Delta H_{ap} = 4800 \text{ cal mole}^{-1},$$

and $$\Delta H_{id} = 6200 \text{ cal mole}^{-1} \text{ at } 25°.$$

Dacre and Wyatt (1961) measured directly the heat of the reaction

$$HB(HSO_4)_4 + KHSO_4 = KB(HSO_4)_4 + H_2SO_4 \tag{70}$$

and assuming that $HB(HSO_4)_4$ is a strong acid and correcting for the solvolysis of the $H_3SO_4^+$ ion they obtained a value of $5\cdot0 \pm 0\cdot2$ kcal mole^{-1} for ΔH_{ap}, in good agreement with the more indirectly determined value given above. It is our opinion that the cryoscopic data at 10° is the most accurate data available on the self-dissociation so this was used in conjunction with the above values of ΔH_{ap} and ΔH_{id} to obtain the self-dissociation constants at 25° and 40° given in Table III. The values (Gillespie and Robinson, 1964) do not however agree particularly well with the values given above for 25°.

The heat of infinite dilution of a saturated solution of 2,4,6-trinitrotoluene is less than 100 cal mole^{-1} and the heat of solution of the solid, 4·6 kcal mole^{-1}, is close to the heat of fusion (Kirkbride and Wyatt, 1958). These observations have been interpreted as indicating that the non-electrolyte probably exists in solution as simple molecules and not in a chemically solvated form, and that departures from ideality in these solutions are mainly due to entropy rather than thermal effects (Kirkbride and Wyatt, 1958). It is possible however that the heat required to break the solvent hydrogen bonds when the solute molecule is inserted is approximately equal to the heat evolved in the formation of hydrogen bonds between the nitro-groups of the solute and the solvent and that the agreement between the heat of solution and the heat of fusion is coincidental.

6. Spectroscopy of Sulphuric Acid Solutions

(a) *Infra-red and Raman Spectra.* There has been considerable interest in the Raman spectra of sulphuric acid solutions, particularly of the H_2O–SO_3 system, over many years, but the infra-red spectra of sulphuric acid and its solutions have only been studied quite recently. This was due to the impossibility of studying the infra-red spectrum of sulphuric acid using conventional cell material such as sodium chloride whereas for Raman spectra measurements a glass cell may be used. The recent infra-red work was done with thin films of sulphuric acid between silver chloride plates, or sodium chloride plates protected with a thin polythene film.

The constitution of oleum solutions has been examined by several workers using Raman spectroscopy and recently Giguere and Savoie (1960) have reported infra-red measurements. There has also been much work on the vibrational spectra of solutions of water in sulphuric acid. These results are discussed in a later section, (Section III A).

Only a very few other sulphuric acid solutions have been studied by infrared and Raman spectroscopy. An important early application of Raman spectroscopy was the proof of the formation of the linear NO_2^+ ion in solutions of N_2O_5 and nitric acid in sulphuric acid (Ingold *et al.*, 1950), by the observation of the single line at 1400 cm^{-1} in the Raman spectrum which may be assigned to the nitronium ion and other lines, e.g. 1050 cm^{-1} attributable to the HSO_4^- ion.

(b) *Visible and Ultra-violet Spectroscopy.* Differences in the visible and ultra-violet absorption spectra of bases and their conjugate acids have been utilized in determining their degrees of ionization in sulphuric acid–water mixtures, particularly for acidity function measurements (Section II B, 7). Similar measurements have been carried out on solutions of nitro compounds in oleum. Other important applications of visible and ultra-violet spectroscopy to solutions of sulphur dioxide in oleum (Gold and Tye, 1952), and in support of the formation of acylium ions (Section IV H) and carbonium ions (Section IV, I) in sulphuric acid have also been reported.

(c) *Nuclear Magnetic Resonance Spectroscopy.* In solutions of metal hydrogen sulphates in sulphuric acid, because there is rapid proton exchange between the HSO_4^- ion and the solvent, the proton chemical shifts would be expected to be a linear function of the concentration expressed as a proton fraction, p, according to the expression

$$\delta = \delta_{H_2SO_4} + p(\delta_{HSO_4^-} + \delta_{H_2SO_4}). \tag{71}$$

Figure 12 shows that various metal hydrogen sulphates give linear but nevertheless different plots of δ against p (Gillespie and White, 1960; Birchall and Gillespie, 1964). It must be concluded that the metal ions cause a shift in the proton resonance by virtue of their interaction with the solvent. The largest down field shifts are produced by the ions that other measurements show to be the least solvated. The simplest interpretation of these

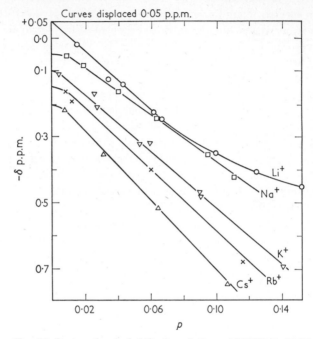

FIG. 12. Proton chemical shifts for solutions of $MHSO_4$ in H_2SO_4.

results is that the HSO_4^- ion produces a large down-field shift and that cation-solvent interaction produces a high-field shift. The observed order of the shifts then agrees with the extents of solvation determined by other methods. Since hydrogen-bonding is known to produce a low-field shift (Pople et $al.$, 1959) the high-field shift caused by solvated ions can presumably be attributed to there being fewer hydrogen bonds between the solvation layer and the bulk solvent than between the solvent molecules themselves. In other words there exists a region of disordered structure, containing relatively few hydrogen bonds, between the solvation layer and the normal structure of the bulk solvent.

The large shift to low field produced by HSO_4^- is of interest. The electron density around the proton in an isolated HSO_4^- would be expected to be greater than around the protons in a sulphuric acid molecule and therefore an isolated HSO_4^- ion would be expected to have a proton resonance at higher field than H_2SO_4. The shift to low field must be due to a strong interaction with the solvent. The negatively charged oxygen atoms of the HSO_4^- ion probably polarize OH bonds from surrounding sulphuric acid molecules and also form hydrogen bonds with them. This conclusion throws some doubt on the earlier assumption that the HSO_4^- ion is not solvated.

Proton chemical shifts have been used to estimate the degree of ionization of water in sulphuric acid (Hood and Reilly, 1959; Gillespie and White, 1960) and although the results obtained agree reasonably well with Raman spectral data (Young, 1951) the assumptions on which the method is based cannot be easily justified and the agreement may be fortuitous.

7. *Hammett Acidity Function Measurements*

Hammett and Deyrup (1932) showed that a convenient quantitative measure of acidity is the Hammett acidity function H_0 which is based on the relative degree of protonation of suitable neutral bases in very dilute solution in an acid medium. The acidity function is given by

$$H_0 = -\log a_{H^+} \left(\frac{f_B}{f_{BH^+}} \right) \tag{72}$$

where a_{H^+} is the activity of hydrogen ions, and f_B and f_{BH^+} are the activity coefficients of a suitable indicator base and its conjugate acid. The expression for H_0 may also be conveniently expressed in the form

$$H_0 = pK_{BH^+} - \log \frac{[BH^+]}{[B]} \tag{73}$$

when $[BH^+]/[B]$ is the indicator ratio (the ratio of the concentrations of protonated to unprotonated base).

Hammett and Deyrup (1932) were the first to evaluate H_0 for the water–sulphuric acid system and H_0 for oleums has been measured by Brand and co-workers (Brand, 1950; Brand et al., 1952). This work has been summarized by Paul and Long (1957).

Experimentally the indicator ratio, $[BH^+]/[B]$, in a particular medium has been measured spectrophotometrically by observing the extinction coefficient, ϵ, of very dilute solutions of the base in the medium and comparing it with the extinction coefficients of the fully ionized base, ϵ_{ion}, and unionized base, ϵ_b, at the same wavelength. Then

$$[BH^+]/[B] = \frac{\epsilon - \epsilon_b}{\epsilon_{ion} - \epsilon}. \tag{74}$$

When direct determination of pK_{BH^+} is not feasible it is evaluated by stepwise comparison of the indicator ratios of the base B in solutions of gradually increasing acidity, with those of another base C, for which the value of pK_{CH^+} is known, since for a particular acidity

$$H_0 = pK_{BH^+} - \log \frac{[BH^+]}{[B]} = pK_{CH^+} - \log \frac{[CH^+]}{[C]} \tag{75}$$

i.e. $$\mathrm{pK_{BH^+} - pK_{CH^+}} = \log\frac{[\mathrm{BH^+}]}{[\mathrm{B}]} - \log\frac{[\mathrm{CH^+}]}{[\mathrm{C}]}. \tag{76}$$

The underlying assumption is that

$$\frac{f_{\mathrm{BH^+}} \times f_{\mathrm{C}}}{f_{\mathrm{B}} \times f_{\mathrm{CH^+}}} = 1 \tag{77}$$

where f_{B} and f_{C} are the activity coefficients of the bases and $f_{\mathrm{BH^+}}$ and $f_{\mathrm{CH^+}}$ those of their conjugate acids. An experimental test of the stepwise procedure is that

$$\log\frac{[\mathrm{BH^+}]}{[\mathrm{B}]} - \log\frac{[\mathrm{CH^+}]}{[\mathrm{C}]}$$

shall remain constant with variation of acidity. If this condition is satisfied then the H_0 scale has been assumed to be independent of the indicators

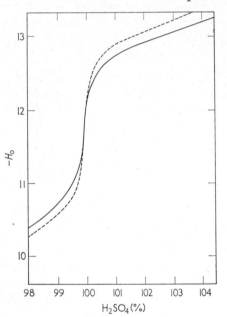

Fig. 13. H_0 for concentrated sulphuric acid and oleum. —, experimental curve; – – – –, calculated curve.

used for its measurement. However, Yates has recently shown that measurements of the H_0 scale for aqueous sulphuric acid, (5–80% H_2SO_4), using a series of overlapping substituted aromatic amides as indicators give different values from those obtained on the basis of substituted aromatic anilines (Yates et al., 1964). The difference has been attributed to a difference in the extent of solvation of BH^+ by the medium.

In 1963, Jorgenson and Harrter re-evaluated the Hammett acidity function scale for water–sulphuric acid solutions more concentrated than

60% H_2SO_4. They showed that some of the previously measured pK values (Hammett and Deyrup, 1932) are in error and that the indicators used by previous workers do not form a suitable set for stepwise comparison. By using a uniform overlapping series of indicators consisting solely of primary anilines a new H_0 scale for sulphuric acid solutions has been established which is progressively more negative with increasing H_2SO_4 concentration than the Paul and Long scale. The weakest base used by Jorgenson and Harrter was picramide, (pK = $-10\cdot10$); this enabled the H_0 scale to be evaluated up to about 99% H_2SO_4.

TABLE XVII

H_0 Values for the H_2O–SO_3 System at Compositions Near to H_2SO_4

%H_2SO_4	H_0
96·0	−10·03
97·0	−10·21
98·0	−10·40
99·0	−10·72
99·5	−11·00
100·0	−12·08
100·5	−12·58
101·0	−12·74
101·5	−12·83
102·0	−12·92
103·0	−13·06
104·0	−13·20
105·0	−13·34
106·0	−13·50

Recently R. J. Gillespie and E. A. Robinson (unpublished results) have re-determined a number of indicator ratios in concentrated aqueous sulphuric acid and in oleum. Their measurements using picramide as the indicator are in good agreement with those of Jorgenson and Harrter. The other indicators used were substituted nitrobenzenes which appear to overlap successfully with the primary anilines. Some of the previous values for the extinction coefficients of fully ionized aromatic nitro compounds reported by Brand et al. (1952) were found to be in error. These errors can be attributed either to the difficulty of evaluating extinction coefficients in media where the indicator is undergoing slow sulphonation, or, in the case of very weak bases, such as 2 : 4 dinitrotoluene, to incomplete protonation of the base even in the most acidic solvent studied. By using highly acidic media such as fluorosulphuric acid, solutions of antimony pentafluoride in fluorosulphuric acid, and solutions of the strong acid $HB(HSO_4)_4$ in sulphuric acid it was possible to obtain what are believed to be more reliable values of ϵ_{ion} for some of the weaker bases. From these results a new H_0 scale was evaluated for concentrated aqueous sulphuric acid and oleums (Fig. 13, Table XVII).

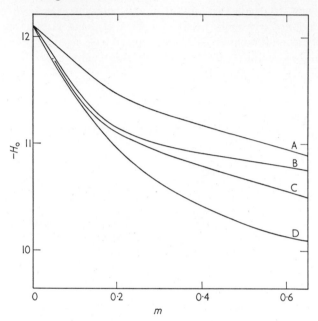

FIG. 14. H_0 for some electrolyte solutions in sulphuric acid: A, $H_3O^+ \cdot HSO_4^-$; B, $C_6H_5COOH_2^+ \cdot HSO_4^-$; C, $Na^+ \cdot HSO_4^-$; D, $K^+ \cdot HSO_4^-$.

Various attempts have been made to justify theoretically the H_0 values for concentrated sulphuric acid solutions. These have recently been discussed by Jorgenson and Harrter (1963) who conclude that no simple explanation such as that given by Deno and Taft (1954), which was based on the supposed ideality of sulphuric acid solutions, suffices below 95% H_2SO_4. Even in 100% H_2SO_4, the H_0 functions of solutions of bases such as benzoic acid, $NaHSO_4$, $KHSO_4$ and water are not identical (Fig. 14), showing that activity effects cannot be neglected. Nevertheless the H_0 scale in the region of 100% H_2SO_4 in the H_2O–H_2SO_4–SO_3 system can be correlated reasonably well with the change in the concentration of $H_3SO_4^+$ ions (Fig. 13), since for the equilibrium between protons and solvated protons

$$H_2SO_4 + H^+ = H_3SO_4^+ \tag{78}$$

$$K = a_{H^+}\left(\frac{a_{H_2SO_4}}{a_{H_3SO_4^+}}\right) \tag{79}$$

which gives $\quad H_0 = -\log[H_3SO_4^+]\left(\frac{f_B}{f_{BH^+}}\right)f_{H_3SO^+} + \dfrac{K}{a_{H_2SO_4}} \tag{80}$

where the a's refer to activities, the f's to activity coefficients, and $[H_3SO_4^+]$ is the concentration of $H_3SO_4^+$ ions. For dilute solutions in sulphuric acid it is reasonable to assume that $a_{H_2SO_4}$ is constant and if the activity coefficient terms can be neglected.

$$H_0 = -\log[H_3SO_4^+] + k \qquad (81)$$

where k is a constant. At the composition H_2SO_4 and at $25°$ $[H_3SO_4^+] = 0.135$ m, and the change in $[H_3SO_4^+]$ with composition is most readily compared with the observed H_0 scale by calculating H_0 relative to the observed value of -12.08 for 100% H_2SO_4, i.e.

$$[H_0]_{calc.} = -\log[H_3SO_4^+] - 13.95. \qquad (82)$$

The calculated values are compared with the experimental values in Fig. 13. The calculated values are slightly too low in aqueous acid and slightly too high in oleum although the two curves have a similar shape. It has been shown that in aqueous sulphuric acid aromatic nitro compounds give larger depressions of freezing point than in 100% sulphuric acid (Gillespie and Robinson, 1957a). Similarly it has been shown that in dilute oleum solutions the

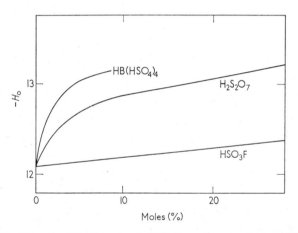

FIG. 15. The Hamett acidity function for solutions of some acids in sulphuric acid.

depressions that are produced by polynitro-compounds which behave as non-electrolytes are smaller than would be expected (Brayford and Wyatt, 1955). In aqueous acid the electrolyte $H_3O^+.HSO_4^-$ causes a salting-out effect, while in oleum there is a salting-in effect. This is consistent with the difference between the calculated and observed H_0 values.

The variation of H_0 with composition in the H_2SO_4–$HB(HSO_4)_4$, H_2SO_4–HSO_3F and H_2SO_4–$H_2S_2O_7$ systems are shown in Fig. 15 (Barr et al., 1965). H_0 measurements have also been reported for the H_2SO_4–HSO_3Cl system by Palm (1956.)

III. Inorganic Solutes

A. THE SOLUTES WATER AND SULPHUR TRIOXIDE

The existence of a number of compounds in the H_2O–SO_3 system has long been recognized. For example phase diagram studies show congruent melting points for the following compounds: $H_2SO_4.4H_2O$ ($-28.366°$); $H_2SO_4.2H_2O$ ($-39.51°$); $H_2SO_4.H_2O$ ($8.56°$); H_2SO_4 ($10.37°$); and $H_2S_2O_7$ ($35.15°$), and the compounds $H_2SO_4.6H_2O$ and $H_2SO_4.3H_2O$ melt in-congruently and are transformed into the four-hydrate at $-53.73°$ and $-36.56°$, respectively (Gable et al., 1950; Giauque et al., 1952; Kunzler and Giauque, 1952a). The numerous and extensive studies of aqueous sulphuric acid will not be considered further here: the discussion will be limited to dilute solutions of water in sulphuric acid. Freezing point measurements (Gillespie, 1950a; Bass et al., 1960) have shown that water is apparently incompletely ionized in sulphuric acid and a dissociation constant $K_{H_2O} = 1$ mole kg^{-1}, has been obtained. However there is no indication of incomplete dissociation in the electrical conductivities of solutions of water in sulphuric acid (Gillespie et al., 1960). This observation is most easily explained by assuming that the incompleteness of the ionization of water is due to the formation of ion-pairs, $H_3O^+.HSO_4^-$, and that the life-time of an $H_3O^+.HSO_4^-$ ion-pair is less than the average time taken for proton transfer in the conduction by HSO_4^- ions. Recent spectroscopic work by E. A. Robinson (un-published results) appears to support the formation of $H_3O^+.HSO_4^-$ ion-pairs and frequencies of 1140 and 1300 cm^{-1} can be assigned to the SO stretching vibrations of this species.

Recently Giguere and Savoie (1960) have investigated the infra-red spectra of solutions of water in sulphuric acid and similar measurements have been reported by Walrafen and Dodd (1961). Many workers have studied the Raman spectra of aqueous sulphuric acid solutions and Young (1959) claimed that for sulphuric acid solutions having compositions between H_2SO_4 and $H_2SO_4.H_2O$, the species $H_5SO_5^+$ is present in addition to H_2SO_4, HSO_4^-, and H_3O^+. Presumably $H_5SO_5^+$ is the monosolvated H_3O^+ ion, ($H_3O^+.H_2SO_4$). Cryoscopic measurements also indicate that the H_3O^+ ion is solvated, probably with two H_2SO_4 molecules (Bass et al., 1960) and Wyatt (1960) found it necessary to assume the formation of $H_3O^+(H_2SO_4)$ in order to account for the partial molar heat content of water in sulphuric acid.

Lehmann (1953) has summarized data on the phase diagram of the H_2SO_4–SO_3 system and claims the existence of $H_2S_2O_7$, $H_2S_3O_{10}$, $H_2S_4O_{13}$, and $H_2S_8O_{25}$. Cryoscopic studies showed that a weak acid, presumably $H_2S_2O_7$, is present in dilute solutions of SO_3 in sulphuric acid (Gillespie, 1950b). The dissociation constant was found to be $K_{H_2S_2O_7} = 0.014$ moles kg^{-1}, (Bass et al., 1960). Conductivity measurements at $10°$ and $25°$ are consistent with the degree of ionization of $H_2S_2O_7$ expected on the basis of this constant (Gillespie *et al.*, 1960) and the position of the conductivity minimum in conductimetric titration of dilute oleum with a strong base has also been shown (Flowers *et al.*, 1960b) to be consistent with $K_{H_2S_2O_7} = 0.014$. The freezing point depressions obtained when small amounts of ammonium sulphate were added to dilute oleum could be interpreted only if higher polysulphuric acids and their ions were assumed to be present in the system in addition to $H_2S_2O_7$, $HS_2O_7^-$, and $S_2O_7^{2-}$. In particular $H_2S_3O_{10}$ was shown to be present even at concentrates as low as 0.15 molal and the initial decrease in the freezing point depression of an 0.4 molal solution when $(NH_4)_2SO_4$ was added could be explained only if $H_2S_4O_{13}$ was assumed to be present (Gillespie, 1950b).

The constitution of oleum solutions has been examined by several workers using Raman spectroscopy (Millen, 1950c; Walrafen and Young, 1960; Gillespie and Robinson, 1962b) and Giguere and Savoie (1960) have measured the infra-red spectra. All the workers are in agreement that the spectra give evidence for the formation of $H_2S_2O_7$ and the spectra have been analysed by comparison with the spectrum of $S_2O_5F_2$ which is isoelectronic with $H_2S_2O_7$ (Gillespie and Robinson, 1962b). There has been, however, some controversy concerning the spectral evidence for the formation of $H_2S_3O_{10}$. In 1960 Walrafen and Young claimed that the spectra could be accounted for without having to take into account any polysulphuric acid more complex than $H_2S_2O_7$. However the presence of $H_2S_3O_{10}$, as well as $H_2S_2O_7$ in oleum solutions more concentrated than 12% SO_3 has been proved unambiguously by comparison of the spectra of oleums with those of $S_2O_5F_2$ and $S_3O_8F_2$ (Gillespie and Robinson, 1962b). It was shown that a diagnostic feature of the vibrational spectrum of a trisulphuryl compound is the appearance of two frequencies near to 700 cm^{-1}, whereas in the case of a disulphuryl compound there is only one frequency in this part of the spectrum. In relatively dilute oleums there is a single vibrational frequency near to 730 cm^{-1}, ($S_2O_5F_2$ 733 cm^{-1}), while in more concentrated oleums there are two lines at approximately 690 and 735 cm^{-1}, ($S_3O_8F_2$ 699 and 724 cm^{-1}). Other details of the spectra also confirm the occurrence of $H_2S_3O_{10}$ in oleum solutions. Very recently Walrafen (1964) has accepted the evidence for the occurrence of $H_2S_3O_{10}$ and has confirmed it by observations on the intensities of certain spectral lines. Unfortunately the spectrum of $S_4O_{11}F_2$ shows no definite diagnostic features compared to that of $S_3O_8F_2$ and so it was not possible to confirm the presence of $H_2S_4O_{13}$ conclusively by comparison of oleum spectra with that of $S_4O_{11}F_2$. However the SO_2 symmetric stretch, which has a frequency of 1195 cm^{-1} in H_2SO_4, 1224 cm^{-1} in oleum of the composition $H_2S_2O_7$, and 1230 cm^{-1} at the composition $H_2S_3O_{10}$, gradually moves to even higher frequencies as the concentration of SO_3 in oleum increases, until at 92.2% SO_3 it is near to 1260 cm^{-1}. This continuous shift in the frequencies attributed to SO_2 symmetric stretches has been interpreted as indicating that increasing amounts of polysulphuric acids such as $H_2S_4O_{13}$, and even higher polyacids, are formed in very strong oleums (Gillespie and Robinson, 1962b). The SO_2 symmetric stretching frequency in the acyclic SO_3 polymer, which is presumably a very high molecular weight polysulphuric acid, since its formation from the liquid trimer is catalysed by traces of water, is also at 1260 cm^{-1}. In moderately strong oleums the monomer SO_3 is also found to be present and in very strong oleums both the monomer and the trimer $(SO_3)_3$ are present. The Raman spectra of solutions of SO_3 in D_2SO_4 have also been investigated and can be interpreted in a similar way to the H_2SO_4–SO_3 system (Gillespie and Robinson, 1962b).

B. BORON

Boric acid is very soluble in sulphuric acid, and various compounds of boric acid and boric oxide with sulphuric acid have been reported. One of these compounds has the composition H_3BO_3 . $3SO_3$ (d'Arcy, 1889), and it may be regarded as boron tri(hydrogen sulphate), $B(HSO_4)_3$. On the basis of his measurements of freezing point depressions Hantzsch suggested that this compound is formed when boric oxide is dissolved in sulphuric acid (Hantzsch, 1907). More recent freezing point measurements (Flowers et al., 1956b) have shown that $\nu = 6$ for solutions of both H_3BO_3 and B_2O_3, whereas the formation of $B(HSO_4)_3$ would give $\nu = 7$ and $\nu = 8$ for boric acid and boric oxide, respectively,

$$H_3BO_3 + 6H_2SO_4 = B(HSO_4)_3 + 3H_3O^+ + 3HSO_4^- \tag{83}$$

$$B_2O_3 + 9H_2SO_4 = 2B(HSO_4)_3 + 3H_3O^+ + 3HSO_4^-. \tag{84}$$

Conductivity measurements show that for boric acid $\gamma = 2$ and for boric oxide $\gamma = 1$, which again is not in agreement with equations (83) and (84) which require $\gamma = 3$ in both cases. If boron tri(hydrogen sulphate) combines with a hydrogen sulphate ion to form the boron tetra(hydrogen sulphate) ion

$$B(HSO_4)_3 + HSO_4^- = B(HSO_4)_4^- \tag{85}$$

by analogy with

$$BF_3 + F^- = BF_4^- \tag{86}$$

and

$$B(OH)_3 + OH^- = B(OH)_4^- \tag{87}$$

equations (83) and (84) can be rewritten as follows

$$H_3BO_3 + 6H_2SO_4 = B(HSO_4)_4^- + 3H_3O^+ + 2HSO_4^- \tag{88}$$

and

$$B_2O_3 + 9H_2SO_4 = 2B(HSO_4)_4^- + 3H_3O^+ + HSO_4^-. \tag{89}$$

Now $\nu = 6$ and $\gamma = 2$ for boric acid, and $\nu = 6$ and $\gamma = 1$ for boric oxide in agreement with the experimental results.

The conclusion that the boron tetra(hydrogen sulphate) ion is formed in these solutions is of great interest since, as it apparently does not undergo solvolysis, the corresponding acid $HB(HSO_4)_4$ must be a relatively strong acid of the sulphuric acid solvent system. Solutions of the free acid can be prepared by dissolving boric acid or boric oxide in oleum instead of sulphuric acid in which case the H_3O^+ ion is removed by the reaction

$$H_3O^+ + SO_3 = H_3SO_4^+ \tag{90}$$

and the overall equations are

$$H_3BO_3 + 3H_2S_2O_7 = H_3SO_4^+ + B(HSO_4)_4^- + H_2SO_4 \tag{91}$$

and $\quad B_2O_3 + 3H_2S_2O_7 + 4H_2SO_4 = 2H_3SO_4^+ + 2B(HSO_4)_4^-. \tag{92}$

Cryoscopic and conductimetric measurements confirm these reactions and show that the acid $HB(HSO_4)_4$ is extensively ionized, $K_b = 0\cdot4$ moles kg^{-1} (Flowers et al., 1956b). A solution of $HB(HSO_4)_4$ can be titrated conductimetrically with a strong base, such as $KHSO_4$ (Flowers et al., 1960b).

$$KHSO_4 + HB(HSO_4)_4 = KB(HSO_4)_4 + H_2SO_4. \tag{93}$$
$$\text{base} \qquad \text{acid} \qquad\qquad \text{salt} \qquad\quad \text{solvent}$$

The conductivity minimum occurs at

$$\frac{n_{KHSO_4}}{n^i_{HB(HSO_4)_4}} = 0\cdot98,$$

where n_{KHSO_4} is the number of moles of base added to a solution of acid containing initially $n^i_{HB(HSO_4)_4}$ moles of tetra(hydrogen sulphato) boric acid. The freezing point of the solution hardly changes as $KHSO_4$ is added up to the composition

$$\frac{n_{KHSO_4}}{n^i_{HB(HSO_4)_4}} = 1\cdot0.$$

This is because the $H_3SO_4^+$ ion is replaced by an equal concentration of K^+ ions and the concentration of $B(HSO_4)_4^-$ ions remains constant; hence the total number of solute particles remains unchanged. After the composition of minimum conductivity the conductivity increases and the freezing point of the solution decreases as a consequence of the addition of excess $KHSO_4$.

Concentrated solutions of $HB(HSO_4)_4$ have been investigated by means of Raman spectroscopy (Gillespie and Robinson, 1962c). The spectra of these solutions are rather complex but apart from the frequencies that can be reasonably assigned to the species $H_3SO_4^+$, H_2SO_4, and $B(HSO_4)_4^-$ there are other bands which are due to $H_2S_2O_7$ and $H_2S_3O_{10}$. These polysulphuric acids are presumably formed in condensation processes between $B(HSO_4)_4^-$ ions giving polymeric ions containing B—O—B bonds, e.g.

$$2B(HSO_4)_4^- = \left[(HSO_4)_2B \overset{\displaystyle O}{\underset{\displaystyle \underset{S}{O \quad O}}{\diagup\diagdown}} B(SO_4H)_2 \right]^{2-} + H_2S_2O_7 + H_2SO_4 \tag{94}$$

II

Thompson and Greenwood (1959) claim to have obtained the acid $HB(HSO_4)_4$ as a wet solid by the reaction of BCl_3 with sulphuric acid:

$$BCl_3 + 4H_2SO_4 = HB(HSO_4)_4 + 3HCl. \tag{95}$$

In view of the evidence from the Raman spectra of concentrated solutions of this acid that elimination of $H_2S_2O_7$ occurs to give B—O—B links (Gillespie and Robinson, 1962c), and in view of the complex structures of the salts it seems unlikely that the wet solid was in fact pure $HB(HSO_4)_4$. It is more likely that the product of the reaction is a mixture of polysulphatoboric acids with sulphuric acid and disulphuric acid having the overall composition $HB(HSO_4)_4$.

Salts of tetra(hydrogen sulphato) boric acid of the general composition $M^I B(SO_4)_2$, $M^{II}[B(SO_4)_2]_2$, and $M^{III}[B_2O(SO_4)_3]$ have been prepared by the reaction between the corresponding sulphates, boric acid and sulphur trioxide (Schott and Kibbel, 1962), e.g.

$$(NH_4)_2SO_4 + 2B(OH)_3 + 6SO_3 = 2NH_4[B(SO_4)_2] + 3H_2SO_4. \tag{96}$$

On heating the calcium, strontium, or barium salt elimination of SO_3 gave the compound $M^{II}[B_2O(SO_4)_3]$. $NH_4[B(SO_4)_2]$ was also prepared by the reaction of boron nitride with sulphuric acid

$$BN + 2H_2SO_4 = NH_4[B(SO_4)_2]. \tag{97}$$

All the compounds are very hygroscopic and sensitive to hydrolysis; they are believed to contain highly polymeric anions.

Attempts to obtain salts, such as $KB(HSO_4)_4$ by the neutralization of solutions of $HB(HSO_4)_4$ in sulphuric acid have not been successful. In order to obtain a crystalline product it was necessary to prepare considerably more concentrated solutions of the complex boric acid than those used in the physical measurements, and under these conditions the solid sodium, potassium, ammonium, and strontium salts that were obtained had a ratio of sulphate to boron of less than four (Gillespie and Robinson, 1962d). This behaviour is analogous to the behaviour of the borate ion in aqueous solution, which has the formula $B(OH)_4^-$ in dilute solution (Edwards et al., 1955) although many borates which separate from concentrated solution contain complex ions such as $B_4O_7^{2-}$ and $B_6O_{11}^{4-}$ formed by polymerization of $B(OH)_4^-$ and $B(OH)_3$ through the elimination of water.

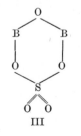

III

It was found (Gillespie and Robinson, 1962d) that the compositions of the salts and the results of cryoscopic and conductimetric measurements on the salts could be satisfactorily explained by assuming that they contain anions with structures based on the six-membered ring III, such as IV and V.

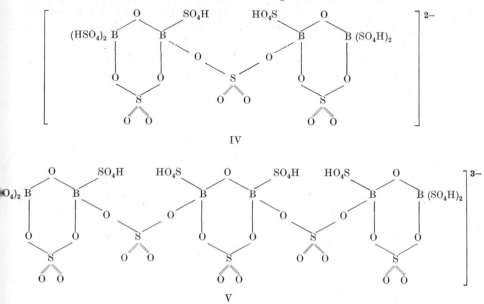

IV

V

C. SILICON

The experimental values of ν and γ for hexamethyldisiloxane (Rice, 1948; Newman *et al.*, 1949; Flowers *et al.*, 1963), indicate that it ionizes according to the equation

$$[(CH_3)_3Si]_2O + 3H_2SO_4 = 2(CH_3)_3Si.SO_4H + H_3O^+ + HSO_4^-. \qquad (98)$$

Price (1948) suggested that trimethylsilicon hydrogen sulphate ionizes further to give the trimethylsiliconium ion

$$(CH_3)_3Si.SO_4H = (CH_3)_3Si^+ + HSO_4^- \qquad (99)$$

but there is no evidence from the cryoscopic or conductimetric measurements that this occurs to any appreciable extent (Flowers *et al.*, 1963). The results of measurements on solutions of trimethylethoxysilane, triethylethoxysilane and trimethylsilanol (Newman *et al.*, 1949) show that they also react to give the corresponding trialkylsilicon hydrogen sulphates.

$$R_3SiOEt + 3H_2SO_4 = R_3Si.SO_4H + EtSO_4H + H_3O^+ + HSO_4^- \qquad (100)$$

$$R_3Si.OH + 2H_2SO_4 = R_3Si.SO_4H + H_3O^+ + HSO_4^-. \qquad (101)$$

Trimethylsilyl sulphate has been prepared by the reaction of oleum on hexamethyldisiloxane (Sommer *et al.*, 1946).

Recently Reavill (1964) has commented on the unsuitability of tetramethylsilane when used in nuclear magnetic resonance spectroscopy as an internal reference standard for sulphuric acid solutions. He has shown that $(CH_3)_4Si$ is immiscible with sulphuric acid but on shaking at room temperature forms methane and trimethylsilyl sulphate.

The experimental results for dimethyldiethoxysilane (Flowers *et al.*, 1963) are in good agreement with the formation of the corresponding di(hydrogen sulphate)

$$(CH_3)_2Si(OEt)_2 + 5H_2SO_4 = (CH_3)_3Si(HSO_4)_2 + 2EtSO_4H + 2H_3O^+ + 2HSO_4^- \tag{102}$$

and results for the compound $[(CH_3)_2SiO]_4$ are also consistent with the formation of dimethylsilicon di(hydrogen sulphate) (Price, 1948)

$$(CH_3)_2SiO_4 + 12H_2SO_4 = 4(CH_3)_2Si(SO_4H)_2 + 4H_3O^+ + 4HSO_4^-. \tag{103}$$

Methyltriethoxysilane differs from the compounds discussed above in that both ν and γ show a definite concentration dependence: ν decreases from 8·4–7·7 while γ decreases from 2·8–2·2 over the concentration range 0·01–0·06 molal (Flowers *et al.*, 1963). Presumably the low observed values of ν and γ, and their concentration dependence are due to polymerization of the methylsilicon trihydrogen sulphate. The general equation for the formation of linear polymers may be written

$$CH_3Si(OEt)_3 + (6+3/n)H_2SO_4 = \frac{1}{n}\left[HSO_4-\underset{\underset{SO_4H}{|}}{\overset{\overset{CH_3}{|}}{Si}}-O-\left(\underset{\underset{SO_4H}{|}}{\overset{\overset{CH_3}{|}}{Si}}-O \right)_{n-2}-\underset{\underset{SO_4H}{|}}{\overset{\overset{CH_3}{|}}{Si}}-SO_4H \right]$$

$$+ 3EtHSO_4 + \left(2+\frac{1}{n}\right)H_3O^+ + \left(2+\frac{1}{n}\right)HSO_4^- \tag{104}$$

	n	$\nu = 7 + \dfrac{3}{n}$	$\gamma = 2 + \dfrac{1}{n}$
dimer	2	8·5	2·5
trimer	3	8·0	2·3
tetramer	4	7·75	2·25

It is possible that these polymers are better formulated as containing six-membered rings with bridging sulphate groups formed by the elimination of sulphuric acid from the linear polymer VI:

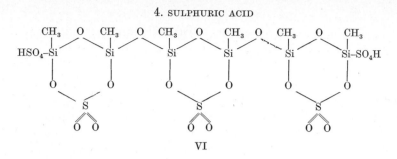

VI

This is consistent with the proposed structures for complex sulphato compounds of boron and arsenic eg. III and XV. The formation of a mixture of these polymers would account satisfactorily for the experimental observations.

The results of a cryoscopic study of tetraphenylsilane, tetrabenzylsilane and hexaphenyldisilane (Szmant et al., 1951) can only be interpreted if it is assumed that complete cleavage of all the Si—C bonds occurs with the formation of the corresponding aryl sulphonic acids, which were isolated from the solutions. The cleavage of Si—C bonds is well known to be caused by a variety of acidic and basic reagents and kinetic studies have been made of the rate of the cleavage of phenyltrimethylsilane by sulphuric acid (Deans and Eaborn, 1959). However, the formation of $Si(HSO_4)_4$ or of the anions $Si(HSO_4)_5^-$ or $Si(HSO_4)_6^{2-}$

$$Ph_4Si + 12H_2SO_4 = Si(HSO_4)_4 + 4PhSO_3H + 4H_3O^+ + 4HSO_4^- \qquad (105)$$

$$Ph_4Si + 12H_2SO_4 = Si(HSO_4)_5^- + 4PhSO_3H + 4H_3O^+ + 3HSO_4^- \qquad (106)$$

$$Ph_4Si + 12H_2SO_4 = Si(HSO_4)_6^{2-} + 4PhSO_3H + 4H_3O^+ + 2HSO_4^- \qquad (107)$$

is not in agreement with the cryoscopic results. It was found that ν decreases from 10·8–10·3, and γ from 2·7–2·5 over the concentration range 0·005–0·03 molal. Thus it appears likely that polymerization occurs and the cryoscopic and conductimetric results for Ph_4Si (Flowers et al., 1963), and the cryoscopic results for tetrabenzylsilane and hexaphenyldisilane (Szmant et al., 1951), and for $[(CH_3)_3SiO]_4Si$ (Price, 1948) can be reasonably accounted for in terms of the formation a three-dimensional oxy(hydrogen sulphate)polymer, e.g.

$$SiPh_4 \rightarrow 4PhSO_3H + \frac{1}{2}n[Si_2O_3(HSO_4)_2]_{\frac{n}{2}} + 2\cdot5H_3O^+ + 2\cdot5HSO_4^-$$

$$(108)$$

$$Si[OSi(OCH_3)_3]_4 \rightarrow 4(CH_3)_3Si \cdot SO_4H + \frac{1}{2}n[Si_2O_3(HSO_4)_2]_{\frac{n}{2}} + 2\cdot5H_3O^+ +$$

$$2\cdot5HSO_4^-.$$

$$(109)$$

The compounds $Si(OEt)_4$, $Ph_3Si.OH$, $Ph_2Si(OH)_2$, $Si(OAC)_4$, and $(naphthyl)_3Si.OH$ appear to react with sulphuric acid to give insoluble polymers.

D. TIN AND LEAD

Stannic acid and stannic sulphate are almost insoluble in sulphuric acid, but a number of salts of sulphostannic acid, $H_2Sn(HSO_4)_6$, have been prepared by evaporating mixtures of stannic oxide, a metal sulphate, and sulphuric acid (Weinlaud and Kuhl, 1907; Druce, 1924), e.g. $Rb_2Sn(SO_4)_3$, $K_2Sn(SO_4)_3$, $Ag_2Sn(SO_4)_3.3H_2O$, $CaSn(SO_4)_3.3H_2O$, $PbSn(SO_4)_3.3H_2O$. All the hydrated salts contain three molecules of water, and they may reasonably be formulated as salts of tri(hydrogen sulphato)stannic acid, $H_2Sn(OH)_3(HSO_4)_3$, e.g. $Ag_2Sn(OH)_3(HSO_4)_3$. Evidence for the existence of hexa(hydrogen sulphato)stannic acid, $H_2Sn(HSO_4)_6$, in solution in sulphuric acid has been obtained (R. J. Gillespie and E. A. Robinson, 1965) from a study of the freezing points and conductivities of solutions of tetraphenyltin, triphenyltin hydroxide, and tin tetra-acetate in sulphuric acid. The results of these measurements are consistent with the following modes of ionization:

$$Ph_4Sn + 14H_2SO_4 = H_2Sn(HSO_4)_6 + 4PhSO_3H + 4H_3O^+ + 4HSO_4^- \quad (110)$$

$$Ph_3Sn.OH + 13H_2SO_4 = H_2Sn(HSO_4)_6 + 3PhSO_3H + 4H_3O^+ + 4HSO_4^- \quad (111)$$

$$Sn(OAc)_4 + 10H_2SO_4 = H_2Sn(HSO_4)_6 + 4AcOH_2^+ + 4HSO_4^-. \quad (112)$$

The values of ν and γ which decrease with increasing concentration are consistent with an equilibrium between the free acid and its anions.

$$H_2Sn(HSO_4)_6 + HSO_4^- = HSn(HSO_4)_6^- + H_2SO_4 \quad (113)$$

$$HSn(HSO_4)_6^- + HSO_4^- = Sn(HSO_4)_6^{2-} + H_2SO_4. \quad (114)$$

Brubaker (1955) has investigated solutions of Sn^{IV} in aqueous solutions of sulphuric acid of various strengths by means of spectrophotometric and electromigration studies and by studying the equilibrium between hydrous stannic oxide and aqueous sulphuric acid solutions. He concludes that in dilute solution, hydrous stannic oxide is in equilibrium with $Sn(SO_4)^{2+}$ while in concentrated solutions there is an equilibrium between $Sn(SO_4)^{2+}$, $Sn(SO_4)_2$ and $H_2Sn(SO_4)_3$.

Tetramethyltin dissolves rapidly in sulphuric acid with evolution of methane, according to the equation

$$(CH_3)_4Sn + H_2SO_4 = (CH_3)_3Sn.HSO_4 + CH_4. \quad (115)$$

A similar reaction has been observed between tetramethyltin and concentrated solutions of hydrogen halides (Coates, 1960). Cryoscopic and conductimetric measurements indicate that the trimethyltin hydrogen sulphate thus formed is substantially ionized to give a trimethyltin cation

$$(CH_3)_3Sn.HSO_4 = (CH_3)_3Sn^+ + HSO_4^-. \quad (116)$$

This reaction may also be written as

$$(CH_3)_3Sn.HSO_4 + H_2SO_4 = (CH_3)_3Sn.SO_4H_2^+ + HSO_4^- \qquad (117)$$

and it is not possible to distinguish between these two possibilities by cryoscopic and conductimetric measurements. A study of the infra-red spectra of concentrated solutions has been made (E. A. Robinson, unpublished results), and although it is difficult to interpret the spectra in detail, they are more complex than would be expected for the trimethyltin cation $(CH_3)_3Sn^+$. Recent infra-red studies of solid trimethyltin salts such as the perchlorate, nitrate, carbonate, and tetrafluoroborate have led to the conclusion that these compounds do not contain $(CH_3)_3Sn^+$ cations, but that the anions are covalently bound to tin in a five co-ordinated trigonal bipyramidal structure (Clark and O'Brien, 1963; Hathaway and Webster, 1963; Okawara *et al.*, 1963). X-Ray studies of $(CH_3)_3SnF$ show that there is trigonal bipyramidal co-ordination of the tin in a structure involving fluorine bridges (Clark *et al.*, 1963). In aqueous solution trialkyltin cations probably exist in solvated forms, e.g. $R_3SnOH_2^+$, rather than the planar ion R_3Sn^+ (Coates, 1960). It is therefore likely that the cation present in sulphuric acid is $[(CH_3)_3Sn.SO_4H_2]^+$ or $[(CH_3)_3Sn(SO_4H_2)_2]^+$. Trimethyltin sulphate gives $\nu = 4$ and $\gamma = 2$ in accord with the ionization

$$[(CH_3)_3Sn]_2SO_4 + 4H_2SO_4 = 2(CH_3)_3Sn.SO_4H_2^+ + 2HSO_4^- \qquad (118)$$

and is thus a strong base although the corresponding hydroxide is only a weak base in water.

Di-n-butyltin diacetate reacts with sulphuric acid to give three hydrogen-sulphate ions per solute molecule ($\gamma = 3$) (R. J. Gillespie and E. A. Robinson, unpublished results). For the reaction

$$(n-Bu)_2Sn(OAc)_2 + 4H_2SO_4 = (n-Bu)_2Sn(HSO_4)_2 + 2AcOH_2^+ + 2HSO_4^- \quad (119)$$

which might be expected by analogy with the behaviour of dialkylsilicon compounds, $\gamma = 2$; the observed γ-value is consistent only with the formation of a singly charged tin cation, e.g.

$$(n-Bu)_2Sn(OAc)_2 + 5H_2SO_4 = (n-Bu)_2Sn(HSO_4)_2H^+ + 2AcOH_2^+ + 3HSO_4^-.$$
$$(120)$$

Di-n-butyltin di(hydrogen sulphate) appears to behave as a strong base.

Methylstannonic acid is only slowly soluble in sulphuric acid, doubtless as a consequence of its polymeric nature. The observed values of ν and γ vary from 6 to 5 and from 3 to 2, respectively, with increasing concentration, and are consistent with the reaction

$$CH_3Sn.O.OH + 5H_2SO_4 = CH_2Sn(HSO_4)_2 + 2H_3O^+ + 2HSO_4^- \qquad (121)$$

followed by ionization of $CH_3.Sn(HSO_4)_3$ as a weak base

$$CH_3.Sn(HSO_4)_3 + H_2SO_4 = CH_3.Sn(HSO_4)_3H^+ + HSO_4^-. \qquad (122)$$

In contrast to the behaviour of silicon, all the tin compounds investigated are completely converted to the corresponding sulphato compounds, which is consistent with the smaller electronegativity of tin. The basicity of the tin hydrogen sulphates decreases as the number of hydrogen sulphate groups attached to the tin atom increases. Thus R_3SnSO_4H, and $R_2Sn(SO_4H)_2$ are strong bases, while $RSn(SO_4H)_3$ is a weak base, and $Sn(HSO_4)_4$ is an acid.

It has been suggested that the solutions of lead tetra-acetate in sulphuric acid from which $Pb(SO_4)_2$ is obtained, and the greenish yellow solutions obtained by the electrolysis of sulphuric acid using lead electrodes, contain the acid $H_2Pb(SO_4)_3$, since the potassium and ammonium salts, $K_2Pb(SO_4)_3$ and $(NH_4)_2Pb(SO_4)_3$ can be obtained from the solutions (Dolezalek and Finkh, 1906; Esch, 1903). The insoluble salts $(NH_4)_2Pb(SO_4)_3$, $K_2Pb(SO_4)_3$, $Rb_2Pb(SO_4)_3$, and $Cs_2Pb(SO_4)_3$ have also been prepared by treating an acid solution of $Pb(SO_4)_2$ with a solution of metal sulphate in sulphuric acid (Elbs and Fischer, 1901).

Cryoscopic and conductimetric measurements show that lead tetra-acetate, like tin tetra-acetate, is fully converted to the tetra(hydrogen sulphate) (Gillespie and Robinson, 1957b and unpublished results). Since this behaves as an acid it may be regarded as hexa(hydrogen sulphato) plumbic acid

$$Pb(OAc)_4 + 10H_2SO_4 = H_2Pb(HSO_4)_6 + 4AcOH_2^+ + 4HSO_4^-. \quad (123)$$

From the variation of the values of ν and γ with concentration, (ν varies from 8·2—7·5 and γ from 3·4—2·5, over the concentration range 0·005—0·55 molal), it was possible to deduce values for the two dissociation constants of this acid at 25°:

$$H_2Pb(HSO_4)_6 + H_2SO_4 = H_3SO_4^+ + HPb(HSO_4)_6^- \quad K_1 = 1·2 \times 10^{-2} \text{ moles kg}^{-1} \quad (124)$$

$$HPb(HSO_4)_6^- + H_2SO_4 = H_3SO_4^+ + Pb(HSO_4)_6^{2-} \quad K_2 = 1·8 \times 10^{-3} \text{ moles kg}^{-1}. \quad (125)$$

On gently warming below 100°, the yellow solution of lead tetra-acetate in sulphuric acid deposits bright yellow plumbic sulphate, $Pb(SO_4)_2$; above 100° decomposition occurs to give oxygen and a precipitate of plumbous sulphate. Plumbic sulphate has also been prepared from PbF_4 and concentrated sulphuric acid (Brauner, 1894). Like $Sn(SO_4)_2$ it is insoluble in sulphuric acid. It seems reasonable to suppose that the insolubility of $Pb(SO_4)_2$ and the salts $M_2Pb(SO_4)_3$ is due to their being polymerized by sulphate bridges, although their structures are not known.

E. NITROGEN AND PHOSPHORUS

Solutions of nitric acid, metallic nitrates and dinitrogen pentoxide in sulphuric acid have long been known to be efficient reagents in aromatic nitration (Gillespie and Millen, 1948). The idea that the nitrating species under certain conditions might be the nitronium ion was suggested by several workers but no good evidence for the existence of NO_2^+ as a stable entity was available until Ingold and co-workers (Gillespie et al., 1950; Goddard et al., 1950; Ingold et al., 1950) studied by means of cryoscopy and Raman spectroscopy, solutions of nitric acid and some oxides of nitrogen in sulphuric acid and other acids, and also prepared stable salts of NO_2^+. The quantitative formation of NO_2^+ in solutions of nitric acid in sulphuric acid has also been confirmed by conductimetric measurements (Gillespie and Wasif, 1953c). In the case of nitric acid solutions in sulphuric acid the cryoscopic ν-value is close to 4 and electrical conductivity measurements give $\gamma = 2$, as required by the equation,

$$HNO_3 + 2H_2SO_4 = NO_2^+ + H_3O^+ + 2HSO_4^-. \tag{126}$$

The Raman spectrum of these solutions contains two strong lines at 1050 cm^{-1} and 1400 cm^{-1} which cannot be attributed to the solvent or solute molecules. The former is diagnostic of the HSO_4^- ion and the latter, which is polarized, is readily assigned to the linear NO_2^+ ion, for which just one polarized line is expected in the Raman spectrum. This interpretation of the spectrum has been confirmed by an investigation of the Raman spectra of mixtures of nitric acid with other strong acids and of the salts $NO_2^+.ClO_4^-$ and $NO_2^+.HS_2O_7^-$ (Millen, 1950b). The Raman spectrum of HNO_3 in oleum consists of the spectrum of oleum with the addition of two other lines, one at 1400 cm^{-1} the symmetric stretching frequency of the NO_2^+ ion, and another at 1075–1095 cm^{-1} which is due to the $HS_2O_7^-$ ion (Chedin, 1936, 1937; Millen, 1950a). Cryoscopic measurements show that nitric acid ionizes in excess dilute oleum to produce the NO_2^+ ion (Gillespie and Graham, 1950) according to the equation

$$HNO_3 + 2H_2S_2O_7 = NO_2^+ + HS_2O_7^- + 2H_2SO_4. \tag{127}$$

Ogg and Ray (1956) have investigated the [14]N n.m.r. spectrum of solutions of nitric acid in oleum and have observed the nitrogen resonance of the NO_2^+ ion as a single broad peak, the breadth reflecting the effect of a large quadrupole interaction due to the unsymmetrical environment. Comparison with the similar broad spectrum of the linear azide ion provides further evidence that the nitronium ion is linear. The infra-red spectra of solutions of nitric acid in sulphuric acid have been investigated by Marcus and Fresco (1957) who observed the strong asymmetric stretching frequency of the NO_2^+ ion at 2360 cm^{-1}.

Metal nitrates and dinitrogen pentoxide have similarly been shown to give the nitronium ion according to the equations (Gillespie et al., 1950; Millen, 1950b):

$$KNO_3 + 3H_2SO_4 = NO_2^+ + K^+ + H_3O^+ + 3HSO_4^- \tag{128}$$

$$N_2O_5 + 3H_2SO_4 = 2NO_2^+ + H_3O^+ + 3HSO_4^-. \tag{129}$$

Dinitrogen trioxide and metal nitrites react with sulphuric acid to give fully ionized nitrosonium hydrogen sulphate

$$N_2O_3 + 3H_2SO_4 = 2NO^+ + H_3O^+ + 3HSO_4^- \qquad (130)$$

$$NaNO_2 + 3H_2SO_4 = NO^+ + Na^+ + H_3O^+ + 3HSO_4^- \qquad (131)$$

and dinitrogen tetroxide behaves as nitrosyl nitrate since it gives a mixture of nitronium and nitrosonium hydrogen sulphate (Gillespie *et al.*, 1950; Millen, 1950b):

$$N_2O_4 + 3H_2SO_4 = NO_2^+ + NO^+ + H_3O^+ + 3HSO_4^-. \qquad (132)$$

Like triphenylamine, triphenylphosphine is a strong base, being fully protonated according to the equation

$$Ph_3P + H_2SO_4 = Ph_3PH^+ + HSO_4^-. \qquad (133)$$

In addition it undergoes rather slow sulphonation and/or oxidation.

Phosphoric acid behaves as a strong base, as is shown, for example, by cryoscopic and conductimetric measurements on KH_2PO_4 (Gillespie *et al.*, 1965), which give $\nu = 4$ and $\gamma = 2$, in agreement with ionization according to the equation

$$KH_2PO_4 + 2H_2SO_4 = K^+ + H_4PO_4^+ + 2HSO_4^-. \qquad (134)$$

For potassium diphosphate $\nu = 12$ and $\gamma = 5$ indicating that diphosphoric acid dehydrates sulphuric acid to give the $P(OH)_4^+$ ion (Gillespie *et al.*, 1965)

$$K_4P_2O_7 + 7H_2SO_4 = 4K^+ + 2P(OH)_4^+ + HS_2O_7^- + 5HSO_4^-. \qquad (135)$$

Cryoscopic and conductimetric measurements have shown that trimeric phosphonitrilic chloride $(PNCl_2)_3$ accepts 1·2 protons in sulphuric acid while the tetramer is more extensively protonated accepting approximately 2·0 protons (Paddock, 1964).

F. ARSENIC, ANTIMONY, AND BISMUTH

Arsenic pentoxide is insoluble in sulphuric acid at room temperature, and only dissolves to a very small extent at temperatures near the boiling point of the acid. Arsenious oxide, on the other hand, is moderately if rather slowly soluble in sulphuric acid. Cryoscopic and conductimetric measurements (Gillespie and Robinson, 1963a) have shown that it ionizes in an analogous manner to N_2O_3, forming $AsO.HSO_4$,

$$As_2O_3 + 3H_2SO_4 = 2AsO.HSO_4 + H_3O^+ + HSO_4^-. \qquad (136)$$

Whereas the ionization of $NO.HSO_4$ is complete however, that of $AsO.HSO_4$ is only approximately 50% complete in a 0·05 molal solution of As_2O_3. If As_2O_3 behaved like N_2O_3, values of $\nu = 6$ and $\gamma = 3$ would be expected and at very low concentrations the observed values of ν and γ are indeed reasonably consistent with the formation of fully ionized $AsO.HSO_4$. The simplest explanation of the observed decrease in ν from 6·0–4·8 and in γ from 2·6–2·1 as the concentration of As_2O_3 increases from $0.01–0.07$ molal is that $AsO.HSO_4$ is incompletely ionized

$$AsO.SO_4H \rightleftharpoons AsO^+ + HSO_4^-. \tag{137}$$

Values of ν and γ decreasing towards 4 and 1, respectively, as the concentration of As_2O_3 increases, would then be expected. The experimental observations are reasonably consistent with this mode of reaction and an approximately constant value of the dissociation constant of $AsO.HSO_4$ ($K = 12$ moles kg^{-1}), may be calculated. However the decrease in ν is more rapid than that for γ. This may be explained by assuming that $AsO.HSO_4$ polymerizes at higher concentrations, for example, by the formation of a dimer,

$$As_2O_3 + 3H_2SO_4 = (AsO.HSO_4)_2 + H_3O^+ + HSO_4^-. \tag{138}$$

The ready formation of a white precipitate having the composition $As_2O_3.SO_3$ even from quite dilute solutions is also consistent with the formation of polymers for which structures VII or VIII seem reasonable

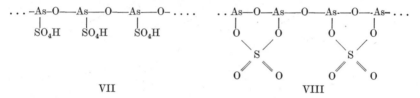

VII   VIII

An additional sulphuric acid molecule is needed to terminate such a chain, giving an –OH group at one end and a –HSO_4 group at the other end:

HO–As–O—As—O—As—O- ..... -As—O—As–SO$_4$H
    SO$_4$H SO$_4$H SO$_4$H   SO$_4$H SO$_4$H

IX

The first two members of this series of polymers then represent solvated forms of $AsO.HSO_4$ and $(AsO.HSO_4)_2$, i.e. $HOAs(HSO_4)_2$ and $(HO)(SO_4H)AsOAs(SO_4H)_2$.

Similarly the species written above as AsO^+ is probably more correctly written in one of the solvated forms X or XI, which can be derived from $HOAs(HSO_4)_2$ by loss of HSO_4^- or by proton addition; similar dimeric ions XII and XIII are also possible.

HO–$\overset{+}{As}$–SO$_4$H   H$_2\overset{+}{O}$–As–SO$_4$H
                                   SO$_4$H

X   XI

HO–As–O–$\overset{+}{As}$–SO$_4$H   H$_2\overset{+}{O}$–As–O–As–SO$_4$H
  SO$_4$H   SO$_4$H SO$_4$H

XII   XIII

It is unfortunate that the cryoscopic and conductimetric measurements do not enable one to distinguish between AsO^+ and the solvated forms X and XI. Raman spectroscopy, which established that NO^+ and NO_2^+ exist in solution in sulphuric acid in the unsolvated forms (Ingold *et al.*, 1950) cannot be used because solutions of sufficient concentration to give satisfactory spectra of the dissolved species cannot be obtained.

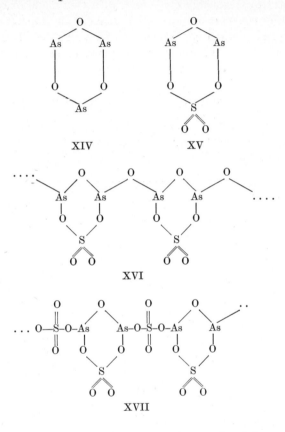

Early workers reported the preparation of several sulphato compounds of arsenic (III), e.g. $As_2O_3.SO_3$; $As_2O_3.2SO_3$; $As_2O_3.3SO_3$ (Adie, 1890; Stavenhagen, 1893; Mellor, 1922a) which are closely related to the species that have been found to occur in 100% H_2SO_4 and in oleum. In general oxygen compounds of arsenic (III) are found to have only single bonds to oxygen and As_4O_6 contains the six-membered ring XIV. Therefore it is postulated that the ring (XV) is an important structural unit in the sulphato compounds of arsenic (III). The ring (XV) is analogous to the ring (III) proposed for the sulphato compounds of boron. On this basis $As_2O_3.SO_3$ may be formulated as XVI and $As_2O_3.2SO_3$ as XVII.

Antimony trioxide is sparingly soluble in 100% sulphuric acid at its boiling point. On cooling white prisms of $Sb_2O_3.3SO_3$, i.e. $Sb_2(SO_4)_3$, are deposited (Mellor, 1922b). Other complexes obtained from aqueous sulphuric acid are $Sb_2O_3.2SO_3$ and $Sb_2O_3.SO_3$. Several workers have shown that these compounds are not fully hydrolysed by water and compounds such as $SbO.SO_4H$ and $(SbO)_2SO_4$ can be obtained. Clearly the behaviour of Sb_2O_3 in sulphuric acid is analogous to that of As_2O_3 but fully sulphated forms are preferentially formed under milder sulphating conditions. This reflects the lower electronegativity of Sb(III) compared to As(III). A number of salts of the acid $HSb(SO_4)_2$ have been prepared (Mellor, 1922b). They are insoluble in sulphuric acid at room temperature. It has been suggested that these salts contain discrete $Sb(SO_4)_2^-$ anions in which the two sulphate groups are chelated to antimony. However their insolubility in sulphuric acid makes it more probable that they contain polymeric anions in which sulphate groups bridge between antimony atoms.

Bismuth(III) sulphate is formed by evaporating Bi_2O_3 with sulphuric acid or from the nitrate and sulphuric acid. It is slowly hydrolysed in hot water to the bismuthyl compound $(BiO)_2SO_4$. Both the oxide and sulphate are very sparingly soluble in sulphuric acid at normal temperatures. Alkali metal salts, $MBi(SO_4)_2$, are formed when a metal sulphate is added to a boiling solution of Bi_2O_3 in concentrated sulphuric acid. These salts are very sparingly soluble in sulphuric acid and are similar in nature to the corresponding compounds of antimony (Mellor, 1922c).

G. VANADIUM, CHROMIUM, AND MANGANESE

Mishra and Symons (1962) have proposed on the basis of conductimetric measurements that V_2O_5 dissolves in 100% H_2SO_4 to give an equilibrium mixture of $VO(HSO_4)_3$ and $HOVO(HSO_4)_2$. A more extensive cryoscopic and conductimetric investigation has shown that in very dilute solution both V_2O_5 and NH_4VO_3 ionize to give only $VO(HSO_4)_3$ according to the equations

$$V_2O_5 + 9H_2SO_4 = 2VO(HSO_4)_3 + 3H_3O^+ + 3HSO_4^- \qquad (139a)$$

$$NH_4VO_3 + 6H_2SO_4 = VO(HSO_4)_3 + 2H_3O^+ + NH_4^+ + 3HSO_4^- \quad (139b)$$

and that with increasing concentration polymeric species such as $[VO(HSO_4)_2]_2O$ are formed (Gillespie et al., 1965).

Mishra and Symons (1962) have studied solutions of K_2CrO_4 in sulphuric acid and dilute oleum. They found that the solutions were relatively stable and that the conductimetric γ-value $\simeq 3$. This is consistent with the reaction

$$K_2CrO_4 + 4H_2SO_4 = \underset{\underset{O}{\overset{\|}{}}}{\overset{\overset{O}{\overset{\|}{}}}{HO-Cr}}-O-\underset{\underset{O}{\overset{\|}{}}}{\overset{\overset{O}{\overset{\|}{}}}{S}}-OH + 2K^+ + H_3O^+ + 3HSO_4^-. \qquad (140)$$

Chromatosulphuric acid H_2CrSO_7 has been previously described by Gilbert et al. (1922).

Potassium permanganate dissolves in slightly aqueous sulphuric acid to give green solutions. Solutions less concentrated than 0·01 molal were found to be stable for 24–36 hours in the absence of reducing agents but eventually deposited MnO_2 (Royer, 1961). More concentrated solutions quickly became turbid and precipitated a green solid which decomposed to MnO_2. Even for dilute solutions the decomposition was quite rapid when the solvent was anhydrous H_2SO_4 or oleum. Royer (1961) found that the cryoscopic ν-value varies with concentration from approximately six for a 0·00358 molal solution to approximately 4·2 for an 0·0145 molal solution, which was turbid. The cryoscopic ν-value also decreased with time to give a limiting value of approximately four after 3–12 hours. The conductimetric γ-value was found to decrease with time from approximately 2·6–2·0 in about 20 minutes at 25°. By extrapolation to zero time an initial γ-value of approximately 3·0 was obtained. Royer interpreted these results in terms of the formation of the permanganyl ion according to the following equation

$$KMnO_4 + 3H_2SO_4 = K^+ + H_3O^+ + MnO_3^+ + 3HSO_4^- \tag{141}$$

and he attributed the decrease in ν and γ with time and with increasing concentration to the precipitation of insoluble permanganyl hydrogen sulphate

$$KMnO_4 + 3H_2SO_4 = K^+ + H_3O^+ + 2HSO_4^- + (MnO_3SO_4H)_{solid}. \tag{142}$$

Mishra and Symons (1962) found that $KMnO_4$ decomposes slowly in 100% sulphuric acid and rapidly in dilute oleum to give oxygen and manganese dioxide or tervalent manganese. They found a γ-value of 2·0–2·2 but they do not mention any variation of this value with time. They also prefer to take the average of Royers ν-values, which is approximately 5, and to ignore the variation with time; consequently they favour the reaction

$$KMnO_4 + 3H_2SO_4 = K^+ + H_3O^+ + MnO_3SO_4H + 2HSO_4^-. \tag{143}$$

These authors also carried out a conductimetric titration in which $KMnO_4$ was added to dilute oleum. They found the conductivity minimum at approximately half the r value for a similar titration with $KHSO_4$ (r = moles of solute/ moles of $H_2S_2O_7$). Since the latter minimum is at $r = 0·56$ the minimum with $KMnO_4$ is at approximately 0·28. They propose that the reaction

$$KMnO_4 + 2H_2S_2O_7 = MnO_3SO_4H + K^+ + H_2S_2O_7^- + H_2SO_4 \tag{144}$$

would explain their results, but this would in fact give a conductivity minimum at $r = 0·36$. Provided the decomposition to give oxygen and MnO_2 may be justifiably ignored the conductimetric titration may be best explained by assuming the occurrence of further sulphation to give $MnO_2(SO_4H)_3$ according to the equation

$$KMnO_4 + 3H_2S_2O_7 = MnO_2(SO_4H)_3 + K^+ + HS_2O_7^- + H_2SO_4 \tag{145}$$

which would give a conductivity minimum at $r = 0\cdot26$ in close agreement with the observed value.

Unfortunately one must conclude that on the basis of the inadequate experimental evidence presented above no firm conclusions can be drawn concerning the behaviour of $KMnO_4$ in sulphuric acid.

H. SULPHUR, SELENIUM, AND TELLURIUM

Sulphur dioxide is moderately soluble in sulphuric acid (Miles and Carson, 1946) and gives a solution which has an electrical conductivity which is very slightly greater than that of the solvent (R. J. Gillespie and E. A. Robinson, unpublished results). This appears to be due to a very slight ionization according to the equation

$$SO_2 + H_2SO_4 = HSO_2^+ + HSO_4^- \qquad (146)$$

although Gold and Tye (1950) found very little change in the absorption spectrum of sulphur dioxide and oleum, and they concluded that there was very little interaction with the solvent and no evidence for any appreciable protonation. The solubility of sulphur dioxide is greater in oleum and increases rapidly with increase in the SO_3 concentration, i.e. with increasing acidity of the solvent (Miles and Carson, 1946). This suggests that the basicity of sulphur dioxide is essentially responsible for its solubility in sulphuric acid and oleum, presumably because of the formation of a hydrogen-bonded complex which precedes the proton transfer accompanying ionization

$$H_2SO_4 + SO_2 \rightarrow HSO_3.OH \cdots O\!\!=\!\!S\!\!=\!\!O \rightarrow HSO_4^- + {}^+HO\!\!=\!\!S\!\!=\!\!O. \quad (147)$$

It has been known for many years that selenium dioxide is soluble in sulphuric acid to give a bright yellow solution (Meyer and Langer, 1927). More recently it has been shown (Flowers *et al.*, 1959) that in dilute solutions it behaves as a weak base

$$SeO_2 + H_2SO_4 \rightleftharpoons HSeO_2^+ + HSO_4^- \quad K_b = 4\cdot4 \times 10^{-3} \qquad (148)$$

forming the $SeO.OH^+$ ion. It is probable that the unionized portion of the selenium dioxide is present as the hydrogen sulphate, $SeO(OH)(SO_4H)$. The reaction of selenium dioxide with sulphuric acid would then be more correctly written

$$SeO_2 + H_2SO_4 \rightarrow SeO(OH).HSO_4 \rightleftharpoons SeO.OH^+ + HSO_4^-. \qquad (149)$$

Small amounts of the ion $HSe_2O_4^+$ (XVIII) are also present in dilute solution of SeO_2 in sulphuric acid, together with unionized diselenious hydrogen sulphate, $Se_2O_3(OH)(HSO_4)$ (XIX).

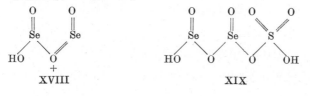

Relatively large amounts of this dimeric ion and probably higher polymeric ions are formed with increasing concentration of SeO_2.

When selenium dioxide is added to an oleum (Flowers *et al.*, 1959) the conductivity decreases and passes through a minimum when one mole of SeO_2 has been added to each mole of disulphuric acid originally present in the oleum. The simplest interpretation of this result is that a largely unionized complex $SeO_2.H_2S_2O_7$ is formed. This can probably be formulated as $SeO(HSO_4)_2$. Confirmation of such an unionized species is obtained from freezing point measurements which show that at the composition of minimum conductivity $\nu = 1\cdot3$ for an initially $0\cdot1$ M solution of $H_2S_2O_7$. There is also some evidence for the existence of the corresponding derivative of diselenious acid, i.e. $Se_2O_3(HSO_4)_2$.

It is somewhat surprising that tellurium dioxide is insoluble in sulphuric acid (Mellor, 1922d) since compounds such as $2TeO_2.SO_3$ (Brauner, 1889) have been described and since it is soluble in acids such as HNO_3, $HClO_4$, and HSO_3F, from which solutions compounds such as $2TeO_2.HNO_3$ (Kon and Blois, 1958) and $2TeO_2.HClO_4$ (Fichter and Scmid, 1916) have been isolated. All these compounds can be regarded as derivatives of ditellurous acid, e.g. $Te_2O_3(OH)(NO_3)$, $Te_2O_3(OH)(ClO_4)$, and $Te_2O_3(SO_4)$. It seems likely that TeO_2 does form a sulphate when treated with sulphuric acid but that being highly polymeric it is insoluble.

I. HALOGENS

Recent measurements (R. J. Gillespie and E. K. Robinson, unpublished results) have shown that hydrogen chloride reacts quantitatively at low concentrations with sulphuric acid to give chlorosulphuric acid.

$$HCl + H_2SO_4 = HClSO_3 + H_3O^+ + HSO_4^-.$$

Many chlorides also react in a similar manner, e.g.

$$(CH_3)_3C_6H_2COCl + H_2SO_4 = (CH_3)_3C_6H_2CO^+ + HClSO_3 + H_3O^+ + 2HSO_4^-. \tag{150}$$

Perchloric acid and chlorosulphuric acid behave as very weak acids (Barr *et al.*, 1961).

Solutions of iodic acid in sulphuric acid have been studied by the cryoscopic and conductimetric techniques by Arotsky *et al.* (1962) and by Gillespie and Senior (1964). The more extensive experiments of the latter authors show that iodic acid is not simply protonated as proposed by Arotsky *et al.*,

$$HIO_3 + H_2SO_4 = H_2IO_3^+ + HSO_4^- \tag{151}$$

but reacts to form unionized iodyl hydrogen sulphate $IO_2.HSO_4$

$$HIO_3 + 2H_2SO_4 = IO_2.HSO_4 + H_3O^+ + HSO_4^- \tag{152}$$

which is probably present in solution in solvated and polymerized forms such as XX and XXI. A white solid that separates from the solution on standing is probably a long-chain or three-dimensional polymer such as XXII or XXIII. There is no evidence that either of the simple ions IO_2^+ or $H_2IO_3^+$ exist in appreciable concentrations in sulphuric acid.

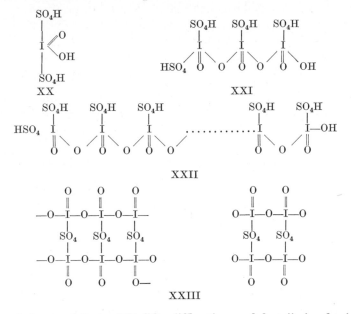

Yellow iodous sulphate $(IO)_2SO_4$, "Chretiens sulphate", is obtained by reacting iodine with iodic acid in sulphuric acid (Chretien, 1895, 1896). Infra-red studies have shown that this compound and the related $(IO)_2SeO_4$ and $IO.IO_3$ are probably ionic and contain the polymeric iodyl ion $(IO^+)_n$ (Dasent and Waddington, 1960). In solution in sulphuric acid iodosyl sulphate reacts with nitrobenzene to give m-iodosonitrobenzene suggesting that the simple iodosyl cation is present in the sulphuric acid solutions. More reactive substrates such as benzene and chlorobenzene give a quantitative yield of the diaryliodonium sulphate. Masson and Hanby (1938) suggested that this latter product arises from I^{3+} ions present in small concentration in equilibrium with the IO^+,

$$IO^+ + 2H^+ = I^{3+} + H_2O \qquad (153)$$

the formation of the diaryl iodonium sulphate taking place in the following manner

$$I^{3+} + RH = H^+ + RI^{2+} \qquad (154)$$
$$RI^{2+} + RH = H^+ + R_2I^+. \qquad (155)$$

The above equilibrium should shift to the right with the removal of water and indeed the yellow sulphate is transformed to a white compound in oleum

7

(Masson and Argument, 1938). This compound has the composition $I_2(SO_4)_3.H_2SO_4$; it may be regarded as a partially desolvated form of $I(HSO_4)_3$. Cryoscopic and conductimetric measurements on solutions of iodosyl sulphate in sulphuric acid show (R. J. Gillespie and J. B. Senior, unpublished results) that it is not a non-electrolyte as claimed by Arotsky *et al.* (1962) but is converted to the hydrogen sulphate, which is about 50% ionized in the dilute solutions studied

$$(IO)_2SO_4 + H_2SO_4 \rightleftharpoons IO^+ + 2HSO_4^-. \tag{156}$$

In dilute oleum $IO.HSO_4$ forms the more sulphated dimer $I_2O(HSO_4)_4$ and with excess oleum the fully sulphated iodine tri(hydrogen sulphate), $I(HSO_4)_3$. The white solid that results from the action of oleum on iodosyl sulphate is the partially desolvated form $I(SO_4)(HSO_4)$ which possibly has the linear polymeric structure XXIV or is the similar ionic compound $[I(SO_4)^+]_nHSO_4^-$ while the normal sulphate $I_2(SO_4)_3$ is no doubt a three-dimensional polymer such as XXV.

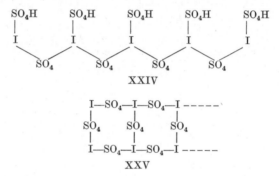

Iodine dioxide, $(IO_2)_n$, behaves as expected as a compound of I(III) and I(V) and dissolves in sulphuric acid to give $IO_2.HSO_4$ and $IO.HSO_4$ (R. J. Gillespie and J. B. Senior, unpublished results).

Masson (1938) showed that iodine dissolves in solutions of iodosyl sulphate in concentrated sulphuric acid giving brown solutions, which react smoothly with chlorobenzene to give a mixture of chlorotriiodobenzenes and a precipitate of elementary iodine. The rapidity of the reaction and the fact that the brown solute is stable only in strongly acid media, led to the conclusion that the iodine was present in a cationic form. From the stoichiometry of the reactions with chlorobenzene of solutions containing different ratios of iodine to iodosyl sulphate, Masson deduced the existence of the ions I^+, I_3^+, and I_5^+.

The freezing points and conductivities of sulphuric acid solutions containing iodine and iodic acid have been studied. At the mole ratio $I_2/HIO_3 = 7.0$ the observed values of ν and γ are in excellent agreement with the formation I_3^+ according to the equation

$$HIO_3 + 7I_2 + 8H_2SO_4 = 5I_3^+ + 3H_3O^+ + 8HSO_4^-. \tag{157}$$

Although more iodine can be dissolved in such solutions to give mole ratios $I_2/HIO_3 > 7.0$, the freezing points and conductivities of the solutions remain constant and independent of the amount of iodine added. This can only be due to the formation of I_5^+

$$I_3^+ + I_2 = I_5^+. \tag{158}$$

At the mole ratio $I_2/HIO_3 = 2.0$ the formation of I^+ would be represented by the equation

$$HIO_3 + 2I_2 + 8H_2SO_4 = 5I^+ + 3H_3O^+ + 8HSO_4^- \tag{159}$$

for which $\nu = 16$, $\gamma = 8$ and $\nu - \gamma = 8$. If $IHSO_4$ were a non-electrolyte the corresponding equation would be

$$HIO_3 + 2I_2 + 8H_2SO_4 = 5IHSO_4 + 3H_3O^+ + 3HSO_4^- \tag{160}$$

$$\nu = 11, \qquad \gamma = 3 \text{ and } \nu - \gamma = 8.$$

It was found that ν decreased from 8.5–7.7, γ from 3.5–3.3 and $\nu - \gamma$ from 5.0–4.4 with increasing concentration. These results are not in agreement with the quantitative formation of either I^+ or $I.HSO_4$. Much better agreement with the observed values is given by the equation

$$4IHO_3 + 8I_2 + 17H_2SO_4 = 5I_3^+ + 7H_3O^+ + 5IO.HSO_4 \tag{161}$$

$$\nu = 8.5–7.25, \ \gamma = 4.25–3, \ \nu - \gamma = 4.25.$$

As $IO.HSO_4$ is known to be partially ionized, the values for ν and γ quoted above represent extreme values corresponding to degrees of dissociation of 0 and 100% respectively. The observed values of ν and γ are a little higher than would be expected in the most dilute solutions studied and this may indicate that at these concentrations a small amount of I^+ or $I.HSO_4$ is present. The disproportionation of I^+ can be written

$$4I^+ + H_2O + 2HSO_4^- = IO^+ + I_3^+ + 2HSO_4^- \tag{162}$$

and it is clear that the equilibrium will be shifted in favour of an increasing amount of disproportionation with increasing concentration.

It has been claimed that the deep blue solutions formed by dissolving iodine in oleum contain I^+ and that absorption bands observed at 640, 500 and 410 mμ may be attributed to this species (Symons, 1957). The brown solutions containing I_3^+ have absorption maxima at 290 and 460 mμ. Solutions containing the solutes in the mole ratio $I_2/HIO_3 = 2.0$, corresponding to the stoichiometric formation of I^+, have the strong absorption band at 640 mμ characteristic of I^+ and also a strong band at 460 mμ overlapping with the 500 and 410 mμ bands of I^+. The relative intensities of the absorptions indicate that in the particular solutions studied about one-third of the iodine was present as I^+, the rest having undergone disproportionation (Symons, 1957). As the solutions were much more dilute than those used in the cryoscopic studies the smaller extent of disproportionation is not surprising.

Addition of ICl or IBr to a solution containing iodine and iodic acid in the mole ratio $I_2/HIO_3 = 2$ gave results very similar to those obtained on adding iodine and it was concluded that the I_2Cl^+ and I_2Br^+ ions are formed respectively.

J. TRANSITION METAL COMPLEXES

It has been shown, by observing the appearance of the characteristic high-field resonance in the n.m.r. spectrum due to hydrogen bonded to a transition metal, that a number of metal, carbonyl and cyclopentadienyl complexes protonate on the metal in sulphuric acid (Davison *et al.*, 1962a). For example the triphenylphosphine and triphenylarsine iron carbonyls $PPh_3Fe(CO)_4$, $AsPh_3Fe(CO)_4$, $(PPh_3)_2Fe(CO)_3$ and $(AsPh_3)_2Fe(CO)_3$ all give stable yellow solutions in 98% sulphuric acid. The proton resonance spectra of these solutions show high-field proton resonances attributable to Fe–H at $\tau \sim 18$. The relative intensities of the high-field lines and the phenyl groups show that the carbonyls function as monoacid bases, e.g.

$$Fe(CO)_4PPh_3 + H_2SO_4 = HFe(CO)_4PPh_3^+ + HSO_4^-. \qquad (163)$$

A number of tricarbonyl arenes of chromium dissolve readily in sulphuric acid solution to give yellow solutions which may contain the corresponding conjugate acids, but they decompose rather rapidly.

The purple-red binuclear compounds $[\pi\text{--}C_5H_5Mo(CO)_3]_2$ and $[\pi\text{--}C_5H_5W(CO)_3]_2$ give red-brown solutions in sulphuric acid which decompose only slowly in the absence of air and which contain the protonated complexes. The chemical shifts in the n.m.r. spectrum of the proton bound to the metal are exceptionally large, $\tau = 30\text{--}40$. Additional evidence that the hydrogen is directly associated with the metal atom comes from the observation of satellite peaks in the spectra of the tungsten compounds which may be attributed to spin-coupling of the proton with the ^{183}W tungsten isotope. The satellite spectrum shows that the proton is in some way associated with both metal atoms in these complexes and from a detailed consideration of the spectrum it was concluded that the proton undergoes rapid intramolecular exchange between the two tungsten atoms.

The binuclear iron complex $[\pi\text{--}C_5H_5Fe(CO)_2]_2$ is soluble in sulphuric acid and gives a high-field line in the n.m.r. spectrum with a relative area to the $\pi\text{--}C_5H_5$ line of 1 : 10 clearly showing that $[\pi\text{--}C_5H_5Fe(CO)_2]_2$ is monobasic. Cryoscopic studies have given slightly high ν-values of 2·3 and 2·4. The reason for this is not known and unfortunately there appear to have been no other cryoscopic studies of compounds of this type with which comparison might be made. The neutral compound has a band in the infra-red spectrum at 1785 cm^{-1} which has been attributed to a bridging carbonyl group. This band is absent in the spectrum of the sulphuric acid solution. It is also absent in the mull spectrum of the hexafluorophosphate salt obtained by treating a solution of the compound in HF with phosphorus pentachloride. The protonated species therefore appears to have two —$C_5H_5Fe(CO)_2$ units linked by a metal–metal bond and the proton can be considered to be in a position comparable to that in the tungsten and molybdenum species and undergoing rapid intramolecular exchange.

Carbonyl–olefin–metal complexes behave differently on protonation in sulphuric acid (Davison *et al.*, 1962b). No transition metal–hydrogen bond is formed; instead the proton adds to the olefin ligand to give what can be regarded as "carbonium ions" bound to and stabilized by the carbonyl metal portion. Tricarbonylcyclo-octatetrane iron is readily soluble in sulphuric acid to give a red solution. The proton n.m.r. spectrum does not contain any high-field line characteristic of a metal–hydrogen bond and the spectrum is consistent with protonation on the ring to give the tricarbonylbicyclo(5,10) octadieniumiron cation

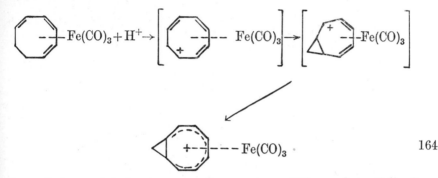

164

Somewhat surprisingly, however, the spectrum differs substantially from that of the free bicyclo(5,10)octadienium cation (Section IV I, 1).

Tricarbonylcycloheptatriene ion is protonated in sulphuric acid to give the $C_7H_9Fe(CO)_3^+$ cation.

$$Fe(Co)_3 - \!\!-\!\!\!\!\bigcirc \quad + H^+ \quad \rightarrow \quad \bigcirc\!\!-\!\!-Fe(CO)_3 \qquad 165$$

A number of cyano complexes have been investigated in acid solution and it has been shown that they protonate on the cyano groups and not on the metal atom (Schilt, 1963). For example $H[Fe(phen)(CN)_4]$ gives a bright yellow solution in concentrated sulphuric acid. From the changes in the visible spectrum that occur on dilution of the solution with water it was concluded that the $[Fe(phen)(CNH)_4]^{3+}$ ion is formed. Contrary to earlier reports it was found that tris-(1,10 phenanthroline)iron(II) and the analogous 2,2-bipyridine complex do not possess any measurable affinity for acids. The gradual change in colour that occurs in solutions of these complexes in concentrated sulphuric acid is due to oxidation.

K. CHELATION BY THE SULPHATE GROUP

We have formulated various sulphato compounds as containing bridging sulphate groups as in **XXVI** rather than bidentate sulphate groups as in **XXVII**

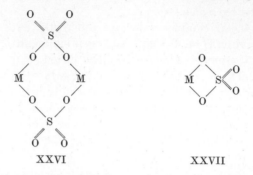

XXVI   XXVII

as there appears to be no direct evidence that the sulphate group behaves as a dichelate group whereas several compounds are known where it apparently functions as a bridging group.

In the case of the sulphato-boron compounds, it is of interest to compare the proposed structures with that of methylene sulphate which has been shown (Baker and Field, 1932) to be dimeric in benzene and therefore presumably has structure **XXVIII** rather than **XXIX**

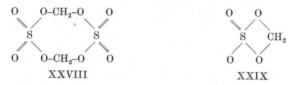

XXVIII   XXIX

Since boron has nearly the same radius as carbon, it is reasonable that sulphato-boron compounds should have similar structures. Comparison with trimethylene sulphate is also appropriate. This compound is monomeric in benzene (Baker and Field, 1932) and can therefore be formulated as in **XXX** containing a six membered ring.

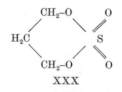

XXX

Chelation by the sulphate group seems possible in many compounds e.g. $H_3Fe(SO_4)(C_2O_4)_2$, $H_3Fe(SO_4)_2.C_2O_4$, $M_2Pb(SO_4)_3$, $K_3Ce(SO_4)_3.H_2O$, $Sb_2(SO_4)_3$, etc. However in all of these cases there is no direct evidence to support this kind of bonding and it is possible that the structures are more complex than the simple molecular formula implies and contain bridging sulphate groups. There are several compounds in which the presence of a bridging sulphate group appears to be established. For example, the compound diethyl germanium sulphate has been shown by cryoscopy to be dimeric in acetone (Anderson, 1950) and therefore presumably has structure **XXXI** and structures such as **XXXII** have been suggested for the salts formed by the reaction of chelating diamines with bis(tetraethyl digold sulphate) (Evans and Gibson, 1941).

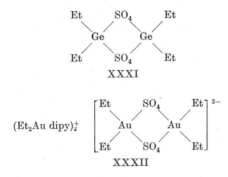

XXXI

$(Et_2Au \; dipy)_2^+$
XXXII

Several cases are known where the sulphate group behaves as a bridging group between two metal atoms which are also joined by some other bridging group such as NH_2, OH, or H_2O. Nakamoto and co-workers (1957) have examined the infra-red spectrum of **XXXIII** and have concluded that the sulphate group has C_{2v} symmetry and is therefore a bridging group. However Barraclough and Tobe (1961) claim that it is not easy to distinguish between a bridging sulphate group and a chelate sulphate group on the basis of the infra-red spectrum.

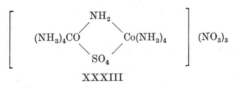

XXXIII

IV. ORGANIC SOLUTES

A. SIMPLE BASES

Many ketones, aldehydes, carboxylic acids, anhydrides, ethers, amines, amides, nitriles, nitro compounds, sulphoxides, sulphones, and some ethylenic and aromatic hydrocarbons are simply converted to their conjugate acids (Gillespie and Leisten, 1954). In cases where ionization is incomplete relative basicities have been measured by cryoscopic, conductimetric and spectroscopic methods. Results of such measurements are given in Table XVIII.

TABLE XVIII

Dissociation Constants for Weak Bases

Base	Conductimetric	Cryoscopic	Spectroscopic	Titration*
p-Butylnitrobenzene	—	$0 \cdot 10^d$	$0 \cdot 10^h$	—
p-Nitrotoluene	$0 \cdot 095^a$ $0 \cdot 105^g$	$0 \cdot 094^d$	$0 \cdot 080^e$ $0 \cdot 090^h$	—
o-Nitrotoluene	$0 \cdot 067^a$ $0 \cdot 073^g$	$0 \cdot 062^d$	—	—
m-Nitrotoluene	$0 \cdot 023^a$ $0 \cdot 028^g$	$0 \cdot 020^d$	$0 \cdot 021^e$ $0 \cdot 025^h$	$0 \cdot 024^f$
Nitrobenzene	$0 \cdot 010^a$ $0 \cdot 013^g$	$0 \cdot 011^d$	$0 \cdot 007^e$ $0 \cdot 0096^h$	$0 \cdot 013^f$
p-Chloronitrobenzene	$0 \cdot 004^a$ $0 \cdot 0057^g$	$0 \cdot 003^a$	$0 \cdot 005^e$ $0 \cdot 0042^h$	—
o-Chlorobenzene	$0 \cdot 0024^g$	—	—	—
m-Chlorobenzene	$0 \cdot 0013^g$	—	$0 \cdot 0011^h$	—
Nitromethane	$0 \cdot 0025^a$	$0 \cdot 004$†	—	—
Acetonitrile	$0 \cdot 16^b$	—	—	—
Benzonitrile	$0 \cdot 07^b$	—	—	—
Dimethylsulphone	$0 \cdot 0148^c$	$0 \cdot 0150^c$	—	$0 \cdot 0145^c$
Diethylsulphone	$0 \cdot 0119^c$	$0 \cdot 0120^c$	—	$0 \cdot 0123^c$
Di-n-propylsulphone	$0 \cdot 0051^c$	$0 \cdot 0048^c$	—	$0 \cdot 0052^c$
Di-n-butylsulphone	$0 \cdot 0039^c$	$0 \cdot 0041^c$	—	$0 \cdot 0040^c$
Tetramethylenesulphone	$0 \cdot 0039^c$	$0 \cdot 0036^c$	—	$0 \cdot 0036^c$
2,4-Dinitrotoluene	$0 \cdot 0005^g$	—	$0 \cdot 0006^e$	
1,2-Dinitrobenzene	$0 \cdot 0003^g$	—	—	
1,3-Dinitrobenzene	$0 \cdot 0003^g$	—	—	
1,4-Dinitrobenzene	$0 \cdot 0003^g$	—	—	

* Titration of base against solution of $H_2S_2O_7$ in H_2SO_4.

† Measured in slightly aqueous H_2SO_4.

[a] Gillespie and Solomons (1957).

[b] Liler and Kosanovic (1958).

[c] Hall and Robinson (1964).

[d] Gillespie and Robinson (1957).

[e] R. J. Gillespie and E. A. Robinson, unpublished experiments.

[f] Flowers et al. (1960).

[g] Liler (1962).

[h] Brand et al. (1952).

B. POLYBASIC COMPOUNDS

The position and extent of protonation of a polybasic compound depends on the intrinsic basicity of each group, their spatial separation and the mesomeric interaction between them.

The intrinsic basicity of an amino group is such that, generally, in a polyamine the amino groups are all protonated regardless of their position in the molecule. Thus o-phenylene diamine produces a threefold depression of the freezing point indicating diprotonation (Leisten, 1964) and it has been shown by conductivity measurements that all four of the nitrogen atoms of

TABLE XIX

ν Factors for Some Organic Compounds

Compound	Formula	ν
Benzil	Ph.CO.CO.Ph	1·8
Dibenzoylmethane	Ph.CO.CH$_2$.CO.Ph	2·1
Dibenzoylpropane	Ph.CO.[CH$_2$]$_3$.CO.Ph	3·0
Dibenzoylpentane	Ph.CO.[CH$_2$]$_5$.CO.Ph	2·9
Dibenzoylhexane	Ph.CO.[CH$_2$]$_6$.CO.Ph	3·0
Dibenzoylheptane	Ph.CO.[CH$_2$]$_7$.CO.Ph	3·0
Anthraquinone		2·0–2·2
Oxalic acid	HO$_2$C.CO$_2$H	1·3
Malonic acid	HO$_2$C.CH$_2$.CO$_2$H	2·0
Succinic acid	HO$_2$C.[CH$_2$]$_2$.CO$_2$H	2·5
Glutaric acid	HO$_2$C.[CH$_2$]$_3$.CO$_2$H	2·6
Suberic acid	HO$_2$C.[CH$_2$]$_6$.CO$_2$H	2·6
Sebacic acid	HO$_2$C.[CH$_2$]$_8$.CO$_2$H	2·6
m-Benzoylbenzoic acid		2·5
p-Benzoylbenzoic acid		2·5
Glycine	HO$_2$C.CH$_2$.NH$_2$	2·2
β-Alanine	HO$_2$C.[CH$_2$]$_2$.NH$_2$	2·7
γ-Amino-n-butyric acid	HO$_2$C.[CH$_2$]$_3$.NH$_2$	2·9
5-Amino-n-pentanoic acid	HO$_2$C.[CH$_2$]$_4$.NH$_2$	3·0
p,p'-Dimethylaminobenzophenone	Me$_2$N⟨ ⟩.CO.⟨ ⟩NMe$_2$	3·5

hexamethylene tetramine are protonated (Gillespie and Wasif, 1953c). It is remarkable then that guanidine which is a strong base in water should be found to add only 1·3 protons (Williams et al., 1953). This incompleteness in the second stage of ionization illustrates the importance of resonance interaction between the basic groups. The monoprotonated ion is considerably stabilized by resonance and the addition of a second proton would result in the loss of a large amount of resonance energy.

Measurements of the basicities of aromatic ketones and carboxylic acids by means of their ultra-violet absorption spectra in sulphuric acid–water mixtures has shown that they are weaker bases than aniline by a factor of approximately 10^{-10} (Flexser et al., 1935; Flexser and Hammett, 1938; Stewart and Yates, 1958, 1960). This difference is reflected in the behaviour in sulphuric acid of polyamines on the one hand and of diketones, dicarboxylic acids and ketocarboxylic acids on the other hand. Thus when the two basic groups are sufficiently close together these latter compounds are only monoprotonated in sulphuric acid but in a series of related compounds in which the distance between the two basic groups is progressively increased the degree of protonation increases. This is shown by the v-values obtained from cryoscopic measurements given in Table XIX (Hammett and Deyrup, 1933; Newman and Deno, 1951a; Wiles, 1953; Wiles and Baughan, 1953). The failure of the dicarboxylic acids to attain a maximum v-value of three has not been explained. In the case of amino acids and amino ketones it might be expected that the amino group would be fully protonated and would decrease the basicity of the carbonyl or carboxyl group by an amount that would decrease with increasing separation of the groups. That this is the case is shown by the v-values given in Table XIX.

Although aliphatic ethers appear to be fully protonated in sulphuric acid conjugation of the methoxyl group with an aromatic system reduces the bascity of the methoxyl group considerably. For example, 1-methoxy, 2-methoxy and 1 : 2-dimethoxy anthraquinone are all monoprotonated in sulphuric acid as is anthraquinone itself (Wiles, 1953). However in 1,4-dimethoxy, 1,5-dimethoxy, and 1,4,5,8-tetramethoxyanthraquinone the second carbonyl group is activated by the methoxyl group and protonates, thus these compounds accept two protons (Wiles, 1953). Anisole and many of its derivatives are rather rapidly sulphonated in sulphuric acid but it has been found that in fluorosulphuric acid at $-80°$ anisole is protonated on the ring carbon in the *para* position rather than on the methoxyl oxygen (Birchall and Gillespie, 1964). Although aniline protonates on the nitrogen it is noteworthy that the v-values obtained for bis-(dimethylaminophenyl)phenyl-carbinol and tris-(dimethylaminophenyl)carbinol indicate that although carbonium ion formation is complete the protonation of the amino groups is not (Newman and Deno, 1951b). Thus it appears that the conjugation of the amino group with the carbonium ion centre reduces its basicity to such an extent that it is not completely protonated in 100% sulphuric acid.

C. AMIDES AND UREAS

Amides behave as strong bases in sulphuric acid (Oddo and Scandola, 1909a) but there has for a long time been uncertainty as to the site of protonation. N.m.r. studies of solutions of amides in sulphuric acid have provided evidence for the now generally accepted view that amides protonate on oxygen rather than on nitrogen. It has been shown, for example, that the relative areas of the nitrogen proton resonance and the methyl group resonance of acetamide in sulphuric acid are in the ratio 2 : 3 (Bunton *et al.*, 1962). If protonation was on nitrogen, the two peaks of equal area would be obtained. It has also been shown that spin–spin coupling between the nitrogen protons and the methyl-protons of N-methyl acetamide in 100% sulphuric acid produces a doublet spectrum for the methyl group, whereas N-protonation would have produced a triplet spectrum (Berger *et al.*, 1959). In sulphuric acid at room temperature it is not possible to observe a separate signal in the n.m.r. spectrum for the protonated carbonyl group because of rapid exchange with the solvent. However in fluorosulphuric acid at low temperatures exchange with the solvent is slowed down sufficiently that a signal from the $C={O}H^+$ group is observed at very low field (Birchall and Gillespie, 1963; Gillespie and Birchall, 1963).

Leisten has studied the rate of hydrolysis of a number of amides in 100% H_2SO_4 (Leisten, 1960)

$$R.C(OH^+)NHR + HSO_4^- + 2H_2SO_4 \rightarrow RCO_2H_2^+ + RNH_3^+ + HSO_4^- + HS_2O_7^-. \tag{166}$$

He finds that as the composition of the medium is changed from aqueous sulphuric acid towards 100% H_2SO_4 the usual A2 mechanism, involving a bimolecular attack of a water molecule on the amide conjugate acid, is replaced by the A1 mechanism in which the rate determining step is the unimolecular heterolysis of the N-protonated amide

$$RC\overset{+}{\underset{\diagdown NHR}{\diagup OH}} \underset{\longleftarrow}{\overset{\text{Fast}}{\longrightarrow}} RC\underset{\overset{+}{NH_2R}}{\diagup O} \tag{167a}$$

$$RCONH_2R^+ \xrightarrow{\text{Slow}} RCO^+ + RNH_2 \tag{167b}$$

$$RNH_2 + H^+ \xrightarrow{\text{Fast}} RNH_3^+ \tag{167c}$$

$$RCO + H_2O \xrightarrow{\text{Fast}} RCO_2H^+. \tag{167d}$$

In order to explain the observation that addition of an acid such as $H_2S_2O_7$ or HSO_3Cl increases the rate while addition of a base such as water decreases the rate Leisten proposed that the reaction is subject to general acid catalysis as a consequence of the fact that step (c) occurs synchronously with step (a).

It has been shown by means of cryoscopic measurements that urea, urethane and N-methylurethane are monoprotonated in sulphuric acid (Holstead *et al.*, 1953). This conclusion has been confirmed in the case of urea by conductimetric measurements and it has also been shown that tetramethylurea is completely monoprotonated and is probably diprotonated to the extent of about 10% in a 0·05 M solution (T. Birchall, J. Gauldie and R. J. Gillespie, unpublished work).

D. ESTERS

The esters of carboxylic acids generally undergo hydrolysis in sulphuric acid. However a number of esters such as methyl and ethyl benzoate and ethyl acetate react only slowly at room temperature and freezing point measurements show that initially they are simply protonated. On pouring the sulphuric acid solutions onto ice the ester is recovered in good yield (Kothner, 1901; Hantzsch, 1907; Oddo and Scandola, 1910). It is generally assumed, but has not been proved, that protonation occurs on the carbonyl oxygen.

Graham (1943) showed that the hydrolysis of methyl benzoate is of zero order with respect to water in 98–100% sulphuric acid. He concluded that the reaction is unimolecular. Leisten (1956) has measured the rate cyroscopically in aqueous H_2SO_4, 100% H_2SO_4 and in dilute oleum. He showed that the first-order rate constant is independent of the initial concentration of the ester and therefore of the concentration of hydrogen sulphate ion, since methyl benzoate is ionized as a strong base. These results therefore eliminate the possibility of a rate-determining attack by hydrogen sulphate ion on the conjugate acid. The rates are similar in slightly aqueous acid and in 100% acid and a little greater in oleum, clearly indicating that water is not involved in the rate-determining step. Unimolecular heterolysis can proceed by either acyl–oxygen fission ($A_{AC}1$) or alkyl–oxygen fission ($A_{AL}1$).

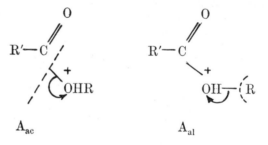

Electron-donating substituents in R′ should aid, and in R retard $A_{AC}1$ heterolysis but have the opposite effects on $A_{AL}1$ heterolysis. Conversely electron-attracting substituents in R′ should retard and in R aid the $A_{AC}1$ heterolysis but have contrary effects in the $A_{AL}1$ case. Graham (1943) found that the rate of hydrolysis of methyl p-toluate was four times that of methyl benzoate and concluded that the mechanism was $A_{AC}1$. Qualitative comparisons of rate have been made for a large number of esters by Kuhn and Corwin (1948) and by Bradley and Hill (1955) and all their results show the effects predicted for the $A_{AC}1$ mechanism. The rate of hydrolysis of alkyl benzoates varies in the following manner Me > Et < i–Pr < t–Bu indicating a change in mechanism between Et and i–Pr. Leisten showed that the introduction of a p-nitro group into ethyl benzoate leads to a sixtyfold decrease in rate whereas in the case of isopropyl benzoate it leads to a two hundredfold increase. Thus the change in mechanism in the hydrolysis of this series of esters is from $A_{AC}l$ in the case of methyl and ethyl benzoate to $A_{AL}l$ in the cases of isopropyl and tertbutyl benzoate. These esters give an initial ν value of 2·0 which increases as hydrolysis proceeds to a limiting value of 3·0. Thus the overall equation for the hydrolysis may be written

$$PhCO_2Me + 2H_2SO_4 = PhCO_2H_2^+ + HSO_4^- + MeHSO_4. \qquad (168)$$

By introducing sufficiently electron-attracting substituents in R it is possible to cause even the ethyl esters to hydrolyse by alkyl–oxygen fission. Thus it has been found that the rate of hydrolysis of their ethyl esters increases in the series p-nitro $<$ 4-chloro-3-nitro $<$ 3,5-dinitrobenzoic acid (Kershaw and Leisten, 1960)

Methyl mesitoate gives a constant ν-value of 5 (Treffers and Hammett, 1937) indicating that it undergoes rapid and complete hydrolysis, presumably by acyl–oxygen fission, to give a stable acyl ion.

$$C_6H_2Me_3CO_2Me + 2H_2SO_4 = C_6H_2Me_3CO^+ + H_3O^+ + MeHSO_4 + 2HSO_4^-. \qquad (169)$$

It is noteworthy that esters of mesitoic acid are hydrolysed only with great difficulty in aqueous solution. Their ionization in sulphuric acid consequently provides a useful method of hydrolysing such esters; the free acid is easily recovered by pouring the solution onto ice. The reverse process, the esterification of mesitoic and related acids which is difficult by normal methods can also be carried out conveniently by pouring a sulphuric acid solution into the required alcohol (Newman, 1940).

E. CARBOXYLIC ANHYDRIDES

Acetic and benzoic anhydrides give fourfold depressions of the freezing point of 100% sulphuric acid (Gillespie, 1950c), but in slightly aqueous sulphuric acid $\nu = 2$ (Leisten, 1955). Conductivity measurements indicate the formation of one hydrogen sulphate ion from each molecule of anhydride (Flowers et al., 1956). These results provide strong evidence for the following mode of ionization

$$(RCO)_2O + 3H_2SO_4 = 2RCO_2H_2^+ + HS_2O_7^- + HSO_4^- \qquad (170)$$

in 100% H_2SO_4 and

$$(RCO)_2O + H_2SO_4 + H_3O^+ = 2RCO_2H_2^+ + HSO_4^- \qquad (171)$$

in aqueous sulphuric acid.

Phthalic anhydride gives a freezing point depression in 100% sulphuric acid that is only 10–15% greater than for a non-electrolyte (Hantzsch, 1907; Oddo and Casalino, 1917a; Leisten, 1960) and conductivity measurements show that it gives 1·14–1·18 hydrogen sulphate ions (Flowers *et al.*, 1956a). This is very probably due to incomplete protonation. However in slightly aqueous sulphuric acid it produces a much smaller freezing point depression because of conversion to protonated phthalic acid (Leisten, 1961).

$$\text{(structure)}\ \text{CO}{>}\text{O} + \text{H}_3\text{O}^+ = \text{(structure)}\ \text{CO}_2\text{H}_2^+ , \text{C}_2\text{OH} \tag{172}$$

Complete conversion to the conjugate acid of phthalic acid would give $\nu = 0$. Phthalic acid gives a slightly greater than twofold depression of the freezing point of slightly aqueous sulphuric acid as a consequence of the formation of its conjugate acid

$$\text{(structure)}\ \text{CO}_2\text{H}, \text{CO}_2\text{H} + \text{H}_2\text{SO}_4 \rightarrow \text{(structure)}\ \text{CO}_2\text{H}_2^+, \text{CO}_2\text{H} + \text{HSO}_4^- \tag{173}$$

and possibly some further slight protonation on the second carboxyl group. However in sulphuric acid containing HSO_4^- and HS_2O_7^- phthalic acid gives ν-values of only slightly greater than unity (Leisten, 1961) because HS_2O_7^- dehydrates the acid to give the anhydride,

$$\text{(structure)}\ \text{CO}_2\text{H}, \text{CO}_2\text{H} + \text{HS}_2\text{O}_7^- = \text{(structure)}\ \text{CO}{>}\text{O} + \text{HSO}_4^- + \text{H}_2\text{SO}_4 \tag{174}$$

for which $\nu = 1$ if no further protonation occurs. Clearly the equilibrium between the acid and the anhydride is critically balanced in the region of 100% sulphuric acid and a slight excess of water shifts the equilibrium to the acid side while a slight excess of sulphur trioxide shifts it to the anhydride side. Maleic acid and anhydride behave in a similar manner. Succinic acid also behaves similarly except that the second stage of protonation of the acid is about 50% complete and the anhydride is also about 50% converted to its conjugate acid in sulphuric acid containing small amounts of HSO_4^- (Leisten, 1961).

F. ETHERS

Aliphatic ethers behave as strong or moderately strong bases in sulphuric acid giving initial ν-values of two or less (Oddo and Scandola, 1910; Gillespie and Leisten, 1954; Jaques and Leisten, 1961). Such solutions are however not generally stable and the freezing point of the solution decreases. In the case of diethyl and certain other aliphatic ethers Oddo and Scandola (1910) were able to isolate small quantities of the corresponding alkyl hydrogen sulphates after the ethers had stood for a short time in solution in sulphuric acid. This result and the fact that the ν-value eventually reaches a constant limiting value of approximately four indicates that complete solvolysis occurs according to the equation

$$RR'O + 3H_2SO_4 = RHSO_4 + R'HSO_4 + H_3O^+ + HSO_4^-. \qquad (175)$$

From the rate of variation of ν with time rates of solvolysis have been obtained for a number of ethers (Jaques and Leisten, 1961). The results are consistent with a mechanism in which the rate-determining step is a unimolecular fission of the conjugate acid or of some other ether–solvent complex to produce the more stable of the two possible carbonium ions. Somewhat surprisingly the rate of solvolysis is reduced by added hydrogen sulphate and even more by added water. If the complex undergoing unimolecular fission were the conjugate acid, hydrogen sulphates and water should both have the same effect. Therefore the following pre-equilibrium has been postulated (Jaques and Leisten, 1961) in order to account for the solvent effects

$$RR'OH^+ + SO_3 \rightleftharpoons RR'SO_4H^+ \qquad (176)$$

followed by

$$R\overset{\frown}{-}O-R' \rightarrow R^+ + R'SO_4H \qquad (177)$$
$$\underset{SO_3H}{|}$$

The carbonium ion formed by the heterolysis unites rapidly with a hydrogen sulphate ion. The observed solvent effects would be expected for this mechanism because the solvent-self-dissociation in which SO_3 is formed

$$2H_2SO_4 = SO_3 + HSO_4^- + H_3O^+ \qquad (178)$$

is repressed more strongly by water than by hydrogen sulphate ion alone. Preliminary experiments on aryl alkyl ethers have indicated that in some cases at least the mechanism is different and it is the conjugate acid that undergoes heterolysis (Jaques and Leisten, 1961). However, in view of the fact that at low temperatures in fluorosulphuric acid anisole has been shown to protonate on an aromatic carbon rather than on oxygen, further studies are clearly needed before the nature and mechanism of the reaction of aromatic ethers with sulphuric acid are established with certainty.

G. NITRILES

Hantzsch (1908) found by means of cryoscopic measurement that nitriles are not completely ionized in sulphuric acid. This conclusion has recently been confirmed by conductometric measurements and dissociation constants of 0·16 and 0·07 have been obtained for acetonitrile and benzonitrile respectively (Liler and Kosanovic, 1958). However solutions of these nitriles are not stable and hydrolysis to the corresponding amide occurs

$$RCN + 2H_2SO_4 = RCONH_2 + H_2S_2O_7. \qquad (179)$$

The rates of the reactions were followed by measuring the change in the conductivity of the solutions (Liler and Kosanovic, 1958). In both cases the hydrolysis was found to be second order and it was concluded that the rate determining step in the reaction is the attack of HSO_4^- ions on the conjugate acid of the nitrile

$$RCNH^+ + HSO_4^- = RCONH_2 + SO_3. \qquad (180)$$

H. CARBOXYLIC ACIDS

Most aliphatic and many aromatic carboxylic acids behave as fully ionized simple bases (Hantzsch, 1907; Oddo and Casalino, 1917b; Gillespie and Leisten, 1954). However electron-withdrawing substituents can reduce the basicity so that ionization is incomplete. Thus although acetic acid is a strong base, dichloracetic acid is a weak electrolyte and trichloracetic acid is a non-electrolyte (Gillespie and Wasif, 1953c).

Some substituted benzoic acids, e.g. mesitoic acid, undergo a complex ionization involving the elimination of water and the formation of a stable acyl ion (Treffers and Hammett, 1937)

$$Me_3C_6H_2CO_2H + 2H_2SO_4 = Me_3C_6H_2CO^+ + H_3O^+ + 2HSO_4^-. \qquad (181)$$

Mesitoic acid has $\nu = 4$, and $\gamma = 2$ (Treffers and Hammett, 1937; R. J. Gillespie and E. A. Robinson, unpublished results); on dilution of the sulphuric acid solution with water the acid is obtained and on dilution with methanol the methyl ester is obtained. Other acids, for example, 2,3,5,6-tetramethyl- and pentamethylbenzoic acids, behave in the same way (Newman and Deno, 1951a). 2,6-Dimethylbenzoic acid and 3,5-dibromo-2,4,6-trimethylbenzoic acid, which give $\nu = 3.5$ and 2.4 respectively, are believed to ionize partly in the above "complex" manner and partly as simple bases. A very similar type of ionization has been observed for certain aromatic keto-acids. For example, o-benzoylbenzoic acid has a ν-value of 4, which has been considered to indicate the following ionization (Newman et al., 1945):

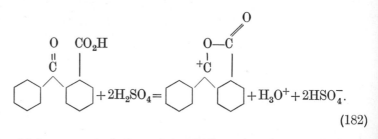

$$\qquad\qquad\qquad\qquad\qquad\qquad\qquad\qquad\qquad (182)$$

Other acids which appear to behave in a similar manner are o-mesitoyl-benzoic, 1,8-naphthaldehydic, and 4,5-phenanthaldehydic acid (Newman et al., 1945).

A number of carboxylic acids are unstable in sulphuric acid and decompose to give carbon monoxide

$$RCO_2H + 2H_2SO_4 = R^+ + CO + H_3O^+ + 2HSO_4^- \qquad (183)$$

e.g. formic acid

$$HCO_2H + H_2SO_4 = CO + H_3O^+ + HSO_4^- \qquad (184)$$

oxalic acid

$$(CO_2H)_2 + 2H_2SO_4 = CO + CO_2 + H_3O^+ + HSO_4^- \qquad (185)$$

α-keto acids

$$PhCO.CO_2H + 2H_2SO_4 = PhCO_2H_2^+ + CO + HSO_4^- \qquad (186)$$

α-hydroxy-acids

$$\begin{array}{c} CH_2CO_2H \\ | \\ CH(OH)CO_2H \end{array} + 2H_2SO_4 = \begin{array}{c} CH_2CO_2H \\ | \\ CH(OH)^+ \\ | \quad -H^+ \\ \downarrow \\ CH_2CO_2H \\ | \\ CHO \end{array} + H_3O^+ + CO + 2HSO_4^- \qquad (187)$$

and triphenylacetic acid, diphenyl acetic acid, and bis-(p-chlorophenyl)-acetic acid (Welch and Smith, 1953; Gillespie and Leisten, 1954). Dicyclohexylacetic acid and 2,4,6-trimethylcyclohexane carboxylic acid also evolve carbon monoxide but the other products of the reactions have not been identified (Welch and Smith, 1953). The kinetics of the decompositions have been studied in the case of formic (de Right, 1933), oxalic (Lichty, 1907; Wiig, 1930; Liler, 1963), citric (Wiig, 1930), benzoylformic (Elliot and Hammick, 1951), triphenylacetic (Dittmar, 1929), and malic acids (Whitford, 1925). In each case the reaction is first order with respect to the organic compound and the rate decreases with increasing water content of the solvent. Liler (1963) has studied the decomposition of oxalic acid by means of conductimetric measurements. The initial conductivities enabled the degree of ionization of oxalic acid to be determined and the results agree well with previous cryoscopic measurements which showed that oxalic acid is only about 30% protonated (Oddo and Casalino, 1917b; Wiles, 1953). The decomposition rates obtained by Liler agree well with those found earlier by using a permanganate titration to follow the reaction (Lichty, 1907). She found that the rate of decomposition is proportional to the concentration diprotonated oxalic acid rather than proportional to the concentration of the monoprotonated species. Hence she concluded that the reaction occurs by a unimolecular decomposition of the diprotonated species which is present at very low concentration. On the basis of his observation that the slope of the plot of the logarithm of the rate constant against H_0 was approximately equal to two, Hammett had previously come to the same conclusion (Hammett, 1940).

I. CARBONIUM IONS

1. *Aromatic Hydrocarbon Conjugate Acids and Positive Ions*

Carbonium ions have been obtained by protonation and by oxidation of aromatic hydrocarbons in sulphuric acid although other reactions such as sulphonation and dealkylation also often occur. Thus mesitylene is sulphonated (Deno *et al.*, 1959) and hexamethylbenzene (Leisten, 1964b) undergoes simultaneous demethylation and sulphonation; they both give the same product, namely mesitylene trisulphonic acid. However anthracene and 3,4-benzpyrene give the stable conjugate acids XXXIV and XXXV (Gold and Tye, 1952). More extensive studies of the protonation of aromatic hydrocarbons have been carried out in other acidic solvents such as HF and HSO_3F under conditions where more stable solutions can be obtained than in sulphuric acid (McCauley and Lier, 1951; Reid, 1954; Dallinga *et al.*, 1958; Mackor *et al.*, 1958; MacClean and Mackor, 1961, 1962; Birchall and Gillespie, 1964).

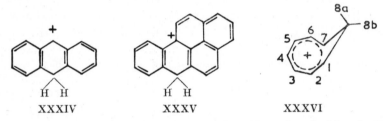

XXXIV   XXXV   XXXVI

Cyclo-octatetraene dissolves in 98% sulphuric acid to give the bicyclo-(5,10)-octadienyl cation (von Rosenberg *et al.*, 1962). The n.m.r. spectrum suggests that the cation has the structure XXXVI as the H_{2-6} signals occur in the aromatic region, the H_1 and H_7 signals are at abnormally low field and H_{8a} is highly shielded, presumably, in view of its position above the ring, by the ring current effect.

Electron spin resonance measurements have shown that radical cations are formed in dilute solutions by oxidation of hydrocarbons such as anthracene, napthacene, and perylene in sulphuric acid (Weissman *et al.*, 1956; Carrington *et al.*, 1959). 9-Methyl and 9,10-dimethyl anthracene are oxidized to the corresponding cations by persulphate in sulphuric acid but xylene is oxidized to 2,5-dimethylbenzosemiquinone (Bolton and Carrington, 1961; Brivati *et al.*, 1961). This latter radical can also be prepared by the reduction of a sulphuric acid solution of the quinone with sodium dithionate (Bolton and Carrington, 1961). The relation of these results to the spectroscopic results which show that anthracene is converted to its conjugate acid is not clear. Possibly the major product is the conjugate acid and only a rather small amount of this is converted to the radical ion. It has indeed been pointed out that the ability of a hydrocarbon to form a positive ion in sulphuric acid follows the ease of protonation (Kon and Blois, 1958) and it has been suggested that this can be understood in terms of the following sequence of reactions

$$A + H_2SO_4 = AH^+ + HSO_4^- \tag{188a}$$

$$AH^+ + A = AH + A^+ \tag{188b}$$

$$AH + 2H_2SO_4 = A^+ + 2H_2O + SO_2 + HSO_4^-. \tag{188c}$$

However there is no real evidence in support of this mechanism.

2. Tri-aryl Carbonium Ions

It has long been known that when triphenyl methanol is dissolved in sulphuric acid it ionizes according to the equation

$$Ph_3COH + 2H_2SO_4 = Ph_3C^+ + H_3O^+ + 2HSO_4^- \tag{189}$$

to give a stable yellow solution. This mode of ionization is demonstrated by the absorption spectrum of the solution which is very similar to that of the electrically conducting solution of triphenyl methyl chloride in sulphur dioxide (Hantzsch, 1921; Gold and Hawes, 1951), by freezing point depression measurements which give $\nu = 4$ (Hantzsch, 1908; Oddo and Scandola, 1909b), and by the reaction of the sulphuric acid solution with alcohols to form ethers

$$Ph_3C^+ + ROH = Ph_3C.OR + H^+. \tag{190}$$

The tri-p-methyl, tri-p-chloro and tri-p-nitro derivatives of triphenyl-methanol have also been shown to ionize in the same manner (Newman and Deno, 1951b). In the case of the tri-amino and tris-p-dimethylamino derivatives it was found that the carbonium ion is formed but only two of the three amino groups are protonated (Newman and Deno, 1951b). It appears therefore that in these cases the carbonium ion is best represented by the quinonoid structure XXXVII.

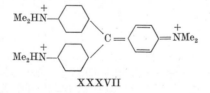

XXXVII

3. Di-aryl Carbonium Ions

A number of stable carbonium ions of this type can be prepared by dissolving the corresponding alcohol or olefin in sulphuric acid. For example

$$Ph_2C{=}CH_2 + H_2SO_4 = Ph_2\overset{+}{C}.CH_3 + HSO_4^- \tag{191}$$

$$Ph_2C\begin{array}{c} OH \\ \diagdown \\ CH_3 \end{array} + H_2SO_4 = Ph_2\overset{+}{C}.CH_3 + H_3O^+ + 2HSO_4^-. \quad (192)$$

Thus 1,1-diphenyl ethylene gives an initial twofold depression of the freezing point of sulphuric acid and diphenylmethyl carbinol gives an initial fourfold depression (Gold and Tye, 1952). The cations are not completely stable as the freezing points of the solutions decrease somewhat with time. The ultra-violet spectra of the sulphuric acid solutions of 1,1-diphenylethylene and triphenylethylene, and anthracene were found to be very similar with peaks at 2050–3150 and at 4250–4350Å. This similarity is easily understood if the species obtained in the three cases are protonated at those positions which simple-molecular orbital calculations predict would yield the most stable classical ion, i.e.

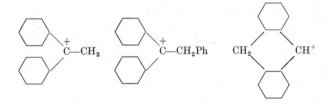

Di-*p*-chlorophenylmethylcarbinol and di-*p*-chlorophenylcarbinol and di-mesityl carbinol all give $\nu = 4$, and hence form the corresponding carbonium ions although in the latter case the solution is not completely stable; probably sulphonation occurs (Newman and Deno, 1951b). Diphenyl carbinol also gives an initial ν-value of somewhat greater than four, indicating carbonium ion formation, but rather rapid reaction with the solvent, presumably sulphonation, occurs (Welch and Smith, 1950). Somewhat more stable solutions may be prepared by dissolving the benzhydrol in carbon tetra-chloride and extracting with sulphuric acid. Solutions prepared in this way, on pouring into water, methanol, and glacial acetic acid, give dibenzhydryl ether, methylbenzyhdryl ether and benzhydryl acetate respectively (Welch and Smith, 1950).

4. *Mono-aryl Carbonium Ions*

Benzyl alcohol was first shown by Cannizzaro (1854) to yield a pink insoluble polymer in sulphuric acid. *p*-Chlorobenzyl alcohol similarly gives a red polymer. Heptamethyl benzyl alcohol and α,α,2,4,6-pentamethyl-benzylalcohol give ν-values which vary rapidly with time but, by extra-polation to zero time, initial values of approximately four have been obtained (Newman and Deno, 1951b). On dilution, a sulphuric acid solution of α,α,2,4,6-pentamethylbenzyl alcohol gives 2-mesitylpropylene in a yield which decreases with the time of solution. There is evidence that sulphonation occurs to give water-soluble products. The mesityldimethyl carbonium ion that is formed in this way is also obtained when α,2,4,6-tetramethylstyrene is dissolved in sulphuric acid. In this case extrapolation to zero time gave the expected ν-value of approximately two. Although cryoscopic work indicates that all mono-aryl carbonium ions and most di-aryl carbonium ions are unstable in sulphuric acid solution, and undergo sulphonation or polymerization, several workers have claimed that stable solutions of a wide variety of di-aryl and mono-aryl carbonium ions can be prepared by suitable procedures which keep the concentrations of all species with which the carbonium ion might react to a minimum. The best procedure appears to be to dilute an acetic acid solution of the appropriate alcohol with excess sulphuric acid or to extract a cyclohexane solution with a large excess of sulphuric acid (Grace and Symons, 1959; Williams, 1962). Unfortunately the solutions prepared in this way are too dilute to enable confirmatory cryoscopic or conductimetric measurements to be made. The only evidence that carbonium ions are in fact formed in these solutions is the observation that all the solutions have an absorption band in the visible ultra-violet spectrum at approximately 400 mμ. Grace and Symons (1959) obtained rather high extinction coefficients of approximately 10^4 but Williams (1962) has pointed out that the extinction coefficient is not independent of concentration and he gives values for most carbonium ions that are much smaller than those obtained by Grace and Symons.

Deno et $al.$ (1959, 1960) attempted to obtain solutions in aqueous sulphuric acid of a number of mono-aryl carbonium ions. They observed the characteristic absorption at 400 mμ but none of the solutions were stable and this absorption disappeared rather rapidly in many cases. They found that pentamethyl benzyl alcohol disproportionates to hexamethylbenzene and pentamethylbenzaldehyde.

5. Dipositive Carbonium Ions

Cryoscopic measurements on sulphuric acid solutions of tetraphenyl-p-xylene glycol and tetraphenylphthalein are consistent with their ionization to form dipositive carbonium ions (Hart et $al.$, 1963).

$$(C_6H_5)_2C \overset{|}{\underset{OH}{}} \!\!\!\!\!\!\!\!\! -\!\!\!\bigcirc\!\!\!- \!\!\! C(C_6H_5)_2 \overset{|}{\underset{OH}{}} + 4H_2SO_4 = (C_6H_5)_2 \overset{+}{C} -\!\!\!\bigcirc\!\!\!- \overset{+}{C}(C_6H_5)_2$$
$$+ 2H_3O^+ + 4HSO_4^- \qquad (193)$$

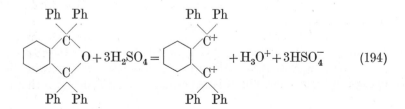

$$+ H_3O^+ + 3HSO_4^- \qquad (194)$$

On dilution of the sulphuric acid solutions with water the original compounds are recovered. Solutions of tetraphenyl-*o*-xylene glycol and the *meta* compound have absorption spectra that are very similar to that of the *para* compound and the solutions of the *meta* compound gives the glycol on dilution while the solution of the *ortho* compound gives tetraphenylphthalein. It is therefore concluded that these compounds also give the corresponding dipositive carbonium ions.

Hart and Fish (1958, 1960, 1961) have claimed that another type of dipositive carbonium ion, which they call an extraordinary dipositive carbonium ion, is obtained when trichloromethylpolymethylbenzenes are dissolved in sulphuric acid. For example in the case of trichloromethyl-mesitylene they obtained a *v*-factor of five and other evidence which they interpreted as indicating ionization according to the equation

$$(CH_3)_3C_6H_2CCl_3 + 2H_2SO_4 = CH_3^+ \langle\rangle = \overset{+}{C}\text{-}Cl + 2HCl + 2HSO_4^-. \quad (195)$$

However this interpretation ignores the reaction of HCl with sulphuric acid to give chlorosulphuric acid (Section III I)

$$HCl + 2H_2SO_4 = HClSO_3 + H_3O^+ + HSO_4^-. \quad (196)$$

Re-investigation (Gillespie and Robinson, 1964, and unpublished results) has shown that a monopositive and not a dipositive carbonium ion is in fact formed.

$$(CH_3)_3C_6H_2CCl_3 + 3H_2SO_4 = CH_3 \langle\rangle \overset{+}{-}CCl_2 + HClSO_3 + H_3O^+ + 2HSO_4^- \quad (197)$$

6. *Aliphatic Carbonium Ions*

The allylic cation XXXVIII is formed by adding a mixture of the dienes XXXIXa and XXXIXb to concentrated sulphuric acid. This is shown by the twofold depression of the freezing point and the n.m.r. spectrum of the solutions which has four bands with chemical shifts from tetramethyl silane of 1·98, 6·67, 6·93 and 9·79 p.p.m. and relative areas of 1 : 4 : 6 : 6 (Deno *et al.*, 1962a).

Tricyclopropylcarbinol gives an initial *v*-value of four in sulphuric acid and the alcohol is recovered in 63% yield on dilution with ice (Deno *et al.*, 1962b). It has been suggested that these results indicate the formation of the tri-cyclopropylcarbonium ion. It is somewhat surprising however that the n.m.r.

spectrum consists of a single line only. The solution has a maximum ultra-violet absorption at 270 mμ (Deno *et al.*, 1962b).

But-1-ene, but-2-ene, pent-1-ene and pent-2-ene all dissolve in concentrated sulphuric acid ($>75\%$) and on dilution secondary hydrogen sulphates are obtained (Norris and Jouber, 1927). Isobutylene, trimethylethylene and 2-methyl but-1-ene dissolve readily in acid as dilute as 60% and dilution with water produces tertiary alcohols, although this may be due to rapid hydrolysis of the tertiary hydrogen sulphate originally formed. It seems likely therefore that in 100% sulphuric acid, olefins in general dissolve initially to form alkyl hydrogen sulphates. In all cases except that of ethylene, which gives the stable ethyl hydrogen sulphate, subsequent oxidation and polymerization reactions occur. However these polymerization reactions, and the alkylation of paraffins and aromatic hydrocarbons by olefins that takes place in the presence of sulphuric acid, strongly suggest that alkyl carbonium ions are formed by the ionization of alkyl hydrogen sulphates in sulphuric acid but there is no evidence to indicate that the degree of ioniza-tion is large.

XXXVIII XXXIXa XXXIXb

Ethanol gives a constant ν-value of 3 and $\gamma = 1$, indicating the formation of ethyl hydrogen sulphate, (Oddo and Scandola, 1909b; Gillespie, 1950b; Gillespie and Wasif, 1953c). n-Propyl and other straight chain primary alcohols give initially pale yellow solutions and an approximately threefold depression of the freezing point, indicating the formation of the alkyl hyd-rogen sulphate (Hantzsch, 1908). The ν-values however increase markedly with time and obvious subsequent reactions occur leading to a deepening of the colour of the solutions to a dark red or brown, the evolution of sulphur dioxide, and the separation of a colourless hydrocarbon layer. Some branched chain alcohols give initial ν-values between 2 and 3 which increase rapidly with time because of similar reactions to those that occur with most of the straight chain alcohols. Tertiary alcohols give initial ν-values of approxi-mately two (Hantzsch, 1908; Oddo and Scandola, 1909b; Newman *et al.*, 1949). This has generally in the past been attributed to oxonium ion formation. However recent work (Leisten, 1961a), which showed that in an H_2SO_4–$HS_2O_7^-$–HSO_4^- solvent the initial freezing point depression is very small, confirms a different interpretation that was first suggested by the results of studies in methanesulphonic acid (Craig *et al.*, 1950) namely that t-butanol is immediately dehydrated and polymerized

$$C_4H_9OH + H_2SO_4 = 1/n(C_4H_8)_n + H_3O^+ + HSO_4^-. \qquad (198)$$

By preparing very dilute solutions of olefins or alcohols by the method that was originally used for arylolefins and alcohols Rosenbaum and Symons (1960) have claimed that stable solutions of tertiary alkyl carbonium ions can be formed. Their evidence is that for alcohols and halides an intense absorption band at 293 mμ develops over a period of up to seven days, and that the same band develops very rapidly for most olefins. They attribute this band to the alkylcarbonium ion as they were unable to detect the formation of any sulphur dioxide or of any of a large number of possible oxidation products. Deno *et al.* (1959), claim that the species formed are alkenyl cations.

7. *Polyenes*

The higher polyenes dissolve in sulphuric acid to give coloured solutions, the intensity of the colour increasing with increasing chain length (Kuhn and Winterstein, 1928). It has recently been claimed that 1,6-diphenyl-hexatriene is immediately oxidized in 100% H_2SO_4 to the corresponding dipositive ion (M^{2+}) (de Boer and van der Meij, 1962). However Leisten and Walton (1963) have shown by means of cryoscopic experiments that sulphur dioxide is not an important product of the reaction and that two moles of water are formed per mole of hexatriene. They therefore conclude that the product is a protonated hexatriene disulphonic acid formed according to the equation

$$C_6H_5.CH=CH.CH=CH=CH.C_6H_5+3H_2SO_4$$
$$\rightarrow [SO_3H.C_6H_4.(CH)_6C_6H_4.SO_3H]H^+. \qquad (199)$$

The site of protonation was not established.

J. AROMATIC SULPHONATION

Ingold (1953b) has discussed work on aromatic sulphonation prior to 1953 and has concluded that the kinetics in slightly aqueous sulphuric acid are consistent with SO_3 as the reactive species, rather than $H_3SO_4^+$, HSO_3^+, or S_2O_6, since the rate of sulphonation varies as the first power of the concentration of the aromatic compound and as the inverse square of the concentration of water. Brand and co-workers (Brand, 1950; Brand and Horning, 1952; Brand *et al.*, 1959) have studied aromatic sulphonation by sulphuric acid over a wide range of solvent composition from aqueous acid to oleum and have shown that for a number of solutes the variation of the first order rate constant with solvent composition varies almost linearly with $-H_0+\log a_{SO_3}$, where H_0 is the Hammett acidity function of the solvent and a_{SO_3} is the activity of sulphur trioxide. The possibility that the reactive species is HSO_3^+ was eliminated on the grounds of a slower rate of sulphonation in deuterated solvent than in proto-solvent, because their spectrometric measurements led to the conclusion that DSO_3^+ should be more abundant in D_2SO_4 than HSO_3^+ would be in H_2SO_4. However it has been shown conductimetrically that m-nitrotoluene is less ionized in D_2SO_4 than in H_2SO_4 (Flowers et al., 1958) and it has been shown recently that D_2SO_4 is probably a weaker acid and a weaker base than H_2SO_4 (Hall and Robinson, 1964), so that their argument may not be sound. However their conclusion that HSO_3^+ is not the reactive species is probably correct as SO_3 is a very weak base. For example, SO_3 gives a non-conducting solution in fluorosulphuric acid, which is a considerably stronger acid than sulphuric acid (Barr et al., 1964). Thus the concentration of the protonated species must be exceedingly small in slightly aqueous sulphuric acid or dilute oleum so that it is improbable that it is the reagent involved in sulphonation in these media. The mechanism of the reaction may be written as follows:

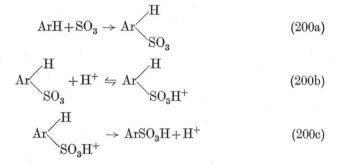

$$ArH + SO_3 \rightarrow Ar\begin{matrix} H \\ SO_3 \end{matrix} \qquad (200a)$$

$$Ar\begin{matrix} H \\ SO_3 \end{matrix} + H^+ \rightleftharpoons Ar\begin{matrix} H \\ SO_3H^+ \end{matrix} \qquad (200b)$$

$$Ar\begin{matrix} H \\ SO_3H^+ \end{matrix} \rightarrow ArSO_3H + H^+ \qquad (200c)$$

REFERENCES

Adie, R. H. (1890) *J. chem. Soc.* **57**, 450.
Anderson, H. H. (1950) *J. Amer. chem. Soc.* **72**, 194.
Arotsky, J., Mishra, H. C. and Symons, M. C. R. (1962) *J. chem. Soc.*, 2582.
Baker, W. and Field, F. B. (1932) *J. chem. Soc.* 86.
Barr, J., Gillespie, R. J. and Robinson, E. A. (1961) *Can. J. Chem.* **39**, 1266.
Barr, J., Gillespie, R. J. and Thompson, R. C. (1964) *Inorg. Chem.* (in the press).
Barraclough, C. G., and Tobe, M. L. (1961) *J. chem. Soc.* 1993.
Bass, S. J. and Gillespie, R. J. (1960) *J. chem. Soc.* 814.
Bass, S. J., Gillespie, R. J. and Oubridge, J. V. (1960b) *J. chem. Soc.* 837.
Bass, S. J., Gillespie, R. J. and Robinson, E. A. (1960c) *J. chem. Soc.* 821.
Bass, S. J., Flowers, R. H., Gillespie, R. J., Robinson, E. A. and Solomons, S. (1960a) *J. chem. Soc.* 4315.
Berger, A., Lowenstein, A. and Meirboum, S. (1959) *J. Amer. chem. Soc.* **81**, 62.
Bergius, F. (1910) *Z. physikal. chem.* **72**, 338.
Birchall, T. and Gillespie, R. J. (1963) *Canad. J. Chem.* **41**, 2642.
Birchall, T. and Gillespie, R. J. (1964) *Canad. J. Chem.* **42**, 502.
Bolton, J. R. and Carrington, A. (1961) *Proc. chem. Soc.* 385.
Bradley, A. and Hill, M. E. (1955) *J. Amer. chem. Soc.* **77**, 1575.
Brand, J. C. D. (1946) *J. chem. Soc.* 585.
Brand, J. C. D. (1950a) *J. chem. Soc.* 997.
Brand, J. C. D. (1950b) *J. chem. Soc.* 1004.

Brand, J. C. D. and Horning, W. C. (1952) *J. chem. Soc.* 3922.

Brand, J. C. D., Horning, W. C. and Thornley, M. B. (1952) *J. chem. Soc.* 1374.

Brand, J. C. D., James, J. C. and Rutherford, A. (1953) *J. chem. Soc.* 2447.

Brand, J. C. D., Jarvie, A. W. P. and Horning, W. C. (1959) *J. chem. Soc.* 3844.

Brauner, B. (1889) *J. chem. Soc.* **55**, 382.

Brauner, B. (1894) *Z. anorg. chem.* **7**, 11.

Brayford, J. R. and Wyatt, P. A. H. (1955) *J. chem. Soc.* 2453.

Brivati, J. A., Hulme, R. and Symons, M. C. R. (1961) *Proc. chem. Soc.* 384.

Brubaker, C. H. (1955) *J. Amer. chem. Soc.* **77**, 3265.

Bunton, C. A., Figgis, B. N. and Nayak, B. (1962) *In* "Advances in Molecular Spectroscopy", Vol. I, p. 209. Pergamon Press, Oxford.

Cannizzaro, S., von (1854) *Ann. der Chem.* **92**, 113.

Carrington, A., Dravieko, F. and Symons, M. C. R. (1959) *J. chem. Soc.* 947.

Chedin, J. (1936) *C. R. Acad. Sci., Paris* **292**, 220.

Chedin, J. (1937) *Ann. Chim.* **8**, 243.

Chretien, P. (1895) *Ann. chim. Phys.* **15**, 367.

Chretien, P. (1896) *C. R. Acad. Sci., Paris* **123**, 814.

Clark, H. C. and O'Brien, R. J. (1963) *Inorg. Chem.* **2**, 1020.

Clark, H. C., O'Brien, R. J. and Trotter, J. (1963) *Proc. chem. Soc.* 85.

Coates, G. E. (1960) *In* "Organometallic Compounds", p. 184. Wiley, New York.

Couture, A. M. and Laidler, K. J. (1956) *Canad. J. Chem.* **34**, 1209.

Craig, R. A., Garrett, A. B. and Newman, M. S. (1950) *J. Amer. chem. Soc.* **72**, 163.

Dacre, B. and Wyatt, P. A. H. (1961) *J. chem. Soc.* 568.

Dallinga, G., Mackor, E. L. and Verrigin Stuart, A. A. (1958) *Mol. Phys.* **1**, 123.

d'Arcy, R. H. (1889) *J. chem. Soc.* **55**, 159.

Dasent, W. E. and Waddington, T. C. (1960) *J. chem. Soc.* 3350.

Davison, A., McFarlane, W., Pratt, L. and Wilkinson, G. (1962a) *J. chem. Soc.* 3653.

Davison, A., McFarlane, W., Pratt, L. and Wilkinson, G. (1962b) *J. chem. Soc.* 4821.

Deans, F. B. and Eaborn, C. (1959) *J. chem. Soc.* 2299, 2303.

de Boer, E. and van der Meij, P. H. (1962) *J. chem. Soc.* 139.

Deno, N. C. and Taft, R. W. (1954) *J. Amer. chem. Soc.* **76**, 244.

Deno, N. C., Groves, P. T. and Saires, G. (1959) *J. Amer. chem. Soc.* **81**, 5790.

Deno, N. C., Groves, P. T., Jarvzelski, J. J. and Lugash, M. N. (1960) *J. Amer. chem. Soc.* **82**, 4719.

Deno, N. C., Richey, H. G., Hodge, J. D. and Wisotsky, M. J. (1962a) *J. Amer. chem. Soc.* **84**, 1498.

Deno, N. C., Richey, H. G., Lia, J. S., Hodge, J. D., Houser, J. J. and Wisotsky, M. J. (1962b) *J. Amer. chem. Soc.* **84**, 2016.

de Right, R. E. (1933) *J. Amer. chem. Soc.* **55**, 4761.

Dittmar, H. R. (1929) *J. Phys. chem.* **33**, 533.

Dolezalek, F. and Finkh, K. (1960a) *Z. anorg. chem.* **50**, 82.

Dolezalek, F. and Finkh, K. (1906b) *Z. anorg. chem.* **51**, 320.

Druce, J. G. F. (1924) *Chem. News.* **128**, 33. *C.A.* **18**, 976.

Edwards, J. O. Morrison, G. C., Ross, V. F. and Schultz, J. W. (1955) *J. Amer. chem. Soc.* **77**, 166.

Elbs, K. and Fischer, F. (1901) *Z. elektrochem.* **7**, 343.

Elliott, W. W. and Hammick, D. L. (1951) *J. chem. Soc.*, 3402.

Esch, W. (1903) *Chem. Ztg.* **27**, 297.

Evans, R. V. G. and Gibson, C. S. (1941) *J. chem. Soc.* 109.

Flexser, L. A. and Hammett, L. P. (1938) *J. Amer. chem. Soc.* **60**, 885.

Flexser, L. A., Hammett, L. P. and Dingwall, A. (1935) *J. Amer. chem. Soc.* **57**, 2103.

Flowers, R. H., Gillespie, R. J., and Oubridge J. V. (1956a) *J. chem. Soc.* 607.

Flowers, R. H., Gillespie, R. J. and Oubridge, J. V. (1956b) *J. chem. Soc.* 1925.

Flowers, R. H., Gillespie, R. J. and Robinson, E. A. (1959) *J. inorg. and nuclear Chem.* **9**, 155.

Flowers, R. H., Gillespie, R. J. and Robinson, E. A. (1960a) *J. chem. Soc.* 845.

Flowers, R. H., Gillespie, R. J. and Robinson, E. A. (1960b) *Canad. J. Chem.* **58**, 1363.

Flowers, R. H., Gillespie, R. J., Oubridge, J. V. and Solomons, S. (1958) *J. chem. Soc.* 667.

Flowers, R. H., Gillespie, R. J. and Robinson, E. A. (1963) *Canad. J. Chem.* **41**, 2464.

Flowers, R. H., Gillespie, R. J. and Wasif, S. (1956) *J. chem. Soc.* 607.

Flowers, R. H., Gillespie, R. J., Robinson, E. A. and Solomons, C. (1960c) *J. chem. Soc.* 4327.

Gable, C. M., Betz, H. F. and Marron, S. H. (1950) *J. Amer. chem. Soc.* **72**, 1445.

Giauque, W. F., Horning, E. E., Kunzler, J. E. and Rubin, T. R. (1952) *J. Amer. chem. Soc.* **74**, 62.

Giguere, P. A. and Savoie, R. (1960) *Canad. J. Chem.* **38**, 2467.

Giguere, P. A. and Savoie, R. (1963) *J. Amer. chem. Soc.* **85**, 287.

Gilbert, L. F., Buckley, H. and Masson, I. (1922) *J. chem. Soc.*, 1934.

Gillespie, R. J. (1950a) *J. chem. Soc.* 2493.

Gillespie, R. J. (1950b) *J. chem. Soc.* 2516.

Gillespie, R. J. (1950c) *J. chem. Soc.* 2542.

Gillespie, R. J. (1950d) *J. chem. Soc.* 2997.

Gillespie, R. J. (1959) *Rev. Pure and Applied Chem. (Australia)*, **9**, 1.

Gillespie, R. J. (1960) *J. chem. Soc.* 2516.

Gillespie, R. J. and Birchall, T. (1963) *Canad. J. Chem.* **41**, 148.

Gillespie, R. J. and Cole, R. H. (1956) *Trans Faraday Soc.* **52**, 1325.

Gillespie, R. J. and Graham, J. (1950) *J. chem. Soc.* 2532.

Gillespie, R. J. and Leisten, J. A. (1954) *Quart. Rev. (London)*, **8**, 40.

Gillespie, R. J. and Millen, D. J. (1948) *Quart. Rev. (London)*, **2**, 277.

Gillespie, R. J. and Oubridge, J. V. (1956) *J. chem. Soc.* 80.

Gillespie, R. J. and Robinson, E. A. (1957a) *J. chem. Soc.* 4233.

Gillespie, R. J. and Robinson, E. A. (1957b) *Proc. chem. Soc.* 145.

Gillespie, R. J. and Robinson, E. A. (1959) "The Sulfuric Acid Solvent System". *In* "Advances in Inorganic Chemistry and Radiochemistry", Vol. I, p. 385. Academic Press, New York.

Gillespie, R. J. and Robinson, E. A. (1962a) *Canad. J. Chem.* **40**, 644.

Gillespie, R. J. and Robinson, E. A. (1962b) *Canad. J. Chem.* **40**, 658.

Gillespie, R. J. and Robinson, E. A. (1962c) *Canad. J. Chem.* **40**, 784.

Gillespie, R. J. and Robinson, E. A. (1962d) *Canad. J. Chem.* **40**, 1009.

Gillespie, R. J. and Robinson, E. A. (1963a) *Canad. J. Chem.* **41**, 450.

Gillespie, R. J. and Robinson, E. A. (1963b) *Canad. J. Chem.* **41**, 2074.

Gillespie, R. J. and Senior, J. B. (1964) *Inorg. Chem.* **3**, 440.

Gillespie, R. J. and Solomons, C. (1957) *J. chem. Soc.* 1796.

Gillespie, R. J. and Wasif, S. (1953a) *J. chem. Soc.* 209.

Gillespie, R. J. and Wasif, S. (1953b) *J. chem. Soc.* 215.

Gillespie, R. J. and Wasif, S. (1953c) *J. chem. Soc.* 221.

Gillespie, R. J. and White, R. F. M. (1958) *Trans. Faraday Soc.* **54**, 1846.

Gillespie, R. J. and White, R. F. M. (1960) *Canad. J. Chem.* **38**, 1371.

Gillespie, R. J., Hughes, E. D. and Ingold, C. K. (1950b) *J. chem. Soc.* 2473.

Gillespie, R. J., Oubridge, J. V. and Solomons, C. (1956) *J. chem. Soc.* 1804.

Gillespie, R. J., Robinson, E. A. and Solomons, C. (1960) *J. chem. Soc.*, 4320.

Gillespie, R. J., Graham, J., Hughes, E. D., Ingold, C. K. and Peeling, E. R. A. (1950a) *J. chem. Soc.* 2504.

Gluekauf, E. (1955) *Trans. Faraday Soc.* **51**, 1235.

Goddard, D. R., Hughes, E. D. and Ingold, C. K. (1950) *J. chem. Soc.* 2559.

Gold, V. and Hawes, B. M. W. (1951) *J. chem. Soc.* 2102.

Gold, V. and Tye, F. L. (1950) *J. chem. Soc.* 2932.

Gold, V. and Tye, F. L. (1952) *J. chem. Soc.* 2172.

Grace, J. A. and Symons, M. C. R. (1959) *J. chem. Soc.* 958.

Graham, J. (1943) Ph.D., Thesis (London).

Greenwood, N. N. and Thompson, A. (1959) *J. chem. Soc.* 3474.

Gurney, R. W. (1953) *In* "Ionic Processes in Solution". McGraw-Hill, London.

Hall, S. K. and Robinson, E. A. (1964) *Canad. J. Chem.* **42**, 1113.

Hammett, L. P. (1940) *In* "Physical Organic Chemistry", p. 284. McGraw-Hill, New York.

Hammett, L. P. and Deyrup, A. J. (1932) *J. Amer. chem. Soc.* **54**, 2721.

Hammett, L. P. and Deyrup, A. J. (1933) *J. Amer. chem. Soc.* **55**, 1900.

Hantzsch, A. (1907) *Z. physikal. chem.* **61**, 257.

Hantzsch, A. (1908) *Z. physikal. chem.* **65**, 41.

Hantzsch, A. (1921) *Ber. dtsch. chem. Ges.* **54B**, 2573.

Hart, H. and Fish, R. W. (1958) *J. Amer. chem. Soc.* **80**, 5894.

Hart, H. and Fish, R. W. (1960) *J. Amer. chem. Soc.* **82**, 5419.

Hart, H. and Fish, R. W. (1961) *J. Amer. chem. Soc.* **83**, 4460.

Hart, H., Sulzberg, J. and Rafos, R. R. (1963) *J. Amer. chem. Soc.* **85**, 1800.

Hathaway, B. J., and Webster, D. E. (1963) *Proc. chem. Soc.* 14.

Holstead, C., Lamberton, A. H. and Wyatt, P. A. H. (1953) *J. chem. Soc.* 3341.

Hood, G. C. and Reilly, C. A. (1957) *J. chem. Phys.* **27**, 1126.

Ingold, C. K. (1953a) *In* "Structure and Mechanism in Organic Chemistry", p. 400. G. Bell, London.

Ingold, C. K., Millen, D. J. and Poole, H. G. (1950) *J. chem. Soc.* 2576.

Jaques, C. and Leisten, J. A. (1961) *J. chem. Soc.* 4963.

Jones, G. and Dole, M. (1929) *J. Amer. chem. Soc.* **51**, 2590.

Jorgenson, M. J. and Harrter, D. R. (1963) *J. Amer. chem. Soc.* **85**, 878.

Kendall, J., Adler, J. H. and Davidson, A. W. (1921) *J. Amer. chem. Soc.* **43**, 979.

Kershaw, D. N. and Leisten, J. A. (1960) *Proc. chem. Soc.* 84.

Kirkbride, B. J. and Wyatt, P. A. H. (1957) *Trans. Faraday Soc.* **54**, 483.

Kirkbride, B. J. and Wyatt, P. A. H. (1958) *J. chem. Soc.* 2100.

Kon, H. and Blois, M. S. (1958) *J. chem. Phys.* **28**, 743.

Kothner, von P. (1901) *Ann. der chem.* **319**, 1.

Kuhn, L. P. and Corwin, A. H. (1948) *J. Amer. chem. Soc.* **70**, 3370.

Kuhn, L. P. and Winterstein, A. (1928) *Helv. chim. acta* **11**, 87.

Kunzler, J. E. (1953) *Anal. Chem.* **25**, 93.

Kunzler, J. E. and Giauque, W. F. (1952a) *J. Amer. chem. Soc.* **74**, 804.

Kunzler, J. E. and Giauque, W. F. (1952b) *J. Amer. chem. Soc.* **74**, 3472.

Kunzler, J. E. and Giauque, W. F. (1952c) *J. Amer. chem. Soc.* **74**, 5271.

Lehmann, H. A. (1953) *Ber. dtsch. chem. Ges.* **21**, 17.

Leisten, J. A. (1955) *J. chem. Soc.* 298.

Leisten, J. A. (1956) *J. chem. Soc.* 1572.

Leisten, J. A. (1960) *J. chem. Soc.* 545.

Leisten, J. A. (1961) *J. chem. Soc.* 2191.

Leisten, J. A. (1964a) *J. chem. Soc.* (in the press).

Leisten, J. A. (1964b) *J. chem. Soc.* (in the press).

Leisten, J. A. and Walton, P. R. (1963). *Proc. chem. Soc.*, 60.

Leisten, J. A. and Walton, P. R. (1964). *J. chem. Soc.* (in the press).

Lichty, D. M. (1907) *J. Phys. Chem.* **11**, 225.

Liler, M. (1962). *J. chem. Soc.* 4272.

Liler, M. (1963) *J. chem. Soc.* 3106.

Liler, M. and Kosanovic, Dj. (1958). *J. chem. Soc.* 1084.

Mackor, E. L., Hofstra, A. and van der Waals, J. H. (1958) *Trans. Faraday Soc.* **54**, 66, 187.

MacClean, C. and Mackor, E. L. (1961) *Mol. Phys.* **4**, 241.

MacClean, C. and Mackor, E. L. (1962) *Disc. Faraday Soc.* **34**, 165.

Marcus, R. A. and Fresco, J. M. (1957) *J. chem. Phys.* **26**, 1665.

Masson, I. (1938) *J. chem. Soc.* 1708.

Masson, I. and Argument, C. (1938) *J. chem. Soc.*, 1702.

Masson, I. and Hanby, W. E. (1938) *J. chem. Soc.* 1699.

McCauley, D. A. and Lier, A. P. (1951) *J. Amer. chem. Soc.* **73**, 2013.

Mellor, J. W. (1922a) "A Comprehensive Treatise on Inorganic and Theoretical Chemistry," Vol. 9, p. 332. Longmans Green, London.

Mellor, J. W. (1922b) "A Comprehensive Treatise on Inorganic and Theoretical Chemistry", Vol. 9, p. 580. Longmans Green, London.

Mellor, J. W. (1922c) "A Comprehensive Treatise on Inorganic and Theoretical Chemistry", Vol. 9, p. 698. Longmans Green, London.

Mellor, J. W. (1922d) "A Comprehensive Treatise on Inorganic and Theoretical Chemistry", Vol. 11, p. 117. Longmans Green, London.

Meyer, J. and Langer, M. (1927) *Ber. dtsch. chem. Ges.* **60**, 285.

Miles, F. D. and Carson, T. (1946) *J. chem. Soc.* 786.

Millen, D. J. (1950a) *J. chem. Soc.* 2589.

Millen, D. J. (1950b) *J. chem. Soc.* 2600.

Millen, D. J. (1950c) *J. chem. Soc.* 2606.

Mishra, H. C. and Symons, M. C. R. (1962) *J. chem. Soc.* 4411.

Mountford, G. A. and Wyatt, P. A. H. (1964) *J. chem. Soc.* 518.

Nakomoto, K., Fujita, J., Tanaka, S. and Kobayashi, M. (1957) *J. Amer. chem. Soc.* **79**, 4904.

Newman, M. S. (1940) *J. Amer. chem. Soc.* **63**, 2431.

Newman, M. S. and Deno, N. C. (1951a) *J. Amer. chem. Soc.* **73**, 3651.

Newman, M. S. and Deno, N. C. (1951b) *J. Amer. chem. Soc.* **73**, 3644.

Newman, M. S., Craig, R. A. and Garrett, A. B. (1949) *J. Amer. chem. Soc.* **71**, 869.

Newman, M. S., Kuivila, H. and Garrett, A. B. (1945) *J. Amer. chem. Soc.* **67**, 704.

Norris, J. F. and Jouber, J. M. (1927) *J. Amer. chem. Soc.* **49**, 873.

Oddo, G. and Casalino, A. (1917a) *Gazzetta.* **47**(ii), 232.

Oddo, G. and Casalino, A. (1917b) *Gazzetta.* **47**(ii), 200.

Oddo, G. and Scandola, E. (1908) *Gazzetta.* **38**, 603.

Oddo, G. and Scandola, E. (1909a) *Gazzetta.* **39**(i), 569.

Oddo, G. and Scandola, E. (1909b) *Gazzetta.* **39**(ii), 1.

Oddo, G. and Scandola, E. (1910) *Gazzetta.* **40**(ii), 163.

Ogg, R. A. and Ray, J. D. (1956) *J. chem. Phys.* **25**, 1285.

Okawara, R., Hathaway, B. J. and Webster, D. E. (1963) *Proc. chem. Soc.* 13.

Paddock, N. (1964) *Quart. Rev.* (*London*) **18**, 168.

Palm, V. A. (1956) *Proc. Russ. Acad. Sci.* (*Chemistry*) **108**, 249.

Pascard, R. (1955) *C. R. Acad. Sci., Paris*, **240**, 2162.

Paul, M. A. and Long, F. A. (1957) *Chem. Revs.* **58**, 935.

Pople, J. A., Schneider, W. G. and Bernstein, H. J. (1959) "High Resolution Nuclear Magnetic Resonance". McGraw-Hill, New York.

Price, F. P. (1948) *J. Amer. Soc.* **70**, 871.

Reavill, R. E. (1964) *J. chem. Soc.* 519.

Reid, C. (1954) *J. Amer. chem. Soc.* **76**, 3264.

Robinson, E. A. (1964) Unpublished experiments.

Robinson, R. A. and Stokes, R. H. (1948) "Electrolyte Solutions", p. 223. Butterworths, London.

Rosenbaum, J. and Symons, M. C. R. (1960) *Mol. Phys.* **3**, 205.

Royer, J. L. (1961) *J. inorg. and nuclear Chem.* **17**, 159.

Schilt, A. A. (1963) *J. Amer. chem. Soc.* **85**, 904.

Schott, G. and Kibbel, H. U. (1962) *Z. anorg. chem.* **314**, 104.

Somiya, T. (1927) *Proc. Imp. Acad. (Japan)* **3**, 76.

Sommer, L. H., Petruska, E. W., Kerr, G. T. and Whitmore, F. C. (1946) *J. Amer. chem. Soc.* **68**, 156.

Stavenhagen, A. (1893) *Z. anorg. chem.* **6**, 284.

Stewart, R. and Yates, K. (1958) *J. Amer. chem. Soc.* **80**, 6355.

Stewart, R. and Yates, K. (1960) *J. Amer. chem. Soc.* **82**, 4059.

Symons, M. C. R. (1957) *J. chem. Soc.* 387.

Szmant, H. H., Devlin, O. M. and Brost, G. A. (1951) *J. Amer. chem. Soc.* **73**, 3059.

Thompson, A. and Greenwood, N. N. (1959) *J. chem. Soc.* 736.

Treffers, H. P. and Hammett, L. P. (1937) *J. Amer. chem. Soc.* **59**, 1708.

von Rosenberg, J. L., Mahler, J. E. and Pettit, R. (1962) *J. Amer. chem. Soc.* **84**, 2842.

Walrafen, G. E. (1964) *J. chem. Phys.* **40**, 2326.

Walrafen, G. E. and Dodd, D. M. (1961) *Trans. Faraday. Soc.* **57**, 1286.

Walrafen, G. E. and Young, T. F. (1960) *Trans. Faraday Soc.* **56**, 1419.

Weinland, R. F. and Kuhl, H. (1907) *Z. anorg. chem.* **54**, 244.

Weissman, S. I., de Boer, E., and Conradi, J. J. (1956) *J. chem. Phys.* **26**, 963.

Welch, C. M. and Smith, H. A. (1950) *J. Amer. chem. Soc.* **72**, 4748.

Welch, C. M. and Smith, H. A. (1953) *J. Amer. chem. Soc.* **75**, 1412.

Whitford, E. L. (1925) *J. Amer. chem. Soc.* **47**, 953.

Wicke, Von E. and Eigen, M. (1953) *Z. Elektrochem.* **57**, 319.

Wiig, E. O. (1930) *J. Amer. chem. Soc.* **52**, 4729, 4737, 4742.

Wiles, L. A. (1953) *J. chem. Soc.* 996.

Wiles, L. A. and Baughan, E. C. (1953) *J. chem. Soc.* 933.

Williams, G. and Hardy, M. L. (1953) *J. chem. Soc.*, 2560.

Williams, J. F. A. (1962) *Tetrahedron* **18**, 1487.

Wyatt, P. A. H. (1953) *J. chem. Soc.* 1175.

Wyatt, P. A. H. (1960) *Trans. Faraday Soc.* **56**, 490.

Wyatt, P. A. H. (1961) *Trans. Faraday Soc.* **57**, 773.

Yates, K., Stevens, J. B. and Katriskey, A. R. (1964). To be published.

Young, T. F. (1951) *Record of chem. Progress* **12**, 81.

Young, T. F. (1959). *In* "The Structure of Electrolytic Solutions" (Hamer, ed.) Chapter 4. Wiley, New York.

CHAPTER 5

Co-ordinating Solvents

RUSSELL S. DRAGO AND K. F. PURCELL

Chemistry Department, University of Illinois, Urbana, Illinois, U.S.A.

I. Introduction.. 211
II. Criteria for Establishing Co-ordination....................................... 215
    A. Ultra-violet and Visible Spectroscopy.................................. 215
    B. Infra-red Spectroscopy.. 216
    C. Nuclear Magnetic Resonance Spectroscopy............................... 217
    D. Cryoscopy... 219
    E. Conductivity.. 219
III. Energetics of the Co-ordination Process 220
    A. Statement of the Problem.. 220
    B. Evaluation of the Energy Terms.. 222
IV. Solute Behaviour in Selected Solvents. 226
    A. NN-Dimethylacetamide (DMA).. 228
    B. N-Methylacetamide (NMA)... 230
    C. Dimethyl sulphoxide (DMSO).. 230
    D. Nitromethane and Nitrobenzene (NM,NB)................................. 234
    E. Acetone (Ac).. 237
    F. Methanol and Ethanol (MeOH,EtOH)...................................... 239
    G. Pyridine (Py)... 241
    H. Acetonitrile (MeCN) 243
    I. Tetramethylene Sulphone (Sulpholane–$TMSO_2$)......................... 245
V. Generalizations... 247
References... 249

I. INTRODUCTION

Solvent co-ordination of solutes and its ramifications are very important in non-aqueous solvent chemistry. If an inorganic solute dissolves in a solvent, solution is nearly always accompanied by solvent co-ordination. This co-ordination involves a specific interaction of the Lewis acid–base type between the solvent and solute. In the absence of significant interactions in "non-co-ordinating solvents", such as saturated hydrocarbons, CCl_4, fluorocarbons etc., very few inorganic materials dissolve. Consequently, the majority of investigations in inorganic chemistry have been carried out in co-ordinating solvents. It is our feeling that the considerations outlined in this chapter are pertinent to the description of non-aqueous solvent chemistry in co-ordinating media.

In the past, explanations of solute behaviour in many solvents have ignored solvent co-ordination and emphasized the self-ionization of the solvent. For example, the behaviour of solutions of Lewis acids and bases in the solvent $POCl_3$ is correlated by considerations involving the self-ionization of this solvent

$$POCl_3 \leftrightharpoons POCl_2^+ + Cl^-. \tag{1}$$

An acid is defined as a solute capable of increasing the concentration of the cationic species, $POCl_2^+$, and a base as a solute capable of increasing the concentration of the anion, Cl^-. Addition of $FeCl_3$ to $POCl_3$ produces $FeCl_4^-$ and supposedly $POCl_2^+$, hence $FeCl_3$ is an acid. This model for non-aqueous solvent behaviour is referred to as the Solvent Systems Concept (Gutmann, 1959). In order to illustrate the application of this concept and in order to establish an alternate model of solute–solvent interactions based on the premise of solvent co-ordination, the systems $POCl_3$–$FeCl_3$ and $PO(OEt)_3$–$FeCl_3$ will be discussed.

The ultra-violet absorption spectra of dilute solutions of ferric chloride ($\sim 10^{-4}$ M) in phosphorus oxychloride demonstrate that the tetrachloroferrate(III) ion, $FeCl_4^-$, is one of the principal absorbing species present (Baaz et al., 1960). No conclusive evidence is available to establish the presence of $POCl_2^+$, in this solution. At higher concentrations of $FeCl_3$ (about 0·1 M) in the absence of sufficient chloride ion from the solvent to convert all the $FeCl_3$ to $FeCl_4^-$, the existence of a red addition compound $FeCl_3(POCl_3)_x$ is proposed. The essential equilibria are represented by the Solvent Systems Concept as:

$$FeCl_3 + POCl_3 \leftrightharpoons Cl_3FeClPOCl_2 \rightleftharpoons POCl_2^+ + FeCl_4^-. \tag{2}$$

The colour transformation from red to yellow is completely reversible upon dilution or concentration. Addition of a source of chloride ion to red $FeCl_3$ solutions converts the colour to the characteristic yellow colour of $FeCl_4^-$.

Conductimetric titrations of ferric chloride solutions in phosphorus oxychloride (Gutmann and Baaz, 1959) with soluble chlorides give sharp inflections at a mole ratio of one chloride ion to one $FeCl_3$ molecule. According to the Solvent Systems Concept, the net ionic equation describing this titration is

$$POCl_2^+ + Cl^- \rightleftharpoons POCl_3. \tag{3}$$

The complete equation for the titration of ferric chloride is then represented by

$$R_4N^+Cl^- + POCl_2^+FeCl_4^- \rightleftharpoons R_4N^+FeCl_4^- + POCl_3. \tag{4}$$

Contrary to the Solvent System formulation of a chlorine co-ordinated addition compound (equation (2)), X-ray structure determinations and Raman and infra-red investigations indicate that the oxygen is the co-ordination position in several adducts of the $POCl_3$ molecule. X-Ray single crystal studies (Lindquist and Branden, 1959; Branden and Lindquist, 1960) on the addition compounds $SbCl_5 . OPCl_3$ and $(TiCl_4 . OPCl_3)_2$ show that both metals are octahedrally co-ordinated and bonded to the oxygen atom of the $POCl_3$ molecule. The Raman spectra of the compounds $AlCl_3 . OPCl_3$ and $GaCl_3 . OPCl_3$ indicate that co-ordination occurs through the oxygen (Gerding et al., 1960). The infra-red spectra of phosphoryl halide addition compounds with $TiCl_4$, $SnCl_4$ and $TiBr_4$, also support the assignment of oxygen as the co-ordinating atom (Sheldon and Tyree, 1958).

Proponents of the solvent system concept (Lindquist, 1958; Baaz and Gutmann, 1959) argue that although the oxygen co-ordinated species exist in the solid, or under conditions of the Raman and infra-red spectral studies, two competitive equilibria (oxygen co-ordination at high solute concentration and solvent ionization to produce chloride at low solute concentration) occur in $POCl_3$ solutions and are responsible for the observed phenomena. Thus the problem of the species present in dilute solutions of $FeCl_3$ in $POCl_3$ remains unresolved.

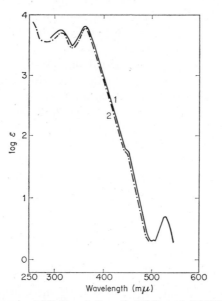

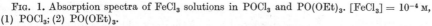

FIG. 1. Absorption spectra of $FeCl_3$ solutions in $POCl_3$ and $PO(OEt)_3$. $[FeCl_3] = 10^{-4}$ M, (1) $POCl_3$; (2) $PO(OEt)_3$.

In an attempt to demonstrate that the behaviour and reactions of $FeCl_3$ in $POCl_3$ could be accounted for without invoking removal of chloride ion from the solvent, i.e. solvent ionization, the behaviour of $FeCl_3$ in a non-chlorine containing solvent was studied (Meek and Drago, 1961). Triethyl phosphate was selected because of its structural similarity to $POCl_3$. Triethyl phosphate is expected to be a slightly better donor than $POCl_3$ but the similarity is such that vastly different co-ordination behaviour would not be expected. The similarity of dilute solutions of $FeCl_3$ in $POCl_3$ and $PO(OEt)_3$ is illustrated in Fig. 1. Absorption bands characteristic of $FeCl_4^-$ are observed in both solvents.

Use of triethyl phosphate as a solvent excludes the possibility of the tetrachloroferrate ion being formed from a chloride ion liberated by a

8

self-ionization of the solvent, as has been postulated for $POCl_3$. The following set of equilibria (5) is suggested to explain the formation of $FeCl_4^-$ in both $PO(OEt)_3$ and $POCl_3$ and to account for the principal species present.

$$FeCl_3 + Y_3PO \rightleftharpoons (FeCl_3OPY_3) \rightleftharpoons FeCl_{3-x}(OPY_3)_{1+x}^{x+} + xFeCl_4^-. \qquad (5)$$

This representation of the equilibria is in agreement with the experimental evidence that demonstrates oxygen co-ordination in the $POCl_3$ addition compounds. The infra-red spectra of $PO(OEt)_3$ co-ordinated to iron species also indicate that co-ordination of the solvent molecule occurs via the phosphoryl oxygen atom (Meek and Drago, 1961). Comparison of equations (2) and (5) demonstrates the essential difference between the Solvent System Concept and our proposed explanation of the equilibria. The species present at equilibrium differ according to the two models. This latter explanation will be referred to as the Co-ordination Model.

Conductimetric titrations were carried out (Meek and Drago, 1961) in triethyl phosphate to demonstrate further the similarity in behaviour of $PO(OEt)_3$ and $POCl_3$. Sharp breaks in the conductivity curves were obtained at a 1 : 1 molar ratio for the titration of both $FeCl_3$ and $SbCl_3$ with chloride ion. These breaks correspond to the formation of $FeCl_4^-$ and $SbCl_4^-$ ions. Analogous behaviour, noted above, has been reported to occur in $POCl_3$. According to our scheme, the equations for the titration involve the conversion of all iron(III) species to the $FeCl_4^-$ ion:

$$f_1 \ FeCl_2(OPY_3)_4^+ + 2f_1 \ Cl^- \rightarrow f_1 \ FeCl_4^- \qquad (6a)$$

$$f_2 \ FeCl(OPY_3)_5^+ + 3f_2 \ Cl^- \rightarrow f_2 \ FeCl_4^- \qquad (6b)$$

$$f_3 \ Fe(OPY_3)_6^{3+} + 4f_3 \ Cl^- \rightarrow f_3 \ FeCl_4^- \qquad (6c)$$

$$f_4 \ FeCl_3(OPY_3) + f_4 \ Cl^- \rightarrow f_4 \ FeCl_4^-, \qquad (6d)$$

where f_i is the fraction of total Fe present as the ith species. Since the iron to chlorine ratio in a solution of $FeCl_3$ is 1 : 3, one mole of chloride ion per mole of $FeCl_3$ will be required to convert all the iron to $FeCl_4^-$. That this is so is substantiated by the spectrophotometric data. These equations should be contrasted with those proposed according to the Solvent System Concept (equations (3) and (4)).

All of the properties of ferric chloride solutions in phosphorus oxychloride which have been used to support the Solvent System Concept have been reproduced in triethyl phosphate. This indicates that solvent ionization is not a requirement to explain the equilibria and chemical reactions that occur when Lewis acids are dissolved in phosphorus oxychloride. When one compares equilibria in different solvents, the Co-ordination Model focuses attention on the donor or acceptor properties of the solvent and the solvating ability of the solvent. Consequently, the behaviour of acidic solutes in donor organic solvents is in many respects similar to the behaviour of these materials in many oxyhalide and oxide solvents. Although the main concern in this chapter will be with "organic" solvents, the above discussion of $POCl_3$ and $PO(OEt)_3$ is presented to emphasize the fact that the concepts developed here may very well apply in most solvents.

In this chapter our interest will be with developing general concepts suggested by the Co-ordination Model and applying these considerations to non-aqueous solvent behaviour. We shall deal first with methods of establishing co-ordination and determining the species present in solution. This will be followed by a description of the energetics of the solvent–solute interactions and a formulation of the species in solution in different solvents. Both of these considerations are a direct outgrowth of the Co-ordination Model. Finally we shall discuss solute behaviour in a series of typical co-ordinating solvents from the standpoint of qualitatively correlating the species formed with the principal solvent properties. As far as possible, data will be presented that are pertinent to the problem of estimating the essential solvent parameters. A limited number of typical solvents will be discussed.

II. CRITERIA FOR ESTABLISHING CO-ORDINATION

One of the first concerns in discussing solvent co-ordination is the criteria for determining whether or not solvent co-ordination occurs. Whatever experiment is selected, the criteria must invariably rely on a difference in physical properties of the free donor or acceptor and the co-ordinated species. Since changes in electronic structure are expected when co-ordination of the Lewis acid–base type occurs, various spectroscopic techniques can be employed. Cryoscopic and conductimetric techniques have also been employed to advantage. In this section we shall briefly describe the results of some selected studies which establish co-ordination.

A. ULTRA-VIOLET AND VISIBLE SPECTROSCOPY

A very early application of this technique involved the spectroscopic study of iodine in different solvents. The wavelength of the $\pi^* \to \sigma^*$ transition of I_2 is shorter in solvents in which co-ordination occurs than in non-coordinating solvents. The transition occurs at 520 mμ in the gas phase, 517 mμ in CCl_4, 520 mμ in heptane, and 500 mμ in benzene where co-ordination occurs and at shorter wavelengths in more basic solvents (Benesi and Hildebrand, 1949). In donor solvents, co-ordination to iodine is also accompanied by the appearance of a new charge-transfer band in the ultra-violet spectrum (Andrews and Keefer, 1961).

The electronic spectra of transition metal ions are especially valuable not only for establishing solvent co-ordination but also for determining the co-ordination number and structure of these ions dissolved in solvents. When a complex that exists in solution can be isolated as a solid, the stoichiometry of the complex can be determined by analysis and it becomes a simple matter to determine the co-ordination number and structure of the ion. A solution structure can often be inferred from electronic spectra of the complex. The generalized spectra of the first transition series ions with their various structures have been reported (Dunn, 1960).

The solution species which result when $FeCl_3$ is dissolved in certain solvents represent examples for which the isolatable solids are not the same as the species in solution (Drago et al., 1965a,b). In the $FeCl_3$–DMA system (DMA is dimethylacetamide), the spectrum of the various chloro-species had to be determined by examination of the spectroscopic changes in $Fe(DMA)_6(ClO_4)_3$ solutions as a function of added chloride ion. The species present were inferred from the existence of isobestic points and from the spectroscopic changes over different concentration ranges.

The system $CoCl_2$–pyridine was examined by Katzin and Gebert (1950 a, b, c) in the solvent acetone by visible spectroscopy. The method of Job (Job, 1928) was employed to obtain the stoichiometry of the $CoCl_2$–pyridine complexes. It has been explicitly pointed out by Woldbye (1955) that this method, unless used cautiously, can be unreliable. In the case at hand, the method appears valid and yields the result that complexes with pyridine to cobalt ratios of $1:1$ and $2:1$ can exist in acetone. A Job's study of the effect of pyridine on the spectrum of $CoCl_4^{2-}$ in acetone also showed the existence of a $1:1$ complex formulated as $CoCl_3py^-$ (py is pyridine). Similarly, Fine (1962) has recently studied the formation of CoX^+, CoX_2, CoX_3^- and CoX_4^{2-} in acetone ($X = Cl, Br, I$). The unfilled co-ordination positions are occupied by acetone molecules e.g. CoX_3ac^- (ac is acetone).

Another example of an application of spectrophotometry to the general problem of solvent co-ordination involves the $(Co(acac)_2)_n$–pyridine system in benzene as the "inert" medium (acac is acetonylacetone) (Fackler, 1963). Equilibrium constants for the formation of the several $Co(acac)_2$–pyridine species were obtained, i.e. $(Co(acac)_2)_2.py$; $Co(acac)_2.py$; and $Co(acac)_2.2py$.

A general discussion of the study of complex formation by spectrophotometry and the mathematical treatment of the data is given by Newman and Hume (1957).

B. INFRA-RED SPECTROSCOPY

Since co-ordination affects the electron distribution in a molecule, changes in the force constants of various bonds and hence changes in their vibrational frequency occur upon complex formation. Consequently, the infra-red spectrum of the solute and/or the solvent can be used as a criterion for co-ordination but the absence of a shift is not always a reliable criterion for the absence of co-ordination. It is essential that such studies be carried out in solution, for it is well known that a change in the spectrum of a compound occurs on change of state (liquid to solid). For example, the spectrum of a solvent molecule trapped in a solid lattice may differ appreciably from the spectrum of the solvent in the liquid or gaseous state. A difference detected when the spectrum of the proposed adduct is examined as a solid cannot be utilized rigorously to establish co-ordination.

In addition to indicating co-ordination, changes in the infra-red spectrum of a donor molecule can often be employed to indicate the position of co-ordination in the donor. For example, it has been shown that $CH_3CON(CH_3)_2$ co-ordinates through oxygen with the Lewis acids I_2, C_6H_5OH (Schmulbach and Drago, 1960; Joesten and Drago, 1962a,b), and several metal ions (Bull et al., 1963; Drago et al., 1963b). Toward many first row transition metal ions it has been shown that the oxygen atom of dimethylsulphoxide is the donor (Cotton and Francis, 1960; Meek et al., 1960; Cotton and Francis, 1961; Drago and Meek, 1961), but sulphur is the donor atom in the $Pd((CH_3)_2SO)_4^{2+}$ complex (Cotton and Francis, 1960). In both $CH_3CON(CH_3)_2$ and $(CH_3)_2SO$, co-ordination through oxygen drains electron density out of the oxo-bond, lowering the bond order, and decreasing the force constant and frequency of the oxo stretching vibration.

A complication which is sometimes encountered with the infra-red technique should be mentioned. Co-ordination gives rise to another effect which instead of decreasing actually increases the vibration frequency of the bond under examination. This is called the *kinematic effect* and arises from the formation of the new bond (i.e. the co-ordination bond). For example, when acetonitrile co-ordinates to an acceptor the C—N stretching motion must now occur at the expense of changes in the acceptor-nitrogen bond distance, in effect coupling these two vibrations. This push-pull effect acts to increase the frequency of the C—N vibration. Another effect, which acts to increase the C—N force constant, results from the hydridization change of nitrogen upon complexation. According to isovalent hybridization arguments (Bent, 1961), co-ordination by nitrogen increases the *s* character in the C—N bond (the N hybrid orbital). Since the drain of σ-electron density from the C—N group is small in many complexes, co-ordination to the nitrogen of nitriles often results in an increased frequency for the C—N vibration. It is to be emphasized that the above effects and the drain of electron density out of the π- and σ-bonds work simultaneously and only the net effect is measured by the direction of the frequency shift.

Another effect which seems to be of importance for ligands with low lying π^*-orbitals (empty) is that of back bonding. If the acid possesses electrons in π-type orbitals which are of the same symmetry and nearly the same energy as the empty ligand π^*-orbitals, π-bonding involving these orbitals can occur (Orgel, 1960). This brings about a decrease in force constant of the donor multiple bond.

C. NUCLEAR MAGNETIC RESONANCE SPECTROSCOPY

This method has tremendous potential for demonstrating co-ordination. For example, when a hydrogen bonding interaction occurs, the chemical shift of the proton involved in the interaction usually moves to lower field. This shift is evidence for "co-ordination" of the proton (Shoolery *et al.*, 1955; Korinek and Schneider, 1957). In a very interesting experiment Schneider and Reeves (1957) have shown that in benzene solution the proton in $CHCl_3$ undergoes a pronounced shift to high field amounting to 1·40 p.p.m. at infinite dilution. This shift was employed to establish the existence of a hydrogen-bonding interaction between the chloroform proton and benzene as a donor. The shift to high field suggests that the chloroform proton is directed at approximately right angles to the plane of the aromatic ring and in the vicinity of the six-fold rotation axis. In this position, the proton shift to high field arises from the magnetic anisotropy of the ring current in benzene.

The thallium-proton coupling constant of $(CH_3)_2TlClO_4$ has been found to be very sensitive to the solvent (Shier and Drago, 1965). In those solvents where the thallium co-ordination number is 6 and the CH_3TlCH_3 moiety linear, coupling constants in the range 410–475 c/s were found and the magnitude of the coupling constant paralleled solvent donor properties.

It has also been found (Onak *et al.*, 1959; Landesman and Williams, 1961) that co-ordination of donor molecules to many boron compounds causes a shift of the [11]B resonance to higher field in the adduct. For example, δ in BCl_3 is at about 35 p.p.m. lower field than in BCl_4^-, $BCl_3O(C_2H_5)_2$ and $BCl_3C_5H_5N$. Similar shifts in the [11]B resonance have been employed to determine whether or not co-ordination has occurred to the weak Lewis acid $B(OEt)_3$.

An n.m.r. technique for establishing the co-ordination number of certain solutes has been recently described (Jackson *et al.*, 1960). The essentials of the technique are illustrated by considering one of the reported systems. The [17]O nuclear magnetic resonance spectra of aqueous solutions ($H_2^{17}O$) of Al^{3+} show a single [17]O resonance including both bulk and co-ordinated water. Upon addition of Co^{2+}, two separate resonances are observed—one for H_2O bound to Al^{3+} and the other for solvent water exchanging rapidly with water bound to the paramagnetic Co^{2+} ion. The paramagnetic Co^{2+} ion gives rise to a large contact shift which is averaged over all water molecules not firmly bound to Al^{3+}. This causes a shift in the bulk water resonance and the two separate peaks due to bulk water and water co-ordinated to Al^{3+} can be distinguished. The same result was obtained when Be^{2+} and Ga^{3+} were substituted for Al^{3+} but not when Mg^{2+}, Sn^{2+}, Ba^{2+}, Hg^{2+} or Bi^{3+} solutions were examined. The sensitivity of these experiments was limited by the [17]O enrichment available and co-ordination numbers could not be accurately obtained. Connick and Fiat (1963), using H_2O enriched to 12% in [17]O and a more sensitive measuring technique, performed essentially the same experiments and found co-ordination numbers 6 and 4 for Al(III) and Be(II), respectively. This appears to be a very promising technique for non-aqueous solvent work.

In another experiment Swinehart and Taube (1962) used proton n.m.r. to establish the co-ordination number of Mg^{2+}. Using various mixed $MeOH-H_2O$ (mole ratio $\sim$10 : 1) solutions of $Mg(ClO_4)_2$ and cooling the samples to $-75°C$ they observed separate resonances for MeOH and H_2O both bound and free. Their calculations give a solvation number for MeOH of 5·0 and of H_2O of 0·7, yielding a total co-ordination number for magnesium(II) (solvent) of 5·7. The deviation from 6·0 is attributed to perchlorate co-ordination.

D. CRYOSCOPY

Although of limited use in studying more complex solutes in solution, simple 1 : 1 association can be convincingly demonstrated with this technique. A case in point is the studies of Voitovich and Barabanova (1961) who examined, by the method of continuous variations, $POCl_3-MX_n$ interactions in nitrobenzene. By plotting δt, the deviation of $C_6H_5NO_2$ freezing point from the additive value for the solutes, against mole·% MX_n, they observed a maximum at 1 : 1 $POCl_3 : MX_n$ for $FeCl_3$ and $AlCl_3$ (the conductivities of solutions of 1 : 1 composition were shown to be negligible).

E. CONDUCTIVITY

In the general case, this method is too involved to yield a great deal of information, yet in certain instances this method is of great value. Conductivity measurements were used by de Maine and Koubek (1959) to establish ionization of $FeCl_3$ when it is dissolved in $MeNO_2$ or $MeNO_2$ solutions in CCl_4. The Onsager equation holds for $FeCl_3$ concentrations from $2·5 \times 10^{-2}$ M to $8·5 \times 10^{-2}$ M. In studying $FeCl_3-MeNO_2$ solutions spectrophotometrically (visible region), they also find that the "effective molar extinction coefficient" (optical density $\div$ total iron concentration) is a linear function of the iron concentration. The linear conductivity and spectrophotometric relationships are reported to be consistent only with equations (7) or (8):

$$2FeCl_3(sol) \overset{K_1}{\rightleftharpoons} Fe_2Cl_6(sol) \tag{7a}$$

$$Fe_2Cl_6(sol) \overset{K_2}{\rightleftharpoons} FeCl_2^+(sol) + FeCl_4^-(sol) . \tag{7b}$$

or

$$2FeCl_3(sol) \overset{K_1}{\rightleftharpoons} Fe_2Cl_6(sol) \tag{8a}$$

$$Fe_2Cl_6(sol) \overset{K_3}{\rightleftharpoons} Fe_2Cl_5^+(sol) + Cl^-(sol). \tag{8b}$$

It is necessary that K_1 be very small and K_2 (or K_3) be large. The species $FeCl_3(sol)$ is probably $MeNO_2FeCl_3$ and equations (7) are most probably correct.

III. ENERGETICS OF THE CO-ORDINATION PROCESS

In applying the Co-ordination Model, the first step involves formation of the initial adduct between the Lewis acid (a dative acceptor of electron density) and the Lewis base (a dative donor of electron density). Next one considers the subsequent reactions that this adduct can undergo. Very frequently ionization occurs in these subsequent steps. In many instances the subsequent reaction may occur to such an extent that the initial adduct may not exist in significant concentrations at equilibrium.

A. STATEMENT OF THE PROBLEM

The essential properties of a solvent that determine the extent of solute ionization can be most simply described by considering the hypothetical solute MX dissolved in a solvent. Assuming that all MX molecules have at least p molecules of solute attached, the equilibrium in solution can be formulated as:

$$\text{MXS}_{p(\text{sol})} + \text{S}_{(\text{sol})} \leftrightharpoons \text{MS}^+_{p+1(\text{sol})} + \text{X}^-_{(\text{sol})}. \tag{9}$$

This formulation represents a simple case in that it assumes only a fixed co-ordination number for M equal to $p+1$. The thermochemical cycle in Fig. 2(a) can then be written to describe the important enthalpy contributions

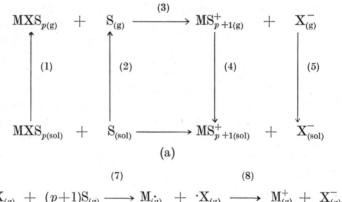

FIG. 2. Born-Haber cycles for the solution process.

to the equilibria. The contribution of enthalpy effects to the position of equilibrium in solution is determined by the difference in the heats of solvation of MXS_p and MS_{p+1}^+, the solvation of X^-, the latent enthalpy of evaporation of S and the difference in donor strength of X^- and the solvent as measured by the difference in the gaseous heats of formation of $MXS_p + S$ and $MS_{p+1}^+ + X^-$. In a donor solvent, specific interaction occurs, i.e. co-ordination, with the solute as indicated by step (3), and non-specific interactions as indicated by steps (1), (4), and (5). The term non-specific solvation will be employed to describe dipolar solvent interaction where co-ordination cannot occur, e.g. dipolar interactions of the solvent outside the first co-ordination sphere with certain metal complexes. As will be seen shortly, it is possible in certain circumstances to have contributions to steps (1), (4), and (5) from specific interactions of the hydrogen-bonding type between the solvent and an anion or a fully co-ordinated complex.

For some purposes it may be more convenient to break up step (3) into the steps in Fig. 2(b). In Fig. 2(b), (6) is the heat of dissociation of MXS_p into p molecules of S and gaseous MX, (7) the heat of dissociation of MX, (8) the ionization potential and electron affinity of M and X, and (9) the heat of co-ordination of M^+ with $p+1$ molecules of S. This cycle is equivalent to step (3) in Fig. 2(a) but provides a different path for determining the energy associated with

$$MXS_{p(g)} + S_{(g)} \rightleftharpoons MS_{p+1}^+ + X_{(g)}^-. \tag{10}$$

In addition to all the above effects, there are three additional important considerations.

(1) In order that the position of equilibrium parallel the net enthalpy change of all the steps in the cycle for different solvents and solutes, the net entropy change in these solvents must be constant or linearly related to the net enthalpy change.

(2) When extensive ion-pairing occurs, additional species must be added to the cycle and contributions to the energetics from this effect must be considered. The term ion-pairing will be employed to mean cation–anion association in which the anion is not in the first co-ordination sphere of the cation. The extent of ion-pairing can be estimated from the solvent dielectric constant or more accurately from conductivity studies of non-acidic ionic solutes in the solvent. The energy from this type of interaction is very significant in low dielectric solvents and is a very important factor in explaining why dissociation of solutes into ions occurs in these solvents.

(3) When different solutes are compared in a given solvent, differences in solute co-ordination number will be very important. The energies of the steps will be greatly influenced by entropy effects and hybridization changes.

For a more complex system than MX, e.g. $FeCl_3$, a large number of species must be considered:

$$FeCl_3S + Cl^- \rightleftharpoons FeCl_4^- + S \tag{11a}$$

$$FeCl_3S + 3S \rightleftharpoons FeCl_2S_4^+ + Cl^- \tag{11b}$$

$$FeCl_2S_4^+ + S \rightleftharpoons FeClS_5^{2+} + Cl^- \tag{11c}$$

$$FeClS_5^{2+} + S \rightleftharpoons FeS_6^{3+} + Cl^-. \tag{11d}$$

In this case, each equilibrium can be represented by a cycle similar to that for MX and the resulting species at equilibrium will depend on the competitive equilibria for each step. When solid phases are present in the system, the problem is further complicated by the lattice energies of the solid phases.

If the entropy and extent of ion-pairing are considered, a knowledge of the enthalpies corresponding to all the steps in the energy cycle for different solutes and solvents would produce a clear understanding of the important factors which affect the position of equilibrium for various solutes dissolved in different solvents. Unfortunately, for most systems, direct measurement of the energies corresponding to all these steps is not possible. The approach we shall employ in this chapter will consequently be one of indirect estimate of the relative magnitudes of these effects towards different solutes in different solvents.

B. EVALUATION OF ENERGY TERMS

The energy of step (3) of Fig. 2 can be qualitatively estimated from a knowledge of the co-ordination behaviour of the donor solvent. For this purpose it is necessary to study donor properties towards a variety of acids and to take care to employ criteria which actually measure donor strength. Stability constants and pK_B data do not provide this information, for these constants describe the complex free energy changes that can be represented by a cycle similar to that for MX. The term *donor strength* will be employed to indicate the relative co-ordinating ability of a donor measured in the absence of solvation as indicated by the enthalpy of adduct formation. *Basicity* will be employed to indicate the relative position of a donor–acceptor equilibrium in a solvent. Reliable data on donor properties can be obtained by measuring donor–acceptor interactions in the gas phase or in a non-coordinating solvent (such as CCl_4, hexane, etc.) where the difference in enthalpy of solvation of the donor plus acceptor and the adduct is small. In order to understand solvent donor properties, enthalpies should also be investigated over a wide range of different acid types for a given solvent. This is to be done so that intelligent predictions of interaction energies can be made for systems for which the enthalpies corresponding to donor–acceptor interactions cannot be directly measured. Some significant reversals in donor properties are observed. For example, it was found (Niedzielski *et al.*, 1965) that Et_2O is a stronger donor towards phenol (enthalpy of adduct formation, $\Delta H = -5 \cdot 0$ kcal mole^{-1}) than Et_2S ($\Delta H = -4 \cdot 6$ kcal mole^{-1}) but Et_2S is a better donor towards iodine ($\Delta H = -7 \cdot 8$ kcal mole^{-1}) than

$Et_2O(\Delta H = -4 \cdot 2 \text{ kcal mole}^{-1})$. A similar reversal in donor strength towards these two acids was found for the donors $CH_3CON(CH_3)_2$ and $CH_3CSN(CH_3)_2$ (Niedzielski *et al.*, 1965). For these systems it is proposed that the distortable sulphur donor interacts more strongly with the distortable acid iodine than the mole polar oxygen donor but the oxygen donor interacts more strongly with the polar acid phenol. The term distortability refers to the ease with which electron density at the bonding site in the acceptor or donor can be polarized when these molecules have the electronic configurations that they have in the adduct. This phenomenon should be general.

There have been many attempts to infer the magnitude (enthalpy) of the donor–acceptor interaction from the shift upon co-ordination of a donor or acceptor vibration frequency. It has been shown that the difference in the —OH stretching frequency of phenol in free phenol and in a hydrogen-bonded adduct is linearly related to the enthalpy of adduct formation (Joesten and Drago, 1962a,b). There have been many other literature articles in which the magnitude of a frequency shift has been assumed to indicate the magnitude of donor–acceptor interaction. For example, the decrease in carbonyl stretching frequency of acetophenone upon complex formation with the following acids has been reported (Susz and Chaladon, 1958): (parentheses contain the decrease in absorption maximum in cm^{-1}) $HgCl_2$ (18), $ZnCl_2$ (47), BF_3 (107), $TiCl_4$ (118), $AlCl_3$ (120), $FeCl_3$ (130), $AlBr_3$ (130). It should be emphasized that the phenol relationship is the only frequency shift–enthalpy relationship that has been established at the present time. Indeed, in a dramatic illustration, it has been shown (Meek *et al.*, 1962) that even though $(CH_3)_2SO$ and $(CH_2CH_2)_2SO$ interact to the same extent with cobalt in $Co(R_2SO)_6^{2+}CoCl_4^{2-}$ (as evidenced by identical positions in the spectrochemical series toward Ni^{2+}) the frequency shifts of the oxo-bond vibrations are 51 cm^{-1} and 88 cm^{-1}, respectively. An incorrect conclusion regarding the magnitude of the interaction would result from the use of infra-red data. Complications arise in this example and frequently in other systems because of coupling of ligand vibrational modes.

Although there is no definite experimental confirmation, it may be possible, for certain systems, to infer solvent donor strengths toward certain cationic Lewis acids from the spectrochemical series. For example, the following Dq values have been reported (Drago *et al.*, 1963b) for six co-ordinate Ni^{2+} complexes: NH_3 (1080 cm^{-1}), H_2O (860 cm^{-1}), $(CH_3)_2SO$ (773 cm^{-1}), $CH_3CON(CH_3)^2$ (769 cm^{-1}). These results parallel the expected donor order. The need of defining the acid in formulating a donor order is essential not only because of differences in the importance of distortability and electrostatic interactions for different acids but also because of steric effects. For example, it was found (Joesten and Drago, 1965) that the donor order of amides of general formula $R_1CONR_2R_3$ (where R_i is CH_3 or H) towards iodine and phenol increases as the number of methyl groups is increased.

However, the Dq values (Drago *et al.*, 1963b) (for NiS_6^{+2}) are in the order

$$HCON(CH_3)_2 > HCON(CH_3)H > CH_3CONH_2 \gg CH_3CON(CH_3)_2 >$$
$$CH_3CON(CH_3)H.$$

When the amides are co-ordinated to metal ions, a steric repulsion arises between co-ordinated ligands if R_1 and R_3 are both alkyl. Figure 3 illustrates

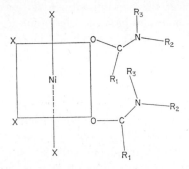

FIG. 3. Illustration of steric interactions between amide ligands in $Ni(amide)_6^{2+}$. Reproduced with permission from the *Journal of the Chemical Society*.

the nature of this steric effect. Only two ligands are illustrated and the concept is simplified to describe the effect. When R_1 is H there is a pronounced decrease in steric repulsion, a stronger interaction of the metal ion with the ligand results, and Dq is large compared to the case where R_1, R_2, and R_3 are methyl groups. This steric effect also is reduced in acetamide where both R_2 and R_3 are hydrogen and only R_1 is methyl. An appreciable steric effect is encountered when R_1 and R_3 are methyl, and also when all R_i groups are alkyl. When R_1 and R_3 are methyl the stable rotamer is the one in which the methyl groups are trans to each other because of steric interactions between R_1 and R_2 when they are both alkyl. Within a given main category, slight inductive effects can be detected as evidenced by the order listed above. A similar steric effect is operative in the six co-ordinate chromium(III) complexes.

When there is considerable metal to ligand π-bonding, Dq is much greater than anticipated from the measured donor strength with non-π-bonding acids. In a π-bonded complex, of which $Ni(CH_3CN)_6^{2+}$ is an example, Dq is a poor criterion of the donor strength of the ligand toward the metal ion.

In summary then, in the course of interpretation of the behaviour of solutes in various solvents, solvent donor properties should be estimated by examining all quantitative data available. Most weight should be given to those results obtained with acids that are most like the solute under consideration.

The problem of estimating the energies associated with steps (1), (4), and (5) of Fig. 2 is even more difficult. In the absence of specific interactions, the solvation will be predominately of the charge-dipole type. And when the solvent dielectric constant is related primarily to the dipole moment of the solvent, non-specific solvation energies should parallel the dielectric constant. Polar solvent molecules will interact most strongly with the most highly charged species and shift the equilibrium in the direction of these species.

It is known that the extent of ion-pairing will also depend on the solvent dielectric constant. The force, F, of attraction or repulsion between two charged species is given by:

$$F = \frac{q_1 q_2}{\epsilon r^2} \tag{12}$$

where q_1 and q_2 are the charges on the two species separated by a distance r in a *homogeneous* medium of dielectric constant ϵ. If the medium is a solvent, the charge-dipole interactions of the solvent with the ions will result in partial charge distribution over the solvent layers about the ions. As a result charge is dispersed, the ions' electric fields are rapidly attenuated, and ion-pairing will decrease. A high dielectric constant solvent attentuates the electric field of an ion more rapidly than a solvent with a low dielectric constant. In the absence of specific interactions, the $K_{assoc.}$ of a tetra-alkyl ammonium halide, measured from conductivity data, and the energy of solvation should parallel the dielectric constant of the solvent. Since co-ordination does not occur to the tetra-alkyl ammonium halides, the solvent donor properties should not affect this interaction.

The dielectric constant is a poor criterion of solvation if specific interactions of the Lewis acid–base type are possible between the co-ordinated solute and the solvent, for these effects usually are energetically more important than the non-specific dielectric effects. Examples of these specific interactions are the hydrogen bonding of certain solvents with the anion, e.g. Cl^-, and the hydrogen-bonding interaction of a donor solvent molecule with co-ordinated protonic ligands, e.g. $Co(NH_3)_6^{3+}$. In the current absence of better criteria, the salt association constant, $K_{assoc.}$, for alkylammonium salts and the Z-values of Kosower (1958a,b,c) can be utilized to estimate solvation energies. The Z-value is obtained from the solvent dependence of the charge transfer transition which the ion-pair 1-ethyl, 4-carbomethoxy pyridinium iodide undergoes. The wavelength of the band maximum for a given solvent is reported as a transition energy (in kcal mole^{-1}) and is referred to as the Z-value for that solvent. Since the ground state of the ion-pair is ionic, its energy is lowered by a highly solvating solvent while the energy of the neutral excited state is raised, for its dipole is oriented in a different direction from that of the ion-pair. Consequently the energy of the transition or Z-value will be higher for a polar or distortable solvent. Hydrogen-bonding solvents undergo specific interaction with the anion and consequently lead to appreciable stabilization of the ground state. This gives rise to very large Z-values. Referring to the cycle for MX, this is equivalent to saying that the Z-value will contain an energy contribution from an interaction like step (5) of Fig. 2. It is interesting to point out that although the dielectric constants of methanol and formamide are 32·6 and 109·5, respectively, the respective Z-values are 83·6 kcal mole^{-1} and 83·3 kcal mole^{-1} because of the effect just described. The values of $K_{assoc.}$ for alkylammonium halides in various solvents can also be employed to provide evidence regarding solvation. Dielectric constant and anion solvation both affect $K_{assoc.}$. We feel that this criterion, $K_{assoc.}$, is one of the best measures we have of the solvating properties of solvents.

IV. Solute Behaviour in Selected Solvents

Very few investigations of solute behaviour in non-aqueous solvents have been carried out in enough detail to provide information regarding the

Table I

Physical Properties of NN-Dimethylacetamide

M.p. (°C)	20[a]
B.p. (°C)	165·0[a]
Specific conductivity (ohm^{-1} cm^{-1})	0·8–2·0 × 10^{-7} [b]
Density (g/cm^3) at 25°C	0·9366[b]
Dielectric constant at 25°C	37·8[b]
Viscosity (centipoise) at 25°C	0·919[b]
Z–Value (kcal mole^{-1})	66·9[c]
Dq toward Ni(II) (cm^{-1})	769[d]
Data for formation of the I_2 adduct	
$\quad -\Delta H$ (kcal mole^{-1})	4·0[e]
$\quad K$ (l mole^{-1})	6·9
Data for formation of the phenol adduct	
$\quad -\Delta H$ (kcal mole^{-1})	6·4[f]
$\quad K$ (l mole^{-1})	134

[a] Beilstein, 1962.
[b] Lester et al., 1956.
[c] D. Hart, personal communication.
[d] Drago et al., 1963b.
[e] Drago et al., 1961.
[f] Joesten and Drago, 1962a,b.

structure of the species present in solution. Consequently a knowledge of the effect of a solvent on many solutes is unknown and a complete understanding of the relative importance of the essential solvent properties is lacking. Because of this lack of information, only a somewhat sketchy synopsis of this important subject can be given at present. It is not our purpose to give

TABLE II

Conductance Data for NN-Dimethylacetamide[a]

Electrolyte	Λ_0	$K_{assoc.}$	Electrolyte	Λ_0	$K_{assoc.}$
KNO_3	71·6	25	Et_4NBr	75·9	20
$NaNO_3$	71·2	50	Pr_4NBr	69·4	20
$NaBr$	69·0	17	Me_3NPhSO_3Ph	59·3	25
$NaSO_3Ph$	56·8	33			

[a] Lester *et al.*, 1956.

an exhaustive review of the data which is available and only a few characteristic solvents will be discussed to demonstrate the line of reasoning which is suggested by the Co-ordination Model. After a discussion of the properties and behaviour of certain solutes in some solvents, a brief general discussion

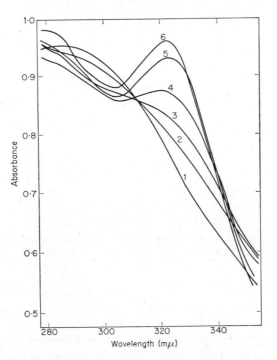

FIG. 4. Effect of chloride ion on the ultra-violet spectrum of $Fe(ClO_4)_3$ in NN-Dimethylacetamide. $[Fe(ClO_4)_3] = 1·28 \times 10^{-4}$ M; $[Cl^-]$: (1) $= 0$, (2) $= 0·36 \times 10^{-4}$ M, (3) $= 0·73 \times 10^{-4}$ M, (4) $= 1·09 \times 10^{-4}$ M, (5) $= 1·46 \times 10^{-4}$ M, (6) $= 2·19 \times 10^{-4}$ M. Reproduced with permission from the *Journal of the Chemical Society*.

will be presented in which an attempt will be made to correlate the existing data with the main properties of the different solvents. In view of the limited information available some of the interpretations in this latter section should be regarded as tentative. We hope this discussion will indicate an approach which can unify solute behaviour in non-aqueous solvents and will stimulate further research in this area.

A. NN-DIMETHYLACETAMIDE (DMA)

The physical properties of DMA are given in Table I. The limiting conductances, Λ_0, for several 1 : 1 electrolytes in DMA at 25°C are contained

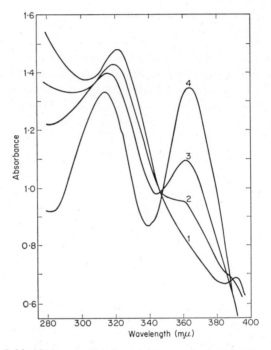

Fig. 5. Effect of chloride ion on the ultra-violet spectrum of $Fe(ClO_4)_3$ in NN-dimethyl-acetamide. [$Fe(ClO_4)_3$] = 2 0×10⁻⁴ M; [Cl⁻]: (1) = 4·54×10⁻⁴ M, (2) = 5·66×10⁻⁴ M, (3) = 6·79×10⁻⁴ M, (4) = 9·05×10⁻⁴ M. Reproduced with permission from the *Journal of the Chemical Society*.

in Table II. Lithium salts are completely dissociated at concentrations up to 0·02 M and $\lambda_{0Li^+} < \lambda_{0Na^+}$ (Lester *et al.*, 1958).

An extensive study of the iron-chloro species formed in dilute solutions of ferric chloride in DMA has been carried out (Drago *et al.*, 1965a,b). The ultra-violet absorption spectra of $Fe(DMA)_6(ClO_4)_3$ as a function of added chloride is presented in Figs. 4 and 5. Addition of Cl⁻ up to a mole ratio of 1·8 to 1 results in the loss of the maximum at 287 which is attributed to

$Fe(DMA)_6^{3+}$. Absorbance increases in the 320 mμ region achieving a maximum at 323 mμ at a Cl$^-$ to Fe^{3+} ratio of 1·8 to 1. This peak is attributed to $FeCl_2^+$. At wavelengths longer than 340 the absorbance is seen to increase initially (Cl$^-$: Fe^{3+} ratio of 0·6 to 1) and then decrease. Concurrently, *one* isobestic point is observed at Cl$^-$: Fe^{3+} ratios up to and including 0·9 to 1. Over this range the absorbances at wavelengths around 290 mμ decrease (up to and including 0·9 to 1) and then increase, and decrease again at the higher (>2) Cl$^-$ ratios. At a Cl$^-$ to Fe^{3+} ratio exceeding 2 to 1, the spectrum characteristic of $FeCl_4^-$ appears with two isobestic points and maxima at 314 mμ and 364 mμ. The spectra in Fig. 4 are consistent with the formation of $FeCl^{2+}$ and $FeCl_2^+$ with the latter beginning to form at 0·9 to 1 Cl$^-$ to Fe^{3+}. The presence of three species at Cl$^-$ ratios from 0·9–1·8 to 1 is certain from the loss of the isobestic point at 316mμ. Figure 5 illustrates the formation of $FeCl_4^-$ from $FeCl_2(DMA)_4^{2+}$ without detectable amounts of $FeCl_3(sol)$. Figure 5 also demonstrates that when ferric chloride (curve 3) is dissolved in DMA the principle species present in dilute solutions are $FeCl_2(DMA)_4^+$ and $FeCl_4^-$. Though exact values were not measured for the formation constants, K_n, of species $FeCl_n^{3-n}$, the following order accounts for the above behaviour.

$$K_3 \ll K_1 < K_2 \lesssim K_4.$$

By means of the following equations, the behaviour of $FeCl_3$ in DMA is seen to be adequately described by the Co-ordination Model:

$$DMA + FeCl_3 \rightleftharpoons FeCl_3.DMA \quad \text{(initial adduct)} \qquad (13a)$$

$$FeCl_3.DMA + 3DMA \rightleftharpoons FeCl_2(DMA)_4^+ + Cl^- \qquad (13b)$$

$$Cl^- + FeCl_3.DMA \rightleftharpoons FeCl_4^- + DMA. \qquad (13c)$$

Since the structure of the initial adduct is not known, the following set of equations could also describe the behaviour of $FeCl_3$ in DMA:

$$2FeCl_3 + DMA \rightleftharpoons Fe_2Cl_6.DMA \qquad (14a)$$

$$Fe_2Cl_6.DMA + 3DMA \rightleftharpoons FeCl_2(DMA)_4^+ + FeCl_4^-. \qquad (14b)$$

This latter reaction gives rise to a simple mechanism for forming $FeCl_4^-$ by attack of DMA on $Fe_2Cl_6.DMA$:

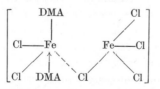

Buffagni and Dunn (1961) have carried out a very thorough study of the system $CoCl_2$–DMA. The spectra (visible region) can be interpreted in terms of the existence of the species $CoCl_4^{2-}$, $Co(DMA)_6^{2+}$, $CoCl_3(DMA)^-$ and $CoCl(DMA)_5^+$. Apparently the neutral species, $CoCl_2(DMA)_2$ or $CoCl_2(DMA)_4$, exists in very low concentration as was found for the species

$FeCl_3.DMA$. The behaviour of the $CoCl_2$–DMA system is also seen to be readily interpreted by the Co-ordination Model by writing equations similar to those above for $FeCl_3$.

B. N-METHYLACETAMIDE (NMA)

The physical properties and conductance data obtained for this solvent are presented in Tables III and IV.

TABLE III

Physical Properties of N-Methylacetamide

M.p. (°C)	29·5[a]
B.p. (°C)	206[c]
Specific conductivity (ohm^{-1} cm^{-1}) at 40°C	1–3×10^{-7} [a]
Density (g/cm^3) at 40°C	0·9420[a]
Dielectric constant at 40°C	165·5[a]
Viscosity (centipoise) at 40°C	3·019[a]
Z–Value (kcal mole^{-1})	77·9[b]
Dq toward Ni(II) (cm^{-1})	752[c]
Data for formation of the phenol adduct	
$-\Delta H$ (kcal mole^{-1})	4·7 ± 3[d]

[a] Dawson et al., 1957.
[b] D. Hart, personal communication.
[c] Drago et al., 1963b.
[d] Joesten, 1962.

An interesting trend in anion solvation is obvious from the λ_0^- of Cl^-, Br^-, and I^-. In hydrogen bonding solvents (those with an acidic proton) like NMA, it is to be expected that anion solvation would be high. This solvation energy consists, to a large extent, of the energy from the specific interaction

$$|\overline{X}| \ldots H \ldots N\!-\!COCH_3$$
$$\mid$$
$$CH_3$$

Limiting anionic conductance should inversely parallel the extent of hydrogen bonding and this is the order observed for NMA, i.e. λ_0^- increases $Cl^- < Br^- < I^-$.

The studies of Drago et al. (1965a,b) are also consistent with extensive anion solvation. The ultra-violet spectrum of $FeCl_3$ in NMA indicates the presence of only FeS_6^{3+} and Cl^-. This strikingly demonstrates the importance of anion solvation and dielectric constant (or Z-value) for this solvent since the donor strength of NMA is nearly the same as that of DMA.

C. DIMETHYL SULPHOXIDE (DMSO)

The physical properties of DMSO are tabulated in Table V and the limiting conductances of several 1 : 1 electrolytes are presented in Table VI. These salts are completely dissociated in DMSO at least up to concentrations of 10^{-3} M. Dimethyl sulphoxide appears to be a better solvating solvent than DMA.

TABLE IV

Conductance Data for N-Methylacetamide

Electrolyte	Λ_0	$K_{assoc.}$
KCl[a]	17·9	
NaCl[a]	17·8	
KBr[a]	19·0	
NaBr[a]	18·9	
KI[a]	20·7	
NaI[a]	20·1	
CsBr[a]	20·1	
Et$_4$NBr[a]	22·1	
Et$_4$NPi[a]	21·3	
HCl[b]	20·7[b]	
HPi[b]	20·9	0
NH$_4$ClO$_4$[b]	26·5	0
NH$_4$NO$_3$[b]	26·5	0
NH$_4$NO$_3$[b]	24·2	0
KClO$_4$[b]	25·2	0
KSCN[b]	24·5	0
KNO$_3$[b]	22·9	0
KPi[b]	20·2	0
NaClO$_4$[b]	25·0	0
NaSCN[b]	24·2	0
NaNO$_3$[b]	22·7	0
NaPi[b]	20·2	0

[a] French and Glover, 1955.
[b] Dawson et al., 1957.

Preliminary investigations (Drago et al., 1965a,b) indicate that $FeCl_4^-$ is unstable in DMSO and ionizes to produce cationic Fe(III) species. These species are most probably $Fe(DMSO)_6^{3+}$ and cationic iron chloro species.

The behaviour of $CoCl_2$ in DMSO and in solutions of Cl^- in DMSO has been studied by P. Van Der Voorn (unpublished results) and by Buffagni and Dunn (1961). The spectra of these solutions are given in Fig. 6. Comparing these spectra with the molar extinction curves of $CoCl_2$, $CoCl_3^-$ and $CoCl_4^{2-}$ reported by Fine (1962) one may make a few qualitative statements about the solution species which exist under the conditions of these experiments. The solution of $CoCl_2$ most certainly contains the tetrahedral species $CoCl_2(DMSO)_2$ and

TABLE V

Physical Properties of Dimethylsulphoxide

M.p. (°C)	$18 \cdot 4^a$
B.p. (°C)	$189 \cdot 0^a$
Specific conductivity (ohm^{-1} cm^{-1})	$3 \times 10^{-8}{}^a$
Density (g/cm^3) at 25°C	$1 \cdot 096^a$
Dielectric constant at 25°C	$46 \cdot 6^a$
Viscosity (centipoise) at 25°C	$1 \cdot 96^a$
Z–Value (kcal mole^{-1})	$71 \cdot 1^b$
Dq towards Ni(II) (cm^{-1})	773^c
Data for formation of the I$_2$ adduct	
$-\Delta H$ (kcal mole^{-1})	$4 \cdot 4^d$
K (l mole^{-1})	$11 \cdot 6$
Data for formation of the phenol adduct	
$-\Delta H$ (kcal mole^{-1})	$6 \cdot 5^d$
K (l mole^{-1})	182

[a] Sears et al., 1956a.
[b] Kosower, 1958a.
[c] Meek et al., 1962.
[d] Drago et al., 1963a.

$CoCl_3(DMSO)^-$; the formation of the anionic complex is accompanied by the formation of octahedral Co^{2+} species and absorption due to these species is observed below 550 mμ. As the concentration of $Cl^-(Ph_3NMeCl)$ is increased the spectra indicate progressive formation of $CoCl_3(DMSO)^-$ and $CoCl_4^{2-}$.

TABLE VI

Conductance Data for Dimethylsulphoxide[a]

Electrolyte	Λ_0	Electrolyte	Λ_0
KI	38·2	NaNO$_3$	40·8
NaI	37·6	KClO$_4$	39·1
KBr	38·4	NaClO$_4$	38·3
NaBr	38·0	KPi	31·7
KSCN	43·5	NaPi	31·1
NaSCN	43·0	Bu$_4$NI	35·0
KNO$_3$	41·5	Me$_3$NPhI	37·8

[a] Sears et al., 1956a.

Buffagni and Dunn (1961) reported that a solution of $CoCl_4^{2-}$ in DMSO contains approximately 20% tetrahedral species ($CoCl_4^{2-}$ and $CoCl_3(DMSO)^-$; the remainder of the Co^{2+} is present as the various octahedral forms.

An interesting effect is observed (Meek, 1962) in $NiCl_2$–DMSO solutions. At room temperature such solutions possess the light green colour of 6 co-ordinate Ni(II) complexes (visible spectra indicate octahedral Ni(II))

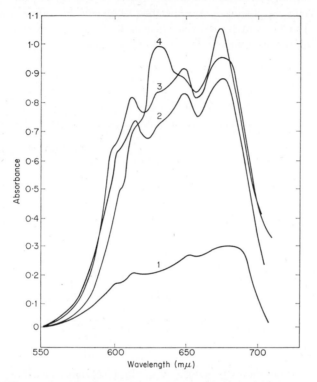

FIG. 6. Effect of chloride ion on visible spectrum of $CoCl_2$ in dimethylsulphoxide. (1) $[CoCl_2] = 0.002$ M; (2) $[Co^{2+}] = 0.003$ M, $[Cl^-] = 0.012$ M; (3) $[Co^{2+}] = 0.003$ M, $[Cl^-] = 0.024$ M; (4) $[Co^{2+}] = 0.003$ M, $[Cl^-] =$ large excess. Reproduced with permission from the *Journal of the Chemical Society*.

which are probably $Ni(DMSO)_6^{2+}$ and $NiCl(DMSO)_5^+$. Upon heating to approximately 50°C, the originally green solution turns to an intense deep blue characteristic of tetrahedral nickel. This colour change is completely reversible and upon heating a solution at 50°C for 6 hours, large blue crystals deposit. Analysis of these crystals is consistent with the formation of the mixed complex $Ni(DMSO)_6^{2+}NiCl_4^{2-}$. This is the same compound obtained from DMSO solutions of $NiCl_2$ upon addition of C_6H_6 at room temperature. This latter case is an example of a situation where the solid isolated and that in solution at room temperature are quite different.

D. NITROMETHANE AND NITROBENZENE (NM, NB)

The physical properties of nitromethane and nitrobenzene are presented together in Table VII.

It is very difficult to interpret the results obtained in the solvent nitromethane because of the difficulty in purifying this material. Two purification procedures are noted by Buffagni and Dunn (1961). It is probably safe to assume that unless purification is specified in an article, impure material was employed. Purification by distillation can be hazardous. Conductances for some electrolytes are given in the succeeding table.

TABLE VII

Physical Properties of Nitromethane and Nitrobenzene

	CH_3NO_2	$C_6H_5NO_2$
M.p. (°C)	$-28 \cdot 5^a$	$5 \cdot 8^a$
B.p. (°C)	$101 \cdot 3^a$	$210 \cdot 8^a$
Specific conductivity (ohm^{-1} cm^{-1}) at 25°C	$6 \cdot 56 \times 10^{-7}$ ^{a}	$9 \cdot 1 \times 10^{-7}$ ^{a}
Density (g/cm^3) at 25°C	$1 \cdot 1312^a$	$1 \cdot 193^a$
Dielectric constant at 30°C	$35 \cdot 9^a$	$34 \cdot 8^a$
Viscosity (centipoise) at 30°C	$0 \cdot 595^a$	$1 \cdot 634^a$
Z–Value (kcal mole^{-1})	—	—
Dq toward Ni(II)	—	—
$-\Delta H$ (kcal mole^{-1})(from $\Delta\nu_{OH}$ towards phenol)	$1 \cdot 9^b$	$2 \cdot 04^b$

[a] Weissberger et al., 1955.
[b] Joesten, 1962.

Interesting behaviour of solutions in these solvents has been noted and studied by several authors. They are fairly good solvating solvents (in the non-specific sense) and dissolve many electrolytes. Dissociation of molecular species into ions is often observed. The $K_{assoc.}$ for Bu$_4$NBr in C$_6$H$_5$NO$_2$ at 25°C is 46 (Sodek and Fuoss, 1950). As co-ordinating solvents they occupy positions at the weak end of the scale but they can and do act as Lewis bases.

The donor strength of CH$_3$NO$_2$ and C$_6$H$_5$NO$_2$ are unknown at present. It is reported (Drago et al., 1963a) that the —O—H frequency shift of phenol cannot be used to measure the donor strength of sulpholane, (CH$_2$CH$_2$)$_2$SO$_2$, because the phenol interacts with both oxygens. A similar effect is expected with nitro compounds so the enthalpies in Table VII represent lower limits and the actual values will have to be measured directly.

The crystal field parameter Dq has not been reported but there are indications that nitromethane displaces certain ligands from the co-ordination sphere of metal ions. This could occur through a hydrogen-bonding interaction of the donor ligand with CH_3NO_2 and does not necessarily imply nitromethane co-ordination. However, there is more direct evidence for nitromethane co-ordination. A most interesting study is the one of de Maine

TABLE VIII

Molar Conductance Data for Nitromethane

Salt	Λ_{molar}	Concentration
$Fe(HMPA)_6(ClO_4)_3$[a]	236	0·0005
$Cr(HMPA)_6(ClO_4)_3$[a]	253	0·005
$Al(HMPA)_6(ClO_4)_3$[a]	241	0·0005
$Fe(HMPA)_4(ClO_4)_2$[a]	185	0·002
$Mg(HMPA)_4(ClO_4)_2$[a]	153	0·001
$Co(HMPA)_4(ClO_4)_2$[b]	178	0·0105
$Ni(HMPA)_4(ClO_4)_2$[b]	184	0·005
$Zn(HMPA)_4(ClO_4)_2$[b]	180	0·002
$(Ph_3AsMe)_2NiCl_4$[c]	173	0·0005
$(Ph_3AsMe)_2CoI_4$[c]	151	0·0005
$(Et_4N)_2MnCl_4$[c]	200	0·0005
$(Ph_3AsMe)I$[c]	85	0·0005
$(Et_4N)I$[c]	97	0·0005
$Co(diars)_2(ClO_4)_2$[c]	177	0·0005
$Co(diars)_3(ClO_4)_3$[c]	262	0·0005

[a] Donoghue and Drago, 1963.
[b] Donoghue and Drago, 1962.
[c] Gill and Nyholm, 1959.

and Koubek (1959) on the system $FeCl_3-CH_3NO_2$ and the ternary system $FeCl_3-CH_3NO_2-CCl_4$. Beer's Law is not obeyed by solutions of $FeCl_3$ in CH_3NO_2 but on the other hand, for a given solvent composition, a linear relationship is found at all wavelengths when the ratio of optical density to total $FeCl_3$ is plotted against total $FeCl_3$. Conductivity measurements made on these solutions revealed normal behaviour in that the Onsager equation described the equivalent conductance as a function of $FeCl_3$ concentration, $[\Lambda = \Lambda_0 - (\alpha + \beta\Lambda_0)\sqrt{C}]$. Reference should be made to the original paper for details but these phenomena reportedly are only consistent with either one or the other of the following equilibria

$$FeCl_{3\ (sol)} + FeCl_{3\ (sol)} \rightleftharpoons \text{``complex''} \rightleftharpoons FeCl_4^-{}_{(sol)} + FeCl_2^+{}_{(sol)} \qquad (15a)$$

$$FeCl_{3\ (sol)} + FeCl_{3\ (sol)} \rightleftharpoons \text{``complex''} \rightleftharpoons Fe_2Cl_5^+{}_{(sol)} + Cl^-_{(sol)}. \qquad (15b)$$

In these equilibria, the concentration of the "complex" (probably Fe_2Cl_6) must be extremely small to account for the linear relationships mentioned above. By analogy with other solvents described herein, the equilibria in (15a) are preferred.

Buffagni and Dunn (1961) have made a thorough spectrophotometric study of solutions of $CoCl_2$ in nitromethane. The spectroscopic properties of these solutions as a function of Cl^- concentration are satisfactorily ration-

TABLE IX

Physical Properties of Acetone

M.p. (°C)	-95.4^a
B.p. (°C)	56.2^a
Specific conductivity (ohm^{-1} cm^{-1}) at 25°C	5.8×10^{-8} ^{a}
Density (g/cm^3) at 25°C	0.7851^a
Dielectric constant at 25°C	20.7^a
Viscosity (centipoise) at 30°C	0.2954^a
Z–Value (kcal mole^{-1})	65.7^b
Data for formation of I_2 adduct	
$-\Delta H$ (kcal mole^{-1})	2.5^c
K (l mole^{-1})	0.85
Data for formation of phenol adduct	
$-\Delta H$ (kcal mole^{-1})	3.3^c
K (l mole^{-1})	13.5

[a] Weissberger et al., 1955.
[b] Kosower, 1958a.
[c] Drago et al., 1963b.

alized on the basis of the following equilibria in which NM symbolizes CH_3NO_2

$$CoCl_2 + 2NM \rightleftharpoons CoCl_2(NM)_2 \qquad (16a)$$

$$CoCl_2(NM)_2 + Cl^- \rightleftharpoons CoCl_3(NM)^- + NM \qquad (16b)$$

$$CoCl_3(NM)^- + Cl^- \rightleftharpoons CoCl_4^{2-} + NM. \qquad (16c)$$

The existence of the first equilibrium described above is supported by the conductance of a solution of $CoCl_2$ in CH_3NO_2. No ionic species can be detected by this technique. In addition, careful examination of all the spectra revealed the absence of any "octahedral" complexes.

Gagnoux et al. (1958) interpreted the infra-red spectra of

$$p\text{-}RC_6N_4NO_2\text{-}MX_n \quad \text{and} \quad CH_3NO_2\text{-}MX_n$$

to indicate co-ordination by the nitro compounds; for the expected lowering of the $-N\underset{O}{\overset{O}{<}}$ asymmetric stretching frequency is observed. However, this work must be viewed with caution as spectra were obtained on solids. It is obvious that there is need for more definitive work with this solvent.

E. ACETONE (Ac)

The physical properties and some conductance data for acetone are presented in Tables IX and X.

TABLE X

Conductance Data for Acetone

Electrolyte	Λ_0	$K_{assoc.}$
Bu$_4$NI[a]	180·2	164
KSCN[a]	202·2	294
KI[b]	193·0	
NaI[b]	191·0	
KBr[b]	196·0	
NaBr[b]	194·0	
KSCN[b]	208·0	
NaSCN[b]	200·0	
KNO$_3$[b]	202·0	
NaNO$_3$[b]	200·0	
KClO$_4$[b]	196·0	
NaClO$_4$[b]	194·0	
KPi[b]	166·0	
NaPi[b]	159·0	

[a] Sears *et al.*, 1956a.
[b] Sears *et al.*, 1956b.

Very recently Fine (1962) has studied the formation of CoX_n^{2-n} complexes (X = Cl⁻, Br⁻, I⁻) in acetone. He established the presence of CoX_2, CoX_3^-, and CoX_4^{2-} complexes in solution. Their spectra indicate that they are all of tetrahedral symmetry. In this study it was *assumed* that acetone occupies the co-ordination positions unoccupied by X⁻. Using the concept of average ligand field (Jorgensen, 1956; Cotton *et al.*, 1961) (apparently valid for ligands near one another in the spectrochemical series), a value of Dq' (where Dq' is the ligand field splitting parameter for a tetrahedral complex) for acetone was calculated using known values of Dq' for the halides. The value $(4·3 \pm 0·4) \times 10^3$ cm⁻¹, which when multiplied by 9/4 to convert to an approximate 10 Dq for an octahedral field of acetone molecules about Co(II), produces a surprisingly high value of 9700 cm⁻¹. Fine also calculates equilibrium quotients for the formation of these complexes. This data is presented in Table XI.

A conductivity study (Dawson and Belcher, 1951) of $FeCl_3$ in acetone indicates the solute is incompletely dissociated. The ions are apparently univalent. This system may parallel that of nitromethane discussed above. More work is required on this system.

Friedman and Planc (1963) have published an interesting study of Cu(II) solvation in water–acetone mixtures. The absorption spectra of these solutions as a function of mole % H_2O are adequately explained by the equilibria

$$Cu(H_2O)_6^{2+} + ac \rightleftharpoons Cu(H_2O)_5ac^{2+} + H_2O \tag{17a}$$

and

$$Cu(H_2O)_5ac^{2+} + ac \rightleftharpoons Cu(H_2O)_4ac_2^{2+} + H_2O. \tag{17b}$$

These authors conclude that the ligand field strengths for water, acetone, and ethanol are qualitatively

$$water \geqq acetone \geqq ethanol.$$

TABLE XI

Equilibrium Quotients for CoX_n^{2-n} Species

Quotient	Cl⁻	Br⁻	I⁻
$\dfrac{[CoX_2]}{[Co^{2+}][X^-]^2}$	3×10^9	2×10^9	$> 10^9$
$\dfrac{[CoX_3^-]}{[CoX_2][X^-]}$	$> 10^5$	$> 10^5$	$2 \cdot 2 \times 10^4$
$\dfrac{[CoX_4^{2-}]}{[CoX_3^-][X\ ]}$	$5 \cdot 4 \times 10^2$	42	16

Katzin and Gebert (1950a,b,c) have studied several Co(II) salts in acetone and found behaviour paralleling that already discussed. The salts $Co(SCN)_2$, $CoCl_2$, and $Co(NO_3)_2$ all form anion complexes of the type CoX_3^- and CoX_4^{2-} with increasing X^- concentration. Unfortunately for our purpose, anhydrous salts were not used in this work and the complexes most certainly contain co-ordinated H_2O. The existence of aquo complexes is suggested by a ternary phase diagram published by Katzin and Ferraro (1950) showing the solid complexes $Co(NO_3)_2.6H_2O$, $Co(NO_3)_2.4H_2O$, $Co(NO_3)_2.3H_2O$, $Co(NO_3)_2.2H_2O$, and *probably* $Co(NO_3)_2.2ac$.

Koch (1950) has proposed the existence of an unusual species in acetone solutions of KI and AgI. Although AgI is insoluble in acetone, three moles of AgI reportedly dissolve per mole of KI in this solvent and the conductance of KI solutions is much lower when AgI is present. The formation of $I(AgI)_3^-$ was proposed to account for this. The same behaviour is observed for HgI_2. Further verification and/or study of this system would be interesting.

Studies of 1 : 1 adduct formation between various Lewis acids and aldehydes and aromatic or aliphatic ketones have been carried out by Susz (1959), by Gagnoux *et al.* (1958) and by Susz and Chalandon (1958). The only conclusion that can be drawn from these studies is that co-ordination occurs.

F. METHANOL AND ETHANOL (MeOH, EtOH)

The physical properties of these solvents are given in Table XII. A few conductance values are given in Table XIII.

TABLE XII

Physical Properties of Methanol and Ethanol

	MeOH	EtOH
M.p. (°C)	-97.5^a	-114.5^a
B.p. (°C)	64.51^a	78.3^a
Specific conductivity (ohm^{-1} cm^{-1}) at 25°C	$1.50 \times 10^{-9\,a}$	$1.35 \times 10^{-9\,a}$
Density (g/cm³) at 25°C	0.7868^a	0.7851^a
Dielectric constant at 25°C	32.6^a	24.3^a
Viscosity (centipoise) at 25°C	0.5445^a	1.078^a
Z–Value (kcal mole^{-1})	83.6^b	79.6^b
Dq toward Ni(II) (cm^{-1})	850^c	—
Data for formation of I_2 adduct		
$-\Delta H$ (kcal mole^{-1})	1.90^d	2.10^d
K (l mole^{-1})	0.47	0.45

[a] Weissberger *et al.*, 1955.
[b] Kosower, 1958a.
[c] V. Imhof, unpublished results.
[d] Tsubomura and Lang, 1961.

When dilute solutions of ferric chloride in methanol are examined spectrophotometrically (Drago *et al.*, 1965a,b) only cationic iron-chloro species are found—no tetrachloroferrate. This is predicted if one considers that methanol is a strong base toward first row transition metal cations ($Dq = 850$ cm^{-1}) and is a good solvating solvent as evidenced by the Z–Value and $K_{assoc.}$ for Bu$_4$NBr. Its dielectric constant is misleading with respect to its ionizing ability. The specific hydrogen-bonding interaction with anions probably is responsible for the high Z–Value and the dissociation of the anionic iron–chloro species.

One might question the $K_{assoc.}$ values for MgX^+ contained in Table XIII. If anion solvation were large, $K_{assoc.}$ would be expected to increase $K_{Cl^-} < K_{Br^-} < K_{I^-}$. If $Cl^- > Br^- > I^-$ is the order of anion donor strength toward the divalent cation Mg^{2+} and one considers that methanol is required to displace or extract the anion from the metal ion, the results can be accounted for. The magnitude of the $K_{assoc.}$ demonstrate strikingly the effect of a divalent cation on ion association relative to monovalent cations.

TABLE XIII

Conductance Data for MeOH and EtOH

Electrolyte	Λ_0	K_{as}	Solvent
LiBr[a]	89·1	—	MeOH
AgNO$_3$[c]	—	73·8	MeOH
KSCN[e]	115·7	11·0	MeOH
MgCl$_2$[b]	41·8	600·0	EtOH
MgBr$_2$[b]	44·6	215·0	EtOH
MgI$_2$[b]	47·2	180·0	EtOH
Bu$_4$NBr[d]	96·7	26·0	MeOH

[a] Sears et al., 1955a.
[b] Dawson and Golben, 1952.
[c] Busby and Griffiths, 1963.
[d] Sodek and Fuoss, 1950.
[e] Sears et al., 1955b.

Katzin (1952) has published spectrophotometric data which further support the above described solvent properties for alcohols. Spectra of $Ni(SCN)_2$ solutions in iso-C_3H_7OH indicate the existence, in significant amounts, of only $Ni(SCN)^+$ and $Ni(SCN)_2$ up to ratios of 4 to 1 of SCN^- to Ni^{2+}. Up to a ten-fold excess of chloride ion to cobalt, only $CoCl^+$ and $CoCl_2$ are detected. Much larger concentrations of Cl^- are needed to form $CoCl_3^-$. The same spectrum is obtained when either $CoCl_2$ or $CoCl_4^{2-}$ is added to this alcohol. The same is true for cobalt(II) bromide. At greater than a four-fold excess of SCN^- to cobalt, the species $Co(SCN)_2$ and $Co(SCN)_3^-$ are claimed but no $Co(SCN)_4^{2-}$ is reported in the solvents iso-C_3H_7OH and C_4H_9OH.

Several workers have carried out investigations in mixed alcohol–water mixtures but, as mentioned above, it is often difficult to interpret results from mixed solvents. In an interesting study, Mackor (1951) has investigated the stability of the AgI_2^- complex in mixed acetone–water and methanol–water solvents. Stability increases on going from water to acetone–water but not on going to methanol–water. Also, K_{form} for AgI_2^- is the same in methanol–acetone as it is in acetone–water mixtures. This study illustrates the similarities between alcohols (particularly methanol) and water. This work is consistent with the hydrogen-bonding propensity of alcohols.

G. PYRIDINE (Py)

The physical properties of this compound are presented in Table XIV and conductance data are given in Table XV.

TABLE XIV

Physical Properties of Pyridine

M.p. (°C)	$-41\cdot8^a$
B.p. (°C)	$115\cdot6^a$
Specific conductivity (ohm^{-1} cm^{-1}) at 25°C	$4\cdot0 \times 10^{-8}$ [a]
Density (g/cm^3) at 30°C	$0\cdot97281^a$
Dielectric constant at 25°C	$12\cdot3^a$
Viscosity (centipoise) at 30°C	$0\cdot829^a$
Z–Value (kcal mole^{-1})	$64\cdot0^b$
Dq toward Ni(II) (cm^{-1})	$\sim 1000^c$
Data for formation of I_2 adduct	
$\quad -\Delta H$ (kcal mole^{-1})	$7\cdot8^d$
$\quad K$ (l mole^{-1})	269
Data for formation of phenol adduct	
$\quad -\Delta H$ (kcal mole^{-1})	$8\cdot07^e$
$\quad K$ (l mole^{-1})	—

[a] Weissberger et al., 1955.
[b] Kosower, 1958a.
[c] Rosenthal and Drago, 1965.
[d] Tsubomura and Lang, 1961.
[e] Joesten, 1962.

Preliminary experiments (D. Hart, personal communication) on the stability of $FeCl_3$ and $FeCl_4^-$ in pyridine reveal that $FeCl_4^-$ is not formed from $FeCl_3$ in pyridine. The species are probably Fe_2Cl_6 and $py \rightarrow FeCl_3$. However, $FeCl_4^-$ has some stability in pyridine. Since addition of Cl^- to a pyridine solution of $FeCl_4^-$ results in an increase in absorbance at 316 and 365 mμ there is some dissociation of $FeCl_4^-$. The nature of the other species has not been ascertained.

A study of adducts of pyridine and substituted pyridines with $SbCl_5$ and phosphorus acids of the type PX_nF_{5-n} has been reported by Holmes et al. (1963). Molecular weights and conductivity measurements were interpreted to indicate that ionization does not occur and only 1 : 1 adducts are formed in nitrobenzene solution. They report enthalpies of adduct formation which were determined calorimetrically in nitrobenzene but which were not corrected for differences in non-specific solvation of the base and adduct.

As mentioned in Section II, Katzin (1950b) has studied the formation of pyridine complexes of $CoCl_2$ in various solvents. The existence of 1:1 and 2:1 py-$CoCl_2$ complexes in acetone has been established. The ion py$CoCl_3^-$ can be obtained when excess Cl^- is added to this system. These authors claim to have isolated $Co(py)_6Cl_2$, but Rosenthal and Drago (1965) have not been able to isolate this complex.

TABLE XV

Conductance Data for Pyridine

Electrolyte	Λ_0	$K_{assoc.}$
NH_4Pi^a	80·5	3580
KPi^a	65·7	10,000
$NaPi^a$	60·5	23,200
$LiPi^a$	58·6	12,000
$AgClO_4{}^a$	81·9	524
$AgNO_3{}^a$	86·9	1070
$PyHNO_3{}^a$	102·2	19,600
Bu_4NOAc^a	76·0	5880
$Bu_4NNO_3{}^a$	76·6	2700
Bu_4NI^a	73·1	2440
Bu_4NBr^a	75·3	4000
Bu_4NPi^a	57·7	780
KI^b	80·2	—
NaI^b	75·2	—
KBr^b	82·9	—
$NaBr^b$	77·9	—
$KNO_3{}^b$	84·7	—
$NaNO_3{}^b$	79·6	—

[a] Audrieth and Kleinberg, 1953.
[b] Sears et al., 1956b.

An interesting study by Fackler, mentioned under Section II, illustrates nicely the effect of a co-ordinating solvent on solute species. A similar study of the system $(Ni(acac)_2)_3$–C_6H_6–py was also carried out by Fackler (1962). The absorption spectra of benzene solutions of $(Ni(acac)_2)_3$ as a function of pyridine concentration indicate the following behaviour:

$$2(Ni(acac)_2)_3 + 3py \rightleftharpoons 3(Ni(acac)_2)_2 \cdot py \qquad (18a)$$

$$(Ni(acac)_2)_2 \cdot py + 3py \rightleftharpoons 2Ni(acac)_2 \cdot 2py. \qquad (18b)$$

These studies are of interest in that they dramatically illustrate solute aggregation in weakly co-ordinating solvents and the effect of a co-ordinating solvent on these aggregates.

The conductance data in Table XV indicate that electrolytes are extensively associated in pyridine. This is most certainly a result of the low dielectric constant of pyridine. Anion solvation through specific interaction does not occur in pyridine but the cation Li^+ is co-ordinated and solvated more than Na^+ and K^+ as shown by Λ_0 and $K_{assoc.}$ for common anion salts of these cations. Apparently, Na^+ and K^+ possess smaller solvodynamic units.

H. ACETONITRILE (MeCN)

Acetonitrile is the most common of the nitrile solvents and we have chosen to discuss solute behaviour in this solvent. Its physical properties are presented in Table XVI and some conductance data are given in Table XVII.

TABLE XVI

Physical Properties of Acetonitrile

M.p. (°C)	$-45 \cdot 7^a$
B.p. (°C)	$81 \cdot 6^a$
Specific conductivity (ohm^{-1} cm^{-1}) 25°C	$5 \cdot 9 \times 10^{-8\,a}$
Density (g/cm^3) 25°	$0 \cdot 7768^a$
Dielectric constant at 25°C	$36 \cdot 2^a$
Viscosity (centipoise) at 30°C	$0 \cdot 325^a$
Z-Value (kcal mole^{-1})	$71 \cdot 3^b$
Dq toward Ni(II) (cm^{-1})	1026^c
Data for formation of I_2 adduct	
$\quad -\Delta H$ (kcal mole^{-1})	$2 \cdot 3^d$
$\quad K$ (l mole^{-1})	$0 \cdot 40$
Data for formation of phenol adduct	
$\quad -\Delta H$ (kcal mole^{-1})	$3 \cdot 3^d$
$\quad K$ (l mole^{-1})	$5 \cdot 0$

[a] Weissberger et al., 1955.
[b] Kosower, 1958a.
[c] Joesten, 1962.
[d] Drago et al., 1963a.

The conductance data for the alkali metal perchlorates seem to follow the expected trend of increasing solvation: $Cs < Rb < K < Na < Li$. The $K_{assoc.}$ values change inversely to this sequence. From the data on the Me_4N^+ salts it appears that I^- and NO_3^- behave similarly in CH_3CN. The $K_{assoc.}$ values for the halides verify the anticipated sequence of ion solvation $(I^- < Br^- < Cl^-)$.

Marcinkowski (1961) has studied, spectrophotometrically and conducti-metrically, solutions of $CoCl_2$ in CH_3CN. It is claimed that the following equilibria account for the observed properties of the solutions:

$$2CoCl_2 + 6MeCN \rightarrow Co(MeCN)_6^{2+}CoCl_4^{2-} \tag{19a}$$

$$CoCl_4^{2-} + 2MeCN \rightleftharpoons CoCl_4(MeCN)_2^{2-}. \tag{19b}$$

The solute iron(III) chloride dissociates in CH_3CN into cationic and anionic species (Drago and Carlson, 1964):

$$FeCl_3 \rightleftharpoons (MeCN)FeCl_3 \rightleftharpoons FeCl_2(MeCN)_4^+ + Cl^- \tag{20a}$$

$$Cl^- + FeCl_3(MeCN) \rightleftharpoons FeCl_4^- + MeCN. \tag{20b}$$

TABLE XVII

Conductance Data for Acetonitrile

Electrolyte	Λ_0	$K_{assoc.}$
KI[a]	186·7	—
LiClO$_4$[b]	183·4	68·4
NaClO$_4$[b]	192·3	70·9
KClO$_4$[b]	208·2	97·7
RbClO$_4$[b]	203·0	103·7
CsClO$_4$[b]	207·6	144·6
Me$_4$NNO$_3$[c]	200·5	23·0
Bu$_4$NNO$_3$[c]	168·2	7·0
Me$_4$NCl[d]	193·1	77·5
Me$_4$NBr[d]	192·7	41·4
Me$_4$NI[d]	195·3	27·5

[a] Marcinkowski, 1961.
[b] Minc and Werblan, 1962.
[c] Berns and Fuoss, 1961.
[d] Popov and Skelly, 1954.

Barnes and Hume (1963) have studied the complexes formed by copper(II) and bromide ion in acetonitrile. They find $CuBr_4^-$ is stable in this solvent as a "tetrahedral" complex. The complex $CuBr_3^-$ has been formulated, not as a tetrahedral ion, but rather as a five co-ordinate trigonal bypyramidal complex

Beattie and Webster (1963) have studied solutions of PCl_5 and $SbCl_5$ in

CH_3CN by infra-red spectroscopy. They conclude from spectroscopic studies that PCl_5 ionizes as

$$2PCl_5 \rightleftharpoons PCl_4^+ + PCl_6^- \tag{21}$$

while $SbCl_5$ dissociates *and* co-ordinates MeCN:

$$2SbCl_5 \rightleftharpoons SbCl_4(MeCN)_2^+ + SbCl_6^-. \tag{22}$$

Ellendt and Cruse (1952) have published their findings on conductance studies of HgX_2 solutions. They observe formation of the complexes HgX_3^-,

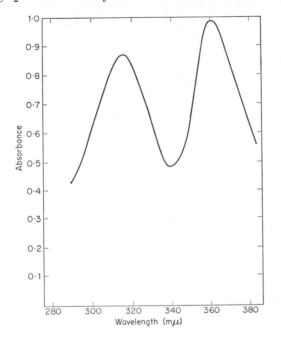

FIG. 7. Absorption spectrum of $FeCl_3$ in tetramethylene sulphone. $[FeCl_3] = 2 \cdot 0 \times 10^{-4}$ M. Reproduced with permission from the *Journal of the Chemical Society*.

HgX_4^{2-}, and $Hg_2X_5^-$. Free energies (in kcal mole^{-1}) of formation of the complexes $Hg_2X_5^-$ and HgX_4^{2-} have been reported for the following reactions in water and acetronitrile:

$$2HgX_2 + R_4NX \rightleftharpoons R_4NHg_2X_5 \tag{23a}$$

and

$$R_4NHgX_3 + R_4NX \rightleftharpoons (R_4N)_2HgX_4. \tag{23b}$$

1. TETRAMETHYLENE SULPHONE (SULPHOLANE–TMSO$_2$)

Sulpholane represents a very interesting non-aqueous solvent, the physical properties of which are listed in Table XVIII. Limiting conductances and $K_{assoc.}$ for a few salts are given in Table XIX.

9

Some inconvenience is encountered in working with sulpholane because of its high melting point (around room temperature). Solutions are more readily handled because of the large molal freezing point depression constant. The solvent 3-methylsulpholane has a somewhat lower melting point.

Many inorganic substances are found to be miscible and soluble in sulpholane. The limited data available indicate a resemblance, as far as solubilities are concerned, to SO_2. The donor properties of sulpholane are very interesting. Toward iodine, the donor strength is comparable to that of benzene. Toward phenol it is proposed that both oxygen atoms co-ordinate to the hydrogen and a greater donor strength is observed toward this acid. The donor properties of sulphones, sulphoxides and sulphites have been reported and the trends interpreted (Drago et al., 1963a). The spectrum of $FeCl_3$ in this solvent is shown in Fig. 7. It appears that $FeCl_4^-$ is stable in this solvent.

TABLE XVIII

Physical Properties of Sulpholane

M.p. (°C)	28·86[a]
B.p. (°C) at 760 mm	283[a]
Specific conductivity (ohm^{-1} cm^{-1}) at 25°C	2×10^{-8} [a]
Dielectric constant (30°C)	44[a]
Density (g/cm^3) 30°C)	1·2615[a]
Viscosity (centipoise) (30°C)	9·87[a]
Molal freezing point depression constant	66·2[a]
Z-Value (kcal mole^{-1})	77·5[c]
Dq toward Ni^{2+}	—
Data for iodine adduct	
$-\Delta H$ (kcal mole^{-1})	2·2[b]
K (l mole^{-1})	0·73
Data for phenol adduct	
$-\Delta H$ (kcal mole^{-1})	5·0[b]
K (l mole^{-1})	17·1

[a] Burwell and Langford, 1959.
[b] Drago et al., 1963a.
[c] D. Hart, personal communication.

Langford and Langford (1962) have investigated the species present when $CoCl_2$ and $Co(ClO_4)_2$ are dissolved in sulpholane. Conductivity measurements of $CoCl_2$ solutions prove the absence of appreciable ionization and a blue solid can be isolated from the blue solutions. This solid possesses the stoichiometry $CoCl_2 \cdot TMSO_2$. From the shape of the visible absorption bands and their intensities, the structure of the complex is proposed to be tetrahedral.

Dissolution of $Co(ClO_4)_2$ in $TMSO_2$ produces a red solution and the complex $Co(TMSO_2)_3(ClO_4)_2$ can be isolated. This complex possesses an absorption spectrum similar to $Co(H_2O)_6^{2+}$. The $\Lambda_{equiv.}$ at a concentration of $1 \cdot 1 \times 10^{-3}$ M is $18 \cdot 4$ ohms^{-1} cm^{-2} (cf. with values for $1 : 1$ electrolytes as given in the table). Both of these complexes are highly unstable with respect to hydrolysis.

TABLE XIX

Conductance Data for Sulpholane[a]

Salt	Λ_0	$K_{assoc.}$
NaSCN	~13·5	48
MeN⬡O$^+$I$^-$	~12·5	77
LiNO$_3$	~10·5	91
Ph$_4$AsCl	~10·5	0
MeNPh$_3$I	—	0

[a] Burwell and Langford, 1959.

V. Some Generalizations

The solute ferric chloride has been investigated in all the solvents discussed in the previous section and this enables some interesting solvent comparisons to be made. It should be emphasized at the start that solutes for which the donor order of the solvents varies from that for ferric chloride will behave differently. Acetonitrile, tetramethylenesulphone, nitromethane and nitro-benzene represent a class of compounds the dielectric constant and solvating ability of which are appreciable ($K_{assoc.}$ for R_4NBr in CH_3CN and $C_6H_5NO_2$ are 41 and 46, respectively; the dielectric constants are in the range 36–40, the Z-values are $71 \cdot 3$ kcal mole^{-1} and 67 kcal mole^{-1}) but the donor strengths are weak towards cationic iron(III). Triethylphosphate and acetone have donor properties that are probably equivalent to the above solvents but are poorer solvating solvents. In all six of these solvents the solute $FeCl_4^-$ is stable and the principle species formed when $FeCl_3$ is added in small amounts are $FeCl_2S_4^+$ and $FeCl_4^-$, i.e. only steps a and b occur in equation (11). The solvent DMA is a better donor toward iron(III) than the above solvents and also a better solvating solvent as evidenced by $K_{assoc.}$ for R_4NBr but the essential species present are still $FeCl_2S_4^+$ and $FeCl_4^-$ when $FeCl_3$ is dissolved and the solute $FeCl_4^-$ is not appreciably dissociated. In DMA as in most of the above mentioned solvents there is probably also some $FeCl_3S$ present but the amount has not been determined. N-Methylacetamide is a solvent whose donor properties are slightly less than DMA but whose solvating ability is greater, because of hydrogen-bonding to chloride and its high dielectric constant. In this solvent $FeCl_4^-$ is not stable and the principle species in dilute $FeCl_3$ solutions at equilibrium are cationic iron complexes and Cl^-. The equilibrium in equation (11) is displaced toward more chloride dissociation than in the case of DMA because of the greater solvating ability of N-methylacetamide.

A comparison of DMA and DMSO is interesting. In the latter solvent the principal species are cationic iron complexes and chloride ion. Tetra-chloroferrate is dissociated in this solvent. The donor properties of DMA and DMSO are similar, though the latter solvent is probably a slightly better donor. The $K_{assoc.}$ for R_4NBr, the Z-value and the dielectric constant all indicate that DMSO is a better solvating solvent than DMA. These two effects (especially the solvating ability) account for the behaviour of $FeCl_3$ and $FeCl_4^-$ in DMSO relative to DMA.

Methanol is a good solvating solvent when specific interactions are possible but only fair when these effects are minor. It is a strong donor toward some acids, e.g. Ni^{2+}, but a weak donor towards distortable (soft) acids, e.g. I_2, Et_3PbCl, etc. Consequently, its behaviour as a solvent will be variable. Towards ferric chloride, strong co-ordination to cationic iron(III) and solvation of chloride ion cause $FeCl_4^-$ to be unstable. Cationic iron species and chloride ion are the principal species in dilute solutions of ferric chloride in methanol.

Pyridine is an interesting solvent for it has strong donor properties especially toward distortable acids but is a poor solvating solvent. The principle species present when $FeCl_4^-$ and $FeCl_3$ are dissolved in pyridine are $FeCl_3 . py$ and $FeCl_4^-$ in the former instance and $FeCl_3 . py$ in the latter.

The results of the experiments with the solute $(Ph_3AsCH_3)_2CoCl_4$ can be similarly interpreted. The species in CH_3NO_2 is reported to be predominantly $CoCl_3S^-$. The structure of the species $CoCl_3S^-$ is not known other than that the symmetry about Co^{2+} is roughly tetrahedral. Addition of $CoCl_2$ to $MeNO_2$ results in a non-conducting solution of $CoCl_2(MeNO_2)_2$.

The two amides and dimethylsulphoxide are sufficiently good bases and possess sufficiently high dielectric constants to displace Cl^- from the metal co-ordination sphere, resulting in the formation of the cationic species CoS_6^{2+}, $CoClS_5^+$ in addition to some $CoCl_3S^-$, $CoCl_4^{2-}$ and Cl^-. The order of stability of $CoCl_4^{2-}$ in these solvents is: $CH_2Cl_2 > CH_3NO_2 > DMA > DMF > DMSO$. For those solvents which have been investigated with both solutes, $CoCl_4^{2-}$ and $FeCl_4^-$, the order is seen to be similar.

In conclusion, we have been able to account for a large amount of non-aqueous solvent chemistry with the Co-ordination Model. In view of the complex nature of the processes being discussed (see Section III) the agreement between predicted and observed behaviour is remarkable. This is undoubtedly due to the fact that the comparisons have involved similar systems where drastic entropy differences are not encountered. The general use of the term "solvating solvent" has also been in the general distinction that there is decreased ion-pairing with increased solvation. Furthermore the spectroscopic techniques employed to examine dissociation of the systems selected are not sensitive to the extent of ion-pairing but mainly depend upon the number and type of the groups in the co-ordination sphere of the metal. The success of the Co-ordination Model in correlating the chemistry discussed above is the strongest argument in support of this model. It is hoped that this limited success will encourage further experimentation so that the limits of this general approach can be ascertained.

REFERENCES

Andrews, L. J. and Keefer, R. M. (1961) "Advances in Inorganic Chemistry and Radiochemistry" (H. J. Emeleus and A. G. Sharpe, eds.) Vol. 3, p. 91. Academic Press, New York.
Audrieth, L. F. and Kleinberg, J. (1953) "Non-Aqueous Solvents", p. 125. Wiley, New York.
Baaz, M. and Gutmann, V. (1959) *Mh. Chem.* **90**, 426.
Baaz, M., Gutmann, V. and Hübner, L. (1960) *Mh. Chem.* **91**, 537.
Barnes, J. C. and Hume, D. N. (1963) *Inorg. Chem.* **2**, 444.
Beattie, I. R. and Webster, M. (1963) *J. chem. Soc.* 38.
Beilstein (1962) "Bielsteins Handbuch Der Organishen Chemie" (H.-G. Boit, ed.), p. 124. Vierte Auflage, Vierter Band, Erstes Teil.
Benesi, H. A. and Hildebrand, J. H. (1949) *J. Amer. chem. Soc.* **71**, 2703.
Bent, H. A. (1961) *Chem. Rev.* **61**, 275.
Berns, D. S. and Fuoss, R. M. (1961) *J. Amer. chem. Soc.* **83**, 1321.
Bränden, C. and Lindquist, I. (1960) *Acta chem. Scand.* **14**, 726.
Buffagni, S. and Dunn, T. M. (1961) *J. chem. Soc.* 5105.
Bull, W. E., Madan, S. K. and Willis, J. E. (1963) *Inorg. Chem.* **2**, 303.
Burwell, R. L. and Langford, C. H. (1959) *J. Amer. chem. Soc.* **81**, 3799.
Busby, R. E. and Griffiths, U. S. (1963) *J. chem. Soc.* 902.
Connick, R. E. and Fiat, D. N. (1963) *J. chem. Phys.* **39**, 1349.
Cotton, F. A. and Francis, R. (1960) *J. Amer. chem. Soc.* **82**, 2986.
Cotton, F. A. and Francis, R. (1961) *J. inorg. nucl. Chem.* **17**, 62.
Cotton, F. A., Goodgame, D. M. L. and Goodgame, M. (1961) *J. Amer. chem. Soc.* **83**, 4690.
Dawson, K. R. and Belcher, R. L. (1951) *Trans. Ky. Acad. Sci.* **13**, 129; *Chem. Abstr.* **45**: 10005 *g*.
Dawson, L. R. and Golben, M. (1952) *J. Amer. chem. Soc.* **74**, 4134.
Dawson, L. R., Wilhoit, E. D., Holmes, R. R. and Sears, P. G. (1957) *J. Amer. chem. Soc.* **79**, 3004.
Donoghue, J. T. and Drago, R. S. (1962) *Inorg. Chem.* **1**, 866.
Donoghue, J. T. and Drago, R. S. (1963) *Inorg. Chem.* **2**, 1158.
Drago, R. S. and Meek, D. W. (1961) *J. phys. Chem.* **65**, 1446.
Drago, R. S., Carlson, R. L. and Hart, D. (1965a) (in the press).
Drago, R. S., Carlson, R. L. and Purcell, K. F. (1965b) (in the press).

Drago, R. S., Wayland, B. and Carlson, R. L. (1963a) *J. Amer. chem. Soc.* **85**, 3125.

Drago, R. S., Carlson, R. L., Rose, N. J. and Wenz, D. A. (1961) *J. Amer. chem. Soc.* **83**, 3572.

Drago, R. S., Meek, D. W., Joesten, M. D. and LaRoche, L. (1963b) *Inorg. Chem.* **2**, 124.

Dunn, T. M. (1960) In "Modern Coordination Chemistry" (J. Lewis and R. Wilkins, eds.), p. 229. Interscience, New York.

Ellendt, G. and Cruse, K. (1952) *Z. phys. Chem.* **201**, 130.

Fackler, J. P., Jr. (1962) *J. Amer. chem. Soc.* **84**, 24.

Fackler, J. P., Jr. (1963) *Inorg. Chem.* **2**, 266.

Fine, D. A. (1962) *J. Amer. chem. Soc.* **84**, 1139.

French, C. M. and Glover, K. H. (1955) *Trans. Faraday Soc.* **51**, 1418, 1427.

Friedman, N. J. and Plane, R. A. (1963) *Inorg. Chem.* **2**, 11.

Gagnaux, P., Janjic, D. and Susz, B. P. (1958) *Helv. chim. Acta*, **41**, 1322.

Gerding, H., Königstein, J. A. and van der Worm, E. R. (1960) *Spectrochim. Acta* **16**, 1881.

Gill, N. S. and Nyholm, R. S. (1959) *J. chem. Soc.* 3997.

Gutmann, V. (1959) *J. Phys. Chem.* **63**, 378.

Gutmann, V. and Baaz, M. (1959) *Mh. Chem.* **90**, 729.

Holmes, R. R., Gallagher, W. P. and Carter, Jr., R. P. (1963) *Inorg. Chem.* **2**, 437.

Jackson, J. H., Lemons, J. F. and Taube, H. (1960) *J. chem. Phys.* **32**, 553.

Job, P. (1928) *Annls. Chim.* [10], **9**, 113.

Joesten, M. D. (1962) Thesis, University of Illinois.

Joesten, M. D. and Drago, R. S. (1962a) *J. Amer. chem. Soc.* **84**, 2037.

Joesten, M. D. and Drago, R. S. (1962b) *J. Amer. chem. Soc.* **84**, 3817.

Joesten, M. D. and Drago, R. S. (1965) (in the press).

Jørgensen, C. K. (1956) *Acta chem. Scand.* **10**, 887.

Katzin, L. I. (1952) *J. chem. Phys.* **20**, 1165.

Katzin, L. I. and Ferraro, J. R. (1950) *J. Amer. chem. Soc.* **72**, 5451.

Katzin, L. I. and Gebert, E. (1950a) *J. Amer. chem. Soc.* **72**, 5455.

Katzin, L. I. and Gebert, E. (1950b) *J. Amer. chem. Soc.* **72**, 5464.

Katzin, L. I. and Gebert, E. (1950c) *J. Amer. chem. Soc.* **72**, 5659.

Koch, F. K. V. (1930) *J. chem. Soc.* 2385.

Korinek, G. J. and Schneider, W. G. (1957) *Canad. J. Chem.* **35**, 1157.

Kosower, E. M. (1958a) *J. Amer. chem. Soc.* **80**, 3253.

Kosower, E. M. (1958b) *J. Amer. chem. Soc.* **80**, 3261.

Kosower, E. M. (1958c) *J. Amer. chem. Soc.* **80**, 3267.

Landesman, H. and Williams, R. E. (1961) *J. Amer. chem. Soc.* **83**, 2663.

Langford, C. H. and Langford, P. O. (1962) *Inorg. Chem.* **1**, 184.

Lester, G. R., Gover, T. A. and Sears, P. G. (1956) *J. phys. Chem.* **60**, 1076.

Lester, G. R., Vaughan, J. W. and Sears, P. G. (1958) *Trans. Ky. Acad. Sci.* **19**, 28.

Lindquist, I. (1958) *Acta chem. Scand.* **12**, 135.

Lindquist, I. and Bränden, C. I. (1959) *Acta crystallogr.* **12**, 692.

Mackor, E. L. (1951) *Rec. Trav. chim.* **70**, 457.

de Maine, P. A. D. and Koubek, E. (1959) *J. inorg. nucl. Chem.* **11**, 329.

Marcinkowski, A. E. (1961) *Dissertation Abstrs.* **22**, 97.

Meek, D. W. (1962) Thesis, University of Illinois, p. 60.

Meek, D. W. and Drago, R. S. (1961) *J. Amer. chem. Soc.* **83**, 4322.

Meek, D. W., Drago, R. S. and Piper, T. S. (1962) *Inorg. Chem.* **1**, 285.

Meek, D. W., Straub, D. K. and Drago, R. S. (1960) *J. Amer. chem. Soc.* **82**, 6013.

Minc, S. and Werblan, L. (1962) *Electrochim. Acta*, **7**, 256.

Newman, L. and Hume, D. N. (1957) *J. Amer. chem. Soc.* **79**, 4571.

Niedzielski, R. J., Drago, R. S. and Middaugh, R. L. (1965) (in the press).

gÀÀÀ

Onak, T. P., Landesman, H., Williams, R. E. and Shapiro, I. (1959) *J. phys. Chem.* **67**, 1533.

Orgel, L. E. (1960) "An Introduction to Transition Metal Chemistry", p. 133. Methuen, London.

Popov, A. I. and Skelly, N. E. (1954) *J. Amer. chem. Soc.* **76**, 5309.

Rosenthal, M. and Drago, R. S. (1965) (in the press).

Schmulbach, C. D. and Drago, R. S. (1960) *J. Amer. chem. Soc.* **82**, 4484.

Schneider, W. G. and Reeves, L. W. (1957) *Canad. J. Chem.* **35**, 251.

Sears, P. G., Holmes, R. R. and Dawson, L. R. (1955b) *Trans. electrochem. Soc.* **102**, 145.

Sears, P. G., Lester, G. R. and Dawson, L. R. (1956b) *J. Phys. Chem.* **60**, 1433.

Sears, P. G., McNeer, R. L. and Dawson, L. R. (1955a) *Trans. electrochem. Soc.* **102**, 269.

Sears, P. G., Wilhoit, E. D. and Dawson, L. R. (1956a) *J. phys. Chem.* **60**, 169.

Sheldon, J. C. and Tyree, S. Y. (1958) *J. Amer. chem. Soc.* **80**, 4775.

Shier, G. D. and Drago, R. S. (1965) (in the press).

Shoolery, J. N., Pimentel, G. C. and Huggins, C. M. (1955) *J. chem. Phys.* **23**, 1244.

Sodek, H. and Fuoss, R. M. (1950) *J. Amer. chem. Soc.* **72**, 301.

Susz, B. P. and Chalandon, P. (1958) *Helv. chim. Acta*, **61**, 1332.

Susz, B. (1959) *C.R. Acad. Sci., Paris* **248**, 2569.

Swinehart, J. H. and Taube, H. (1962) *J. chem. Phys.* **37**, 1579.

Tsubomura, H. and Lang, R. (1961) *J. Amer. chem. Soc.* **83**, 2085.

Voitovich, B. A. and Barabonova, A. S. (1961) *Zh. neorg. Khim.* **6**, 2098; Eng. translation, **6**, 1073.

Weissberger, A., Proskauer, E. S., Riddich, J. A., Toops, E. E. Jr. (1955) "Techniques of Organic Chemistry", Vol. VII. Interscience, New York.

Woldbye, F. (1955) *Acta chem. Scand.* **9**, 299.

CHAPTER 6

Liquid Sulphur Dioxide

T. C. WADDINGTON

School of Molecular Sciences, University of Warwick, Coventry, England

I.	Introduction	253
II.	Solubilities in Liquid Sulphur Dioxide	254
III.	Solvate Formation with Sulphur Dioxide	256
IV.	Electrical Conductivity and Ionization in Liquid Sulphur Dioxide Solutions	260
V.	Electrochemical Studies in Solutions in Liquid Sulphur Dioxide	264
	A. Electrolysis	264
	B. Electrode Potentials	264
VI.	Chemical Reactions in Liquid Sulphur Dioxide	266
	A. Solvolysis	266
	B. Metathetical Reactions	267
	C. Amphoteric Reactions	268
	D. Oxidation–reduction Reactions	271
	E. Complex Formation	272
VII.	Isotopic Exchange Reactions in Liquid Sulphur Dioxide	273
VIII.	Conclusion and Summary	280
	References	282

I. INTRODUCTION

The behaviour of liquid sulphur dioxide as an ionizing solvent has been a subject of extensive study since the work of Walden (1902) and Walden and Centnerszwer (1899, 1902a,b,c, 1903) at the turn of the century. Much of the work in the solvent before 1945 has been summarized by Jander (1949) and by Audrieth and Kleinberg (1953). There has been a fairly recent short review by Elving and Markowitz (1960), and more recently Lichtin (1963) has reviewed the physical chemistry and physical organic chemistry of solutions of electrolytes in the solvent. There seems little point in re-reviewing at length the topics covered in earlier reviews, and these topics will only be dealt with cursorily except where previous interpretations have been in doubt. However, no review has done more than briefly mention the investigations of isotopic exchange in the solvent, so vital to a proper understanding of its mode of action, and these will be discussed at length.

The relevant physical properties of liquid sulphur dioxide are given in Table I. The melting to boiling point range makes sulphur dioxide a very useful solvent, and its vapour pressure is sufficiently low at 0°C that it can be safely handled under its own vapour in sealed glass vessels without special precautions. This is an important consideration, as contamination by water and oxygen must be avoided to prevent complicating side reactions.

TABLE I

Some Physical Constants of Sulphur Dioxide

Property	Value	Temperature (°K)
Melting point (°K)	197·64	—[a]
Boiling point (°K)	263·08	—[a]
Liquid range	65°	
Enthalpy of fusion (kcal mole^{-1})	1·9691	197·64[a]
Enthalpy of vapourization (kcal mole^{-1})	5·96	263·08[a]
Vapour pressure (cm Hg)*	28·48	243[a]
	53·06	253[a]
	115·96	273[a]
	171·4	283[a]
	2456·0	293[a]
Viscosity of liquid (millipoise)	$n = 4·03 - 0·0363T(°C)$	—[b, c]
		—
Dielectric constant of liquid	$D = 95·12 \exp \{-6·676 \times 10^3 T(°K)\}$	—[c, d, e]
	$D = 15·4$	273·4
Dipole moment (Debye)	1·62	256·9[f]
S—O Bond Length (Å)	1·43	—[g]
O—S—O Bond Angle	119·5°	—[g]
Density (g cm^{-3})	1·46	263·1[h]
Specific conductivity (ohm^{-1} cm^{-1})	$3-4 \times 10^{-8}$	—[i, j]
Molar ebullioscopic constant (deg mole^{-1})	1·48	
Molar cryoscopic constant (deg mole^{-1})	0·0393	

* Calculated from

$$\log \quad = -\frac{1867·52}{T} - 0·015865T + 0·000015574T^2 + 13·07540$$

[a] Giauque and Stephenson (1938).

[b] Luchinskii (1938).

[c] Lichtin and Leftin (1956).

[d] Vierk (1950).

[e] Nickerson and McIntosh (1957).

[f] Le Fevre (1953)

[g] Kivelson (1954).

[h] Lichtin and Glazer (1951).

[i] Franklin (1911).

[j] Lichtin (1963).

II. SOLUBILITIES IN LIQUID SULPHUR DIOXIDE

In general, covalent substances are considerably more soluble in liquid sulphur dioxide than ionic compounds. Table II below lists the solubilities in liquid sulphur dioxide of salts of monovalent inorganic cations. It will be seen that only the alkali metal iodides are soluble to the extent of more than a mole per thousand grams of solvent, and that the solubility of most of the others is only a few millimoles. All the tetramethylammonium halides are freely soluble in liquid sulphur dioxide, probably because of their low lattice energies. The solubilities of some salts of divalent and trivalent cations are given in Table III. It will be seen that, with the exceptions of aluminium chloride and antimony trichloride, which are covalent, solubilities are at most

TABLE II

Solubilities in Liquid Sulphur Dioxide of Alkali Metal and other Monovalent Salts [a, b]

Ion	SO_3^{2-}	SO_4^{2-}	F^-	Cl^-	Br^-	I^-	SCN^-	CN^-	ClO_4^-	$CH_3CO_2^-$
Li^+	—	1·55	23·0	2·82	6·0	1490·0	—	—	—	3·48
Na^+	1·37	insol.	6·9	insol.	1·36	1000·0	80·5	3·67	—	8·90
K^+	1·58	insol.	3·1	5·5	40·0	2490·0	502·0	2·62	—	0·61
Rb^+	1·27	—	—	27·2	sol.	sol.	—	—	—	—
Cs^+	—	—	—	—	—	—	—	—	—	—
NH_4^+	2·67	5·07	less than 27 at 50°C	1·67	6·0	580·0	6160·0	—	2·14	141·0
Tl^+	4·96	0·417	insol.	0·292	0·60	1·81	0·915	0·522	0·43	285·0
Ag^+	insol.	insol.	insol.	20·07	0·159	0·68	0·845	1·42	—	1·02

Data refer to 0°C unless otherwise stated. Solubilities are in millimoles per 1000 g sulphur dioxide.

[a] Jander (1949).
[b] Gmelin (1953).

only a few millimoles per thousand grams of solvent. In general, covalent substances are very soluble. Such substances as bromine, iodine monochloride, thionyl chloride, thionyl bromide, boron trichloride, carbon disulphide, phosphorous trichloride, arsenic trichloride and phosphorous oxychloride are miscible with liquid sulphur dioxide in all proportions. Carbon tetrachloride, silicon tetrachloride and the other group IV tetrahalogenides are completely miscible with liquid sulphur dioxide above a critical miscibility temperature which varies from compound to compound (Bond and Beach, 1926; Bond and Stephens, 1929; Bond and Crone, 1934; Bond and Belton, 1945).

The pioneer work of Walden and Centnerszwer (1899, 1902a,b,c, 1903) showed that, with a few exceptions, liquid sulphur dioxide is an excellent solvent for organic compounds. Amines, ethers, esters, alcohols, sulphides, mercaptans and acids, both aliphatic and aromatic, are readily soluble. Aromatic hydrocarbons dissolve readily and so do olefins, but paraffins possess only limited solubility. Halogenated and nitrated aromatic compounds are very soluble. The selective solubility of aromatic hydrocarbons in liquid sulphur dioxide is the basis of the Edeleanu process for refining kerosene. Water is not completely

TABLE III

Solubilities in Liquid Sulphur Dioxide of Divalent and Other Metal Salts [a, b]

Ion	SO_3^{2-}	SO_4^{2-}	F^-	Cl^-	Br^-	I^-	SCN^-	CN^-	ClO_4^-	$CH_3CO_2^-$
Be^{2+}	—	—	—	5·8	—	—	—	—	—	—
Mg^{2+}	—	—	—	1·47	1·3	0·50	—	—	—	—
Ca^{2+}	—	—	—	—	—	—	—	—	—	—
Sr^{2+}	—	—	—	—	—	—	—	—	—	—
Ba^{2+}	insol.	—	—	insol.	insol.	18·15	insol.	—	—	—
Zn^{2+}	—	—	—	11·75	—	3·45	40·4	—	—	—
Cu^{2+}	—	—	—	insol.	—	1·17	—	—	—	—
Hg^{2+}	—	0·338	—	3·8	2·06	0·265	0·632	0·556	—	2·98
Pb^{2+}	—	insol.	2·16	0·69	0·328	0·195	0·371	0·386	—	2·46
Co^{2+}	—	—	—	1·00	—	12·2	insol.	—	—	—
Ni^{2+}	—	—	—	insol.	—	—	insol.	—	—	0·08
Al^{3+}	—	—	—	v. sol.	0·60	5·64	—	—	—	—
Sb^{3+}	—	—	0·56	575·0	21·8	0·26	—	—	—	—
Bi^{3+}	—	—	—	0·60	3·44	—	—	—	—	—

Data refer to 0°C unless otherwise stated. Solubilities are in millimoles per 1000 g SO_2

[a] Jander (1949).
[b] Gmelin (1953).

miscible with liquid sulphur dioxide, but the extent of its solubility at various temperatures has never been accurately determined. Wickert (1938a,b) has reported the existence of a compound $SO_2.H_2O$ which remains as a stable residue upon evaporation of a solution of water in sulphur dioxide at 0°C. He has also reported that the solubility of water in liquid sulphur dioxide at 22°C is 2·3 g per 100 g of SO_2. Conductivity measurements indicate a fair solubility at temperatures below 0°C.

III. SOLVATE FORMATION WITH SULPHUR DIOXIDE

Sulphur dioxide forms stable solvates with many alkali metal halides and other substances, similar to the crystalline hydrates and ammoniates formed with water and ammonia. These solvates have been studied in detail by

Jander and Mesech (1938a,b), by Foote and Fleischer (1931, 1932, 1934), by Ephraim and Kornblum (1916) and by Ephraim and Aellig (1923). In many cases the heat of formation of the adducts has been determined from vapour pressure measurements. The molar ratio of sulphur dioxide to adduct generally varies from one to four, but much higher ratios are sometimes encountered. The information on the alkali metal salts is summarized in Table IV below.

The early workers did not in fact obtain complete phase diagrams of the systems $MX—SO_2$, and in consequence there is probably still a large number of undetected solvate phases in these systems. The mono-adducts with the tetramethylammonium halides are probably best regarded as halosulphinates,

with ions of structure $X—S{\overset{O^-}{\underset{O}{\diagup\diagdown}}}$, by comparison with the halosulphonates.

Their stability decreases in the order $F>Cl>Br>I$. In the alkali metal halide polysolvates one cannot be sure whether the sulphur dioxide is co-ordinated to the cation, the anion or both. But the apparent increase in stability of the iodides over the bromides, and the lack of existence of alkali metal chloride solvates, the reverse of the position with the tetramethyl-ammonium halide mono-solvates, leads one to suspect that the bonding is best regarded as due to charge transfer interactions between the anion and the sulphur dioxide molecules. This is supported by the spectroscopic work of Lippincott and Welch (1961) on the compounds $KI.4SO_2$ and $KNCS.4SO_2$, where the shifts in the vibration frequencies of the sulphur dioxide indicate charge transfer from the negative ion.

With covalent compounds sulphur dioxide forms many solvates, acting in most cases as an electron acceptor through sulphur and only in a few as an electron donor through oxygen. Thus the phase diagram of the boron trifluoride–sulphur dioxide system shows clearly the formation of an $SO_2.BF_3$ adduct (Booth and Martin, 1942). Curiously, the boron trichloride–sulphur dioxide system differs in its behaviour and shows the formation of two immiscible solutions at low temperature, becoming miscible at room temperature (Satenstejn and Viktorov, 1937; Martin, 1945). An adduct with antimony pentachloride, $SO_2.SbF_5$ has also been reported (Aynsley et al., 1951). $SnBr_4$ and $TiCl_4$ both form adducts with SO_2, the formulae reported being $SnBr_4.SO_2$ and $2TiCl_4.SO_2$ (Bond and Belton, 1945). Zirconium tetrachloride also forms a 1 : 1 adduct (Bond and Stephens, 1929).

There is an early report of an adduct $(AlCl_3)_2SO_2$ as well as of $AlCl_3.SO_2$ (Baude, 1904), but subsequent workers appear only to have isolated $AlCl_3.SO_2$ (Silberrad, 1922; Burg and Bickerton, 1945); this compound appears to be dimeric.

Most organic mono-amines form stable mono-adducts with sulphur dioxide. These compounds are usually highly coloured and soluble in liquid

TABLE IV

Solvate Formation with Alkali Metal and Tetramethyl Ammonium Salts and Sulphur Dioxide

Cation	Anion						
	F^-	Cl^-	Br^-	I^-	NCS^-	SO_4^{2-}	$CH_3.CO_2^-$
Li^+	—	—	—	2, −1°, 9·4 [c]	—	—	None
Na^+	—	—	—	2, +15°, 10·01 [c] 4, +5°, 9·63 [c]	2, —, 10·5 [d]	—	1, >80° [d]
K^+	1, [a]	None [b]	4, −1°, 8·38 [b]	4, +6°, 9·67 [c]	0·5, −49°, 11·3 [d] 1, +12·5°, 9·9 [b] 2, —, 9·75 [d]	—	1, >80° [e]
Rb^+	1, [a]	—	—	3, +15·3°, 10·5 [b] 4, +15·5°, 10·9 [c]	0·5, +31·5°, 10·64 [c]	—	1, >50° [e]
Cs^+	—	—	—	3, —, 10·25 [d] 4, +17°, 10·89 [c]	0·5, +19°, 10·14 [c]	—	1, >80° [e]
Me_4N^+	1, +150° [a]	1, +88°, 11·1 [b] 2, +35°, 10·6 [b]	1, +41°, 8·99 [b] 2, +16°, 10·3 [b]	1, +20°, —[a]	—	3, +28°, 11·7 [b] 6, −2·6°, 8·53 [b]	— —

The first figure given represents the number of sulphur dioxide molecules in the solvate per mole of salt; the second, the decomposition temperatures under atmospheric pressure in degrees centigrade; and the third, the heat of decomposition to gaseous sulphur dioxide in kcal mole^{-1}.

[a] Seel and Riehl (1955a,b).
[b] Jander and Mesech (1938a,b).
[c] Ephraim and Kornblum (1916)
[d] Foote and Fleischer (1931, 1932, 1934)
[e] Ephraim and Aellig (1923).

sulphur dioxide (Michaelis, 1891; Andre, 1900; Korezynski and Gleboka, 1920; Hill, 1931; Foote and Fleischer, 1934; Hill and Fitzgerald, 1935; Mesech, 1938; Bright and Jasper, 1941; Bright and Fernelius, 1943; Burg, 1943; Bateman *et al.*, 1944; Jander, 1949; Moede and Curran, 1949; Byrd, 1962). Co-ordination would appear to be through the nitrogen to the sulphur. Diamines may take up two molecules of sulphur dioxide, thus *p*-phenylenediamine gives p-$C_6H_4(NH_2)_2 . 2SO_2$ (Hill and Fitzgerald, 1935; Mesech, 1938) and N,N,N',N'-tetramethyl-*p*-phenylenediamine gives p-$C_6H_4(NME_2)_2.2SO_2$ (Bryd, 1962). The claim of Jander and Wickert (Jander and Wickert, 1936; Wickert and Jander, 1937) that a further reaction takes place:

$$2(C_2H_5)_3N + 2SO_2 \rightarrow \underset{(I)}{2\overset{\text{red}}{(C_2H_5)_3N.SO_2}} \rightarrow \{(C_2H_5)_3N.SO_2\}_2 \rightarrow$$

$$\underset{(II)}{\{(C_2H_5)_3N\}_2\overset{\text{white}}{SO^{2+}SO_3^{2-}}} \tag{1}$$

has been strongly criticized by Bateman *et al.* (1944). They reported that the compound (II), claimed to have been isolated by Jander and Wicker, is in fact $(C_2H_5)_3NH^+.HSO_3^-$, triethylammonium hydrogen sulphite, produced by the action of moisture on the red compound (I), and that the melting point of the hydrogen sulphite (74°–75°) agrees closely with that reported by Jander for compound (II). The conclusions of Bateman *et al.* (1944) are supported by the work of Burg (1943), Hill and Fitzgerald (1931, 1935) and others. Jander *et al.* (1937), report that ammonia itself similarly forms a compound $(H_3N)_2SO^+SO_3^{2-}$ in liquid sulphur dioxide but it seems likely that here again they are observing either the formation of $NH_4^+HSO_3^-$ from moisture in their sulphur dioxide or the formation of HSO_2NH_2, amidosulphonous acid. Triethylamine oxide also forms a stable adduct $Et_3NO.SO_2$ with liquid sulphur dioxide (Lecher and Hardy, 1948). Its structure appears to be

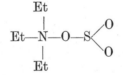

Though from their solubility in liquid sulphur dioxide there is obviously an interaction between alcohols and phenols and sulphur dioxide, the phase diagrams of these systems do not appear to have been studied, and there is only the isolated report of an unstable adduct between phenol and sulphur dioxide (Kashtanov and Sokolova, 1951). Ultra-violet spectroscopic studies have shown that the interaction of sulphur dioxide with ethers and alcohols (de Maine, 1957) is due to the formation of charge transfer complexes and also that charge transfer complexes are formed between sulphur dioxide and a wide variety of aromatic molecules (Andrews and Keefer, 1951; Lichtin *et al.*, 1952; Andrews, 1954).

IV. Electrical Conductivity and Ionization in Liquid Sulphur Dioxide Solutions

Much of the work on electrolytic solutions in liquid sulphur dioxide has been summarized relatively recently (Jander, 1949; Audrieth and Kleinberg, 1953; Elving and Markowitz, 1960). Very recently Lichtin (1963) has thoroughly reviewed the work of the last dozen or so years on conductivity measurements in liquid sulphur dioxide. Nearly all the experimental evidence

Table V

Data for Salts Composed of Spherical and Tetrahedral Ions at 0°C

Ion-pair	Limiting molar conductance (cm² ohm⁻¹ mole⁻¹)	K (mole litre⁻¹ × 10⁴)	a_0 (Å)	$r_+ + r_-$ (Å)
LiBr	189	0·27	2·70	2·55[a]
NaBr	265	0·48	2·87	2·91[b]
KCl	243	0·74	2·96	3·14[c]
KBr	249	1·43	3·28	3·28[c]
KI	244	3·0	3·58	3·50[c]
Me₄NCl	243	10·3	4·96	5·11[d]
Me₄NBr	236	11·8	5·25	5·25[c]
Me₄NI	234	13·9	5·54	5·47[e]
Me₄NClO₄	218	8·4	4·63	6·3[e]
Me₄NBF₄	215	7·9	4·56	6·1[e]
Et₄NBr	215	21	6·8	6·6[e]
Et₄NI	197	39	10·0	8·1[e]

Reproduced with permission from "Progress in Physical Organic Chemistry," Vol. I, Wiley, New York.

[a] Lichtin and Rao (1960).
[b] Lichtin and Kliman (1965)
[c] Lichtin and Leftin (1956).
[d] Lichtin (1963).
[e] Lichtin and Pappas (1957).

on liquid sulphur dioxide is limited to uni-univalent electrolytes. Liquid sulphur dioxide is a solvent of low dielectric constant, so behaviour of the type first described by Kraus and Fuoss (1933) occurs, and a plot of equivalent conductance against concentration shows a minimum. At concentrations above about 10^{-1} M the conductivity is largely due to ion triplets; a minimum is found in the conductivity at about 10^{-1} M, and below this the conductivity increases with decreasing concentration, obeying Ostwald's dilution law. Electrical conductivity at concentrations of less than 10^{-2} M is not significantly complicated by triplet ion formation, and in this region association constants for ion-pair formation may be evaluated. Lichtin (1963) has made extensive use of Shedlovsky's equation (Fuoss and Shedlovsky, 1949) to obtain degrees of dissociation of ion-pairs in liquid sulphur dioxide. Readers are referred to Lichtin's (1963) chapter on "Ionization and Dissociation Equilibria in Solution in Liquid Sulphur Dioxide" for a detailed account of the methods of calculation. Here it is sufficient to say that, by a suitable rearrangement (Daggett, 1951) of Shedlovsky's equation, the conductivity data can be plotted to yield $1/\Lambda_0$ as intercept and $1/K\Lambda_0^2$ as slope, where K is the ion-pair dissociation constant and Λ_0 is the equivalent conductance at infinite dilution. Table V is reproduced from Lichtin's article. Lichtin has also used Bjerrum's theory (Bjerrum, 1926a,b) of ionic association to calculate the distances of closet approach, a_0, in ion-pairs, and these are compared with the sum of the crystal radii, $r_+ + r_-$ of the ions.

TABLE VI

Temperature Dependence of K, Λ_0 and a_0 for KBr

T	Λ_0	$K \times 10^4$	a_0
$-24 \cdot 99$	188	$3 \cdot 62$	$3 \cdot 41 \pm 0 \cdot 03$[a]
$-20 \cdot 58$	202	$2 \cdot 88$	$3 \cdot 34 \pm 0 \cdot 02$[a]
$-15 \cdot 56$	212	$2 \cdot 51$	$3 \cdot 33 \pm 0 \cdot 03$[a]
$-10 \cdot 71$	224	$2 \cdot 11$	$3 \cdot 31 \pm 0 \cdot 03$[a]
$- 8 \cdot 93$	228	$1 \cdot 99$	$3 \cdot 28$[b]
$- 5 \cdot 25$	233	$1 \cdot 80$	$3 \cdot 31 \pm 0 \cdot 02$[a]
$+ 0 \cdot 12$	249	$1 \cdot 43$	$3 \cdot 28$[b]
$+ 6 \cdot 23$	274	$1 \cdot 04$	$3 \cdot 23 \pm 0 \cdot 02$[c]

Reproduced with permission from "Progress in Physical Organic Chemistry", Vol. I, Wiley, New York.

[a] Lichtin and Pappas (1957).
[b] Lichtin and Leftin (1956).
[c] Lichtin and Rao (1961).

The limiting conductances of the salts reported in the table show that, as in water and many other solvents, there must be considerable hydrodynamic transport of solvent associated with the lithium ion. It is interesting, however, that the association behaviour of the lithium ion with bromide, as reflected in the Bjerrum distance, a_0, indicates that there can be little or no "solvent separation" of paired ions. Lichtin reports that in only one case, that of potassium bromide, (Lichtin and Leftin, 1956; Lichtin and Pappas, 1957; Lichtin and Rao, 1961) is there sufficient data for calculation of the dissociation constant for ion-pairs over a range of temperature. Table VI is taken from Lichtin's article. The Bjerrum distance, a_0, changes very little over the range of temperatures from $-24°C$ to $+6°C$ and is in good agreement with the sum of the ionic radii. A plot of $\log K$ against $1/T$ gives a straight line, from which we find $\Delta H_\alpha^\circ = 5 \cdot 25$ kcal mole^{-1} and $\Delta S_\alpha^\circ = -36 \cdot 8$ kcal degree^{-1} mole^{-1} at 0°C. The decrease of K with increasing temperature follows from the temperature dependence of the dielectic constant. The large negative value of ΔS_α° indicates the much greater interaction of the free ions with the solvent than of the ion pair. The increase in the limiting equivalent conductance with increase in temperature is probably due to the hydrodynamic effect of the decrease in viscosity of the solvent.

The conductivity data recorded by earlier workers and their interpretations of it are certainly not as reliable as that of Lichtin and co-workers; however, using a simple Ostwald dilution law, Dutoit and Gyr (1909) obtained values of K of the same order of magnitude as those obtained by Lichtin with the more sophisticated Shedlovsky equation. Some of their results are given in Tables VII and VIII below.

TABLE VII

Dissociation Constants at -15°C in Liquid Sulphur Dioxide Obtained Using the Ostwald Dilution Law

$K \times 10^3$		$K \times 10^3$	
RbBr	0·34	RbI	0·50
KBr	0·35	KI	0·57
NH_4Br	0·16	NH_4I	0·47
Me_4NBr	1·37	Me_4NI	1·66

TABLE VIII

Limiting Equivalent Conductances at -15°C in Liquid Sulphur Dioxide

Anion	Cation			
	$Me_4N_4^+$	Rb^+	NH_4^+	K^+
I^-	199	215	208	207
Br^-	194	211	208	203
SCN^-			~ 174	

The above data refer to the dissociation in liquid sulphur dioxide of ion-pairs of compounds which are essentially ionic in the solid. On the other hand, there are a wide variety of materials, such as triphenylmethylchloride (Walden, 1902), which are covalent in the solid and in many common solvents, but which give conducting solutions in liquid sulphur dioxide.

The van't Hoff i factor has been measured by the ebullioscopic method for variety of solutes (Jander and Mesech, 1939; Jander, 1949) in liquid sulphur dioxide. The factor was defined as the theoretical molecular weight divided by the observed molecular weight, using a molal ebullioscopic constant of 1·45°C per mole. The observations are of necessity confined to fairly concentrated solutions, in which, in the case of electrolytes, one would expect considerable triple ion formation. Some values are given in Table IX below. For all non-electrolytes except water, the mole number is unity within the limits of experimental error. Binary electrolytes give i-values ranging from about 0·4 in very concentrated solutions to greater than unity in more dilute solutions, thus indicating a wide range of associated species.

TABLE IX

Vant' Hoff i-values for a Number of Electrolytes and Non-electrolytes in Liquid Sulphur Dioxide, as a Function of Concentration

| Compound | i-Values at dilutions in litres per mole | | | | | |
	1	2	4	8	16	32
Toluene	—	1·07	—	—	—	—
Napthalene	—	0·99	—	1·03	—	1·01
Acetanilide	—	0·99	—	1·00	—	1·03
ω-Chloro-acetophenone	—	1·05	—	1·03	—	0·89
Tetra-ethyl urea	—	1·08	—	1·01	—	0·90
Acetyl chloride	—	0·83	—	0·75	—	—
$SbCl_3$	—	—	—	1·09	—	1·11
$SbCl_5$	—	0·91	—	0·88	—	—
$SnCl_4$	—	—	—	1·00	—	—
H_2O	—	0·62	—	0·64	—	—
KSCN	0·43	0·50	0·61	0·70	0·78	—
KBr	—	0·55	0·67	0·85	0·95	1·01
KI	0·54	0·63	0·77	0·95	1·08	1·17
$KSbCl_6$	—	1·23	1·25	1·28	1·36	1·42
Me_4NCl	—	1·14	1·05	1·03	1·06	1·22
Me_4NClO_4	—	1·04	1·04	1·10	1·26	1·33
$(Me_4N)_2SO_4$	—	1·03	1·02	1·05	1·27	1·47
Ph_3CCl	—	0·99	1·14	1·26	1·30	—

V. ELECTROCHEMICAL STUDIES IN SOLUTIONS IN LIQUID SULPHUR DIOXIDE

A. ELECTROLYSIS

The nature of the products obtained during the electrolysis of salts in liquid sulphur dioxide has been the subject of conflicting reports. Steele (1907) first investigated the products of electrolysis in liquid sulphur dioxide and reported that sulphur was deposited at the cathode during the electrolysis of potassium or sodium iodide between platinum electrodes in the solvent. He also observed that the current fell quickly from an initially high value to a much lower one. Bagster and Steele (1912a,b) extended this work. They found that, on the electrolysis of a wide range of iodides, both elemental sulphur and sulphite salts were found at the cathode; at a platinum anode free iodide was liberated. Anodes of metals such as zinc and iron passed into solution as the iodides. Centnerszwer and Drucker (1923) obtained results differing from Bagster and Steele on electrolysis of iodides in sulphur dioxide between platinum electrodes. They obtained a cathodic deposit with strongly reducing properties, which careful analysis showed to be a mixture of thio-sulphites and pyrosulphites; no elemental sulphur was found. This was confirmed by Cady and Toft (1925), who electrolysed solutions of potassium iodide, thiocyanate, iodate, chlorate and ferricyanide in liquid sulphur dioxide and found that the cathode products were thiosulphites, pyrosulphites, salts of thionic acids, etc. They attributed the cathodic sulphur found by Bagster and Steele to the presence of some water in the sulphur dioxide. When, however, triphenylmethyl bromide is electrolysed in liquid sulphur dioxide (Schlenk et al., 1910), triphenylmethyl is deposited at the cathode. Since Ph_3CBr is ionized in liquid sulphur dioxide to Ph_3C^+ and Br^-, it seems that here we have a simple cation discharge reaction taking place.

Evidence for the existence of the hydroxonium ion was obtained by Bagster and Cooling (1920) from the electrolysis of a mixture of water and hydrogen bromide in liquid sulphur dioxide. Although neither water nor hydrogen bromide is a conductor in sulphur dioxide, a mixture of the two gives a conducting solution. On electrolysis the cathodic products were water and hydrogen, and the anodic product was bromine. In addition, the quantity of water deposited at the cathode was in agreement with that calculated on the the basis of Faraday's Laws. Electrolysis of bromine, iodine monobromide and iodine trichloride between silver electrodes in liquid sulphur dioxide (Bruner and Bekier, 1913) leads respectively to the deposition of silver bromide, silver iodide and silver chloride at the anode. The cathodic processes were not elucidated.

B. ELECTRODE POTENTIALS

Bagster and Steele (1912a,b) made the earliest measurements of electrode potentials in liquid sulphur dioxide. They found reproducible potentials for cells such as the following:

$$Zn/ZnBr_2(sat),\ SO_2,\ Hg_2Cl_2/Hg.$$

Salts with a common ion affected these potentials in the same way as those of the corresponding aqueous cells. They measured potentials with a quandrant electrometer, since they found that the electrodes polarized extremely easily. They also measured the potentials of the three metals zinc, cadmium and lead in saturated solutions of their salts against a mercurous chloride–mercury electrode. Wickert (1938a,b) measured the potential of the hydrogen electrode ($E = 0\cdot3V$) and the oxygen electrode ($E = 0\cdot2V$) against a mercurous chloride–mercury electrode, using as the electrolyte a solution of hydrogen chloride, of unspecified concentration, in liquid sulphur dioxide. These potentials are of the same order of magnitude as those obtained later by Cruse (1940). Cruse (1940) has made what are certainly the most careful and detailed measurements of electrode potentials in liquid sulphur dioxide. He set up the cells

Pb, $PbCl_2/Cl^-$ in SO_2/Hg_2Cl_2, Hg,
Ag, $AgCl/Cl^-$ in SO_2/Hg_2Cl_2, Hg,
Ag, $AgBr/Br^-$ in SO_2/Hg_2Br_2, Hg,

and measured their e.m.f.'s. The reactions taking place in these cells are respectively as follows:

(a) $Pb(s) + Hg_2Cl_2(s) = PbCl_2(s) + 2Hg(l)$,
(b) $2Ag(s) + Hg_2Cl_2(s) = 2AgCl(s) + 2Hg(l)$,
(c) $2Ag(s) + Hg_2Br_2 = 2AgBr(s) + 2Hg(l)$.

These reactions are of course independent of concentration of halide ions in the sulphur dioxide and of the nature of the solvent, and the thermodynamic data should enable one to calculate the e.m.f.'s. Cruse found that in fact the e.m.f.'s he calculated were not in very good agreement with the measured values, though they were of the right order of magnitude, e.g.

cell (a) E^0 measured $= 0\cdot36V$; E^0 calculated $= 0\cdot55V$;
cell (b) E^0 measured was variable, but initially about $0\cdot04V$;
E^0 calculated $= 0\cdot049V$;
cell (c) E^0 measured was very variable, but initially about $0\cdot06V$;
E^0 calculated $0\cdot048V$.

He found in cells (b) and (c) that the e.m.f. tended to change steadily with time, though that of (a) was fairly steady. He also set up the cells

Ag, $AgBr/HBr$ in SO_2/H_2, Pt and
Ag, $AgCl/HCl$ in SO_2/H_2, Pt

and measured their e.m.f.'s at various hydrogen halide concentrations. As one would predict, there was a straight line relationship between e.m.f. and hydrogen halide concentration. However, the absolute values of the e.m.f.'s did not agree well with those he derived thermodynamically, the measured values being about 0·2V too high.

VI. Chemical Reactions in Liquid Sulphur Dioxide

Solvate and adduct formation with ionic species and covalent molecules in liquid sulphur dioxide have already been discussed. Chemical reactions are discussed below under the following headings: solvolysis, metathetical reactions, amphoteric reactions, oxidation–reduction reactions and complex formation.

A. SOLVOLYSIS

Zinc diethyl reacts in liquid sulphur dioxide even at $-78°C$ to give diethylsulphoxide and zinc oxide (Wickert, 1938a,b):

$$Zn(C_2H_5)_2 + SO_2 \rightarrow ZnO + (C_2H_5)_2SO. \tag{2}$$

Jander (1949) reports that on prolonged standing both alkali metal bromides and iodides react slowly with liquid sulphur dioxide in a sealed tube at room temperature. The precipitate obtained from a solution of potassium iodide, on long standing, was shown by analysis to be an equimolecular mixture of potassium sulphate and sulphur. From a solution of potassium bromide only a precipitate of potassium sulphate was obtained. In the case of the iodide, iodine was formed in solution; whereas in the case of the bromide, bromine and sulphur monobromide were found. Jander suggested the following mechanism for the bromide solvolysis:

$$8KBr + 8SO_2 = 4K_2SO_3 + 4SOBr_2 \tag{3a}$$
$$4SOBr_2 = 2SO_2 + S_2Br_2 + 3Br_2 \tag{3b}$$
$$4K_2SO_3 + 2Br_2 = 2K_2SO_4 \downarrow + 4KBr + 2SO_2 \tag{3c}$$
$$4KBr + 4SO_2 = 2K_2SO_4 + S_2Br_2 + Br_2. \tag{3d}$$

Presumably the same reactions are supposed to take place in the case of the iodide, except that the S_2I_2 is unstable and breaks down to sulphur and iodine, so that the over-all equation is

$$4KI + 4SO_2 = 2K_2SO_4 \downarrow + 2S \downarrow + 2I_2. \tag{4}$$

Lichtin (1963) disputes Jander's results and reports that dilute solutions of bromides and iodides are quite stable when prepared in liquid SO_2 which has been degassed (i.e. oxygen removed), but that, at least for solutions of iodides, instability is associated with the presence of oxygen. Jander (1949) also reports that solutions of alkali metal acetates are also solvolysed in liquid sulphur, even at $-50°C$. The reaction appears to lead to the metal sulphite and to acetic anhydride, considered by Jander to be the decomposition product of an intermediate thionyl acetate. The behaviour of the volatile halides in liquid sulphur dioxide varies. Halides of group IV do not react. Phosphorous pentachloride is readily solvolysed, even at $-50°C$, with the production of phosphorous oxychloride and thionyl chloride:

$$PCl_5 + SO_2 = POCl_3 + SOCl_2. \qquad (5)$$

Phosphorous pentabromide reacts in an analogous way:

$$PBr_5 + SO_2 = POBr_3 + SOBr_2. \qquad (6)$$

Further solvolysis does not occur. Neither antimony trichloride nor antimony pentachloride are solvolysed by liquid sulphur dioxide, and Jander points out that whereas the reaction

$$PCl_5 + SO_2 = POCl_3 + SOCl_2 \qquad (7)$$

is exothermic, both the further solvolysis of $POCl_3$

$$2PCl_5 + 5SO_2 = (P_2O_5) + 5SOCl_2 \qquad (8)$$

and the solvolysis of $SbCl_3$

$$SbCl_3 + SO_2 = (SbOCl) + SOCl_2 \qquad (9)$$

would represent endothermic reactions.

Solvolysis reactions which do occur are

$$NbCl_5 + SO_2 = NbOCl_3 + SOCl_2 \qquad (10)$$
$$WCl_6 + SO_2 = WOCl_4 + SOCl_2 \qquad (11)$$

and $\qquad 2UCl_5 = UCl_6 + UCl_4 \qquad (12a)$

$$UCl_5 + 2SO_2 = UO_2Cl_2 \downarrow + 2SOCl_2. \qquad (12b)$$

B. METATHETICAL REACTIONS

A large number of reactions, called in some cases by Jander (1949) "neutralization reactions", but probably better described as metathetical reactions, have been observed in liquid sulphur dioxide by Jander and co-workers Jander and Wickert, 1936; Jander and Ullman, 1937; (Jander, 1938). Thus, sulphites react with thionyl halides in the solvent to produce chlorides and sulphur dioxide:

$$Cs_2SO_3 + SOCl_2 = 2CsCl + 2SO_2 \qquad (13)$$
$$(Me_4N)_2SO_3 + SOBr_2 = 2Me_4NBr + 2SO_2. \qquad (14)$$

Acetates also react:

$$2Ag(CH_3CO_2) + SOCl_2 = 2AgCl \downarrow + SO(CH_3CO_2)_2 \qquad (15)$$
$$2NH_4(CH_3CO_2) + SOCl_2 = 2NH_4Cl \downarrow + SO(CH_3CO_2)_2. \qquad (16)$$

$SO(CH_3CO_2)_2$ does not appear to have been isolated; it probably breaks up to acetic anhydride and sulphur dioxide. But the compounds $(C_6H_5CH_2CO_2)_2SO$ and $(ClCH_2CO_2)_2SO$ have been isolated and analysed by Jander. Other metathetical reactions are

$$2NH_4SCN + SOCl_2 = 2NH_4Cl \downarrow + SO(SCN)_2 \qquad (17)$$

and

$$4KI + 2SOCl_2 = 4KCl + 2(SOI_2) \qquad (18a)$$
$$= 4KCl \downarrow + 2I_2 + S \downarrow + SO_2. \qquad (18b)$$

The $(SO(SCN)_2)$ appears to be stable in dilute solution in liquid sulphur dioxide at $-15°C$, but, on concentrating the solution, amorphous poly-cyanogen is precipitated. Jander has, however, used solutions of $SO(SCN)_2$ to carry out such reactions as

$$K_2SO_3 + SO(SCN)_2 = 2KSCN + 2SO_2 \qquad (19)$$

and followed them conductimetrically, demonstrating $1:1$ end-points (Fig. 1).

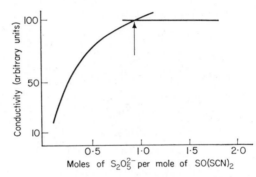

FIG. 1. Conductimetric titration of $SO(SCN)_2$ against $S_2O_5^{2-}$.

In a similar way the reaction between a sulphite and thionyl chloride can be followed conductimetrically (Fig. 2).

C. AMPHOTERIC REACTIONS

Jander (Jander and Immig, 1937; Jander, 1938; Jander and Hecht, 1943; Jander *et al.*, 1944) claims to have demonstrated amphoteric behaviour in liquid sulphur dioxide. When a solution of tetramethylammonium sulphite is added to a solution of aluminium chloride in liquid sulphur dioxide, a voluminous white precipitate of aluminium sulphite is formed. Presumably the metathetical reaction

$$2AlCl_3 + 3(Me_4N)_2SO_3 = Al_2(SO_3)_3 \downarrow + 6Me_4NCl \qquad (20)$$

has taken place. On further addition of tetramethylammonium sulphite, the precipitate redissolves, a complex anion presumably having been formed in solution:

$$Al_2(SO_3)_3 + 3(Me_4N)_2SO_3 = 2(Me_4N)_3Al(SO_3)_3. \qquad (21)$$

On addition of thionyl chloride to this solution the precipitate of aluminium sulphite is regenerated:

$$2(Me_4N)_3Al(SO_3)_3 + 3SOCl_2 = Al_2(SO_3)_3 \downarrow + 6Me_4NCl + 3SO_2. \qquad (22)$$

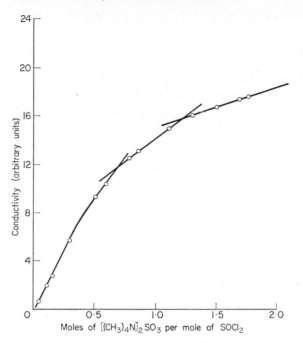

FIG. 2. Conductimetric titration of $S_2O_5^{2-}$ against $SOCl_2$ (Jander and Wickert, 1936).

Jander has followed both reactions conductimetrically and the curves obtained are shown in Figs. 3 and 4.

A similar reaction is observed with gallium trichloride. When tetramethylammonium sulphite is added to a solution of gallium trichloride in liquid sulphur dioxide, a precipitate is formed:

$$2GaCl_3 + 3(Me_4N)_2SO_3 = 6Me_4NCl + Ga_2(SO_3)_2 + 2SO_2 \qquad (23a)$$
$$= 6Me_4NCl + Ga_2O_3.xSO_2. \qquad (23b)$$

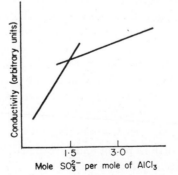

FIG. 3. Conductimetric titration of $(Me_4N)_2SO_3$ against $AlCl_3$ (Jander and Immig, 1937).

When an excess of the sulphite is added, the precipitate redissolves. Similar experiments with stannic chloride show that it too behaves in an analogous way to aluminium and gallium trichlorides. Tin oxide solvate, $SnO_2.xSO_2$, or stannic sulphite, is initially precipitated but dissolves in excess sulphite to give a solution of orthosulphitostannate, $(Me_4N)_4Sn(SO_3)_4$.

Jander also reports that a solution of PCl_3 in liquid sulphur dioxide, which is itself stable and colourless, gives, when a solution of tetramethylammonium sulphite is added at $-40°C$, a flocculent precipitate of phosphorous trioxide:

$$2PCl_3 + 3(Me_4N)_2SO_3 = P_2O_3 + 3SO_2 + 6Me_4NCl. \tag{24}$$

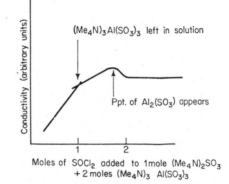

FIG. 4. Conductimetric titration of $SOCl_2$ against $(Me_4N)_2SO_3$ plus $(Me_4N)_3Al(SO_3)_3$ (Jander and Immig, 1937).

On addition of further sulphite the precipitate redissolves, and from this solution the compound $(Me_4N)PO_2SO_2$ has been isolated:

$$P_2O_3 + (Me_4N)_2SO_3 + SO_2 = 2(Me_4N)PO_2SO_2. \tag{25}$$

The reaction has been followed conductimetrically, and Jander (1949) claims to have observed two end-points, the first at 3 moles of sulphite to 2 of PCl_3 and the second at 4 moles of sulphite to 2 of PCl_3 (see Fig. 5).

The solvates of antimony tri- and pentoxides also exhibit amphoretic behaviour in liquid sulphur dioxide. Many metals, whose oxides are amphoteric in water, dissolve in strong hydroxide solutions with the liberation of hydrogen. Jander and Hecht (1943) attempted to demonstrate an analogous situation in liquid sulphur dioxide. Metallic beryllium, aluminium, gallium, antimony and lead gave no reaction with tetramethylammonium sulphite in liquid sulphur dioxide. However, tin does react. With excess tetramethyl-ammonium sulphite the following reaction takes place:

$$Sn + 2(Me_4N)_2SO_3 + 4SO_2 = (Me_4N)_2Sn(SO_3)_3 + (Me_4N)_2S_2O_3. \tag{26}$$

When equimolar proportions of tin and tetramethylammonium sulphite are taken, tin oxide solvate is precipitated:

$$(Me_4N)_2SO_3 + xSO_2 + Sn = SnO_2.xSO_2 + (Me_4N)_2S_2O_3. \tag{27}$$

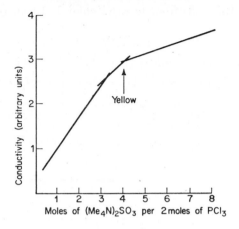

FIG. 5. Conductrimetric titration of SO_3^{2-} against PCl_3.

D. OXIDATION–REDUCTION REACTIONS

A number of oxidation-reduction reactions have been carried out in liquid sulphur dioxide. The sulphur dioxide usually acts merely as an inert carrier in the reactions. Tetramethylammonium sulphite is rapidly oxidized to the sulphate by iodine in the solvent (Jander and Immig, 1937c). A solution of ferric chloride will quantitatively oxidize potassium iodide to iodine:

$$2FeCl_3 + 2KI = 2FeCl_2 + 2KCl + I_2 \qquad (28)$$

and so will a solution of antimony pentachloride:

$$6KI + 3SbCl_5 = 3I_2 + 6KCl + 3SbCl_3. \qquad (29)$$

The $SbCl_3$ interacts with the potassium chloride to yield a precipitate of K_3SbCl_6:

$$6KCl + 2SbCl_3 = 2K_3SbCl_6. \qquad (30)$$

However, addition of excess antimony pentachloride causes this complex to dissolve with decomposition of the complex ion and formation of a hexa-chloroantimonate (V):

$$2K_3SbCl_6 + 6SbCl_5 = 6KSbCl_6 + 2SbCl_3. \qquad (31)$$

The conductimetric titration of $SbCl_5$ against KI in liquid sulphur dioxide is shown in Fig. 6 and shows breaks at mole ratios of $SbCl_5$ to KI of $1:2$ (corresponding to equation (29)) and at $3:2$ corresponding to

$$2KI + 3SbCl_5 = I_2 + 2KSbCl_6 + SbCl_3 \qquad (32)$$

the sum of equations (29), (20) and (31).

Seel et al. (1951a,b) have also recently studied the reactions of nitrosyl compounds with potassium and tetramethylammonium iodides in liquid sulphur dioxide. They all, from nitrosyl chloride to nitrosyl fluoroborate, react as follows:

$$2NOX + 2I^- = 2NO + I_2 + 2X^-.$$ (33)

The reaction of ethyl nitrite (nitrosyl ethoxide!) is as follows:

$$2ON . OEt + 2SO_2 + 2I^- = 2NO + I_2 + 2SO_2(OEt)^-.$$ (34)

With azides the corresponding reactions are

$$NOX + N_3^- = N_2O + N_2 \mid X^-$$ (35)

and $$EtO . NO + N_3^- + SO_2 = N_2O + N_2 + SO_2(OEt)^-.$$ (36)

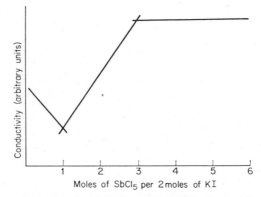

FIG. 6. Conductimetric titration of SbCl$_5$ against KI (Jander and Immig, 1937).

E. COMPLEX FORMATION

The formation of the complexes $K_3Sb(III)Cl_6$ and $KSb(V)Cl_6$ has been described in the previous section. Seel (1943a,b) and Seel and Bauer (1947) have described the preparation and characterization of a series of hexachloro-antimonates in liquid sulphur dioxide. When $NOCl$, CH_3COCl and $PhCOCl$ are titrated against $SbCl_5$ in sulphur dioxide, the conductimetric curves show a sharp break at 1 : 1. The compounds $NO^+SbCl_6^-$, $CH_3CO^+SbCl_6^-$ and $PhCO^+SbCl_6^-$ respectively were isolated. The equivalent conductances of some of these solutions are shown in Table X.

The data on the mixed solution of $SOCl_2$ and $SbCl_5$ given in the table need some comment. Seel, following Jander (1943), formulated the solution of $SOCl_2$ and $SbCl_5$ as $SO^{2+}(SbCl_6^-)_2$. The conductivity data indicate that there is no justification for this. It is worthwhile noting that the only adduct reported between thionyl chloride and antimony pentachloride is $SOCl_2.SbCl_5$ (Lindquist and Einarsson, 1959). No structural data are available for this compound, but one's enthusiasm for formulating this as $SOCl^+SbCl_6^-$ must be considerably dampened both by the conductivity data quoted above and by the fact that the structure of the analogous compound $SeOCl_2.SbCl_5$, as determined by X-ray diffraction (Hermodsson, 1963), shows clearly that the selenium is covalently co-ordinated to antimony through the oxygen atom. Seel *et al.* (1952) have also prepared $NO_2^+SbCl_6^-$ in liquid sulphur dioxide from the reaction of nitryl chloride and antimony pentachloride. Solutions of the compound in liquid sulphur dioxide have conductivities of the same order as $NOSbCl_6$ and $KSbCl_6$. Other complexes that have been obtained in liquid sulphur dioxide are $PhCO^+AlCl_4^-$, from the reaction of aluminium trichloride and benzoyl chloride (Seel and Bauer, 1947), and acetyl fluoroborate, from acetyl fluoride and boron trifluoride (Seel, 1943a,b). A conductimetric titration of boron trichloride against potassium chloride gives a 1 : 1 end-point, indicating the formation of potassium tetrachlorborate in the solvent (Burge *et al.*, 1959).

TABLE X

The Molar Conductances of Some Complexes of $SbCl_5$ in Liquid Sulphur Dioxide [a, b]

	Λ cm^2 ohm^{-1} mole^{-1}	
	0°C	−70°C
$KSbCl_6$	92·8	49·0
$(MeCO)SbCl_6$	80·5	45·3
$(PhCO)SbCl_6$	71·5	37·8
$(NO)SbCl_6$	67·5	50·0
$SOCl_2+2SbCl_5$	0·4	0·7

Dilution = 50 litre mole^{-1}

[a] Seel and Bauer (1947).

[b] Seel (1943b).

As early as 1902, Walden and Centnerszwer (1902a,b, 1903) noted that added iodine increased the conductivity of potassium and rubidium iodides in liquid sulphur dioxide, and that the solubility of iodine itself was greatly increased by the presence of these electrolytes. These effects were a maximum at a ratio of iodide to iodine of 1 : 1, and they attributed them to the formation of metal tri-iodides, MI_3 in solution. They also obtained evidence for the formation of complex iodides of cadmium and mercury, from the increased solubility of cadmium and mercuric iodides in solutions of potassium and rubidium iodides in liquid sulphur dioxide (Walden and Centnerszwer, 1902c).

VII. Isotopic Exchange Reactions in Liquid Sulphur Dioxide

Perhaps the strongest argument against Jander's (1949) proposed ionization mechanism for liquid sulphur dioxide,

$$3SO_2 \rightleftharpoons SO^{2+}+S_2O_5^{2-} \tag{37}$$

and his explanation of the action of $SOCl_2$ as an acid in the solvent

$$SOCl_2 \rightleftharpoons SO^{2+} + 2Cl \qquad (38)$$

comes from isotopic exchange studies in the solvent and in related systems, a comprehensive account of which is given by Norris (1959). The experimental results are summarized in Table XI.

TABLE XI

Summarized Results of Exchange Studies

Solvent	SO_2	$SOCl_2$
SO_2	Direct evidence for ^{18}O exchange [b]	SO_2 dissolved in excess $SOCl_2$ does not exchange *S [c, e]
$(Me_4N)_2S_2O_5$	Rapid *S exchange with solvent SO_2 [c]	
SO_3	Rapid ^{18}O exchange [d, a] No *S exchange [f]	
$SOCl_2$	No *S exchange [c, h] No ^{18}O exchange [i] *S exchange in presence of Cl^-, $SbCl_5$, $AlCl_3$ [c, j, k]	
$SOBr_2$	No *S exchange [c, h] No ^{18}O exchange [i] *S exchange in presence of Cl^-, Br^- [c, j]	*S exchange between $SOCl_2$ and $SOBr_2$ dissolved in SO_2 [g] Also in mixture of $SOCl_2$ and $SOBr_2$ [g]
SCl_2	No *S exchange with SO_2 [e]	Measurable rate of *S exchange with $SOCl_2$. 45% in 2 h at 60°C [e]
Me_4NCl		Rapid *Cl exchange between $SOCl_2$ and Cl^- in SO_2 [l]

[a] Huston (1959).
[b] Lichtin et al. (1964).
[c] Johnson et al. (1951).
[d] Nakata (1943).
[e] Muxart (1950).
[f] Huston (1951).
[g] Johnson and Norris (1957).
[h] Masters and Norris (1955).
[i] Grigg and Lauder (1950).
[j] Herber et al. (1954).
[k] Burge and Norris (1959a, b).
[l] Masters et al. (1956).

Neither $SOCl_2$ or $SOBr_2$ exchange *S or ^{18}O with solvent SO_2 (Grigg and Lauder, 1950; Johnson et al., 1951; Masters and Norris, 1955), but pyrosulphite ion (sulphite dissolved in sulphur dioxide can only be recovered as pyrosulphite) does give rapid *S (Johnson et al., 1951), and presumably ^{18}O exchange, though the ^{18}O measurements do not seem to have been made. This suggests that the thionyl halides, if ionizing at all, are only ionizing as

$$SOX_2 = SOX^+ + X^- \tag{39}$$

and this is supported (A) by the rapid radio-chlorine exchange between thionyl chloride and chloride ions in liquid sulphur dioxide, and (B) by the observation that thionyl chloride and thionyl bromide exchange radiosulphur rapidly and completely in liquid sulphur dioxide, even at $-50°C$. Observation (A) leads to the deduction that either the dissociation is occurring as in equation (39), or the exchange is occurring through an associative equilibrium

$$SOCl_2 + Cl^- \rightleftharpoons SOCl_3^-. \tag{40}$$

Observation (B) leads to the deduction that either a simple dissociation is occurring, again as in equation (39), or there is a direct halide ion transfer, either by

$$SOCl_2 + SOBr_2 \rightleftharpoons SOCl^+ + SOBr_2Cl^- \tag{41}$$

or through a transition complex

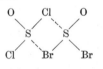

dissociating to uncharged SOClBr species. The exchange of ^{18}O between sulphur dioxide and dissolved sulphur trioxide indicates that the transfer of oxide ions to a really strong acceptor can take place (Nakata, 1959; Huston, 1943), and the failure of *S to exchange (Huston, 1951) confirms that the exchange reaction must either be

$$SO_2 + SO_3 \rightleftharpoons SO^{2+} + SO_4^{2-} \tag{42}$$

or proceed through a transition complex such as

which maintains the nonequivalence of the sulphur atoms. It must be pointed out, however, that the conductivities of sulphur trioxide solutions in sulphur dioxide have only about the same low value as those of $SOCl_2$, i.e. Λ, the equivalent conductance, is $\sim 10^{-1}$ cm^2 ohm^{-1} mole^{-1} in $0\cdot1$ M solution (Jander, 1949).

Attempts have been made to measure the ^{18}O self exchange in liquid sulphur dioxide, but rapid heterogeneously catalysed exchange in the gas phase has made experiments difficult (Huston, 1959). Recently Lichtin et al. (1964), with $S^{16}O_2$ and $S^{18}O_2$ mixtures, have demonstrated by the use of infra-red spectroscopy that homogeneous exchange of oxygen takes place in the gas phase and in solutions of sulphur dioxide in carbon tetrachloride and cyclo-hexane. Exchange is complete within the time of a spectral measurement, i.e. within about ten minutes. They suggest that such exchange takes place via a cyclic intermediate, e.g. $O=S\diamondsuit^{O}_{O}S=O$, and point out that this is supported by the evidence that sulphur dioxide is slightly associated in both liquid and gas (Gmelin, 1953; Clusius et al., 1962).

In contrast to the negligible slow rate of the exchange of *S between thionyl halides and sulphur dioxide, the addition of halide ion is found to catalyse the reaction strongly (Herber et al., 1954; Masters and Norris, 1955). The thionyl bromide–sulphur dioxide *S exchange, studied in detail with tetra-methylammonium bromide (Herber et al., 1954) is independent of thionyl bromide concentration and obeys a rate law

$$d[\text{Exchange}]/dt = k[\text{Me}_4\text{NBr}] \tag{43}$$

k being found to be

$$4\cdot17 \times 10^6 \exp{(-13{,}200/RT)} \text{ sec}^{-1}.$$

A suggested mechanism is

$$\text{SOBr}_2 \underset{k_2}{\overset{k_1}{\rightleftharpoons}} \text{SOBr}^+ + \text{Br}^- \qquad \text{fast} \tag{44}$$

$$*\text{SO}_2 + \text{Br}^- \underset{k_4}{\overset{k_3}{\rightleftharpoons}} *\text{SO}_2\text{Br}^- \qquad \text{fast} \tag{45}$$

$$*\text{SO}_2\text{Br}^- + \text{SO}_2 \underset{k_6}{\overset{k_5}{\rightleftharpoons}} \text{SOBr}^+ + \text{SO}_3^{2-} \qquad \text{slow} \tag{46}$$

which gives a rate law

$$d[\text{Exchange}]/dt = k_3/k_4[\text{SO}_2]^2[\text{Br}^-]. \tag{47}$$

The chloride catalysed exchange of *S between thionyl chloride and solvent sulphur dioxide (Masters and Norris, 1955) obeys a different rate law

$$d[\text{Exchange}]/dt = k[\text{Me}_4\text{NCl}][\text{SOCl}_2][\text{SO}_2]. \tag{48}$$

This reaction has been studied throughout the solvent range from thionyl chloride in excess sulphur dioxide to sulphur dioxide in excess thionyl chloride, and the same rate law is obeyed, though there is a threefold increase in the rate constant in passing from excess sulphur dioxide to excess thionyl chloride. With tetramethylammonium chloride as catalyst in sulphur dioxide solutions, $k = 1\cdot08 \times 10^7 \exp{(-14{,}700/RT)}$ litre^2 mole^{-2} sec^{-1}; a suggested mechanism is

$$*\text{SO}_2 + \text{Cl}^- \underset{k_2}{\overset{k_1}{\rightleftharpoons}} *\text{SO}_2\text{Cl}^- \qquad \text{fast} \tag{49}$$

$$*\text{SO}_2\text{Cl}^- + \text{SOCl}_2 \underset{k_4}{\overset{k_3}{\rightleftharpoons}} *\text{SOCl}_2 + \text{SO}_2\text{Cl}^- \qquad \text{slow} \tag{50}$$

which gives the rate law of equation (48), with k equal to $k_3 k_1/k_2$.

In the above no distinction has been made between "free" halide ion and total halide, i.e. between ion pairs and free halide ions. Conductivity data, of course, indicate that ion pairs predominate in halide solutions in liquid sulphur dioxide (Lichtin, 1963), and it is found that, in the thionyl chloride–sulphur dioxide exchange, tetramethylammonium chloride as catalyst gives rate values about twice those found with comparable concentrations of rubidium chloride. A similar effect was found with tetramethylammonium and rubidium bromides in the exchange of sulphur between thionyl bromide and sulphur dioxide. The rate of thionyl chloride exchange is about seven times that of the thionyl bromide exchange at comparable concentrations, despite an apparently higher activation energy (14·7 kcal mole^{-1} for the chloride as against 13·2 kcal mole^{-1} for the bromide). It may be that the equilibrium in the reaction $SO_2 + X^- \rightleftharpoons SO_2X^-$ is further over to the right in the chloride than in the bromide; this would fall in line with the much higher stability of the SO_2F^- ion. This does not, however, explain the change in mechanism.

The $SOCl_2$–SO_2 exchange also seems to be subject to general catalysis by non-ionic bases. Recently the effect of triethylamine and acetone on the exchange rate has been investigated (Potter, 1962). For triethylamine the rate law

$$d[\text{Exchange}]/dt = k[SO_2][SOCl_2][Et_3N] \qquad (51)$$

was found to be followed over a wide range of reaction conditions, varying from thionyl chloride in liquid sulphur dioxide to sulphur dioxide in liquid thionyl chloride. There was, however, a consistent increase in the rate constant in going from solutions rich in sulphur dioxide to those rich in thionyl chloride. The rate constant was found to be $3·42 \times 10^6 \exp(-13,800/RT)$ litre^2 mole^{-2} sec^{-1} in excess thionyl chloride. In order to cover all conditions the rate law was modified to

$$d[\text{Exchange}]/dt = k[SOCl_2][SO_2.Et_3N] + k'[SO_2][SOCl_2.Et_3N] \qquad (52)$$

the first term dominating in dilute solution of sulphur dioxide in thionyl chloride. Acetone was found to exert only a weak catalytic effect on the exchange reaction, the rate law

$$d[\text{Exchange}]/dt = k[SO_2][SOCl_2][Me_2CO]^2 \qquad (53)$$

being obeyed over the range of concentrations employed. There was no readily apparent variation of k with any reactant concentration, and k was found to be

$$5·3 \times 10^{11} \exp(-24,000/RT) \text{ litre}^3 \text{ mole}^{-3} \text{ sec}^{-1}.$$

The thionyl chloride–sulphur dioxide exchange is also catalysed by antimony pentachloride and aluminium trichloride (Masters and Norris, 1955; Burge and Norris, 1959a,b). These give at comparable concentration about one

10

hundredth and one thousandth of the rates shown by tetramethylammonium chloride. The reaction obeys a rate law

$$d[\text{Exchange}]/dt = k[\text{SbCl}_5][\text{SOCl}_2][\text{SO}_2]. \tag{54}$$

This is consistent with the mechanism

$$*\text{SOCl}_2 + \text{SbCl}_5 \underset{k_2}{\overset{k_1}{\rightleftharpoons}} *\text{SOCl}_2.\text{SbCl}_5 \qquad \text{fast} \tag{55}$$

$$*\text{SOCl}_2.\text{SbCl}_5 + \text{SO}_2 \underset{k_4}{\overset{k_3}{\rightleftharpoons}} *\text{SO}_2 + \text{SOCl}_2.\text{SbCl}_5 \quad \text{slow}. \tag{56}$$

The rate constants appear to be essentially constant over the whole range of composition from excess sulphur dioxide to excess thionyl chloride. $\text{SOCl}_2.\text{SO}_2$ has an equilibrium constant $K = 0.8$ at $0°\text{C}$ and the enthalpy of formation of the adduct is $\Delta H^0 = 3.6$ kcal mole^{-1}; k_3 is 0.875×10^2 exp $(-10,400/RT)$ litre^2 mole^{-2} sec^{-1}. The observed entropy of activation is -51.6 e.u. A comparison of the kinetic data for the various exchange reactions is given in Table XII.

Using mixtures of SbCl_5 and Me_4NCl, the catalytic effect was found to be a minimum at a $\text{Me}_4\text{NCl}:\text{SbCl}_5$ ratio of $1:1$ (Burge and Norris, 1959a,b). A similar minimum was found with Me_4NCl and AlCl_3 mixtures at $1:1$ by the same workers. The structure of the $\text{SOCl}_2.\text{SbCl}_5$ adduct, which can be isolated as a solid, would be of great help in solving the detailed mechanism of the reaction. The structure of the $\text{SeOCl}_2.\text{SbCl}_5$ adduct has been shown to be $\text{Cl}_2\text{SeO} \rightarrow \text{SbCl}_5$, and in view of the low conductivity of $\text{SOCl}_2.\text{SbCl}_5$ in liquid SO_2 it seems reasonable to conclude that the structure of the compound is $\text{Cl}_2\text{SO} \rightarrow \text{SbCl}_5$. The catalytic effect of mixtures of triethylamine and SbCl_5 has also been studied (Potter, 1962). Here again, at a mole ratio of $\text{SbCl}_5:\text{Et}_3\text{N}$ of $1:1$, a minimum in catalytic activity is found; at this point catalytic behaviour is so weak that it is difficult to detect.

Perhaps the most interesting point that emerges from the exchange work is the suggested transition state species that the different inferred mechanisms involve. With thionyl bromide, catalysed by Br^-, the transition species is $\text{SO}_2\text{Br}^-.\text{SO}_2$, formulated as

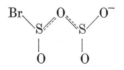

with transfer of an oxide ion. With thionyl chloride catalysed by Cl^- the transition species is $\text{SO}_2\text{Cl}^-.\text{SOCl}_2$, formulated as

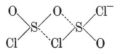

TABLE XII

Summary and Comparison of Kinetic Data on the Catalysed Exchange of *S Exchange between Thionyl Halides and Sulphur Dioxide in Liquid Sulphur Dioxide

	SOCl₂ catalysed by Cl⁻	SOCl₂ catalysed by SbCl₅	SOCl₂ catalysed by Et₃N	SOCl₂ catalysed by Me₂CO	SOBr₂ catalysed by Br⁻
Rate law	$k[Cl^-][SOCl_2][SO_2]$	$k[SOCl_2 . SbCl_5][SO_2]$	$k[SO_2][SOCl_2][Et_3N]$	$k[SO_2][SOCl_2][Me_2CO]^2$	$k[SO_2]^2[Br]$, only $k[Br^-]$ proved
Activation energy (kcal mole⁻¹)	14·7	10·4	14·6 in excess SO₂ 13·8 in excess SOCl₂	24·0	13·2
Pre-exponential factor	$1·08 \times 10^7$	$0·875 \times 10^2$	$3·42 \times 10^6$ in excess SO₂ $2·06 \times 10^6$ in excess SOCl₂	$5·3 \times 10^{11}$	$4·17 \times 10^6$
Entropy of activation (e.u.)	−29	−51·6	−30·7 in excess SO₂	−5·1	−30·4

involving a double bridge, an oxide ion transferring one way and a chloride ion the other. When the thionyl chloride–sulphur dioxide exchange is catalysed by Et_3N the transition species appears to be $(Et_3N.SO_2).SOCl_2$, possibly formulated as

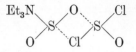

in sulphur dioxide rich solutions and $(Et_3N.SOCl_2).SO_2$, possibly formulated as

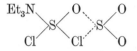

in thionyl chloride rich solutions. The catalytic effect of Lewis acids on the exchange is much weaker, and the suggested mechanism for the exchange catalysed by $SbCl_5$ implies a transition species $(SOCl_2.SbCl_5).SO_2$. Certainly the entropy of activation for this exchange reaction is about twice as high as any of the others, -52 e.u., implying a more complex transition species.

VIII. Conclusion and Summary

In seeking to unify the results of their extensive investigations on the chemistry of liquid sulphur dioxide, Jander and Wickert (1936) adopted a suggestion of Cady and Elsey (1928) and proposed the "sulphito" concept of reactions in liquid sulphur dioxide. This theory is used as a guiding principle by Jander in his monograph in interpreting the reactions he has observed in liquid sulphur dioxide. Liquid sulphur dioxide is assumed to undergo an auto-ionization by the transfer of an oxide ion from one molecule of sulphur dioxide to another:

$$2SO_2 = SO^{2+} + SO_3^{2-} \tag{57}$$

The SO^{2+} and SO_3^{2-} ions are assumed to have a real existence and function similar to those of the hydroxonium, H_3O^+, and hydroxide, OH^-, ions formed during the auto-ionization of water. The reaction between thionyl chloride and a sulphite was considered by Jander to be a neutralization reaction:

$$Cs_2SO_3 + SOCl_2 = 2SO_2 + 2CsCl. \tag{58}$$

Many of the reactions discussed in earlier sections were studied by Jander and interpreted by him in terms of the "sulphito" concept. Of course, it is unnecessary to postulate the occurrence of intermediate ionic species or the involvement of the solvent to explain the metathetical reaction which occur in liquid sulphur dioxide. The reaction

$$(Me_4N)_2SO_3 + SOCl_2 = 2Me_4NCl + 2SO_2 \tag{59}$$

could presumably occur in any inert solvent and does not require SO^{2+}, or even $SOCl^+$ as an intermediate. The reaction can, and probably does, proceed by nucleophilic attack of SO_3^{2-}, or $S_2O_5^{2-}$ on $SOCl_2$, with expulsion of two chloride ions

$$SO_3^{2-} + SOCl_2 \rightleftharpoons (SO_3.SOCl_2^{2-}) \rightarrow (SO_3.SOCl^-) + Cl^- \rightarrow$$
$$(SO_3.SO) + 2Cl^- \rightarrow 2SO_2 + 2Cl^- \qquad (60)$$

and provided that the reaction is fast and the equilibrium

$$SO_3^{2-} + SOCl_2 \rightleftharpoons 2SO_2 + 2Cl^- \qquad (61)$$

sufficiently far over to the right, then a conductimetric titration will show a break at a ratio of $1 : 1$ of SO_3^{2-} to $SOCl_2$. Thus, there is no need to postulate any self-ionization of liquid SO_2. The evidence from studies on isotopic exchange in the solvent indicates in fact that no self-ionization seems to occur. It seems that liquid sulphur dioxide is not a self-ionizing solvent at all. What remains to be explained is the surprising solvent and ionizing powers of liquid sulphur dioxide. Lichtin (1963) has pointed out that once an ionic material has dissolved in liquid sulphur dioxide, its behaviour and conductivity can be rationalized by a theory in which the only solvent parameter is the dielectic constant, $15.36°$ at $0°$. On the other hand, many ionic materials of fairly high lattice energy are much more soluble in liquid sulphur dioxide than its comparatively low dielectic constant would suggest (see Section II). Liquid sulphur dioxide also seems to possess an unusual ionizing power. Thus triphenylmethyl chloride, a substance which is known to be covalent in the crystal and in many common solvents, is an extensively dissociated electrolyte in liquid sulphur dioxide.

The comparison of the ionization of triphenylmethyl chloride in nitrobenzene ($D = 24.5$) and in liquid sulphur dioxide ($D = 15.3$) is, as Lichtin (1963) points out, particularly interesting. Triphenylmethyl chloride is too weak an electrolyte in nitrobenzene for a dissociation constant to be found, whereas in liquid sulphur dioxide it is an electrolyte of much the same ionization as potassium chloride or bromide. This is rather like the behaviour of triphenylmethyl chloride in liquid hydrogen chloride ($D = 9.3$) (Waddington and Klanberg, 1960), where it is an electrolyte comparable in strength to tetramethylammonium chloride. This means that in both liquid sulphur dioxide and liquid hydrogen chloride there must be a specific interaction of the solvent with chloride ions above and beyond the electrostatic, for, both on the basis of its gross dielectric constant and dipole moment, nitrobenzene ($\mu = 4.24$, $D = 34.5$) should be a far better ionizing solvent than either sulphur dioxide ($\mu = 1.62$, $D = 15.4$) or hydrogen chloride ($\mu = 1.03$, $D = 9.3$). This specific interaction in liquid hydrogen chloride is due to hydrogen bonding; in liquid sulphur dioxide there is a good deal of evidence to suggest that it is due at least to charge transfer interactions (Lippincott and Welch, 1961; Lichtin, 1963), if not actual covalent bonding (see Section III).

Spectroscopic studies (Lichtin, 1963) of the complexes of sulphur dioxide with chloride, bromide and iodide ions show that all the halides intensify the electronic spectrum of sulphur dioxide and produce bathochromic shifts. Lippincott and Welch (1961) have identified the complexes of the iodide ion with sulphur dioxide as charge transfer complexes, and it seems reasonable to assume that all the halide ions can form charge transfer complexes with sulphur dioxide. A wide variety of complexes of sulphur dioxide are known and have been discussed in a previous section. It is interesting to note that most of the complexes are with potential electron donors; complexes of sulphur dioxide with electron acceptors are comparatively rare. Lichtin (1963) has calculated from the relative ionizations of substituted trimethyl chlorides that the complexing of chloride ion by sulphur dioxide reduces the free energy of ionization by more than 10 kcal mole^{-1}. Similar effects must occur with bromide and iodide ion and with other monovalent ions such as thiocyanate. Presumably, the free energies of solution of ionic halides and thiocyanates are affected in the same manner, due to specific complexing. Such an effect could produce solubilities $\sim 10^8$ times greater than those to be expected in an "inert" solvent of the same gross dielectic constant.

REFERENCES

Andre, S. (1900) *C. R. Acad. Sci., Paris,* **130,** 174.

Andrews, L. J. (1954) *Chem. Rev.* **54,** 713.

Andrews, L. J. and Keefer, R. M. (1951) *J. Amer. chem. Soc.* **73,** 4169.

Audrieth, L. F. and Kleinberg, J. (1953) "Non-Aqueous Solvents." Wiley, New York.

Aynsley, E. E., Peacock, R. D. and Robinson, P. L. (1951) *Chem. & Ind. (Rev.)* 1117.

Bagster, L. S. and Cooling, G. (1920) *J. chem. Soc.* **117,** 693.

Bagster, L. S. and Steele, B. O. (1912a) *Chem. News,* **105,** 157.

Bagster, L. S. and Steele, B. O. (1912b) *Trans. Faraday Soc.* **8,** 51.

Bateman, L. C., Hughes, E. D. and Ingold, C. K. (1944) *J. chem. Soc.* 243.

Baude, E. (1904) *Ann. Chim. Phys.* **1,** 8.

Bjerrum, N. (1926a) *Ergebn. exakt. Naturw.* **6,** 125.

Bjerrum, N. (1926b) *K. danske vidensk. Selsk. Math.-fys. Medd.* **1,** No. 9, 1.

Bond, P. A. and Beach, H. T. (1926) *J. Amer. chem. Soc.* **48,** 348.

Bond, P. A. and Belton, W. E. (1945) *J. Amer. chem. Soc.* **67,** 1691.

Bond, P. A. and Crone, E. B. (1934) *J. Amer. chem. Soc.* **56,** 2028.

Bond, P. A. and Stephens, W. R. (1929) *J. Amer. chem. Soc.* **51,** 2910.

Booth, H. S. and Martin, D. R. (1942) *J. Amer. chem. Soc.* **64,** 2198.

Bright, J. R. and Fernelius, W. C. (1943) *J. Amer. chem. Soc.* **65,** 637.

Bright, J. R. and Jasper, J. J. (1941) *J. Amer. chem. Soc.* **63,** 3486.

Bruner, L. and Bekier, E. (1913) *Z. phys. Chem.* **84,** 570.

Burg, A. B. (1943) *J. Amer. chem. Soc.* **65,** 1629.

Burg, A. B. and Bickerton, J. H. (1945) *J. Amer. chem. Soc.* **67,** 2261.

Burge, D. E. and Norris, T. H. (1959a) *J. Amer. chem. Soc.* **81,** 2324.

Burge, D. E. and Norris, T. H. (1959b) *J. Amer. chem. Soc.* **81,** 2329.

Burge, D. E., Freund, H. and Norris, T. H. (1959) *J. phys. Chem.* **63,** 1969.

Byrd, W. E. (1962) *Inorg. Chem.* **1**, 762.
Cady, H. P. and Elsey, H. M. (1928) *J. chem. Educ.* **5**, 1425.
Cady, H. P. and Toft, R. (1925) *J. phys. Chem.* **29**, 1075.
Centnerszwer, M. and Drucker, J. (1923) *Z. Electrochem.* **29**, 210.
Clusius, K., Schleich, K. and Bernstein, R. B. (1962) *Helv. chim. acta*, **40**, 252.
Cruse, K. (1940) *Z. Electrochem.* **46**, 571.
Daggett, H. M. (1951) *J. Amer. chem. Soc.* **83**, 4977.
de Maine, P. A. D. (1957) *J. chem. Phys.* **26**, 1036.
Dutoit, P. and Gyr, E. (1909) *J. Chim. phys.* **7**, 189.
Elving, P. J. and Markowitz, J. M. (1960) *J. chem. Educ.* **37**, 75.
Ephraim, F. and Aellig, C. (1923) *Helv. chim. acta*, **6**, 37.
Ephraim, F. and Kornblum, J. (1916) *Ber. dtsch. chem. Ges.* **49**, 2007.
Foote, H. W. and Fleischer, J. (1931) *J. Amer. chem. Soc.* **53**, 1752.
Foote, H. W. and Fleischer, J. (1932) *J. Amer. chem. Soc.* **54**, 3902.
Foote, H. W. and Fleischer, J. (1934) *J. Amer. chem. Soc.* **56**, 870.
Franklin, E. C. (1911) *J. phys. Chem.* **15**, 675.
Fuoss, R. M. and Shedlovsky, T. (1949) *J. Amer. chem. Soc.* **71**, 1497.
Fuoss, R. M., and Kraus, C. A. (1933) *J. Amer. chem. Soc.*, **55**, 2387.
Giauque, W. F. and Stephenson, C. C. (1938) *J. Amer. chem. Soc.* **60**, 1389.
"Gmelin's Handbuch der Anorganische Chemie" System No. 9, Vol. B-1, p. 208. Verlag-Chemie, Weinheim (1953).
Grigg, E. C. M. and Lauder, I. (1950) *Trans. Faraday Soc.* **46**, 1039.
Herber, R. H., Norris, T. H. and Huston, J. L. (1954) *J. Amer. chem. Soc.* **76**, 2015.
Hermodsson, Y. (1963) Private Communication quoted by Lindquist, I., in "Inorganic Adduct Molecules of Oro-compounds", Springer-Verlag, Berlin.
Hill, A. E. (1931) *J. Amer. chem. Soc.* **53**, 2598.
Hill, A. E. and Fitzgerald, T. B. (1935) *J. Amer. chem. Soc.* **57**, 250.
Huston, J. L. (1951) *J. Amer. chem. Soc.* **73**, 3049.
Huston, J. L. (1959) *J. phys. Chem.* **63**, 389.
Jander, G. (1938) *Naturwissenschaften*, **26**, 779.
Jander G. (1949) "Die Chemie in Wasseränlichen Lösungmitteln". Springer-Verlag, Berlin.
Jander, G. and Hecht, H. (1943) *Z. anorg. Chem.* **250**, 287.
Jander, G. and Immig, H. (1937) *Z. anorg. Chem.* **233**, 295.
Jander, G. and Mesech, H. (1938a) *Z. phys. Chem.* A **183**, 121.
Jander, G. and Mesech, H. (1938b) *Z. phys. Chem.* A **183**, 137.
Jander, G. and Mesech, H. (1939) *Z. phys. Chem.* A **183**, 277.
Jander, G. Knöll, H. and Immig, H. (1937a) *Z. anorg. Chem.* **232**, 229.
Jander, G. and Ullman, D. (1937) *Z. anorg. Chem.* **230**, 405.
Jander, G. and Wickert, K. (1936) *Z. phys. Chem.* A **178**, 57.
Jander, G., Wendt, H. and Hecht, H. (1944) *Ber. dtsch. chem. Ges.* **77**, 698.
Johnson, L. F., Jr. and Norris, T. H. (1957) *J. Amer. chem. Soc.* **79**, 1584.
Johnson, R. E., Norris, T. H. and Huston, J. L. (1951) *J. Amer. chem. Soc.* **73**, 3052.
Kashtanov, L. I. and Sokolova, L. N. (1951) *Zh. Obsch. Khim.* **21**, 1484.
Kivelson, H. D. (1954) *J. chem. Phys.* **22**, 904.
Korezynski, A. and Glebocka, M. (1920) *Gazz. chim. ital.* **50**, I, 378.
Lecher, H. Z. and Hardy, W. B. (1948) *J. Amer. chem. Soc.* **70**, 3789.
Le Fevre, R. J. W. (1953) "Dipole Moments". Methuen, London.
Lichtin, N. N. (1963) "Progress in Physical Organic Chemistry", Vol. 1. Wiley, New York.
Lichtin, N. N. and Glazer, H. (1951) *J. Amer. chem. Soc.* **73**, 5537.

Lichtin, N. N. and Kliman, H. (1965) *J. Chem. and Eng. Data*, in the press.

Lichtin, N. N. and Leftin, H. P. (1956) *J. phys. Chem.* **60**, 160.

Lichtin, N. N. and Pappas, P. (1957) *Trans. N.Y. Acad. Sci.* **20**, 143.

Lichtin, N. N. and Rao, K. N. (1960) *J. phys. Chem.* **64**, 945.

Lichtin, N. N. and Rao, K. N. (1961) *J. Amer. chem. Soc.* **83**, 2417.

Lichtin, N. N., Laubicht, I. and Pincher, S. (1964) *Inorg. Chem.* **3**, 537.

Lichtin, N. N., Ullstern, R. E., Jr. and White, J. D. (1952) *J. Amer. chem. Soc.* **74**, 4715.

Lindquist, I. and Einarsson, P. (1959) *Acta chem. scand.* **13**, 420.

Lippincott, E. R. and Welch, F. E. (1961) *Spectrochim. Acta*, **17**, 123.

Luchinskii, G. P. (1938) *J. phys. Chem. Moscow*, **12**, 280.

Martin, D. R. (1945) *J. Amer. chem. Soc.* **67**, 1088.

Masters, B. J. and Norris, T. H. (1955) *J. Amer. chem. Soc.* **77**, 1346.

Masters, B. J., Potter, N. D., Asher, D. R. and Norris, T. H. (1956) *J. Amer. chem. Soc.* **78**, 4252.

Mesech, H. (1938) Dissertation, Greifswald.

Michaelis, A. (1891) *Ber. dtsch. chem. Ges.* **24**, 745.

Moede, J. A. and Curran, C. (1949) *J. Amer. chem. Soc.* **71**, 852.

Muxart, R. (1950) *C.R. Acad. Sci., Paris*, **231**, 1489.

Nakata, S. (1943) *J. chem. Soc., Japan*, **64**, 635.

Nickerson, J. D. and McIntosh, R. (1957) *Canad. J. Res. (Chem.)* **35**, 1325.

Norris, T. H. (1959). *J. phys. Chem.* **63**, 383.

Potter, N. D. (1962) *Diss. Abs.* **23**, 1919.

Satenstejn, A. I. and Viktorov, M. M. (1937) *Acta phys.-chim. URSS.* **1**, 883.

Schlenk, W., Weickel, T. and Herzenstein, A. (1910) *Ann.* **372**, 1.

Seel, F. (1943a) *Z. anorg. Chem.* **250**, 331.

Seel, F. (1943b) *Z. anorg. Chem.* **252**, 24.

Seel, F. and Bauer, H. (1947) *Z. Naturf.* **26**, 397.

Seel, F. and Riehl, L. (1955a) *Z. anorg. Chem.* **282**, 293.

Seel, F. and Riehl, L. (1953b) *Angew. Chem.* **67**, 32.

Seel, F., Boez, A. K. and Nogradi, J. (1951a) *Z. anorg. Chem.* **264**, 298.

Seel, F., Boez, A. K. and Nogradi, J. (1951b) *Z. anorg. Chem.* **264**, 311.

Seel, F., Nogradi, J and Rosse, R. (1952) *Z. anorg. Chem.* **269**, 197.

Silberrad, O. (1922) *J. chem. Soc.* **121**, 1015.

Steele, B. O. (1907) *Chem. News*, **96**, 224.

Vierk, A. L. (1950) *Z. anorg. Chem.* **261**, 279.

Waddington, T. C. and Klanberg, F. (1960) *J. chem. Soc.* 2332.

Walden, P. (1902) *Ber. dtsch. chem. Ges.* **35**, 2018.

Walden, P. and Centnerszwer, M. (1899) *Ber. dtsch. chem. Ges.* **32**, 2862.

Walden, P. and Centnerszwer, M. (1902a) *Z. phys. Chem.* **39**, 513.

Walden, P. and Centnerszwer, M. (1902b) *Z. anorg. Chem.* **30**, 145.

Walden, P. and Centnerszwer, M. (1902c) *Z. anorg. Chem.* **30**, 179.

Walden, P. and Centnerszwer, M. (1903) *Z. phys. Chem.* **42**, 432.

Wickert, K. (1938a) *Z. Electrochem.* **44**, 110.

Wickert, K. (1938b) *Naturwissenshaften*, **26**, 500.

Wickert, K. and Jander, G. (1937) *Ber. dtsch. chem. Ges.* **70** B, 251.

CHAPTER 7

The Halogens and Interhalogens as Solvents

A. G. SHARPE

University Chemical Laboratory, Cambridge, England

I. The Halogens	286
A. Chlorine	287
B. Bromine	287
C. Iodine	288
II. The Interhalogens	290
A. Compounds of Formula AB	290
B. Compounds of Formula AB_3	292
C. Compounds of Formula AB_5	295
D. Compounds of Formula AB_7	297
References	298

The halogens and interhalogens, because of their great reactivity, dissolve only a limited number of substances without causing them to undergo reactions more drastic than ion formation or solvation. Most work on these substances as solvents has been purely qualitative in nature, and even where quantitative data are available their interpretation is often obscure. It is scarcely surprising that this field of inorganic chemistry is one of the less exact areas of physical science: bromine trifluoride, the only one of the solvents to have the status of a reagent of some importance in preparative inorganic chemistry, explodes with water and most organic matter, reacts with asbestos with incandescence, and can be manipulated in quartz apparatus only because the reaction with silica in this form is very much slower than that with the finely-divided material; the iodine chlorides, though they are less violent in their reactions, nevertheless possess the property, inconvenient in electrochemical studies, of readily dissolving gold and platinum. The only technique which has been applied widely is that of measurement of electrical conductivity; this, however, though it provides some indication of the number and mobility of the ions present, gives little information as to their nature. Identification of products liberated at electrodes may throw some light on this problem, but too often the relationship between what carries the current and what is discharged at the electrodes is a subtle one. Even if, as is rarely the case, the structures of solid adducts containing the elements of the solvent are known, far-reaching changes may occur on dissolution, and halogen-exchange processes are often very rapid. Transport and e.m.f. measurements, which have provided so much of our knowledge of the nature of aqueous solutions, have not been made to any profitable extent in halogens and interhalogens. The picture which the following account presents is therefore not a very clear one, and much further work will be needed before the nature of solutions in these substances is well understood.

In this survey, solvents are considered according to formula type, first the halogens themselves and then, in turn, compounds of formula AB, AB_3, AB_5, and AB_7. There is a large literature on the interaction of bromine, iodine, iodine monochloride, or iodine bromide and donor molecules (especially organic bases), but most work on such systems relates to solid phases or to conditions in which the donor molecule is present in large excess; this subject has been reviewed elsewhere recently (Andrews and Keefer, 1961), and will receive only incidental mention here.

I. The Halogens

Little has yet been published concerning solutions in liquid fluorine (though it has been reported that chlorine is only sparingly soluble (Aoyama and Kanda, 1937)), but for the sake of completeness some of its properties Hu *et al.*, 1953) are included with those of chlorine (Giauque and Powell, 1939),

TABLE I

Physical Properties of the Liquid Halogens

	F_2	Cl_2	Br_2	I_2
M.p. (°C)	−220	−101	−7	114
B.p. (°C)	−188	−34	59	183
Specific gravity	1·51 (−190°)	1·57 (−35°)	3·12 (20°)	3·92 (133°)
Dielectric constant	1·52 (−190°)	2·0 (−35°)	3·1 (20°)	11·1 (118°)
Specific conductivity (ohm⁻¹ cm⁻¹)	—	7×10^{-8}	$1·1 \times 10^{-9}(25°)$	$5·2 \times 10^{-5}(114°)$
Heat of vapourization (kcal mole⁻¹) at b.p.	1·56	4·87	7·25	10·6
Entropy of vapourization (cal mole⁻¹ deg⁻¹)	18·5	20·4	22·0	23·1
Viscosity (millipoises)	—	4·9 (−34°)	10·3 (16°)	19·8 (116°)

bromine (Rabinowitsch, 1926), and iodine (Jander, 1949) in Table I. Attention may be directed to the fact that the specific conductivity of chlorine (McIntosh, 1922) appears to be appreciably greater than that of bromine; this value, however, was reported many years ago and should probably be regarded as an upper limit.

A. CHLORINE

Biltz and Meinecke (1923) reported that the chlorides of sodium, potassium, copper(II), cadmium, aluminium, lead(II), cerium(III) and zirconium(IV) are insoluble in liquid chlorine, and that tungsten(VI) chloride is only sparingly soluble. Carbon tetrachloride, silicon tetrachloride, titanium tetrachloride, arsenic trichloride, lead tetrachloride, phosphorus oxychloride, and disulphur dichloride dissolve readily. Biltz and Meinecke found no indication of compound formation in systems of the first four of these compounds and liquid chlorine, but Wheat and Browne (1938) have shown that compounds $CCl_4.nCl_2$, where $n = 0.5$ 1, 2, 3, or 4, exist, and that compound formation also occurs between chlorine and chloroform, methylene chloride, methyl chloride, and hydrogen chloride (Wheat and Browne, 1936a,b). The fact that chloroform and methylene chloride combine with, at most, three and two molecules of chlorine respectively, has been held to indicate that the chlorine atoms of the organic compound are acting as donors. If this is so, however, it is somewhat surprising that Wheat and Browne found no evidence for compound formation in the system carbon tetrachloride–bromine. The following values for the depression of the freezing-point of chlorine by 0.01 mole fraction of the solutes named have been given by Taylor and Hildebrand (1923), but the measurements are those of Waentig and McIntosh (1915).

	$-\Delta T(°C)$		$-\Delta T(°C)$
Acetone	0.190	Carbon tetrachloride	0.210
Ethyl acetate	0.190	Toluene	0.215
Diethyl ether	0.204	Chloroform	0.222
Stannic chloride	0.208		

The theoretical value calculated from the latent heat of fusion is, however, 0.27°. It therefore seems beyond doubt that there exists quite strong interaction between chlorine and the substances named, and the further study of these systems (and their comparison with, e.g. chlorine–hexane, in which interaction should be minimal), might be rewarding. In view of the evidence for the existence of the Cl_3^- ion in aqueous media, the action of liquid chlorine on chlorides of large organic cations also merits study: lattice energy considerations suggest that stable polychloride formation is most likely in such cases. The possibility of complexing with Lewis acids, especially antimony pentachloride, might also prove worth examination.

B. BROMINE

Many halides of non-metals are soluble in bromine, among them being carbon tetrachloride and tetrabromide, boron tribromide, silicon tetrabromide, titanium tetrabromide, stannic bromide, arsenic tribromide and antimony tribromide; there is up to the present time no evidence for compound formation (Biltz and Jeep, 1923; Wheat and Browne, 1936a). Phosphorus trichloride dissolves to form chlorobromides.

Bromine forms addition compounds with many organic bases such as pyridine, quinoline, acetamide, and benzamide; such compounds form conducting solutions in bromine, probably giving $Base_nBr^+$ and Br_3^- ions, but the conductivity is time-variable, suggesting that bromination of the organic molecule is taking place, and the interpretation of the data is obscure (Finkelstein, 1926; Plotnikov and Mikhailowskaya, 1940).

Alkali metal bromides do not dissolve to any appreciable extent in bromine, but bromides of large organic cations do so; a solution of tetrabutylammonium bromide, for example, has an equivalent conductivity of $15 \cdot 7$ ohm^{-1} cm^{-2} at $2 \cdot 01$ M concentration at $25°$. Since the solution is highly viscous, a very high degree of dissociation, presumably with formation of polybromide anions, is indicated (Moessen and Kraus, 1952). Phosphorus pentachloride also forms conducting solutions which appear to contain anionic chlorine; the variation of molar conductivity with concentration is complicated. Phosphorus pentabromide forms similar solutions (Plotnikov and Jakubson, 1928).

C. IODINE

Liquid iodine as a solvent has been investigated more extensively than the other halogens, though no new work has been reported during the last decade; the following account is based largely on a much more detailed one by G. Jander in 1949 (Jander, 1949).

Iodine itself is in some ways an abnormal substance. In the solid, the closest approach of what would usually be designated non-bonded atoms ($3 \cdot 56$ Å) is near enough to the interatomic distance in the molecule ($2 \cdot 68$ Å) to suggest that quite strong intermolecular attraction exists, and the rather high entropy of vapourization at the boiling point suggests that this attraction persists to some extent in the liquid phase. The dielectric constant of the liquid is remarkable in increasing with rise in temperature, from $11 \cdot 1$ at $118°$ to $13 \cdot 0$ at $168°$. The liquid is a much better conductor than the other halogens, but the conductivity, unlike that of the solid, falls with increase in temperature; these results are commonly interpreted as showing that the conductivity is partly metallic and partly electrolytic but the factor that the current-carrying ions are probably thermally unstable should also be borne in mind.

Sulphur, selenium, and tellurium are said to dissolve in liquid iodine without chemical change. Stannic iodide, zinc iodide, antimony tri-iodide, arsenic tri-iodide, mercuric iodide and iodoform also dissolve, and cryoscopic measurements suggest that they do so unchanged. The iodides of calcium, strontium and barium are insoluble, but those of the alkali metals are readily soluble; cryoscopic measurements, however, show that polymeric species are present, the degree of polymerization being greatest for lithium and least for caesium. Conductivities of solutions of alkali metal halides have been measured for the lithium, sodium, potassium, and rubidium salts; the specific conductivity of sodium iodide solutions is lower than those of the other compounds, and varies little with concentration; the specific conductivities of solutions of the other three iodides increase steeply with increasing concentration, reaching maxima at about 10 mole % of the salt. Furthermore, the temperature coefficient of the specific conductivity is reported to be negative for solutions of sodium iodide and positive for solutions of lithium, potassium, and rubidium iodides. It seems clear that triple ions and more complex species, as well as M^+ and I_3^-, are present in such solutions, but it appears profitless to speculate further until the anomalous position of sodium iodide has been confirmed and more detailed studies of all the solutions have been made.

The self-dissociation of liquid iodine has been represented by the equation

$$2I_2 \rightleftharpoons I^+ + I_3^-. \tag{1}$$

On this basis alkali metal iodides, which readily form tri-iodides, have been regarded as bases, and iodine monohalides as acids. Conductimetric titration, of e.g. KI and IBr in molten iodine shows a sharp break at a 1 : 1 molar ratio, which would correspond to the process

$$MI_3 + IX \rightleftharpoons MX + 2I_2. \tag{2}$$

Such a process can also be followed potentiometrically, though since the iodine monohalides are only weak electrolytes in iodine a symmetrical curve is not obtained. A rough estimate of the value for the ionic product $[I^+][I^-]$ has led to a value of 10^{-42}. Recently, however, the species I^+ has been identified beyond reasonable doubt in the blue solutions of iodine in oleum and iodine in iodine pentafluoride, and in each case it has been shown that it is paramagnetic with a moment of 1·7–2·0 Bohr magnetons (Arotsky and Symons, 1962; Aynsley et al., 1963). No measurements of the magnetic susceptibilities of solutions of iodine monohalides in liquid iodine have been reported, but it seems very doubtful whether free I^+ ions are present, and it can only be said that the simplest basis for the self-ionization of iodine appears to involve the formation of I_3^+ and I_3^- ions, and that more complex species may well be involved. Solvolytic reactions in liquid iodine, e.g.

$$KCN + I_2 \rightleftharpoons KI + ICN, \tag{3}$$

and amphoteric behaviour, e.g.

$$HgI_2 + 2KI \rightleftharpoons K_2HgI_4, \tag{4}$$

have also been described.

II. The Interhalogens

A. COMPOUNDS OF FORMULA AB

Of the compounds of this general formula, chlorine monofluoride (m.p. −156°, b.p. −100°), the unstable bromine monofluoride (m.p. about −33°, b.p. about 20°) and monochloride (m.p. about −66°, b.p. about 5°), and the recently reported iodine monofluoride have not been described as solvents, and only iodine monochloride and bromide will be discussed here. Their physical properties are given in Table II, which is based on reviews by Gutmann (1951a,b) and Greenwood (1951, 1956).

TABLE II

Physical Properties of Iodine Monochloride and Bromide

	ICl	IBr
M.p.(°C)	27·2(α), 13·9(β)	41°
B.p. (°C)	100	about 116
Specific gravity	3·13 (45°)	3·76 (42°)
Dielectric constant	—	—
Specific conductivity (ohm^{-1} cm^{-1})	4·6 × 10^{-3}(35°)	3·0 × 10^{-4}(40°)
Heat of vapourization (kcal mole^{-1}) at b.p.	10·0	—
Entropy of vapourization (cal mole^{-1} deg^{-1})	26·7	—
Viscosity (millipoises)	41·9 (28°)	—

One special difficulty attends the interpretation of data on fused iodine monohalides: the compounds are dissociated into free halogens to an appreciable extent. For iodine monochloride the degree of dissociation is 0·4% at 25° and 1·1% at 100°; for iodine monobromide the corresponding figures are 8·8% and 13·4% (Greenwood, 1951).

The electrical conductivity of liquid iodine monochloride is increased considerably when potassium or ammonium chloride is dissolved in it, the equivalent conductances at 35° at infinite dilution being about 32 and 26 ohm^{-1} cm^2 respectively. Other compounds which are appreciably soluble to yield conducting solutions include RbCl, CsCl, KBr, KI, AlCl$_3$, AlBr$_3$, PCl$_5$, pyridine, acetamide, and benzamide. Lithium, sodium, silver, and barium chlorides are sparingly soluble; silicon tetrachloride, titanium tetrachloride, and niobium pentachloride dissolve but have very little effect on the conductivity; antimony pentachloride increases it, though to a much less extent than phosphorus pentachloride. Thionyl chloride, which is miscible in all proportions, acts merely as a diluent, and the conductivity decreases as more thionyl chloride is added. The interpretation of the conductivity data is complicated by the changes in density, viscosity and degree of dissociation which occur on dilution; further information has often been obtained by studies of systems involving iodine monochloride in nitrobenzene solution, but it should not be forgotten that addition of a third component may create further complications.

The self-ionization of iodine monochloride, which has generally been represented as

$$2ICl \rightleftharpoons I^+ + ICl_2^- \tag{5}$$

resembles that of iodine, and doubts about the presence of the free cation (as distinct from species such as I_2Cl^+) which were expressed earlier must be reiterated here. The existence of the ICl_2^- ion in e.g. solid alkali metal salts and $PCl_4^+ICl_2^-$ (Zelezny and Baenziger, 1952) is well established by X-ray methods, but there is no real evidence for the existence of the unsolvated cation; phase studies of the systems $AlCl_3$—ICl and $SbCl_5$—ICl reveal no 1 : 1 compounds, but only 1 : 2 and 1 : 2 and 1 : 3 adducts respectively. These presumably contain the I_2Cl^+ ion analogous to the ICl_2^+ ion present in $ICl_3.AlCl_3$ and $ICl_3.SbCl_5$, which are better represented as $ICl_2^+AlCl_4^-$ and $ICl_2^+SbCl_6^-$ (see later).

In solution in excess of iodine monochloride, the distinction between I^+ and its solvates is for many purposes of minor significance. Thus conductimetric titration of RbCl vs $SbCl_5$ or KCl vs $NbCl_5$ shows a break at 1 : 1 molar ratio, whilst NH_4Cl vs $SnCl_4$ shows a break at 2 : 1 molar ratio, indicating formation of the ion $SnCl_6^{2-}$. The compound $PCl_5.ICl$, which in the solid state is $PCl_4^+ICl_2^-$, behaves as an acid towards $KICl_2$ and as a base towards $SbCl_5$. Organic bases form 1 : 1 or 1 : 2 compounds; these are likely to be N-donor complexes and salts of the type (Base) $I^+ICl_2^-$ respectively. From the preparative viewpoint reactions in fused iodine monochloride are of very limited usefulness, pure products being seldom isolable; the reagent may, however, prove to be useful in stabilizing chloride complexes of elements in high oxidation states.

Fused iodine bromide as a solvent closely resembles iodine monochloride, but stable acids on this solvent system have not yet been isolated. Alkali metal bromides form polyhalides of formula $MIBr_2$, and phosphorus pentabromide gives the compound $IPBr_6$ which, by analogy with the chloro compound, is probably $PBr_4^+IBr_2^-$; in iodine bromide it behaves only as a base. Stannic bromide acts as an acid anhydride and, as may be shown by conductimetric titration, undergoes neutralization reactions such as

$$2RbIBr_2 + SnBr_4 \rightleftharpoons Rb_2SnBr_6 + 2IBr. \tag{6}$$

B. COMPOUNDS OF FORMULA AB₃

Excluding the recently discovered iodine trifluoride (Schmeisser and Scharf, 1960), concerning which very little is known, the compounds in this group are chlorine trifluoride, bromine trifluoride, and iodine trichloride. Their physical properties appear in Table III.

TABLE III*

Physical Properties of Liquid Interhalogens of Formula AB₃

	ClF_3	BrF_3	ICl_3
M.p. (°C)	−83	9	101
B.p. (°C)	12	126	—
Specific gravity	1·84 (12°)	2·80 (25°)	—
Dielectric constant	4·6 (12°)	—	—
Specific conductivity (ohm⁻¹ cm⁻¹)	$6·5 \times 10^{-9}(0°)$	$8·0 \times 10^{-3}(25°)$	$8·5 \times 10^{-3}(101°)$
Heat of vapourization (kcal mole⁻¹) at b.p.	6·6	10·2	—
Entropy of vapourization (cal mole⁻¹ deg⁻¹)	23·1	25·6	—
Viscosity (millipoises)	4·8 (12°)	22·2 (25°)	—

* Banks, Davies and Rudge, 1953.
  Greenwood, 1951.
  Oliver and Grisand, 1952.
  Quarterman, Hyman and Katz, 1957.
  Rogers, Thompson and Speirs, 1954.
  Rogers, Speirs and Panish, 1957.
  Rogers and Garver, 1958.

Iodine trichloride in the molten state (in which there is appreciable dissociation into the monochloride and chlorine) has not been investigated as a solvent, but since the structure of solid iodine trichloride and those of its adducts with potassium chloride, aluminium chloride, and antimony pentachloride are all accurately known, some discussion of this compound is essential here. The solid contains planar dimeric molecules having the structure shown (Boswijk and Wiebenga, 1954).

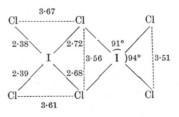

This might be described to a first approximation in terms of an ionic structure with resonance between the two forms ;

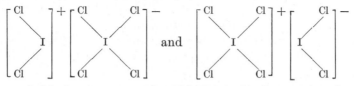

or the central chlorine atoms may be taking part in three-centre bonding. In the planar ion ICl_4^-, present in $KICl_4.H_2O$, the environment of the iodine atom is again unsymmetrical; all the angles are within 1° of 90°, but the I—Cl distances are as shown (Elma, de Boer and Vos, 1963):

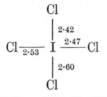

Finally, in the compounds $IAlCl_4$ and $ISbCl_6$ (Vonk and Wiebenga, 1959) the iodine atom has two chlorine atoms at distances of 2·25–2·33 Å plus two more, completing a distorted square, at 2·85–3·00 Å:

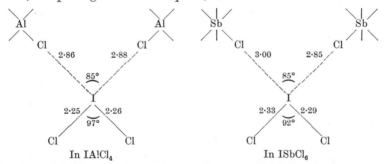

To a first approximation this indicates structures $ICl_2^+AlCl_4^-$ and $ICl_2^+SbCl_6^-$, but the shortness of the I—Cl (bonded to Sb or Al) distances shows there must be substantial cation–anion interaction. Nevertheless, this evidence for the ICl_2^+ and ICl_4^- ions is very important in interpreting the chemistry of adducts of other interhalogens for which no adequate structural data are available.

Although chlorine trifluoride has a very low conductivity and no studies of ionic reactions in it have been reported, it is noteworthy that compounds which may well contain ClF_4^- and ClF_2^+ ions, capable of reacting by the equation

$$ClF_2^+ + ClF_4^- \rightleftharpoons 2ClF_3, \qquad (7)$$

have recently been prepared. The action of fluorine on alkali metal chlorides, bromides, or iodides at 15°–250° results in the formation of the compound

$MClF_4$, where $M = K$, Rb, or Ca, and these must surely contain a ClF_4^- anion; whether they dissolve in liquid chlorine trifluoride does not appear to have been investigated (Asprey, Margrave and Silverthorn, 1961). Chlorine trifluoride forms 1 : 1 complexes with antimony pentafluoride and boron trifluoride (Seel and Detmar, 1958; Selig and Shamir, 1964); both are good conductors and the infra-red spectrum of the second compound strongly suggests it has the structure $ClF_2^+BF_4^-$. There is also n.m.r. evidence which suggests that chlorine trifluoride, which consists of T-shaped molecules in the solid and gaseous states, may in the liquid state be in equilibrium with a low concentration of dimer (Muetterties and Phillips, 1957).

Bromine trifluoride is the only one of the interhalogens which has become a widely used laboratory reagent, chiefly for the preparation of complex fluorides. A number of reviews of its reactions have been given (Gutmann, 1950; Leech, 1956; Ryss, 1960); this account is restricted to instances in which it acts not only as a fluorinating agent but also as a solvent. Bromine trifluoride fluorinates everything which dissolves in it, and a discussion of solubilities is therefore restricted to those of soluble inorganic fluorides. These fall into two groups: alkali metal fluorides, silver(I) fluoride, and barium fluoride; and fluorides of gold(III), boron, titanium(IV), silicon, germanium(IV), vanadium(V), niobium(V), tantalum(V), phosphorus(V), arsenic(V), antimony(V), platinum(IV), ruthenium(V) and a few other metals. Members of both groups have been shown to be conductors in bromine trifluoride, and many form stable adducts, e.g. $AgBrF_4$, $SbBrF_8$, with the solvent. The fact that any member of the first group reacts with a member of the second group to yield a complex halide is easily understood if (by analogy with derivatives of iodine trichloride) derivatives containing BrF_4^- and BrF_2^+ ions are formed and these interact according to an equation such as

$$BrF_2^+SbF_6^- + Ag^+BrF_4^- \rightleftharpoons AgSbF_6 + 2BrF_3. \qquad (8)$$

In a few instances, such as this one, it has been shown by measuring the conductivities of solutions containing different molar ratios of $AgBrF_4$ and $SbBrF_8$ that the conductivity is a minimum at 1 : 1 molar ratio. Stannic fluoride forms a 1 : 2 complex with bromine trifluoride and the reaction of this adduct with $KBrF_4$ can be represented by the equation (Woolf and Eméleus, 1949)

$$(BrF_2^+)_2SnF_6 + 2KBrF_4 \rightleftharpoons K_2SnF_6 + 4BrF_3. \qquad (9)$$

Among a very large number of preparations of fluoro-complexes by means of this reagent the following must suffice to illustrate its scope (Eméleus and Gutmann, 1949; Sharpe, 1950; Woolf, 1950; Sharpe and Woolf, 1951; Sharpe, 1953; Hepworth et al., 1954):

$$Ag + Au \rightarrow AgBrF_4 + BrF_2AuF_4 \rightarrow AgAuF_4 \qquad (10)$$

$$NOCl + SnF_4 \rightarrow (NO)_2SnF_6 \qquad (11)$$

$$N_2O_4 + Sb_2O_3 \rightarrow (NO_2)SbF_6 \tag{12}$$

$$VF_5 + LiF \rightarrow LiVF_6 \tag{13}$$

$$Ru + KCl \rightarrow KRuF_6. \tag{14}$$

Removal of bromine trifluoride from the reaction product is not always easily completed, however; this has been attributed to solvolysis of the product or incomplete interaction of acid and base according to the neutralization equation

$$BrF_2^+ + BrF_4^- \rightleftharpoons 2BrF_3 \tag{15}$$

Stabilization of high oxidation states in bromine trifluoride sometimes occurs; thus although palladium tetrafluoride has not yet been isolated, salts such as K_2PdF_6 are readily obtained from alkali metal chloro-palladites and the reagent (Sharpe, 1953); complexes of chromium(V), e.g. $KCrOF_4$, have also been made in this solvent (Sharpe and Woolf, 1951). It should be pointed out that no acid or base in the bromine trifluoride system has yet been the subject of an adequate structural study; the anion in $KBrF_4$ has been variously reported to be tetrahedral (Siegel, 1956; 1957) or (what seems much more probable) planar (Sly and Marsh, 1957), and the BrF_2^+ ion has not so far been identified conclusively. Since BrF_2 and SbF_5 form a range of compounds (Fischer et al., 1955), it may be that more than one cationic species is involved. However, the analogy with adducts of iodine trichloride is a powerful one, and the value of the reagent in preparative work shows that even if the model for seld-ionization of the interhalogen is not established beyond doubt, it does nevertheless provide a basis on which useful studies can be made.

C. COMPOUNDS OF FORMULA AB_5

Since the recent preparation of chlorine pentafluoride (Smith, 1963) by the action of fluorine on the trifluoride at 350° and 250 atm, pentafluorides of chlorine, bromine, and iodine are all known, and some of their physical properties are given in Table IV. For the first two of these, however, nothing is known of their properties as solvents except that bromine trifluoride and hydrogen fluoride are miscible in all proportions with bromine pentafluoride, and the possibility of complex formation with alkali metal fluorides or, for example, tin(IV) and antimony(V) fluorides, does not seem to have been investigated. [A report of the existence of the compound K_2ClF_7 or $KClF_6.KF$ has been criticized (Emeléus and Sharpe, 1949), and appears to be without foundation.] The properties of iodine pentafluoride have been examined in more detail (Emeléus and Sharpe, 1949; Hargreaves and Peacock, 1960; Muetterties and Phillips, 1957; Rogers and Katz, 1952; Rogers, Thompson and Speirs, 1954; Rogers, Pruett and Speirs, 1955; Rogers, Speirs, Thompson and Panish, 1954; Rogers and Garver, 1958; Woolf, 1950).

A wide range of observations indicate that iodine pentafluoride is an associated liquid, and the observed dependence of the number, widths and positions of the ^{19}F resonances of the compound on temperature has been interpreted in terms of fluorine exchange through a dimeric intermediate (Muetterties and Phillips, 1957). The low specific conductivity of the liquid is greatly increased when potassium iodate or antimony(V) fluoride is dissolved in it; solutions of the former compound liberate iodine at the cathode on electrolysis, and the equivalent conductivity at infinite dilution is $35.5\ ohm^{-1}\ cm^2$. The nature of the ions present has not, however, been established.

TABLE IV

Physical Properties of Interhalogens of Formula AB_5

	ClF_5	BrF_5	IF_5
M.p. (°C)	−100	−61	9·4
B.p. (°C)	—	40·5	100·5
Specific gravity	—	2·46 (25°)	3·19 (25°)
Dielectric constant	—	8 (25°)	36·2 (35°)
Specific conductivity (ohm^{-1} cm^{-1})	—	$9 \times 10^{-8}(25°)$	$5.4 \times 10^{-6}(25°)$
Heat of vapourization (kcal mole^{-1}) at b.p.	—	6·7	9·8
Entropy of vapourization (cal mole^{-1} deg^{-1})	—	23·3	26·5
Viscosity (millipoises)	—	6·2 (24°)	21·9 (25°)

Antimony(V) fluoride and potassium fluoride both combine with iodine pentafluoride to yield compounds of formulae $ISbF_{10}$ and KIF_6 respectively, both of which are readily soluble in hot, and sparingly soluble in cold, iodine pentafluoride. The potassium salt is a well-defined compound which is also obtained by the action of the pentafluoride on potassium nitrate (Aynsley, Nichols and Robinson, 1953) or iodide (Hargreaves and Peacock, 1960), and although the structure of the solid has not been determined by X-ray analysis there seems to be little doubt that the formulation $K^+IF_6^-$ is correct. The nature of the adduct with antimony pentafluoride is more doubtful, but from the conductivity in iodine pentafluoride and the formation of (impure) potassium hexafluorantimonate by the interaction of KIF_6 and $ISbF_{10}$ in iodine pentafluoride, the structure $IF_4^+SbF_6^-$ is suggested. The neutralization process may then be represented by the equation

$$K^+IF_6^- + IF_4^+SbF_6^- \rightleftharpoons KSbF_6 + 2IF_5. \qquad (16)$$

Boron trifluoride also increases the conductivity of iodine pentafluoride, and passage of the gas into a solution of potassium fluoride in the interhalogen compound results in the formation of potassium fluoroborate. Sulphur trioxide is readily soluble and increases the conductivity; distillation of such solutions gives a constant-boiling mixture of composition $IF_5.1\cdot17SO_3$. It is possible that a fluorosulphonate is in fact formed; such compounds have been made by other methods (Roberts and Cady, 1960). Adducts are also formed with dinitrogen pentoxide, molybdenum and tungsten trioxides, and potassium periodate (Aynsley, Nichols and Robinson, 1953). The system $HF—IF_5$ has been studied in detail, but no compound formation has been detected.

A recent examination of the nature of the blue solutions formed when iodine dissolves in iodine pentafluoride shows these to contain the uncoordinated paramagnetic I^+ ion, formed by the reaction

$$IF_5 + 2I_2 \rightleftharpoons 5I^+ + 5IF_6^-. \tag{17}$$

Addition of potassium fluoride, which combines with the interhalogen, shifts the equilibrium towards the left hand side, and the solutions turn brown (Aynsley et al., 1963). Similar blue solutions have been obtained from the oxide I_2O_4 (Aynsley et al., 1953). Iodine(III) is also stable in cold iodine pentafluoride solution; when potassium iodide reacts with the pentafluoride, iodine is liberated and from the resulting solution the compound KIF_4 may be isolated (Hargreaves and Peacock, 1960).

D. COMPOUNDS OF FORMULA AB_7

The only representative of this class known at the present time is iodine heptafluoride, which has only a very narrow liquid range: it melts at 5–6° at 2 atm pressure; the vapour pressure of the solid reaches 760 mm at 4·5°, which is also the boiling point of the slightly supercooled liquid. As Greenwood (1951) has pointed out, the widely quoted value of 26·4 cal mole^{-1} deg^{-1} for the entropy of vapourization (which would suggest an associated liquid) is incorrect, having been calculated from the heat of sublimation of the solid instead of the heat of vapourization of the liquid; the true value must certainly be substantially lower.

Our knowledge of the chemical properties of iodine heptafluoride is very limited. There is no sign of interaction with sodium, potassium, and rubidium fluorides, which do not dissolve in the liquid (Schumb and Lynch, 1950). A brief report has, however, described addition compounds $IF_7.AsF_5$ and $IF_7.3SbF_5$; the structure $IF_6^+AsF_6^-$ was suggested for the former compound, largely on the basis of its decomposition to iodine heptafluoride and potassium hexafluoroarsenate on treatment with potassium fluoride (Seel and Detmar, 1958), but further details have not yet appeared. The present writer is of the opinion that interaction of caesium fluoride and iodine heptafluoride at high pressures and moderate temperatures might lead to the discovery of a compound containing the IF_8^- ion, and it may be that some future publication will describe fluoride transfer by the reaction

$$IF_6^+ + IF_8^- \rightleftharpoons 2IF_7 \tag{18}$$

in iodine heptafluoride solution.

REFERENCES

Andrews, L. J. and Keefer, R. M. (1961) *Adv. inorg. Chem. Radiochem.* **3**, 91.

Aoyama, S. and Kanda, E. (1937) *Bull. chem. Soc. Japan*, **12**, 455.

Arotsky, J. and Symons, M. C. R. (1962) *Quart. Rev.* **16**, 282.

Asprey, L. B., Margrave, J. L. and Silverthorn, M. E. (1961) *J. Amer. chem. Soc.* **83**, 2955.

Aynsley, E. E., Greenwood, N. N. and Wharmby, D. H. W. (1963) *J. chem. Soc.* 5369.

Aynsley, E. E., Nichols, R. and Robinson, P. L. (1953) *J. chem. Soc.* 623.

Banks, A. A., Davies, A. and Rudge, A. J. (1953) *J. chem. Soc.* 732.

Biltz, W. and Jeep, K. (1927) *Z. anorg. Chem.* **162**, 32.

Biltz, W. and Meinecke, E. (1923) *Z. anorg. Chem.* **131**, 4.

Boswijk, K. H. and Wiebenga, E. H. (1954) *Acta crystallogr.* **7**, 417.

Elma, R. J., de Boer, J. L. and Vos, A. (1963) *Acta crystallogr.* **16**, 243.

Emeléus, H. J. and Gutmann, V. (1949) *J. chem. Soc.* 2979.

Emeléus, H. J. and Sharpe, A. G. (1949) *J. chem. Soc.* 2206.

Finkelstein, W. (1926) *Z. phys. Chem.* **121**, 46.

Fischer, J., Liimatainen, R. and Bingle, J. (1955) *J. Amer. chem. Soc.* **77**, 5848.

Giauque, W. F. and Powell, T. M. (1939) *J. Amer. chem. Soc.* **61**, 1970.

Greenwood, N. N. (1951) *Rev. pure appl. Chem.* **1**, 84.

Greenwood, N. N. (1956). *In* Supplement to Mellor's "Comprehensive Treatise on Inorganic and Theoretical Chemistry," II, Part I.

Gutmann, V. (1950) *Angew. Chem.* **62**, 312.

Gutmann, V. (1951a) *Z. anorg. Chem.* **264**, 151.

Gutmann, V. (1951b) *Mh. Chem.* **82**, 156.

Hargreaves, G. B. and Peacock, R. D. (1960) *J. chem. Soc.* 2373.

Hepworth, M. A., Peacock, R. D. and Robinson, P. L. (1954) *J. chem. Soc.* 1197.

Hu, J.-H., White, D. and Johnston, H. L. (1953) *J. Amer. chem. Soc.* **75**, 5642.

Jander, G. (1949) "Die Chemie in Wasserähnlichen Lösungsmitteln Springer-Verlag, Berlin".

Leech, H. R. (1956) *In* Mellor's "Comprehensive Treatise on Inorganic and Theoretical Chemistry," Supplement II, Part I.

McIntosh, D. (1922) *Proc. roy. Soc. Can.* **16**, III, 302.

Moessen, G. W. and Kraus, C. A. (1953) *Proc. nat. Acad. Sci., Wash.* **38**, 1023.

Muetterties, E. L. and Phillips, W. D. (1957) *J. Amer. chem. Soc.* **79**, 322.

Oliver, G. D. and Grisard, J. W. (1952) *J. Amer. chem. Soc.* **74**, 2705.

Plotnikov, W. A. and Jakubson, S. (1928) *Z. phys. Chem.*, **138**, 235.

Plotnikov, W. A. and Mikhailowskaya, V. I. (1940) *Zap. Inst. Khim. U.S.S.R.* **7**, No. 1, 85.

Quarterman, L. A., Hyman, H. H. and Katz, J. J. (1957) *J. phys. Chem.* **61**, 912.

Rabinowitsch, M. (1926) *Z. phys. Chem.* **119**, 81.

Roberts, J. E. and Cady, G. H. (1960) *J. Amer. chem. Soc.*, **82**, 352, 353, 354.

Rogers, M. T. and Garver, E. E. (1958) *J. phys. Chem.* **62**, 952.

Rogers, M. T. and Katz, J. J. (1952) *J. Amer. chem. Soc.*, **74**, 1375.

Rogers, M. T., Pruett, R. D. and Speirs, J. L. (1955) *J. Amer. chem. Soc.* **77**, 5280.

Rogers, M. T., Speirs, J. L. and Panish, M. B. (1957) *J. phys. Chem.* **61**, 366.

Rogers, M. T., Thompson, H. B. and Speirs, J. L. (1954) *J. Amer. chem. Soc.*, **76**, 4841.

Rogers, M. T., Speirs, J. L., Thompson, H. B. and Panish, M. B. (1954) *J. Amer. chem. Soc.* **76**, 4843.

Rogers, M. T., Speirs, J. L., Thompson, H. B. and Panish, M. B. (1956) *J. Amer. chem. Soc.* **78**, 936.

Ryss, I. G. (1960). "The Chemistry of Fluorine and its Inorganic Compounds" (Translation), U.S. Atomic Energy Commission.

Schmeisser, M. and Scharf, E. (1960) *Angew. Chem.*, **72**, 324.

Schumb, W. C. and Lynch, M. A. (1950) *Industr. Engng. Chem. (Industr.)* **42**, 1383.

Seel, F. and Detmar, O. (1958) *Angew. Chem.* **70**, 163, 470.

Selig, H. and Shamir, J. (1964) *Inorg. Chem.* **3**, 294.

Sharpe, A. G. (1950) *J. chem. Soc.* 3444.

Sharpe, A. G. (1953) *J. chem. Soc.* 197.

Sharpe, A. G. and Woolf, A. A. (1951) *J. chem. Soc.* 798.

Siegel, S. (1956) *Acta crystallogr.* **9**, 493.

Siegel, S. (1957) *Acta crystallogr.* **10**, 380.

Sly, W. G. and Marsh, R. E. (1957) *Acta crystallogr.* **10**, 378.

Smith, D. F. (1963) *Science*, **141**, 1039.

Taylor, N. W. and Hildebrand, J. H. (1923) *J. Amer. chem. Soc.* **45**, 685.

Vonk, C. G. and Wiebenga, E. H. (1959) *Acta crystallogr.* **12**, 859.

Waentig, G. and McIntosh, D. (1915) *Proc. roy. Soc. Can.* **9**, 207.

Wheat, J. A. and Browne, A. W. (1936a) *J. Amer. chem. Soc.* **58**, 2410.

Wheat, J. A. and Browne, A. W. (1938) *J. Amer. chem. Soc.* **60**, 371.

Wheat, J. A. and Browne, A. W. (1936b) *J. Amer. chem. Soc.* **60**, 1575, 1577.

Woolf, A. A. (1950) *J. chem. Soc.* 1053.

Woolf, A. A. (1950) *J. chem. Soc.* 3678.

Woolf, A. A. and Emeléus, H. J. (1949) *J. chem. Soc.* 2865.

Zelezny, W. F. and Baenziger, N. C. (1952) *J. Amer. chem. Soc.* **74**, 6151.

CHAPTER 8

Halides and Oxyhalides of Group V Elements as Solvents

D. S. PAYNE

Chemistry Department, The University, Glasgow, Scotland

I. Introduction 301
II. Experimental Methods.. 306
    A. Qualitative Solubility Considerations.................................. 306
    B. The Examination of Solid Phases...................................... 307
    C. The Products of Electron Transfer.................................... 307
    D. Conductivity Measurements.. 307
    E. Transport Number Measurements.. 308
    F. Potentiometric Measurements.. 308
    G. Titrations Using Indicators.. 309
    H. Spectrophotometric Measurements...................................... 309
    I. Viscosity Measurements... 310
    J. Thermodynamic Measurements... 310
    K. Isotopic Exchange Reaction... 310
    L. Ebullioscopic and Cryoscopic Measurements............................ 310
III. Halides as Solvents.. 311
IV. Oxyhalides as Solvents.. 327
 V. Phosphoryl Chloride.. 332
VI. Uses of Group V Halides and Oxyhalides as Solvents......................... 348
References.. 349

I. INTRODUCTION

Immediately after the recognition by Cady (1897) of the resemblances between liquid ammonia and water in the dissolution of inorganic salts, attention was turned to a search for other liquids with similar solvent properties. Brühl (1898) suggested that certain halides of elements such as phosphorus or arsenic might be solvents; the first experimental work, however, concerned antimony trichloride as a cryoscopic solvent (Tolloczko, 1899). Walden's classical investigations into non-aqueous solvents covered the halides and oxyhalides of phosphorus and the halides of arsenic and antimony (Walden, 1900). Certain of these were "good" solvents for inorganic materials and the resulting solutions were usually electrical conductors. The process of dissolution was interpreted in terms of ionization processes involving both solvent and solute. Little interest was shown in these halide and oxyhalide solvents until recent work, notably that of V. Gutmann and his collaborators working in Vienna, re-awakened interest. A large number of investigators have now worked in the field and the experimental techniques for handling these readily hydrolysed solvents are well established and tested. As the following account will show, the scope of this group of compounds as solvents has now been thoroughly examined and the nature of the solution species established in a number of instances. Interest has now turned to a more detailed physico-chemical examination of these systems, indeed for certain aspects of electrochemistry these experimentally difficult solvents offer considerable attractions because of the comparative simplicity of the interactions between solvent and ionic species (Porter and Baughan, 1958).

The elements of Group V, with the exception of nitrogen, give rise to two main series of halides, the trihalides and the pentahalides. Other halides such as tetraiododiphosphine (P_2I_4) and bismuth monochloride (BiCl) are known but are not appropriate to a discussion of solvent properties, as they are not readily accessible in amounts required for solvent investigations. The oxy-halides of this group vary from simple molecular compounds such as the nitrosyl and phosphoryl halides to the solid bismuth oxyhalides with layer structures. The halide and oxyhalide chemistry of nitrogen, phosphorus, arsenic, antimony and bismuth is dominated by the ready attack of nucleo-philic reagents; all the compounds are sensitive to hydrolysis and work must always be carried out under strictly anhydrous conditions, if the results are to be significant. These conditions are readily achieved by working in totally enclosed systems, particularly under vacuum. There is also a general ten-dency for these halides and oxyhalides to react with hydrocarbon greases, so that special arrangements have to be made in handling to avoid contamin-ation of this kind.

The stereochemistries most preferred by the elements phosphorus, arsenic, antimony and bismuth are either the tetrahedral (four co-ordination) or the octahedral (six co-ordination). Indeed phosphorus chemistry, particularly pentahalide chemistry, is dominated by the tetrahedrally disposed phos-phorus atom. Thus phosphorus pentachloride exists as a solid based on the PCl_4^+ ion. The octahedral configuration is perhaps of greater general importance, dominating the formation of complex anions, such as $SbCl_6^-$, and AsF_6^-. The stabilities of these species, particularly the six co-ordinate ones are very much a matter of the size, as well as of the electro-negativity of the attached groups. Only the high electronegativities of fluorine, chlorine and possibly of bromine enable the adequate utilization of the d-orbitals essential to the formation of compounds based on co-ordination numbers above four (Craig et $al.$, 1954). It is, of course, also true that only in the case of fluorine and chlorine are the size relationships favourable to high co-ordination numbers. The electronegativities of phosphorus, arsenic, antimony and bismuth are all very close (2·06–1·67); the corresponding electronegativities of the halogens (4·0–2·2) are significantly higher. The polar character of most of the bonds between the halogens and nitrogen, phosphorus, arsenic, antimony and bismuth leads to the expectation of interactions of these molecules with ions or with other polar molecules. It is this prospect which is of great significance in determining solvent behaviour. In the oxyhalides the oxygen bonds are similarly strongly polar, so that further interactions are possible.

TABLE I

Halides of Group V

	M.p.°	B.p.°	Dielectric constant ϵ	Viscosity (centipoise) η	Density ρ (gcm^{-3})
PF$_3$	−151	−101	—	—	—
PCl$_3$	−112	74	3·5(17°) 4·7(22°)	—	1·56(21°)
PBr$_3$	−40	173	3·9(20°)	—	2·85(15°)
PI$_3$	61	dec. > 200	4·1(c. 65°)	—	—
AsF$_3$	−6	63	5·7(< −6°)	—	2·67(0°)
*AsCl$_3$	−13	130	12·6(17°)	1·225(20°)	2·16(20°)
*AsBr$_3$	35	220	8·8(35°)	5·41(35°) 4·44(40°)	3·33(50°)
AsI$_3$	146	403	7·0(c. 150°)	—	4·69(25°)
SbF$_3$	292	subl. 319	—	—	4·38(21°)
*SbCl$_3$	73	221	33·0(75°)	3·3(95°)	2·44(178°)
*SbBr$_3$	97	280	20·9(c. 100°)	6·81(100°)	4·15(23°)
SbI$_3$	167	401	13·9(c. 175°)	—	4·85
BiF$_3$	725	—	—	—	5·32(20°)
*BiCl$_3$	232	447	—	32·0(260°)	4·75(25°)
BiBr$_3$	218	460	—	—	5·72(25°)
BiI$_3$	408	>500	—	—	5·88(17·5°)
PF$_5$	−94	−84	—	—	—
PCl$_5$	—	subl. 167	2·7(165°) 2·85(liq. at 160°)	—	1·60(160°)
PBr$_5$	<100	dec. > 106	—	—	—
AsF$_5$	−80	−53	—	—	3·40(−73°)
SbF$_5$	7	150	—	—	2·99(23°)
SbCl$_5$	5	∼140	3·2(21°)	2·16(25°)	2·35(20°)
BiF$_5$	<160	230	—	—	5·40(25°)

* Compounds with significant solvent properties.

The characteristic feature of a solvent is its ability to bring into a single phase (the solution), usually liquid, one or more other compounds (the solutes), usually solids. The mechanism of this phenomena is not confined solely to the separation and solvation of ions already present in a crystal lattice, but rather involves the general interaction of solvent molecules and solute, often leading to quite new compounds. The occurrence of these interactions in amounts large enough to be practically significant, and to warrant the use of the term solution and solvent, is controlled by the algebraic sum of a number of free energies. The magnitude and multiplicity of these energy terms vary considerably from system to system. However, in certain classes of compound with certain types of solute the overall energy change is generally favourable, and "good" solvent properties are encountered. Such groups of compounds are the trihalides, particularly those of arsenic and antimony, and the oxyhalides, notably nitrosyl and phosphoryl chlorides.

TABLE II

Oxyhalides of Group V

	M.p.°	B.p.°	Dielectric constant ϵ	Viscosity centipoise η	Density ρ (gcm^{-3})
FNO	−132·5	−60	—	—	1·33(−60°)
*ClNO	−61·5	−6	22·5(−27·5°)	0·586(−27°)	1·59(−6°)
			19·7(−10·0°)	0·547(−20°)	
BrNO	−55·5	∼0	13·4(15·2°)	—	—
FNO$_2$	−166	−72	—	—	1·49(−73°)
ClNO$_2$	−141	−14	—	—	1·41(−15°)
FNO$_3$	−181	−46	—	—	1·51(−46°)
ClNO$_3$	−107 (in vacuum)	18	—	—	—
POF$_3$	−39	−40	—	—	—
*POCl$_3$	1	108	13·9(22°)	1·15(25°)	1·71(0°)
POBr$_3$	56	192	—	—	2·82(45°)

*Compounds with significant solvent properties.

Whilst certain solutes dissolve in the halides and oxyhalides to give non-conducting species, these are not numerically very large and they will not be considered here in detail. Attention will be given largely to solutes which lead to conducting solutions, that is to the role of the halides and oxyhalides as ionizing solvents. Because of the pre-occupation of so much of inorganic chemistry with aqueous solutions, undue emphasis has been given to the consideration of solvent behaviour in terms solely of the dielectric constant. Reference to the physical properties of some of the halides and oxyhalides of Group V elements shown in Tables I and II shows that the dielectric constants, whilst greater than many organic solvents, are not particularly high when compared with solvents such as water ($\epsilon = 81\cdot1$ at 18°), anhydrous hydrogen fluoride ($\epsilon = 83\cdot6$ at 0°) or iodine pentafluoride ($\epsilon = 36\cdot2$ at 25°).

In addition to lowering the forces of Coulombic attraction the solvent is often also involved with the solute as an acceptor or donor of electrons, or as in the case of halides and oxyhalides, of halide ions. In this process of dissolution new chemical species are formed, and it is these which have been of particular interest to many investigators in this field.

The search for a unified approach to ionizing solvents in general has resulted in the application of the terms "acid" and "base" in the discussion of the ionic species involved in widely differing solvents. The Brønsted-Lowry definition of acid and base is clearly not applicable to the halide–oxyhalide solvents. The Lewis acid concept, in which an acid is regarded purely as an electron acceptor, is more nearly applicable, however it is not without its ambiguities. The Solvent-System concept of acids and bases developed by Gutmann and Lindquist (1954) is well suited to the halide solvents, focusing attention as it does on the possibility of ionic transfer processes. The investigation of any solvosystem is primarily a matter of recognizing the nature of the ions present. The interpretation to be placed on these ions, in terms of the solvent-system concept, necessitates the separation of the overall ion forming process into the individual transfer steps, such that "acid"+halide ion = "base" (cf. acid = base+proton, in aqueous systems), or that "base"+ solvent = "acid"+halide ion (cf. acid+solvent = base+proton, in certain aqueous systems). Halide solvents are all aniontropic solvents favouring fluoride, chloride, or iodide ion transfer; the "acids" are anion acceptors and the "bases" anion donors. A halide solvent MX_n may involve the equilibrium:

$$\overset{\overset{\displaystyle X^-_{\text{transfer}}}{\lceil\qquad\qquad\rceil}}{MX_n \quad + \quad MX_n} \quad \rightleftharpoons \quad MX^-_{n+1} + MX^+_{u+1}. \tag{1}$$

$$\text{Acid I} \qquad\qquad \text{Base II} \qquad\qquad\qquad \text{Base I} \qquad \text{Acid II}$$

Such a solvent is ampholytic, reacting as both acid and base. Acids in such a solvent result in a decrease in the solvent halide ion concentration, for example, addition of an acceptor species of the form AX_4 leads to the formation of AX_6^{2-} thus consuming the X^- ions otherwise associated with the solvent. Bases lead to a corresponding increase in halide by the release of halide directly, as with, for example, tetramethylammonium halide. The utility of this concept as a method for a unified treatment of so called "acid–base" reactions is limited by the inherent difficulties associated with identifying with certainty the ionic species present in the solutions and those associated with the solvent. For simple halides the concept is perhaps most easily applied, for example in the case of arsenic trifluoride fluoride ion, transfer may occur thus:

$$AsF_3 \; + \; AsF_3 \; = \; AsF_2^+ \; + \; AsF_4^-.$$

$$\text{Acid I} \quad\;\; \text{Base II} \quad\;\; \text{Acid II} \quad\;\; \text{Base I} \tag{2}$$

Base II is regarded as a fluoride donor, acid I as the fluoride acceptor and similarly base I as the fluoride donor, acid II as the acceptor. Potassium fluoride functions as a base in arsenic trifluoride giving, by fluoride donation, the anion AsF_4^-, whereas antimony pentafluoride functions, as an acid, by fluoride acceptance, giving the cation AsF_2^+ and the anion SbF_6^-.

The application of the solvent-system concept to phosphoryl chloride as a solvent has led to particular uncertainties as regards the interpretation of the species present in the solution; this particular problem will be referred to in greater detail later, here it can be noted that a simpler treatment may well be in terms of a Lewis acid–base interaction (Meek and Drago, 1961). Probably the idea of using the terms "acid" and "base" outside of protonic solvents is unnecessary and should not be attempted except where there is a clear advantage. The view of a cation–anion reaction as a "neutralization" of "acid" and "base" is not necessarily of assistance to our understanding of the system, indeed on the contrary these terms often necessitate additional explanation without adding significantly to the argument.

II. Experimental Methods

Understanding the nature of conducting solutions has always been one of the prime objects in electrochemistry, however, the highly developed theories and experimental techniques which have been evolved deal mainly with aqueous solutions and are not obviously directly applicable to halide and oxyhalide systems. The extension of electrochemical techniques and theories to these halide and oxyhalide solvent systems has recently been started, with results to be described later. The methods which are outlined below for the study of the species in solution cover the foundation work in the field of halide and oxyhalide solvents and only in small part refer to recent precise measurements of a kind similar to the well established work in the water solvent system. Conclusions can only be safely drawn from the results obtained by more than one experimental technique. It is dangerous, although often inescapable, to base conclusions on the result of only one technique.

A. QUALITATIVE SOLUBILITY CONSIDERATIONS

Examination of the solubility characteristics, not necessarily quantitatively, of a wide range of solutes gives an indication of the type of process involved in dissolution, as well as the general features of the solvent. It is of interest to establish at the commencement of an investigation whether typical salts such as the alkali metal halides, the quaternary ammonium halides and selected compounds such as iron(III), tin(IV), titanium(IV), or antimony(V) chlorides are soluble. In certain instances, accompanying colour changes may indicate the formation of complexes. As well as providing an overall picture of the solvent behaviour, this aspect of the investigation usually gives a guide as to the most suitable solutes to employ in later investigations.

B. THE EXAMINATION OF SOLID PHASES

The natures of the solid phases obtained from solutions by changes in concentration, or by changes in temperature, are of particular importance to the study of a solvent. Often these solids are conveniently described as "solvates" where simple addition of molecules of solvent to the solute has apparently occurred, e.g. $SbCl_5.POCl_3$ from antimony(V) chloride in phosphoryl chloride solution. In other cases, the resulting solid can be recognized as a complex between solvent and solute, e.g. $Me_4N^+AsCl_4^-$ from tetramethylammonium chloride in arsenic trichloride solution. The investigation of these solids has in only a few isolated instances been carried to a full X-ray structure determination; in the majority of cases the establishment of the formulae (that is, the ratio of solvent to solute molecules) is all that has been undertaken. By comparing the ratios for a series of solutes, deductions as to the chemical nature of the solvate can sometimes be made. The relation between the species present in solution and the solids obtained from it is difficult to be certain about, since ions present only at very low concentrations may be in equilibrium with the solid phase. However, where a complex ion is recognized in the solid it is reasonable to postulate, until evidence to the contrary is obtained, that this ion is present at a significant concentration in the solution.

C. THE PRODUCTS OF ELECTRON TRANSFER

The effect of electron transfer to a solvent cation can be studied, in certain cases, by the addition of suitable metals. It is especially useful when the product can be readily separated and identified. For example, in the case of nitrosyl chloride, the formation of nitric oxide by addition of zinc has been taken as evidence for the presence of the nitrosonium ion (Addison and Lewis, 1955). However, this method has only a limited applicability because of the difficulty of examining non-volatile or soluble products. An alternative procedure is to electrolyse the solution and to examine the electrode products, but again this is successful only when these are readily separated. In the case of self-ionization of a pure solvent, direct electrolysis presents considerable difficulties because of the very low conductance values. In one case, namely phosphoryl chloride, it has, however, been successfully applied (Spandau *et al.*, 1960).

D. CONDUCTIVITY MEASUREMENTS

In dealing with the halides and oxyhalides as ionizing solvents, conductivity measurements have been very important. The self-ionization of a solvent is a feature of particular interest and a direct experimental approach may be attempted by measurement of the conductivity of the pure liquid. Clearly such measurements can equally well serve as a criterion of purity, since it is usual to find the conductivities of pure liquids to be very low. It is usually assumed that impurities present in the solvent will lead to an increase in conductivity. Measurement of the conductivities of pure halide solvents indicates that there is a trend, which is in line with the expected stability of the anionic and cationic species, thus

$$PCl_3 < AsCl_3 < SbCl_3 < BiCl_3.$$

Whilst measurement of the absolute conductivities is of interest in the application of modern electrolyte theory to these non-aqueous solutions, so far only a limited amount of data, which can be adequately tested by application of the Debye-Hückel Theory, has been collected. Usually it has been found sufficient to examine the change of conductivity in the course of the addition of a solution of one solute to that of another. The resulting changes in conductance depend on the nature of the reaction. Kolthoff and Laitinen (1941) describe the shape of conductimetric titration curves for a number of aqueous acids and bases of varying strengths. There are two essential features, firstly when reaction occurs to give ions of different mobility, or a decrease or increase in the total number of ions, an inflexion in the plot of conductivity against mole ratio occurs at the equivalence point, and secondly, the change of conductivity before or after the equivalence point is regular, often linear, so that the equivalence point may be determined by the simple intersection of two curves. The details of the curves vary greatly depending on a number of factors, but it can be taken that the occurrence of an intersection of two sections at a particular mole-ratio is evidence for a separate chemical entity. This method is particularly well suited to the halide and oxyhalide solvents because of the very great tendency in these solvents for the formation of complex halide ion species from electrolyte and non-electrolyte species.

E. TRANSPORT NUMBER MEASUREMENTS

This is a fundamental method of investigating the ionic species present in solution. However, its application is difficult experimentally in the halide–oxyhalide solvents because of the difficulties associated with measurement of the small changes in anolyte and catholyte composition associated with the passage of practically realizable amounts of current (Gutmann and Himml, 1955).

F. POTENTIOMETRIC MEASUREMENTS

Halide and oxyhalide solvents should respond to electrodes indicating halide ion activity, in the same way as the hydrogen electrode responds to changes in hydrogen ion activity in aqueous solutions. Halide ion mobility is essential to the conduction process just as hydrogen ion mobility is in aqueous solutions. The ion activity is conveniently represented by an expression of the form

$$pX = \log_{10} [X^-],$$

assuming that the activity coefficient can be taken as unity. So far only chloride ion indicators have been employed and their use has been confined to potentiometric titrations. The silver-silver chloride indicator electrode (Andersson and Lindquist, 1955) can be employed in a concentration cell of the type

$$Ag, AgCl \mid Cl^-(c_1) \mid \mid Cl^-(c_2) \mid AgCl, Ag$$

in arsenic trichloride, the reference electrode consisting of a solution of tetramethylammonium chloride of known concentration separated from the titration cell by a ground glass stopper. The silver–silver chloride electrode is not, however, a suitable electrode for solutions in phosphoryl chloride. The metals copper, silver, gold, magnesium, zinc, mercury, aluminium, lead, molybdenum and platinum have been examined as alternatives (Gutmann and Mairinger, 1957): however, only molybdenum is suitable for the construction of a sensitive indicator electrode; the equilibrium $MoCl_2 \rightleftharpoons Mo^{2+} + 2Cl^-$ seems to be involved. For more precise e.m.f. measurements in solutions of high dilution, a calomel electrode and chlorine electrode have been successfully applied (Gutmann, 1959).

G. TITRATIONS USING INDICATORS

The sulphophthaleins, well known as indicators for hydrogen ion in aqueous systems, also function as chloride ion indicators in phosphoryl chloride solution (Gutmann and Hubacek, 1963). The colour changes, which are reversible, are usually different from those encountered in aqueous systems. With these indicators, titrations can be conducted in much the same fashion as in aqueous solutions, the main type of information obtained thereby is of the stoichiometry of the reactions, although it is possible to use these indicators to compare relative chloride donor strength.

H. SPECTROPHOTOMETRIC MEASUREMENTS

The problems of identifying and estimating the relative amounts of species present in solution are particularly suited to spectroscopic investigations. Unfortunately relatively few of the species encountered in halide and oxyhalide solution can be identified unambiguously spectroscopically. In certain instances, notably where the tetrachloroferrate(III) ion was present, the method has been most successful (Baaz et al., 1961a). Infrared methods can give valuable information as to the nature of the solvates, as for example in consideration of the P=O shift in a series of phosphoryl halide complexes as an indication of the existence of an oxygen donor bond (Sheldon and Tyree,

11

1959). The application of Raman spectroscopy has so far been limited, which is unfortunate because this powerful tool is particularly suited to the simple symmetries of the ionic species present in the halide and oxyhalide solvents. Whilst the presence of the NO^+ ion has been established by Raman spectra (Gerding and Houtgraaf, 1953), evidence of comparable reliabliity for other cations postulated as being present in the halides and oxyhalides of Group V has not been obtained.

I. VISCOSITY MEASUREMENTS

The understanding of aqueous solutions has been assisted by studies of the forces of viscous flow; however, outside of this field data is limited. The only measurements available amongst halides and oxyhalides are for melts of the compounds $GaCl_3.POCl_3$ (Greenwood and Wade, 1957) and $GaBr_3.POBr_3$ (Greenwood and Worrall, 1958). Here all that can be deduced is that the unit of flow is a complex unit. From the only other record of viscosity data, namely that of $SbBr_3$ and acetone, no evidence for complex formation is obtained.

J. THERMODYNAMIC MEASUREMENTS

Unfortunately no data has been collected on the energy changes involved in the dissolution process in solvents of the halide and oxyhalide type. Similarly, very little data is available on the thermochemical aspects of the numerous solvates. It is to be hoped that this obvious omission will soon be made good, so that these solvent systems can be properly discussed.

K. ISOTOPIC EXCHANGE REACTION

In discussions involving the species present in solution, evidence concerning rates of exchange, as obtained by the use of isotopic tracers, is particularly relevant, since the extent of halogen interchange between solute and solvent can be recognized and possibly interpreted kinetically. So far only a limited number of experiments has been undertaken, but the results have been very significant in promoting our understanding of the nature of these solutions (Lewis and Sowerby, 1957a; Herber, 1960).

L. EBULLIOSCOPIC AND CRYOSCOPIC MEASUREMENTS

The earliest investigations concerned this aspect of these solvents and recently these measurements have been revived in an investigation of certain complex halides (Gutmann and Mairinger, 1960) and of the nature of titanium(IV), iron(III) and aluminium(III) chlorides (Gutmann and Mairinger, 1961) all in phosphoryl chloride solution. The technique employed consisted of the Swietoslawski ebulliometer employing thermistors for the measurement of the temperature differential.

III. HALIDES AS SOLVENTS

To be of interest as a working solvent, a halide must be available in reasonable quantity, have a m.p. below or conveniently close to room temperature, possess a b.p. above room temperature, be reasonably stable with respect to its elements, and have a suitable dielectric constant, coefficient of viscosity, and latent heat of vapourization. Table I shows those halides which are well suited as solvents. The general chemistry of these halides can be found in two recent reviews (George, 1960; Payne, 1961); nitrogen halides will not be considered, nor will iodides since these compounds are inherently too unstable to serve as effective solvents. It will appear that arsenic(III) and antimony(III) chlorides have been much more thoroughly investigated than any of the other halides; this is in part due to their availability and in part to their very obvious solvent properties and ease of manipulation.

The chemical aspects of solvent behaviour are reflected in the relative donor properties of the compounds. When these donor properties are compared by consideration of, for example, the reaction of the halides of Group V with boron(III) and aluminium(III) chlorides, only phosphorus(III) chloride and bromide are found to display noticeable, albeit feeble, donor characteristics; the trichlorides and tribromides of arsenic and antimony are very feeble donors, if donors at all (Holmes, 1960b). Phosphorus(III) chloride and bromide also show weak acceptor properties in their reaction with trimethylamine (Troost, 1954); similar acceptor properties may be ascribable to arsenic(III) and antimony(III) chlorides in the formation of compounds with trimethylphosphine and triethylamine (Holmes and Bertaut, 1958; Holmes, 1960a). With these feeble acceptor and donor properties, coupled with a low dielectric constant, the solvent properties of phosphorus(III) chloride are very limited. Even substances like iron(III) chloride and tetramethylammonium iodide, readily soluble in most halides, are only sparingly soluble.

Arsenic(III) chloride is a strongly polar molecule, pyramidal in form (Daure, 1929), giving a liquid of appreciable dielectric constant (12·8 at room temperature), which with its wide liquid range ($-18°$ to $+130°$ at atmospheric pressure) coupled with its ability to act as a chloride ion acceptor and donor in complex ion formation leads directly to "good" solvent properties. The extent of chloride ion transfer in pure arsenic(III) chloride, as inferred from the low specific conductivity of $1·4 \times 10^{-7}$ Ω^{-1} cm^{-1} (Andersson and Linquist, 1955) is clearly very small. The suggested self-ionization,

$$2AsCl_3 \rightleftharpoons AsCl_2^+ + AsCl_4^-,$$

implies that the solvent is ampholytic and that, using the solvent-system concept of acids and bases, the $AsCl_3$ molecule is acting in the role of an acid in accepting a chloride ion to give $AsCl_4^-$, and as a base in losing a chloride ion to give $AsCl_2^+$.

Alkali metal chloride complexes of arsenic(III) chloride, such as $Rb_3As_2Cl_9$ and $Cs_3As_2Cl_9$ (Wheeler, 1893a,b) and amine complexes such as

$(EtNH_3)_2AsCl_5$; $(MeNH_3)_3As_2Cl_9$; $Me_2NH_2AsCl_4$, and $(Me_3NH)_2As_3Cl_{11}$

(Petzold, 1933), are obtainable from aqueous systems. Tetra-alkylammonium chlorides are readily soluble in arsenic(III) chloride and from the resulting solu-

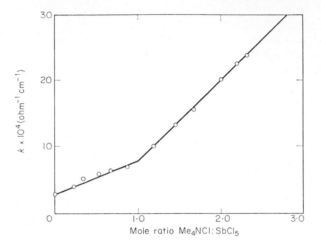

Fig. 1. Conductimetric titration of antimony(V) chloride with tetramethylammonium chloride in arsenic(III) chloride solution at 20°. Reproduced with permission from *Z. anorg. Chem.* (1951) **266**, 340.

tion the corresponding tetrachloroarsenate(III) salts are isolated as white, non-hygroscopic powders (Gutmann, 1951a). It is possible to dissolve a very small amount of potassium chloride in arsenic(III) chloride on heating, and on cooling a solid corresponding to $KAsCl_4$ is obtained (Gutmann, 1951a). By careful crystallization of the tetramethylammonium chloride from arsenic(III) chloride a solvate $Me_4NCl.3AsCl_3$ (possibly $Me_4NAsCl_4.2AsCl_3$ or $Me_4NAs_3Cl_{10}$) is obtained; two of the three arsenic(III) chloride molecules are loosely bound and are lost by heating to 100° at a pressure of 9 mm (Lindquist and Andersson, 1954). In the tetraethylammonium system, evidence for the compounds $Et_4NCl.2AsCl_3$ (possibly $Et_4NAsCl_4.AsCl_3$ or $Et_4NAs_2Cl_7$) and $3Et_4NCl.5AsCl_3$ (possibly $(Et_4N)_3(AsCl_4)_3.2AsCl_3$) is obtained from phase diagrams (Agerman *et al.*, 1958). Gutmann (1951a) lists the solubilities of a wide variety of halides, complex halides, oxides and complex oxides, some cyanides, metals and non-metals. The alkali and ammonium chlorides are only slightly soluble, likewise niobium(V) and tantalum(V) chlorides and the complex salt, $(Me_4N)_2SnCl_6$, whereas aluminium(III), tin(IV), vanadium(IV), iron(III) chlorides and Me_4NSbCl_6 and Me_4NCl, for example, are readily soluble. Walden (1900) drew attention, in his work on arsenic(III) chloride as solvent to the high solubility of a wide range of iodides and this has since been confirmed. Various non-metals such as sulphur, phosphorus and iodide are also readily soluble; the nature of these solutions is unknown. Metals, metal oxides and oxy-salts, such as sulphates or nitrates, are all very sparingly soluble.

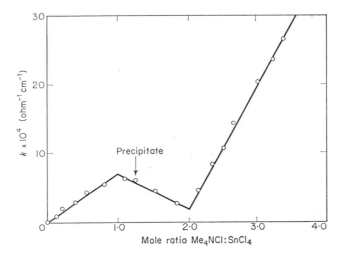

FIG. 2. Conductimetric titration of tin(IV) chloride with tetramethylammonium chloride in arsenic(III) chloride solution at 20°. Reproduced with permission from *Z. anorg. Chem.* (1951) **266**, 340.

Solutions of tetramethylammonium chloride and antimony(V) chloride in arsenic(III) chloride possess high conductivities. Conductimetric titration of these solutions gives the curve shown in Fig. 1, with a break at the $1:1$ composition. A claim to have isolated a small amount of a white solid, with a composition close to $AsCl_3 . SbCl_5$, from the original antimony(V) chloride solution has not been substantiated; however its presence in solution has been assumed. The salt Me_4NSbCl_6 can be obtained from the solution after the titration. The change in conductance has been interpreted in terms of the reaction:

$$Me_4N^+AsCl_4^- + AsCl_2^+SbCl_6^- = Me_4N^+SbCl_6^- + 2AsCl_3 \qquad (3)$$

which is reasonable in so far as the only product appears to be the hexa-chloroantimonate(V) salt. Further, both solutions initially show high conductances and can give solids corresponding, apparently, to the cation and anion expected by chloride ion transfer in arsenic(III) chloride. A solution of tin(IV) chloride titrated with a solution of tetramethylammonium chloride gives a curve of the form shown in Fig. 2. Immediately the $1:1$ ratio has been reached a precipitate of $(Me_4N)_2SnCl_6$ begins to develop. The break at the 1 : 1 ratio has been accounted for by postulating the equilibrium:

$$Me_4NAsCl_4 + SnCl_4 \rightleftharpoons Me_4NSnCl_5 + AsCl_3. \tag{4}$$

The Me_4NSnCl_5 species must then react with further $AsCl_4^-$ to give the hexachlorostannate(IV) ion. Examination of titanium(IV) and vanadium(IV) chlorides in a similar titration showed similar evidence for a 1 : 1 species. Solid materials corresponding approximately to these 1 : 1 compositions have been isolated, but not investigated further. Not all experimenters report the occurrence of definite interactions between arsenic(III) chloride and metal chlorides; for example, a report of the phase study of the system $AsCl_3 - TiCl_4$ states that there was complete miscibility. None of the solutions showed significant electrical conductivity (Eingorn, 1950).

Phosphorus(V) chloride dissolved in arsenic(III) chloride gives a conducting solution which, in distinction to antimony(V) chloride, does not give a break when titrated conductimetrically with a solution of tetramethylammonium chloride. On the basis of this evidence Gutmann (1952d) describes the solution as one containing $PCl_4^+AsCl_4^-$ rather than $AsCl_2^+PCl_6^-$. Cronander (1873a,b,c) observed the formation of a solid $AsCl_3.PCl_5$ from phosphorus(V) chloride dissolved in arsenic(III) chloride; repetition of this work by Kolditz (1957a) has, however, shown that a saturated solution in fact deposits large prism-like crystals of composition $2PCl_5.5AsCl_3$ (m.p. 40°). The solution of this compound in arsenic(III) chloride possesses an appreciable conductance (0·202 M solution, $\kappa = 6·9 \times 10^{-4}$ ohm^{-1} cm^{-1} at 25°), whilst cryoscopic evidence shows the solution contains 2·6 particles per formula weight. Two formulations of the compound are possible:

$$PCl_4^+PCl_6^-.5AsCl_3 \text{ and } PCl_4^+AsCl_4^-.1·5AsCl_3.$$

If the latter were to apply in the solution in arsenic(III) chloride, four particles per formula weight would be expected if dissociation was complete. Other evidence based on the conductance of the compound in acetonitrile supports the formulation as a hexachlorophosphate(V) rather than a tetrachloroarsenate(III), however in solution a proportion (about 30%) of the compound may be present in this latter form. A number of tetrachlorophosphonium(V) salts are conveniently prepared in arsenic(III) chloride solution. For example, $PCl_4^+PCl_5Br^-$ is the product of phosphorus(III) chloride and bromine (Kolditz and Feltz, 1957). Kolditz (1956) has used arsenic(III) chloride as solvent in the conversion of the ionic tetrachlorophosphonium(V) hexafluorophosphate(V) to a mixture of the molecular tetrachlorofluorophosphorane and the ionic tetrachlorophosphonium(V) fluoride.

Tellurium(IV) chloride dissolves in arsenic(III) chloride to give a conducting solution which when titrated conductimetrically with a solution of tetramethylammonium chloride gives breaks at the 1 : 1 and 1 : 2 ratio. At the 1 : 1 ratio a solid of composition $Me_4NCl.TeCl_4.AsCl_3$ can be isolated, which is reasonably formulated as $Me_4N^+AsCl_2^+TeCl_6^{2-}$, and at the 1 : 2 ratio $(Me_4N)_2TeCl_6$, is obtained. The 1 : 1 compound can be regarded as an "acid" salt in the arsenic(III) chloride solvent system (Gutmann, 1952a). By using a solution of phosphorus(V) chloride (Gutmann, 1953) a more complex conductimetric titration curve is obtained with breaks at $2TeCl_4 : 1PCl_5$, $1TeCl_4 : 1PCl_5$ and $1TeCl_4 : 2PCl_5$ and with the separation of the corresponding solids in the form of solvates. Using the idea of the solvo-acid as a basis, Gutmann has suggested that the first of these breaks corresponds to the presence in the solution of $PCl_4^+(AsCl_2^+)_3(TeCl_6^{2-})_2$ formed by reaction of two moles of the solvoacid $(AsCl_2^+)_2TeCl_6^{2-}$ with one mole of the solvo-base $PCl_4^+AsCl_4^-$. The solid $PCl_5.2TeCl_4.3AsCl_3$ very readily loses solvent to give $2TeCl_4.PCl_5$, a known compound (Metzner, 1898). The 1 : 1 compound is given the formulation $PCl_4^+AsCl_2^+TeCl_6^{2-}$ which loses solvent to give the compound $PCl_5.TeCl_4$ (Groeneveld, 1953). With tin(IV) chloride, yet another conductimetric titration curve is obtained with the precipitation of the solids of composition $TeCl_4.2SnCl_4$, $TeCl_4.SnCl_4$ and $2TeCl_4.SnCl_4$. In this case the evidence can be explained if the titrations involve the tellurium(IV) chloride as a solvo-base and the tin(IV) chloride as a solvo-acid thus:

$$(AsCl_2^+)_2SnCl_6^{2-} + TeCl_3^+AsCl_4^- \rightleftharpoons TeCl_3^+AsCl_2^+SnCl_6^{2-} + 2AsCl_3. \qquad (5)$$

Titration of antimony(V) chloride with tellurium(IV) chloride gives a break at the 1 : 1 and 1 : 2 ratio with the precipitation of two solids. In this case also the tellurium(IV) chloride appears to function as solvo-base, giving rise to $TeCl_4.SbCl_5$ or $TeCl_3^+SbCl_6^-$ and $2TeCl_4.SbCl_5.AsCl_3$ or $(TeCl_3^+)_2AsCl_4^-SbCl_6^-$.

Yet another group of compounds, the alkoxychlorostibanes (Kolditz and Engels, 1959), $(RO)_nCl_{5-n}Sb$, dissolve in arsenic(III) chloride to give conducting solutions. With $SbCl_4OEt$ there is an initial equilibrium established involving the ions $SbCl_3(OEt)^+$ and $SbCl_5(OEt)^-$, however a slow reaction with the solvent then occurs to give antimony(V) chloride and $As(OEt)_3$ accompanied by corresponding changes in the conductance. The other members of this group of compounds behave likewise.

Since arsenic(III) chloride is a solvent favouring the formation of chloroanions and chlorocations, it suggests itself as a source of either arsenic(V) chloride, or tetrachloroarsonium(V) hexachloroarsenate(V). Attempts to prepare these compounds have been unsuccessful (George, 1960; Payne, 1961). However, reaction of solutions of phosphorus(V) chloride or antimony(V) chloride with chlorine in arsenic(III) chloride leads to the compounds $PCl_5.AsCl_5$ and $SbCl_5AsCl_2$, both of which appear to contain the $AsCl_4^+$ cation (Gutmann, 1951a,b). The investigation has been extended to an examination of the reaction of various metal halides with arsenic(III) chloride and chlorine, whereby a number of tetrachloroarsonium(V) complexes are produced, for example, $AsCl_4^+AlCl_4^-$ (Kolditz and Schmidt, 1958).

The behaviour of pyridine dissolved in arsenic(III) chloride has been the subject of several investigations since the original observation of Walden that the solution was a conductor (Walden, 1903). Two solvates of compositions Py_2AsCl_3 (Shirey, 1930; Montigie, 1935) and $PyAsCl_3$ (Dafert and Melinski, 1926; Gibson *et al.*, 1930) have been isolated. Pyridine is a medium strong electrolyte (Gutmann, 1954a) functioning thus:

$$C_5H_5N + 2AsCl_3 \rightleftharpoons C_5H_5NAsCl_2^+ + AsCl_4^-. \tag{6}$$

Removal of the solvent at room temperature leaves a solid of composition varying from $C_5H_5N.1\cdot6AsCl_3$ to $C_5H_5N.1\cdot8AsCl_3$. By raising the temperature to 50° loss of arsenic(III) chloride occurs to leave $C_5H_5N.AsCl_3$.

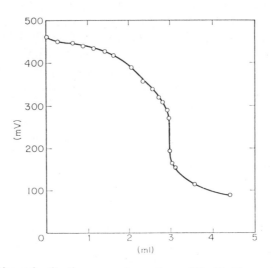

Fig. 3. Potentiometric titration curve for antimony(V) chloride against tetramethylammonium chloride. End point 3·01 ml, calculated on 1 : 1 ratio, 2·96 ml. Reproduced with permission from *Acta chem. Scand.* (1955) **9**, 82.

Solutions of pyridine can be employed in titrations against tin(IV) and vanadium(IV) chlorides when breaks in the conductance at the 1 : 2 ratio are observed and solids containing the $C_5H_5NAsCl_2^+$ cation and the hexachlorostannate(IV) or hexachlorovanadate(IV) are obtained.

The physico-chemical study of arsenic(III) chloride as a solvent has, so far, been limited to a confirmation that the molar conductance of solutions of tetramethylammonium iodide, up to a concentration of $10^{-3}M$, follows the Debye–Hückel–Onsager equation. Potentiometric measurements in arsenic(III) chloride using a silver–silver chloride electrode (Andersson and Lindquist, 1955) have been confined to titrations. The titration of tetramethylammonium chloride with antimony(V) chloride shown in Fig. 3 shows that the electrode is behaving as a pCl electrode for the reaction $SbCl_5 + Cl^- \rightarrow SbCl_6^-$. By assuming that the liquid junction potential can be neglected and that both tetramethylammonium and antimony(V) chlorides are strong electrolytes in arsenic trichloride it can be shown that

$$\tfrac{1}{2}pk = \frac{460 - 215}{60} - \log_{10}[SbCl_5]$$

where k is the ionic product. Whence $pk > 15$ and the ionic product $[AsCl_2^+][AsCl_4^-]$ must be less than 10^{-15}. There are difficulties at present in the way of a more thorough examination of the potentiometric data because of the unknown liquid junction potentials and the uncertainties of activity coefficients in solvents of low dielectric constant. There is, further, a general lack of information on the degree of dissociation of electrolytes in arsenic(III) chloride.

The examination of solutions of arsenic(III) chloride has thus, so far, been confined largely to conductimetry and preparative studies. The evidence for the existence of the tetrachloroarsenate(III) ion in solution is wholly indirect. Such salts as have been isolated lose arsenic(III) chloride with varying ease. Even with the most stable, tetramethylammonium, this occurs at 160°. The $AsCl_4^-$ ion would be expected, on the basis of the distribution of the five electron pairs around a central arsenic atom, to consist of a trigonal bipyramid with one of the positions occupied by a non-bonded electron pair, with a corresponding distortion of the regularity of the structure. The high transport number (0·88–0·97) (Gutmann, 1956) for chloride ion in a solution of tetramethylammonium chloride in arsenic(III) chloride requires for its explanation, the ready transfer of chloride ion from $AsCl_4^-$ to $AsCl_3$, thereby showing the inherent instability of the tetrachloroarsenate(III) ion in these solutions (Lindquist, 1955). The evidence supporting the existence of the $AsCl_2^+$ ion in arsenic(III) chloride solutions is based solely on the interpretation of the changes in conductivity at certain mole ratios in the course of titrations. However, in the absence of alternative explanations, it appears essential to any description of these solutions.

In the case of arsenic(III) fluoride, its physical properties (m.p. $-6°$, b.p. 63°) and its reactivity make it less attractive than the chloride as a solvent. The specific conductivity of $2·4 \times 10^{-5}$ ohm^{-1} cm^{-1} at 25°, is of the same order as bromine trifluoride, iodine pentafluoride, and hydrogen fluoride (Woolf and Greenwood, 1950). Woolf and Greenwood point out that the ease of complex formation of a non-metal fluoride and an alkali-metal fluoride in a suitable solvent is related to the conductivity of the pure anion forming fluoride. Arsenic(III) fluoride has an appreciably higher conductivity than, for example antimony(V) fluoride ($\kappa = 1·2 \times 10^{-8}$ ohm^{-1} cm^{-1}), and it reacts readily with for example potassium fluoride to give $KAsF_4$, whereas antimony(V) fluoride does not (Woolf and Greenwood, 1950). The conductivity of arsenic(III) fluoride is increased markedly by dissolution of, for example, potassium fluoride or antimony(V) fluoride. From the latter solution a solid of composition $AsF_3.SbF_5$, can be isolated, whilst the titration of potassium fluoride and antimony(V) fluoride solutions gives rise to solid $KSbF_6$. It is also suggested, but not confirmed, that the compound $AsF_3.BF_3$ is formed when boron(III) fluoride is passed into a solution of potassium tetrachloroarsenate(III) in arsenic(III) fluoride (Woolf and Greenwood, 1950). Early experiments involving the reaction of arsenic(III) fluoride with halogen were inconclusive. However, Kolditz (1955) has shown that chlorine passed into this solvent at 0° gives a white crystalline substance, shown by conductivity and other studies to be $AsCl_4^+AsF_6^-$. It is somewhat soluble in arsenic(III) chloride and very soluble in arsenic(III) fluoride. Further examination of this reaction in arsenic(III) fluoride solution has shown that it does not proceed under strictly anhydrous conditions, traces of water being essential to ensure a smooth reaction (Dess et $al.$, 1956). Similar restrictions appear to apply to the reaction of bromine and iodine but no AsB_4^+ or AsI_4^+ compounds were isolated (Dess and Parry, 1956). Arsenic(III) fluoride, in part because of its solvent properties and its boiling point, is a good flourinating agent for non-metal chlorides, the reactions, however, rarely go to completion. For example, antimony(V) chloride is converted to tetrachlorostibonium(V) fluoride (Kolditz, 1957b) by the reaction

$$3SbCl_5 + AsF_3 \rightleftharpoons 3SbCl_4^+F^- + AsCl_3. \tag{7}$$

The existence of solid tetrafluoroarsenate(III) salts of K^+, Rb^+ and Cs^+ and the isolation of the compound $AsF_3.SbF_5$ has led to a suggested self-ionization for arsenic(III) fluoride akin to that for the chloride (Gutmann and Baaz, 1959b). The AsF_2^+ cation might be stabilized in solution by a bridged structure involving solvent molecules. The tetrafluoroarsenate(III) cation would be iso-electronic with selenium(IV) fluoride, which has a distorted trigonal bi-pyrimidal structure. Studies employing nuclear magnetic resonance (Muetterties and Phillips, 1957b) techniques have shown that although the tetrafluoroarsenate(III) ion is present in the solid, it does not appear to be a major component of arsenic(III) fluoride solutions of fluorides, since the fluoride undergoes very rapid exchange. Mixtures of boron(III) fluoride and arsenic(III) fluoride, whilst exhibiting a slightly enhanced conductivity did not show resonances other than those arising from the original compounds; the possibility of an unstable compound $AsF_2^+BF_4^-$ mentioned earlier, must on this evidence be suspect. The F^{19} spectrum of an arsenic(III), antimony(V) fluoride mixture showed only one concentration-dependent resonance peak, in a position between the resonances of the pure compounds. It would be expected that any compound between these fluorides would have non-equivalent fluorine atoms and would result in at least two, if not more, peaks in the fluorine spectrum. Probably very rapid exchange occurs through a bridge type structure of the form:

Similar bridged structures have been involved in consideration of the fluoride exchange in halogen fluorides (Muetterties and Phillips, 1957a).

The solvent properties of molten arsenic(III) bromide, first investigated by Walden (1902), have recently been re-investigated by Jander and his co-worker (Jander and Günther, 1958, 1959a,b). The alkali, alkaline earth and transition metal(II) bromides, the salts of oxyacids and the oxides, are not obviously soluble. Certain bromides such as mercury(II), indium(III), tellurium(IV), and bismuth(III) (Rettgers, 1893; Pusin and Makuc, 1938) are moderately soluble, as are arsenic(III) oxide and sulphide, merury(II) and iron(III) chlorides. The quaternary ammonium, boron(III), aluminium(III) (Isbekow and Plotnikow, 1911; Kendall *et al.*, 1923; Pusin and Makuc, 1938), gallium(III), tin(IV), titanium(IV), phosphorus(III) and (V), antimony(III) (Pusin and Löwy, 1926), and selenium(IV) bromides are all very readily soluble. A wide range of organic compounds including hydrocarbons, alcohols, jetones, esters and amines are also freely soluble.

In the case of the quaternary bromides and the organic bases, $\bar{B}$, solvates of the general form $R_4NBr.AsBr_3$ and $B.HBr.AsBr_3$ are common. Conductance measurements suggest that these solvates are more correctly regarded as salts of the tetrabromoarsenate(III) anion. Cryoscopic measurements have shown that in the case of the adducts between free base and arsenic(III) bromide the equilibrium

$$2R_3N + 2AsBr_3 \rightleftharpoons 2R_3N.AsBr_2^+ + 2Br^- \tag{8}$$

is present, although the results are not completely explicable unless associated species such as $(R_3N.AsBr_3)_2$ are also considered. Electrolytic dissociation increases with dilution as for weak electrolytes.

The addition of silver perchlorate to arsenic(III) bromide at 80° leads to decomposition and the evolution of bromine. At 50°, however, the reaction proceeds thus:

$$AsBr_3 + AgClO_4 \rightleftharpoons AsBr_2^+ClO_4^- + AgBr. \tag{9}$$

It is not possible to isolate the compound $AsBr_2^+ClO_4^-$ as such, but the solution is a good conductor and can be employed in conductimetric titrations. By analogy with the other halide solvo-systems a self-ionization process

$$2AsBr_3 \rightleftharpoons AsBr_2^+ + AsBr_4^- \tag{10}$$

is put forward to account for the specific conductivity of the pure solvent of 1.6×10^{-7} ohm^{-1} cm^{-1} at 35°. Most of solutes examined and the reactions studied can be interpreted in terms of the solvent-system of acids and bases

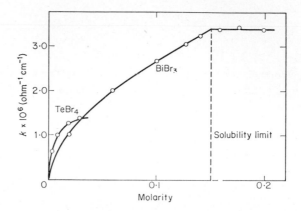

FIG. 4. Specific conductivity of tellurium(IV) and bismuth(III) bromide in arsenic(III) bromide solution at 93°. Reproduced with permission from *Z. anorg. Chem.* (1958) **297,** 100.

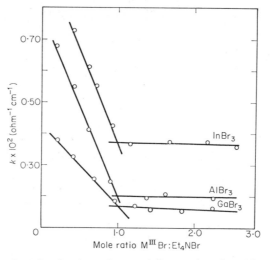

FIG. 5. Conductimetric titration of tetraethylammonium bromide with indium(III), aluminium(III) and gallium(III) bromide in arsenic(III) bromide solution at 93°. Reproduced with permission from *Z. anorg. Chem.* (1959) **298,** 243.

involving the AsBr$_2^+$ and AsBr$_4^-$ ions. The bromides of aluminium(III), gallium(III), indium(III), boron(III), tin(IV), mercury(II), bismuth(III) and tellurium(IV) appear as potential electrolytes with acid properties through their capacity to form complex bromo anions. This capacity is shown by the marked conductivity of their solutions, see, for example, the conductivity of bismuth(III) and tellurium(IV) bromide shown in Fig. 4. Conductimetric titrations between tetraethylammonium bromide and various anion-forming metal bromides are shown in Fig. 5. In the case of aluminium(III) bromide, the equation representing the reaction is

$$Et_4N^+ + Br^- + AsBr_2^+ + AlBr_4^- \rightleftharpoons Et_4N^+ + AlBr_4^- + AsBr_3. \qquad (11)$$

This reaction can be followed potentiometrically using a gold indicator electrode, in which case a slow change in potential occurs until just after the $1:1$ composition is reached and thereafter it remains constant. A variety of salts such as $KAlBr_4$, $CuAlBr_4$, $TlAlBr_4$ can be isolated as a result of "neutralization" reactions of this type. Similar results are obtainable with the other bromides listed above, however, in certain instances such as Pb(II) amphoteric properties emerge. This particular solvent offers a good method for the preparation of a wide range of complex bromides, which are otherwise difficult of access. Using simple metal oxides this solvent can conveniently be applied to the preparation of anhydrous bromides. Arsenic(III) oxide, sulphide and selenide dissolve to give oxy-, thio-, and seleno-bromides, thus:

$$AsBr_3 + As_2O_3 \rightleftharpoons 3AsOBr. \qquad (12)$$

The arsenic(III) bromide system, like the corresponding chloride and fluoride systems, requires more detailed investigation before the correctness of the interpretation of the conductimetric titrations can be regarded as proved. No substantial evidence exists, apart from the conductimetric titration data, for the AsX_2^+ cation which has been postulated as being present in all these arsenic(III) halide solvents. Further investigations are clearly needed here.

   Antimony(III) chloride (m.p. $73°$, b.p. $219°-223°$) was the first solvent of this group to be investigated. The pioneer work of Tolloczko on the cryoscopic properties (Tolloczko, 1901; Frycz and Tolloczko, 1912, 1913), was followed by the classical investigations of Walden (1900), Beckmann (1906) and Klemensiewicz (Klemensiewicz, 1908, 1924; Klemensiewicz and Balowna, 1930, 1931; Klemensiewicz and Zebrowska, 1934). Numerous investigators (Gmelin, 1949) have reported the general features of antimony(III) chloride as a solvent for inorganic and organic substances. In marked contrast to the other halide solvents already referred to, the potassium, rubidium, caesium, ammonium and thallium(I) chlorides, as well as the quaternary ammonium chlorides are easily soluble, at least after heating with the solvent for a short time. Mercury(II) chloride, bromide and iodide, as well as potassium fluoride and potassium bromide, are also readily soluble. Lithium, sodium, tin(II), bismuth(III) and iron(III) chlorides are only slightly soluble. The oxides and salts of a wide range of oxyacids examined were, with the exception of tetramethylammonium sulphate and perchlorate, either insoluble or dissolved with decomposition

(Jander and Swart, 1959a). A large number of addition compounds, mainly with the 1 : 1 ratio, has been reported to be formed with hydrocarbons, and with organic halogen, oxygen and sulphur-containing compounds (Gmelin, 1949). The solubility of proteins and components of nucleic acids in antimony(III) chloride is useful in studies of their NH and OH infra-red absorptions (Lacher *et al.*, 1949). With inorganic compounds the most numerous examples of addition compounds are the double and complex salts of formulae $M^I SbCl_4$, $M_2^I SbCl_5$, $M^I Sb_2 Cl_7$ and $M_3^I Sb_2 Cl_9 (M^I = Li, Na, K, NH_4$, Rb or Cs), $M^{II}(SbCl_4)_2$ and $M^{II} SbCl_5$ (M^{II} = Be, Mg, Ca, Sr or Ba). A wide variety of other inorganic addition compounds has been reported, but their compositions do not appear to be readily rationalized in terms of particular ionic species so that no further mention will be made of them here. The conductivity of antimony(III) chloride (0.85×10^{-6} ohm^{-1} cm^{-1} at 95°) can be interpreted by postulating a self-ionization process, in which chloride is transferred to form a chloroanion:

$$2SbCl_3 \rightleftharpoons SbCl_2^+ + SbCl_4^-. \tag{13}$$

Additions of alkali-metal or quaternary ammonium chlorides lead to a considerable increase in conductivity. The physico-chemical study of these electrolyte solutions will be referred to later.

Application of the methods of conductimetric titration applied in the other halide systems has yielded similar results, incidentally thereby confirming in some measure the interpretations which have been made of the ionization processes, which appear to be generally applicable to the halides. For example, silver perchlorate reacts to give a precipitate of silver chloride and a solution thought to contain $SbCl_2^+ ClO_4^-$. Similarly, aluminium(III), antimony(V) and tellurium(IV) chlorides lead to solutions of high conductance, presumed to contain the appropriate chloroanion, e.g.

$$AlCl_3 + SbCl_3 \rightleftharpoons SbCl_2^+ + AlCl_4^-. \tag{14}$$

Cryoscopic measurements support the formulation of triphenylmethylchloride as a strong electrolyte, giving rise to two ions in solution. Similarly, support is available, from the value of the van't Hoff factor, for accepting other alkali metal and quaternary ammonium chlorides as strong electrolytes, although in these cases there is a much greater concentration dependence of the results. In the case of tellurium(IV) and selenium(IV) chlorides, the van't Hoff factor lies between 0.5 and 1.0. In no case does it fit in with the simple chloride ion transfer, which would, if transfer and dissociation were complete, require a van't Hoff factor of 3; instead it would appear necessary to involve the idea of considerable association, or to admit the possibility of other complex reactions with the solvent antimony(III) chloride resulting in species containing more than one selenium or tellurium per ion or molecule. As well as the more obvious "neutralization" reactions involving tetramethylammonium chloride (presumed to be $Me_4N^+SbCl_4^-$ as the base analogue) titrated with $SbCl_2^+ClO_4^-$ (as the acid analogue), antimony(III) sulphate can be titrated (Jander and Swart, 1959b), the resulting conductimetric titration curve shows breaks at the 6 : 1 ratio, which appear to correspond to:

$$6Me_4N^+SbCl_4^- + Sb_2(SO_4)_3 \rightleftharpoons 3(Me_4N^+)_2SO_4^{2-} + 8SbCl_3 \qquad (15)$$

and a break at 6 : 4 corresponding to the next stage:

$$3(Me_4N^+)_2SO_4^{2-} + 3Sb_2(SO_4)_3 \rightleftharpoons 6Me_4N^+Sb(SO_4)_2^- \qquad (16)$$

giving an overall reaction:

$$4Sb_2(SO_4)_3 + 6Me_4N^+SbCl_4^- \rightleftharpoons 6Me_4N^+Sb(SO_4)_2^- + 8SbCl_3. \qquad (17)$$

Compounds containing this $Sb(SO_4)_2^-$ anion have been recognized elsewhere (Metzl, 1906). Similar complex ions might be expected with the perchlorate ion, however, careful examination of the titration curve obtained in the titration with tetramethylammonium chloride shows only one break corresponding solely to the formal acid–base reaction. Conductimetric and potentiometric (using a gold reference electrode) titrations have established fully the similarities between this system and the arsenic(III) chloride system as far as compounds leading to chloroanions are concerned. A number of solvolytic reactions have been established (Jander and Swart, 1959c), for example potassium bromide and iodide are readily soluble in antimony(III) chloride, the product, in both cases, being $2KCl.SbCl_3$. Potassium fluoride however leads to $KF.2SbCl_3$. Oxides, sulphides, carbonates and acetates are all converted to the corresponding metal halide:

$$3M^{II}O + 2SbCl_3 \rightarrow 3M^{II}Cl_2 + Sb_2O_3. \qquad (18)$$

Kolditz (1957a) has prepared from chloroform solution in the presence of excess antimony(III) chloride the adduct $2PCl_5.4SbCl_3$, closely similar to the arsenic(III) chloride adduct of phosphorus(V) chloride discussed earlier. Cryoscopic measurements in antimony(III) chloride and conductivity measurements in methyl cyanide show this compound to be

$$PCl_4^+PCl_6^-.4SbCl_3.$$

Recent work by Baughan has shown that an ionizing solvent such as antimony(III) halide is ideally suited for studying the interionic effects in solvents of lower dielectric constant than water (Porter and Baughan, 1958; Davies and Baughan, 1961; Baughan, et al., 1963). Cryoscopic measurements using a highly purified sample of the solvent, and fluorene, anthracene, benzophenone and dibenzyl as solutes, gave $k = 15 \cdot 6 \pm 0 \cdot 2$ (deg mole^{-1} kg.). The conductivity data measured at 99° of previous workers (Klemensiewicz, 1908, 1924; Klemensiewicz and Balowna, 1930, 1931; Klemensiewicz and Zebrowska, 1934) for thallium(I) chloride and bromide, potassium chloride and bromide, rubidium chloride and ammonium chloride and bromide gives linear Kohlrausch plots, which can be compared with the theoretical Debye-Hückel-Onsager slopes (Fig. 6). The interionic effects are

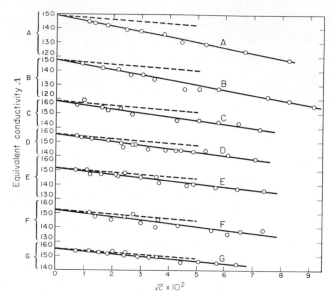

FIG. 6. Kohlrausch plots of the conductivity of halides in antimony(III) chloride measured at 99° (c is molarity). Reproduced with permission from *J. chem. Soc.* (1958) 745, Figure 1.

in keeping with a solvent of dielectric constant 30·4 (cf. methanol and ethanol). The fact that the limiting conductivities of the wide range of bromides and chlorides examined are so close (Λ_0TlCl = 149; TlBr = 148; KCl = 158; KBr = 156; NH$_4$Cl = 152; NH$_4$Br = 152; RbCl = 155) suggests that both chloride and bromide have abnormally high mobilities, which is confirmed by the experimentally determined value of about 0·9 obtained for chloride ion (Frycz and Tolloczko, 1912, 1913). This high transport number, also observed with arsenic(III) chloride, implies a favourable rate for the chloride transfer reaction:

$$\text{SbCl}_3 + \text{SbCl}_4^- \rightarrow \text{SbCl}_4^- + \text{SbCl}_3. \tag{19}$$

Antimony(III) chloride is a much better solvent than arsenic(III) chloride for the alkali halides. Examination of the cryoscopic data in terms of the van't Hoff factors for a number of 1 : 1 electrolytes shows that the i-factors tend to the limiting value of 2 at infinite dilution. The non-ideality of the electrolyte solutions, derived from freezing point data and expressed as the molal osmotic coefficient ϕ, is given by $\phi = 1 - 1 \cdot 86 m_2^{\frac{1}{2}} \sigma (0 \cdot 768 \,\overset{\circ}{a}\, m_2^{\frac{1}{2}}) + b m_2$, where m_2 is the molality of the solute, $\overset{\circ}{a}$ is the distance of closest approach of anion and cation in Angstrom units and b is a constant added to correct for ion solvation. From experimental results with antimony(III) chloride as solvent, it is possible to obtain values for $\overset{\circ}{a}$ and to compare these with values calculated from interatomic distances assuming that the conducting anionic species in solution is $SbCl_4^-$, i.e.

	$\overset{\circ}{a}$ Theoretical	$\overset{\circ}{a}$ Experimental
KCl	5·5	2·1
CsCl	5·9	4·5
Me$_4$NCl	7·7	13·0

The experimental data for potassium and caesium chloride includes effects of association. Since the Bjerrum critical distance for a uni-univalent electrolyte at the melting point of antimony(III) chloride is 7·3 Å, ion pair formation would, in fact, be expected. For tetramethylammonium chloride, which is a strong electrolyte, the observed distances of closest approach exceeds both the critical distance and also the theoretical values, which suggests the presence of, at least, one complete solvation shell around the Me_4N^+ cation. The conductivities of various organic chlorides (Davies and Baughan, 1961) in antimony(III) chloride measured at 75° have shown that these compounds ionize principally by formation of the R_2Cl^+ ion, thus:

$$2RCl \rightleftharpoons R_2Cl^+ + Cl^-. \tag{20}$$

In more dilute solution the more normal process of ionization $RCl \rightleftharpoons R^+ + Cl^-$ occurs. Solutions of aromatic hydrocarbons in antimony(III) chloride are highly coloured and give well resolved electron spin resonance spectra (Baughan et al., 1963). Comparison with the corresponding spectra of solutions of perylene in 98% sulphuric acid, which have been shown to contain a carbonium ion, demonstrates the presence of a positive ion in these solutions. In the case of naphthalene the positive ion differs from that in sulphuric acid in that additional lines appear in the e.s.r. spectrum. The oxidation of hydrocarbons is thus conveniently carried out in antimony(III) chloride solution; the preliminary work which has so far appeared makes it seem likely that this will prove an exceptionally useful general method for the preparation of hydrocarbon cations.

As a result of the availability of precision measurements of the conductivity of triphenylmethyl chloride and tetramethylammonium chloride a more dependable description of this system is available than of any other. Baughan has pointed out that for a number of non-protonic solvents the Walden product $\lambda_0\eta$ of NMe_4^+ is around 0·3, which would correspond to a mobility for the NMe_4^+ ion of about 13 in antimony(III) chloride, giving a transport number for the chloride ion of 0·87. The conductimetric-titration for potassium chloride or triphenylmethyl chloride in antimony(III) chloride solution against antimony(V) chloride shows it to follow a curve typical of a strong acid-strong base in water. The reaction is

$$SbCl_4^- + SbCl_5 \rightleftharpoons SbCl_3 + SbCl_6^-$$ (21)

in which the $SbCl_4^-$ ion is abnormally mobile and the $SbCl_6^-$ ion is not (Jander and Swart, 1959a,b,c). If, in fact, hexachloroantimonate(V) and potassium or triphenylmethyl ions are about equal in mobility, the shape of this curve would imply a high transport number (0·86) for the chloride ion. The evidence for the high mobility of the chloride ion is thus very strong, the mechanism of this conduction is, however, not so well established, although it is convenient to assume that the essential, albeit, perhaps transient species is the tetrachloroantimonate(III) ion. Davies and Baughan (1961) in an attempt to correct the conductivity data for the effects of solvent conductivity have found that their observed specific conductivity for the pure solvent of $4-6 \times 10^{-6}$ ohm^{-1} cm^{-1} at 75° was apparently too great. The self-ionization, which is strongly dependent on pretreatment, appears due principally to impurities (a volatile arsenic(III) chloride or an ammonium salt is suggested) which increase rapidly at 99°, but more slowly at 75°, and hence possibly arise from the glass. Nonetheless, results are at least partially in accord with the solvent ionization scheme:

$$2SbCl_3 \rightleftharpoons SbCl_2^+ + SbCl_4^-.$$

Antimony(III) chloride is thus a solvent in which simple carbonium ions can be obtained and studied in bulk, as well as being a convenient solvent for the physiochemical study of interionic attractions. However, little direct evidence as to exact species present in the solvent, in self ionization, or of complex chloroanions in solution has emerged. Specifically, antimony(III) chloride is a useful solvent for the observation of N—H, O—H and C—H fundamental vibrations in amino acids and proteins (Lacher et al., 1949, 1954).

Antimony(III) bromide has solvent properties for inorganic and organic compounds comparable with the chloride (Jander and Weiss, 1957). Bromides are appreciably more soluble, and from the solutions, compounds such as

$$M_3^I Sb_2 Br_9 \ (M^I = K, NH_4, Rb) \text{ and } M^I SbBr_4 \ (M^I = Tl^I, Me_4N)$$

are obtained. The specific conductivity of the pure solvent is $0·9-1·0 \times 10^{-5}$ ohm^{-1} cm^{-1} at 100° (Jander and Weiss, 1959). As with antimony(III) chloride various conductivity measurements and conductimetric titrations have been employed in the study of the system. The viscosities, conductivities and densities of mixtures of antimony(III) bromide and aluminium bromide have shown the presence of a maximum in the conductivity curve at the

1 : 1 mole ratio, corresponding to a melt of the compound $SbBr_3.AlBr_3$, $SbBr_2^+AlBr_4^-$ (Gorenbein, 1945).

Antimony(III) iodide (m.p. $166.5 \pm 0.5°$) concentration cells employing antimony electrodes at 250° have been employed in a study of a lower iodide of antimony. The resulting oxidation–reduction system can be interpreted in terms of a two electron reduction of antimony(III) iodide. The current in the cell is carried by ions derived from the solvent, presumably SbI_2^+ and SbI_4^-. The conductivity of the molten iodide is considerably increased by the addition of potassium iodide corresponding to an increase in the number of tetraiodoantimonate(III) ions (Corbett and Albers, 1960).

Antimony(V) chloride has poor solvent properties for most inorganic halides. For example mercury(II) chloride dissolves only to the extent of 0.8% at 120°. Antimony(III) chloride, exceptionally, dissolves to give a 20% solution at 40° (Ehrlich and Dietz, 1960). The dissolution of iodine(III) chloride in antimony(V) chloride leads to the formation of the compound $ISbCl_8$ (Vonk and Wiebenga, 1959).

Examination of molten bismuth(III) chloride shows that its most significant solvent property is its ability to dissolve metallic bismuth (Corbett, 1958a,b). The resulting subhalide species is the ion Bi_2^{2+} (Bredig, 1959; Keneshea and Cubicciotti, 1959; Bredig et al., 1960). Beer's Law is obeyed by solutions of bismuth metal in molten bismuth(III) chloride, only in dilute solutions (Boston and Smith, 1958). At high concentrations a change in the spectral profile accompanies the non-adherence to Beer's Law (Boston and Smith, 1962). The overall solvent behaviour is best represented by a family of solution equilibria of which the simplest is $4Bi^+ \rightleftharpoons Bi_4^{4+}$, but which involves others such as $4Bi^+ + 4Bi^{3+} \rightleftharpoons Bi_8^{16+}$ (Boston et al., 1963).

IV. Oxyhalides as Solvents

In view of the bond polarities in the molecules, and the stability of the oxyanions, the oxyhalides suggest themselves as a group of compounds likely to possess useful solvent properties. The oxyhalides differ from the halides in that they can act as oxygen, as well as halogen, donors. They are, in fact, appreciably better halide ion donors than the halides. Although the number of oxyhalides of nitrogen, phosphorus, arsenic, antimony and bismuth is large, only a few have liquid ranges suitable for solvent work. The mixed halides such as $POFCl_2$ and POF_2Cl are not available in quantity and have not been studied. In any case in mixed halides of Group V, re-organization reactions (Schwarzmann and van Wazer, 1959) can occur so that studies in mixed oxyhalide might prove difficult. The general chemistry of the oxyhalides of nitrogen has been examined in detail (George, 1960). However, only nitrosyl chloride has so far been considered as a solvent, no doubt largely because of its ready availability, since there is no reason to think that similar properties will not be found in the other nitrosyl halides and the nitryl and other halides. The oxyhalides of arsenic, antimony and bismuth are more complex, and are solids possessing three dimensional structures, for example antimony oxychloride SbOCl has an infinite sheet of composition $(Sb_6O_6Cl_4)^{2+}$ held together by chloride ions.

Two oxyhalides, nitrosyl chloride (ClNO) and phosphoryl chloride ($POCl_3$), are particularly well suited for use as solvents because of their accessibility and physical properties (Table II). The chemical and physical properties of nitrosyl chloride are the outcome of a polar molecule with two strongly electronegative atoms (Beckham et al., 1951). The nitrogen to chlorine bond length of 1·95 Å is abnormally long (Gerding et al., 1960). Liquid nitrosyl chloride (ϵ = 19·7 at $-10°$ and 22·5 at $-27°$) has notable solvent properties for nitrosonium salts, due to the solvation of the NO^+ ion (Burg and Campbell, 1948; Burg and McKenzie, 1952). The solvated ion arises from the possibility of a stable adduct involving a chlorine bridge, $(O—N—Cl—N—O)^+$, in which the stability is attributed to resonance between structures.

$$[:\ddot{O}\!=\!N\!—\!\ddot{C}l\!—\!N\!=\!\ddot{O}:]^+, \quad [:\ddot{O}\!=\!N\!—\!\ddot{C}l:]:\overset{+}{N}\!\equiv\!O:, \quad \text{and} \quad :O\!\equiv\!\overset{+}{N}:[:\ddot{C}l\!—\!N\!=\!\ddot{O}:].$$

As would be expected, simple cations, such as those of the alkali metals, are not solvated in this way and the solubility of alkali halides are hence much lower than salts of the nitrosonium cation. Compounds such as $NOAlCl_4$, $NOFeCl_4$ and $NOSbCl_6$ are readily soluble and are strong electrolytes. However certain salts, namely, $(NO)_2SnCl_6$, $(NO)_2TiCl_6$ and $NO^+HSO_4^-$ are not soluble.

A number of solids have been isolated in which nitrosyl chloride is combined with a metal or non-metal chloride, usually one known to form chloroanions readily; these compounds can be obtained by dissolving the chloride, or sometimes even the metal, in nitrosyl chloride. In other cases it is necessary to employ a solvent for the reaction, and a variety of solvents including the anhydrous hydrogen halides have been employed (Waddington and Klanberg, 1960a). These solids are either 1 : 1 $MCl_n.NOCl$, as for example with:

$BiCl_3$	(Partington and Whynes, 1948, 1949)
	(Hewitt and Holliday, 1953)
	(Olah and Tolgyesi, 1961)
BF_3	(Waddington and Klanberg, 1960a)
	(Olah and Tolgyesi, 1961)
$AlCl_3$	(Gerding and Houtgraaf, 1953)
	(Burg and Campbell, 1948)
$GaCl_3$	(Partington and Whynes, 1948, 1949)
$InCl_3$	(Partington and Whynes, 1948, 1949)

$TlCl_3$	(Partington and Whynes, 1948, 1949)
$AsCl_3$	(Waddington and Klanberg, 1960a)
	(Lewis and Sowerby, 1957b)
$SbCl_3$	(Waddington and Klanberg, 1960a)
$SbCl_5$	(Burg and Campbell, 1948)
	(Seel, 1943)
	(Seel and Bauer, 1947)
	(Rheinbolt and Wasserfuhr, 1927)
SbF_5	(Waddington and Klanberg, 1960a)
$BiCl_3$	(Rheinbolt and Wasserfuhr, 1927)
	(Sudborough, 1891)
	(van Heteren, 1899)
UO_2Cl_2	(Addison and Hodge, 1961)
$MnCl_2$	(Partington and Whynes, 1948, 1949)
	(Asmussen, 1939)
$FeCl_3$	(Burg and McKenzie, 1952)
	(Rheinbolt and Wasserfuhr, 1927)
	(van Heteren, 1899)
$CuCl$	(Burg and McKenzie, 1952)
	(Sudborough, 1891)
	(Asmussen, 1939)
$AuCl_3$	(Partington and Whynes, 1948, 1949)
	(Sudborough, 1891)
$ZnCl_2$	(Partington and Whynes, 1948, 1949)
	(Sudborough, 1891)
	(Asmussen, 1939)
$HgCl_2$	(Partington and Whynes, 1948, 1949)
	(Rheinbolt and Wasserfuhr, 1927)

or they are 2 : 1, $MCl_n.2NOCl$, as for example with:

$AlCl_3$	(Burg and McKenzie, 1952)
$FeCl_3$	(Burg and McKenzie, 1952)
$ZrCl_4$	(Perrot and Devin, 1958)
	(Gutmann and Himml, 1956)
$ThCl_4$	(Perrot and Devin, 1958)
$PdCl_2$	(Partington and Whynes, 1948, 1949)
$PtCl_2$	(Partington and Whynes, 1948, 1949)
	(Asmussen, 1939)
$SnCl_4$	(Burg and Campbell, 1948)
	(Partington and Whynes, 1948, 1949)
	(Asmussen, 1939)
$PbCl_4$	(Rheinbolt and Wasserfuhr, 1927)
	(Asmussen, 1939).

These adducts can be regarded, in most instances, as chloro-anion salts of the nitrosonium ion, $NO^+MCl_{n+1}^-$ and $(NO^+)_2MCl_{n+2}^{2-}$. The nitrosonium ion, is well established in salts such as $NO^+ClO_4^-$ and $NO^+HSO_4^-$ and the formulation of the adducts of nitrosyl chloride with various chlorides as ionic compounds is in no doubt. The adduct $NOCl.AlCl_3$ shows Raman lines corresponding to the NO^+ and $AlCl_4^-$ ions. The force constant for the NO group, however, suggests that the bonding is not completely ionic in character (Gerding and Houtgraaf, 1953). Transfer of the chloride to the aluminium may not be complete so that the compound might be best regarded as $AlCl_3 \ldots Cl . NO$, rather than $NO^+AlCl_4^-$; however, it is also possible to formulate the solid in such a way that an oxygen bridge between Al and N could occur, e.g.

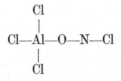

The interpretation of the conductivity of nitrosonium hexachloroantimonate(V) in liquid sulphur dioxide similarly requires the acceptance of a form other than that involving the simple ions (Seel, 1943; Seel and Bauer, 1947). Further detailed structural work on this and other complexes is required before the state of the solids can be known with certainty. The 1 : 2 compounds of aluminium and iron(III) chlorides involve an additional loosely bound molecule of nitrosyl chloride; their dissociation pressures at 0° of 180 mm and 224 mm are in keeping with this interpretation (Burg and McKenzie, 1952).

Solutions of the nitrosonium salts in nitrosyl chloride are good conductors, and typical data at $-20°C$ is

$$NO^+AlCl_4^-, \kappa = 1.17 \times 10^{-2} \text{ ohm}^{-1} \text{ cm}^{-1} \text{ at } 0.098 \text{ M};$$
$$NO^+FeCl_4^-, \kappa = 1.34 \times 10^{-3} \text{ ohm}^{-1} \text{ cm}^{-1} \text{ at } 0.0099 \text{ M};$$
$$NO^+SbCl_6^-, \kappa = 2.35 \times 10^{-2} \text{ ohm}^{-1} \text{ cm}^{-1} \text{ at } 0.140 \text{ M}.$$

The molar conductance of $NO^+FeCl_4^-$ at $-10°$ in nitrosyl chloride can be fitted to the Shedlovsky equation and a value of Λ_0 of 401·2 obtained; the data also leads to values for the degree of dissociation of the tetrachloroferrate(III) compound:

concentration (mole/l)	0·328	0·481	0·704	1·53	2·19	4·65	6·13
degree of dissociation	0·937	0·916	0·885	0·820	0·792	0·717	0·693

This interpretation of the results involves the application of the Debye-Hückel-Onsager theory to the nitrosyl chloride solvo-system, which appears justified. The high value of Λ_0 arises from the high transport number (0·88) of the NO^+ in the system. The high mobility of the nitrosonium ion, which has yet to be confirmed, must involve a chain mechanism for the conductance analogous to the transport of the H^+ ion in the water system (Burg and McKenzie, 1952). High mobilities have been observed for the chloride ion in antimony and arsenic(III) chlorides (Seel *et al.*, 1959), where a chain mechanism must also apply.

The application of the acid–base concept of Gutmann and Lindquist leads to the postulate of a solvent self-ionization equilibrium of the form $ClNO \rightleftharpoons NO^+$ (solvated) $+ Cl^-$ (solvated). Nitrosonium salts thus function as acids and chlorides as bases. The results of conductivity titrations support this as is shown by Fig. 7, in which tetramethylammonium chloride was

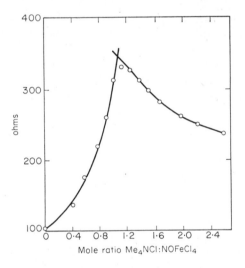

Fig. 7. Conductimetric titration of nitrosonium tetrachloroferrate(III) with tetramethylammonium chloride in nitrosyl chloride solution at $-10°$. Reproduced with permission from *J. Amer. chem. Soc.* (1952) **74**, 3147.

titrated with $NO^+FeCl_4^-$, the decrease in conductivity (increase in resistance) as the titration proceeded is due to the replacement of the highly mobile nitrosonium ion by the less mobile tetramethylammonium ion. Titrations of $NO^+BF_4^-$ and of $NO^+ClO_4^-$ with tetramethylammonium chloride showed a decrease of non-volatile chloride and a corresponding change in conductance, but the reactions were not complete due to solvolysis of the resulting salt. Nitrosonium salts of condensed phosphate anions can be conveniently prepared by dissolving silver salts in nitrosyl chloride:

$$4Ag_3PO_4 + 12ClNO \rightarrow (NO)_2P_4O_{11} + 5N_2O_3 + 12AgCl \qquad (23a)$$

$$3Ag_4P_2O_7 + 12ClNO \rightarrow (NO)_4P_6O_{17} + 4N_2O_3 + 12AgCl \qquad (23b)$$

$$Ag_3P_3O_9 + 3ClNO \rightarrow (NO)P_3O_8 + N_2O_3 + 3AgCl \tag{23c}$$

$$Ag_4P_4O_{12} + 4ClNO \rightarrow (NO)_2P_4O_{11} + N_2O_3 + 4AgCl. \tag{23d}$$

The reactions involve more than the replacement of the silver cation by the nitrosonium ion, the nitrosyl chloride bringing about additional P—O—P bond formation (Seel *et al.*, 1959).

The understanding of the chemistry of nitrosyl chloride solutions has been greatly helped by investigation of exchange using tracer studies. The rapid exchange of ^{36}Cl between nitrosyl chloride and aluminium, gallium, indium(III), thallium(III), iron(III) and antimony(V) chlorides confirms that these compounds exist in solution in the form of complexes, in which the chloride atoms are all equivalent and rapidly exchanged (Lewis and Sowerby, 1957a,b,c). The exchange between metal chlorides which are not significantly soluble, and nitrosyl chloride has also been followed using tracer methods (Lewis and Sowerby, 1956). Zinc, cadmium and mercury(II) chloride showed a rapid exchange between the chlorides and nitrosyl chloride presumed to involve the formation of 1 : 1 complexes. This was followed by a slower heterogenous exchange between the complexes and the solvent. No exchange was observed with chlorides, such as sodium or potassium, which do not form complexes nor with chlorides which form very stable complexes, for example $(NO^+)_2SnCl_6^{2-}$. Silver chloride was found to exchange with liquid nitrosyl chloride only in the presence of light; the exchange therefore probably proceeds through photochemical decomposition.

Nitrosyl fluoride (FNO), has been investigated only with respect to its reactions with metals, many of which it attacks with the formation of the corresponding nitrosonium fluoro-anion salts, for example tin gives $(NO^+)_2SnF_6^{2-}$ (Sokol'skii and Knunyants, 1960). Although no investigation of its solvent properties has yet been made, a large number of nitrosonium fluoro-anion salts have been prepared (Addison and Lewis, 1955).

Nitryl fluoride (NO_2F) and nitryl chloride both have boiling points too low for convenient investigation of their solvent properties. The number of complexes based on the nitronium ion, NO_2^+ is, however, very large (Hetherington and Robinson, 1957), especially with fluoro-anions. The physical properties (Table II) suggest that it is unlikely that an extensive solvo-system chemistry exists, as is found with nitrosyl chloride.

V. PHOSPHORYL CHLORIDE

By far the most extensive investigation of the halides and oxyhalides of Group V elements as solvents has been undertaken with phosphoryl chloride, largely because of its ready availability, convenient liquid range, ease of purification and obvious solvent properties. The investigation of phosphoryl chloride has covered almost every approach to the problem of elucidating solute behaviour in a particular solvent system. However, whilst it is true to say that the general features of the system have thereby been elucidated, there is still need for a considerable amount of work to finally and convincingly demonstrate the exact nature of the ionic equilibria present in the solvent. Since it is clearly of importance in the evaluation of the work that follows, the question of the solvent purity will be considered first. The criterion of purity of the solvent used in the numerous investigations has been that of its specific conductivity. Early work by Walden (1903) employed a sample with a specific conductivity at 25° of 1.7×10^{-6} ohm^{-1} cm^{-1}, but the recent work by Gutmann (1952a) has employed a sample purified by repeated distillation in glass giving a highly purified product with a conductivity of 1.55×10^{-6} ohm^{-1} cm^{-1} at 20°. More recently the need for measurements of conductances of greater precision has led to the purification of the solvent still further, so that the conductivity was reduced to 2×10^{-8} ohm^{-1} cm^{-1} at 20° (Gutmann and Baaz, 1959c). The chief impurities in phosphoryl chloride are polyphosphoryl chlorides and hydrogen chloride, both formed by hydrolysis of phosphoryl chloride; they are removed by careful and repeated fractional distillation. The examination of solvent properties and the measurement of physical properties has to be conducted in special apparatus, usually all glass, designed to avoid, or to minimize, contact with moisture; such apparatus is somewhat restrictive in use and results and observations are never as easily obtainable as with aqueous systems. The conductivity of purified phosphoryl chloride requires in explanation the postulate of a self-ionization process. Walden's original proposal for this involved the formation of a series of cations by the loss of successive chloride ions, but no evidence was then available to substantiate the presence of any such species, and ions with charge beyond one unit are no longer considered to occur. In line with the self-ionization processes postulated, and to some degree substantiated for the halide solvents, phosphoryl chloride might behave thus:

$$POCl_3 + POCl_3 \rightarrow POCl_2^+ + POCl_4^-. \tag{24}$$

Gutmann (1959) has preferred to generalize this equation thus:

$$(POCl_3)_n + (POCl_3)_m \rightleftharpoons (POCl_3)_{n-1} POCl_2^+ + (POCl_3)_m Cl^- \tag{25}$$

in which the $POCl_2^+$ cation and chloride anion are both regarded as solvated. With a specific conductivity as low as 2×10^{-8} ohm^{-1} cm^{-1} the extent of this self-ionization is clearly very small, the ionic product is not greater than 9×10^{-14} (Gutmann and Baaz, 1959c). A potentiometric measurement has given the value 5×10^{-14} (20°) (Gutmann, 1959). Direct electrolysis of pure solvent is not feasible, but the electrolysis of a 0·14 M solution of triethylammonium chloride (Spandau et al., 1960) yields chlorine at the anode and a polymeric solid of composition PO at the cathode,

$$POCl_3 \rightleftharpoons POCl_2^+ + Cl^- \tag{26a}$$

$$\text{Anode} \quad Cl^- \rightarrow \tfrac{1}{2}Cl_2 + e \tag{26b}$$

$$\text{Cathode} \quad 3POCl_2^+ + 3e \rightarrow PO + 2POCl_3. \tag{26c}$$

The ratio of chlorine to phosphorus monoxide was in the ratio $3:1$, as required by the electrode equations. It would appear from this that these ions were in fact the only ones involved in the discharge reactions at the electrode and thus provide strong evidence for a $POCl_2^+$ cation. However, an alternative explanation could be that the triethylammonium ion was discharged at the cathode and reacted with the solvent to give

$$Et_3NH^+ + e \rightarrow Et_3N + [H] \tag{27a}$$

$$3[H] + POCl_3 \rightarrow PO + 3HCl. \tag{27b}$$

Overall equation:

$$3Et_3NH^+ + 3e + POCl_3 \rightarrow PO + 3Et_3NH^+ + 3Cl^-. \tag{27c}$$

Transport number measurements with a solution of tetramethyl-ammonium chloride give an average value of 0.8 for the chloride ion (Gutmann, 1959), closely similar to the values obtained with arsenic(III) and antimony(III) chlorides which are attributed to the occurrence of a chloride transference process. Such a transference in phosphoryl chloride would be in line with the self-ionization process discussed above.

The general features of phosphoryl chloride as a solvent (Gutmann, 1952b) are closely similar to the other halide and oxyhalide solvents already discussed. Thus solutes such as $SiCl_4$, $SiBr_4$, $SnBr_4$ (Oddo and Tealdi, 1903), dissolve readily without dissociation or association. $(CH_3)_4NCl$, $(C_2H_5)_4NCl$, PCl_5, PBr_5, $AsCl_3$, $BiCl_3$, $BiBr_3$, BiI_3, ICl_3, SCl_4 (Oddo and Tealdi, 1903), $PtCl_4$ (Oddo, 1905) are readily soluble but cryoscopic measurements show that they undergo dissociation. The compounds

$AlCl_3$	(Oddo and Tealdi, 1903)
BBr_3	(Oddo and Tealdi, 1903)
$SbCl_5$	(Köhler, 1880)
$SnCl_4$	(Casselmann, 1856)
$TeCl_4$	(Lenher, 1908)
$TiCl_4$	(Ruff and Ipsen, 1903)
BCl_3	(Gustavson, 1871)

all dissolve with evidence of compound formation, likewise $FeCl_3$, but the solubility here is lower. Numerous iodides and bromides are soluble but the colour change accompanying dissolution suggests that some reaction has occurred. Similarly salts of various oxyanions such as potassium dichromate and permanganate dissolve, but with an accompanying reaction. The alkali metal and ammonium chlorides are only slightly soluble. Data for the solubility and conductivities of some of these alkali metal salts is shown in Table

III. In general these salts are not sufficiently soluble to permit them to be used in work with phosphoryl chloride, and it is more convenient to use the quaternary ammonium chlorides instead. The chlorides of the alkaline earth metals, silver(I), mercury(I) and thallium(I) are also only very sparingly soluble.

TABLE III

Solubility and Specific Conductivity of Saturated Solutions of Alkali Metal Salts Measured at 20° and the Equivalent Conductance at a Dilution of $V = 1000$

Salt	Solubility (g/l)	Specific conductivity of saturated solution (ohm^{-1} cm^{-1})	Equivalent conductance at $V = 1000$ l/mole
LiCl	0·05	$6·6 \times 10^{-6}$	4·0
NaCl	0·31	$3·0 \times 10^{-5}$	6·4
KCl	~0·60	$3·4 \times 10^{-5}$	6·7
NH$_4$Cl	0·46	$3·6 \times 10^{-5}$	6·9
RbCl	0·87	$8·3 \times 10^{-5}$	14·6
CsCl	1·26	$1·1 \times 10^{-4}$	16·0
KF	~0·40	$2·6 \times 10^{-5}$	6·4
KBr	0·51	$4·3 \times 10^{-5}$	14·5
KI	~1·71	$1·2 \times 10^{-4}$	23·1
KCN	~0·73	$3·3 \times 10^{-5}$	7·2
KCNO	~0·80	$3·1 \times 10^{-5}$	9·0
KCNS	~0·76	$2·9 \times 10^{-5}$	6·6

The solubilities of quaternary ammonium salts are high (Baaz and Gutmann, 1959b) and the equivalent conductances follow closely values predicted by electrolyte theory. For example, data for the equivalent conductance of tetraethylammonium chloride measured from $1·4 \times 10^{-3}$ to $7·3 \times 10^{-5}$ M follows a linear relationship with $\sqrt{c}$ over much of the concentration range. The Debye-Hückel-Onsager equation can be successfully applied to this data (Gutmann and Baaz, 1959c) and similarly to that for other quaternary ammonium salts (Fig. 8 and Table IV). Walden's rule can be applied to give ionic mobilities for the Et$_4$N$^+$, Pr$_4$N$^+$, Cl$^-$, Br$^-$, I$^-$, and ClO$_4^-$ ions of 25·6, 18·9, 15·6, 27·4, 23·4, 22·7, and 27·8 respectively. These mobilities are confirmed by comparison with those in other solvents (particularly water). The calculated Stokes radii for the ions, derived from the ionic mobility data, supports the solvation of the chloride, bromide and iodide ions; the number of solvent molecules being from 0·5 to 2 per ion. The Stokes radii are confirmed by a consideration of the Bjerrum parameters, obtainable from the conductivity data.

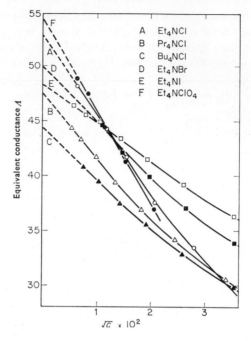

FIG. 8. The conductance of quaternary ammonium salts in phosphoryl chloride at 20° (c in molarity). Reproduced with permission from *Mh. Chem.* (1959) **90**, 260.

TABLE IV

Values of Experimental and Calculated Λ_0 for a Series of Quaternary Ammonium Salts in Phosphoryl Chloride Measured at 20°

Substance	Λ_0 from $\Lambda - \sqrt{c}$	Λ_0 calculated by method of Fuoss[a]
Et_4NCl	53·0	53·0
Pr_4NCl	47·6	46·3
Bu_4NCl	44·4	43·0
Et_4NBr	50·0	49·0
Et_4NI	48·5	48·3
Et_4NClO_4	54·4	53·4

[a] Fuoss, 1935.

Triethylamine is a "potential" electrolyte in phosphoryl chloride; it reacts with the solvent to give a conducting solution (Baaz and Gutmann, 1959a), which is well represented by equilibria:

$$Et_3N + POCl_3 \rightleftharpoons (Et_3N.POCl_2^+ \ Cl^-) \rightleftharpoons Et_3N.POCl_2^+ + Cl^- \qquad (28)$$

whence $\Lambda_0 = 48 \cdot 5 \pm 1$. From the ionic mobility of the chloride ion, the mobility of the cation can be obtained and hence the Stokes radius. This, on comparison with the estimated sizes of the ions $(Et_3N)_2POCl^{2+}$ and $(Et_3N)_3PO^{3+}$ as well as $(Et_3N)POCl_2^+$, confirms the presence in the solution of the latter. The $(Et_3N)POCl_2^+$ ion is presumably tetrahedral in shape, with the phosphorus surrounded by two chlorine atoms, one oxygen and a nitrogen. The equilibrium constant for the system is comparable with that observed for the corresponding aqueous system,

$$Et_3N + H_2O \rightleftharpoons (Et_3NH^+ \ OH^-) \rightleftharpoons Et_3NH^+ + OH^-. \tag{29}$$

The $POCl_2^+$ cation in phosphoryl chloride solution, however, possesses a greater affinity for triethylamine than does the proton in water so that the equilibrium lies well to the right. A solution of triethylamine hydrochloride in phosphoryl chloride gives rise to three equilibria:

$$Et_3NH^+ + POCl_3 \rightleftharpoons Et_3NPOCl_2^+ + HCl$$
$$-Cl^- \updownarrow +Cl^- \qquad\qquad -Cl^- \updownarrow +Cl^-$$
$$Et_3N \cdot HCl \qquad\qquad Et_3N + POCl_3 \tag{30}$$

By examining the conductivity of this system the affinity of the proton for triethylamine in phosphoryl chloride can be shown to be at least not greater that of the $POCl_2^+$ cation. In dilute solution $Et_3N.HCl$ gives Et_3NH^+ and $(Et_3N)POCl_2^+$ in approximately equal proportions. Passage of nitrogen through the solution causes the conductivity to fall, ultimately reaching the value of triethylamine itself (Baaz and Gutmann, 1959c). Conductimetric titrations in phosphoryl chloride solutions of pyridine with vanadium(IV), phosphorus(V) and tantalum(V) chlorides show breaks at the $1:2$ ratio (corresponding to $(Py.POCl_2^+)_2VCl_6^{2-}$) and $1:1$ ratio (corresponding to $Py.POCl_2^+PCl_6^-$ and $Py.POCl_2^+TaCl_6^-$) (Gutmann, 1954b).

Solutions of a number of chloride acceptors such as antimony(V) and boron(III) chloride lead to solutions of high conductance. Antimony(V) chloride is of special interest because the structure of the solid phase obtainable from the solution is known (Fig. 9), and it contains an antimony bonded directly to oxygen (Lindquist and Bränden, 1959; Bränden and Lindquist, 1963). The conductance of solutions of antimony(V) chloride in phosphoryl chloride (Baaz and Gutmann, 1959d) is readily interpreted simply in terms of the equilibrium:

$$Cl_5SbOPCl_3 \rightleftharpoons SbCl_6^- + POCl_2^+ \tag{31}$$

for which an equilibrium constant of 4×10^{-6} has been evaluated. The equilibrium constant for the reaction;

$$SbCl_6^- + POCl_3 \rightleftharpoons Cl_5SbOPCl_3 + Cl^- \tag{32}$$

is not more than 10^{-9}. Mobilities obtainable from the conductance data fit with unsolvated $POCl_2^+$ and $SbCl_6^-$ ions. Although initial experiments gave a transport number for the $POCl_2^+$ ion of 0·95 (Gutmann and Himml, 1955) this has not been confirmed by later work (V. Gutmann, personal communication). Further examination of the solution shows that in concentrated solutions, colloidal aggregates of indefinite composition, presumably involving oxygen co-ordination, appear on standing (Baaz and Gutmann, 1959d). The resulting change is accompanied by a fall in the conductance. Lindquist (Brändén and Lindquist, 1963) has pointed out that the ionic formulation previously postulated (Gutmann, 1952f) for the solid adduct of antimony

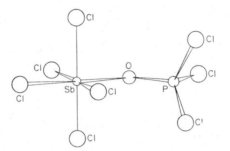

Fig. 9. The structure of $SbCl_5.OPCl_3$. Reproduced with permission from *Acta chem. Scand.* (1963) **17**, 358.

pentachloride and phosphoryl chloride does not have a favourable lattice energy and hence would not be expected to be stable. Other ionization processes are possible in this system, viz.

$$Cl_3POSbCl_5 \rightleftharpoons Cl_3POSbCl_4^+ + Cl^- \qquad (33a)$$

$$\rightleftharpoons Cl_2P^+OSbCl_5 + Cl^-. \qquad (33b)$$

However, the evidence from the conductance titrations of tetramethyl-ammonium chloride and antimony(V) chloride giving $Et_4N^+SbCl_6^-$ would appear to support the presence of an antimony-containing anion. A solid of composition $POCl_3.2SbCl_5$ ($POCl_3.SbCl_4^+SbCl_6^-$) has been reported in phase studies of the system $POCl_3$–$SbCl_5$ (Leman and Tridot, 1959).

In the case of boron(III) chloride there is strong conductimetric and potentiometric evidence to show that the phosphoryl chloride solution of this compound involves the equilibrium (Baaz *et al.*, 1960a):

$$BCl_3.POCl_3 \rightleftharpoons POCl_2^+ + BCl_4^-. \qquad (34)$$

The examination of the solid adduct $BCl_3.POCl_3$ by infra-red techniques has led, however, to conflicting views. On the one hand the structure $POCl_2^+BCl_4^-$ is put forward (Fraser *et al.*, 1960; Gerrard *et al.*, 1961), on the other, an oxygen donor complex (Waddington and Klanberg, 1960b; Peach and Waddington, 1962). As no other example of solids in which phosphoryl chloride acts as a chloride donor are known, the evidence favours the oxygen co-ordinated form. The rapid halogen exchange at $0°$ between phosphoryl chloride and boron(III) chloride which occurs in solutions which are rich in phosphoryl chloride has been found not to occur when boron(III) chloride is in excess (Gutmann, 1952e). The absence of exchange clearly indicates that the species $POCl_2^+$ and BCl_4^- are not present in solution in equilibrium with the component halides. It would thus appear that even in solution the phosphoryl chloride acts as an oxygen donor rather than a chloride donor. The exchange process observed at high concentrations of phosphoryl chloride may be the effect of the high dielectric constant of the solvent promoting an ionic exchange thus:

$$POCl_3 \rightleftharpoons POCl_2^+ + Cl^- \tag{35a}$$

$$Cl^- + Cl_3^*B.OPCl_3 \rightleftharpoons (ClCl_3^*BOPCl_3^-) \rightleftharpoons Cl^{*-} + Cl_3B.OPCl_3. \tag{35b}$$

It is difficult to see why, if at this stage a solvated tetrachloroborate(III) ion is formed, it would not also be formed, at least in an amount sufficient to promote a rapid exchange, in the boron(III) chloride rich system. The conductivity of boron(III) chloride solutions and the conductimetric and potentiometric titration data are difficult to explain without a boron-containing anion. One possible alternative is for the complex to ionize thus:

$$Cl_3B.OPCl_3 \rightleftharpoons Cl_3B.OPCl_2^+ + Cl^- \tag{36}$$

but this would not appear compatible with a break in the conductimetric titration curve of boron trichloride with tetraethylammonium chloride. Spectrophotometric investigation of the iron(III) chloride–boron(III) chloride–phosphoryl chloride system likewise supports the presence of the tetrachloroborate(III) ion in the early stages of the reaction, on addition of further tetraethylammonium chloride the system changes over to one containing the tetrachloroferrate(III) ion. Further experiments on the conductivity of dilute solutions of boron(III) chloride in phosphoryl chloride and vice versa are promised (Herber, 1960). These and other results will be awaited with interest, meanwhile the role of boron(III) chloride as a chloride ion acceptor must be accepted tentatively, the evidence so far would place boron(III) chloride between iron(III) and titanium(IV) chloride in a series of decreasing chloride acceptance.

The aluminium halides have solubilities and conductivities as shown in Table V. The conductivity of aluminium chloride rises to a maximum at around $40°$ and then drops rapidly with increasing temperature. A solvate of formula $AlCl_3.POCl_3$ is obtained only on long standing. Similarly the bromide gives $AlBr_3.POCl_3$, whereas the iodide gives a compound $AlI_3.2POCl_3$ (Gutmann, 1952e). An examination of the phase diagram for aluminium chloride and phosphoryl chloride shows a further two compounds $AlCl_3.2POCl_3$ and $AlCl_3.6POCl_3$ (Groeneveld and Zuur, 1957, 1958). The first of these has been confirmed by a direct preparation (Raman and Murthy, 1960). Gallium(III) chloride behaves in a similar fashion giving solvates $GaCl_3.POCl_3$ and $GaCl_3.2POCl_3$ (Greenwood and Wade, 1957; Greenwood and Perkins, 1957; Greenwood, 1958). Similarly solvates $GaBr_3.POBr_3$ and $GaBr_3.POCl_3$ have been reported. The structures of these solvates have so far only been investigated spectroscopically. Evidence for the structure $POCl_2^+GaCl_4^-$ has come from the Raman spectrum of the molten compound. Ten lines were observed, four of which corresponded in position and polarization to the

TABLE V

Solubility and Conductivities of Aluminium Halides at 20°

	Solubility (g/1000 g) $POCl_3$	Specific conductivities $(ohm^{-1}\ cm^{-1})$			Colour
		0·05 M	0·1 M	0·2 M	
AlF_3	c. 0·5	$4\cdot4\times10^{-6}$			Colourless
$AlCl_3$	60·0	$3\cdot6\times10^{-4}$	$7\cdot7\times10^{-4}$	$1\cdot52\times10^{-3}$	Light yellow
$AlBr_3$	153	$4\cdot5\times10^{-4}$	$9\cdot1\times10^{-4}$	$1\cdot82\times10^{-3}$	Yellow brown
AlI_3	170	$4\cdot0\times10^{-4}$	$8\cdot1\times10^{-4}$	$1\cdot62\times10^{-3}$	Deep red

spectrum of the known $GaCl_4^-$ (tetrahedral, symmetry T_d) and the remaining six lines could be assigned to frequencies caused by $POCl_2^+$ (planar, symmetry C_{2v}) (Woodward et al., 1956; Greenwood, 1958). An examination of the Raman spectra and a detailed examination of the infra-red spectra of these aluminium and gallium halide adducts suggests a contrary view of the structure in which oxygen is held to be the bridging atom (Gerding et al., 1960). The energy change involved in the formation of the gallium(III) chloride complex is

$$GaCl_3(g) + POCl_3(g) \rightleftharpoons GaCl_3.POCl_3(g), \quad \Delta H = -22\cdot6\ \text{kcal.} \quad (37)$$

The evidence so far would appear to support the idea that these solids are in fact essentially oxygen donors, in which perhaps only relatively weak interactions are involved in the crystal lattice.

The nature of the solution of aluminium chloride in phosphoryl chloride is equally uncertain. Conductance titrations such as those between zinc(II), tin(IV) and antimony(V) chlorides with aluminium(III) chloride lead to breaks in the curve, 1 : 2 in the case of tin(IV), and 1 : 1 in the case of antimony(V) and zinc(II). At the same time precipitation of, for example, $2AlCl_3.SnCl_4.2POCl_3$ and $AlCl_3.SbCl_5.3POCl_3$ occurs (Gutmann, 1952f). Similarly, titration of aluminium chloride and tetraethylammonium chloride gives a break at $1:1$ and a curve characteristic of the formation of soluble ionic compound involving a feeble chloride acceptor. Closer examination of the titration of antimony(V) chloride shows that the curve is in fact more complex than the original experiments suggested. The breaks obtained depend on the direction of the titration, for example aluminium chloride with antimony(V) chloride gave no significant break at the $1:1$ composition, but a break at the $1:2$ ($AlCl_3.2SbCl_5$) (*vide supra*), whereas antimony(V) chloride with aluminium(III) chloride gave breaks at $1:1$, $1:2$ ($2AlCl_3.SbCl_5$) and possibly $1:3$ ($3AlCl_3.SbCl_5$). The formation of colloidal micelles during the titration of antimony(V) chloride with aluminium chloride may explain some of the features of the conductimetric curves. The results are made more difficult to interpret by the slow establishment of the equilibrium between solid and solution. The overall picture obtained from conductimetric, potentiometric and preparative studies is one involving several species in solution, which lead to the solvates mentioned earlier. The bonding of the phosphoryl chloride to the aluminium in these solvates is most probably through an oxygen bridge. The $AlCl_4^-$ ion appears to be the only anionic species present; there is no evidence for $AlCl_5^{2-}$ or $AlCl_6^{3-}$ species. The $AlCl^{2+}$ and Al^{3+} species occur solvated thus

$$AlCl(OPCl_3)_5^{2+} \text{ and } Al(OPCl_3)_6^{3+};$$

the corresponding $AlCl_2^+$ ion does not appear to be involved. The system is made complex by the possibility of polymeric species, for example:

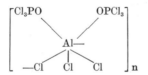

or even more complex two dimensional polymers (Baaz *et al.*, 1960d). Ebullioscopic measurements support the presence of polymeric species breaking down with time, true equilibrium being very slow to attain (Gutmann and Mairinger, 1961). In a 0.3 M solution the transport number of the tetrachloroaluminate ion has the very low value of 0.04. This may be explained by a switch mechanism (Gutmann and Himml, 1955). Similar studies of aluminium chloride in acyl halides have shown that the aluminium is transported to both anode and cathode simultaneously (Wertyporoch and Firla, 1932). The transport experiment does not assist greatly in supporting the postulate of a solvate $POCl_2^+$ and a $AlCl_4^-$ ion, since alternative more complex systems might similarly give a very low transport number.

Titanium(IV) chloride is appreciably soluble in phosphoryl chloride, giving a conducting yellow solution from which a solvate $TiCl_4.2POCl_3$ can be obtained (Gutmann, 1952e). The solvate $TiCl_4.POCl_3$ which can also

12

be obtained has a dimeric structure involving two octahedrally disposed titanium atoms linked through a bridge of two chlorine atoms. The phosphoryl chloride molecules are in the trans positions on a diagonal of the molecule (Bränden and Lindquist, 1960). Three crystal modifications of this compound exist. The oxygen bridge structure for the solid solvates is supported by the infra-red data (Sheldon and Tyree, 1959) and also by the crystal structure of a ternary compound $TiCl_3(OPCl_3)_3^+SbCl_6^-$ (Adolfsson et al., 1960). Conductimetric titrations of titanium(IV) chloride solutions with tetraethylammonium chloride show a maximum at the 1 : 1 ratio followed by a break at the 1 : 2 ratio (Adolfsson et al., 1960); however, another form of the curve has been reported, which although it shows similar breaks at 1 : 1 and 1 : 2 ratios, does not show the maximum (Gutmann, 1952f). Clearly the interpretation of the shape of the conductimetric curves must be treated with caution until reproducible results are available. During the titration tetraethylammonium hexachlorotitanate(IV) is precipitated: it has been observed previously that the presence of solids leads to difficulties in understanding the form of conductimetric curves. Potentiometric experiments in which solutions of titanium(IV) chloride were titrated with tetraethylammonium, antimony(V) and iron(III) chlorides show the existence of the species $TiCl_6^{2-}$, $TiCl_5^-$ solv. and $TiCl_3^+$ solv. in solution. The behaviour of the titanium(IV) chloride depends wholly on the relative donor or acceptor strength of the other chloride. Thus, with antimony(V) chloride, the species predominating can be shown to consist of $Cl_3Ti(OPCl_3)_3^+$ whereas with iron(III) chloride, a much weaker chloride acceptor, photometric measurements show an equilibrium to exist:

$$(TiCl_3 \text{ solv.})^+ (FeCl_4)^- \rightleftharpoons (TiCl_4)_{solv.} + (FeCl_3)_{solv.}. \qquad (38)$$

The ratio of chloride donation and acceptance appears largely dependent on concentration. In very dilute solution titanium(IV) chloride is almost exclusively a donor, in concentrated solution it is often an acceptor (Baaz et al., 1960c). Ebullioscopic results on mixtures of potassium chloride and titanium(IV) chloride in 1 : 1 mole ratio show the presence of a $TiCl_5.POCl_3$ species as well as $TiCl_6^{2-}$. The potassium salt of this ion, $KTiCl_5.POCl_3$ has been isolated as a solid (Gutmann and Mairinger, 1961). The solutions, covering a range of concentrations, thus involve the equilibria:

$$Cl_5Ti.OPCl_3^- + Cl^- \rightleftharpoons TiCl_6^{2-} + POCl_3 \qquad (39a)$$

$$Cl_5Ti.OPCl_3^- + POCl_3 \rightleftharpoons Cl_4Ti(OPCl_3)_2 + Cl^- \qquad (39b)$$

$$Cl_4Ti(OPCl_3)_2 + POCl_3 \rightleftharpoons Cl_3Ti(OPCl_3)_3^+ + Cl^-. \qquad (39c)$$

Tungsten(VI) chloride is readily soluble in phosphoryl chloride to give a red solution. On adding tetraethylammonium, potassium or caesium chlorides a yellow solvated WCl_7^- species is formed, which cannot, however, be isolated as a salt. Other metallic chlorides supply chloride ions for the formation of the WCl_7^- ion, the sequence of donor strengths to tungsten(VI) chloride, as determined by potentiometric and spectraphotometric methods, being

$$Et_4NCl \sim KCl \sim CsCl > ZnCl_2 > AlCl_3 > SnCl_4.$$

There is no evidence to show that tungsten(VI) chloride can behave as a chloride ion donor itself (Baaz et al., 1961g).

Iron(III) chloride dissolves in phosphoryl chloride to give a reddish brown solution at a concentration of 0·01 M, but on dilution the colour changes so that at 10^{-4} M the solution is yellow (Gutmann, 1959). From the solution solid solvates of composition $2FeCl_3.3POCl_3$ (Dadape and Rao, 1955), $FeCl_3.POCl_3$ (Dadape and Rao, 1955; Gutmann and Baaz, 1959e) and $2FeCl_3.POCl_3$ (Ruff, 1904) are obtained. The ultra-violet spectrum of these solutions shows clearly that in the concentrated solution there are no tetra-chloroferrate(III) ion species present, on dilution however the colour change corresponds to the appearance of this ion. The red solution on evaporation gives a brown amorphous solid, but by carefully cooling the solution, or by adding carbon tetrachloride, a red crystalline product of composition $2FeCl_3.3POCl_3$ is obtained (vide supra). It is also possible by pumping both the brown and red materials to obtain the yellow crystalline $FeCl_3.POCl_3$ (vide supra) (Baaz et al., 1960b). The brown coloured solid is a highly con-densed species, rich in phosphoryl chloride. The addition of various chlorides to the red-brown solution produces the absorption characteristic of the tetrachloroferrate(III) ion and there is a corresponding change in the conductivity. The formation of the tetrachloroferrate(III) ion can be con-veniently followed potentiometrically (Baaz et al., 1960c,d; Gutmann and Baaz, 1959e), spectrophotometrically (Baaz et al., 1960b, 1961a,b,c; Gutmann and Baaz, 1959d), conductimetrically (Baaz et al., 1960c,d; Gutmann and Baaz, 1959d), or ebullioscopically (Gutmann and Mairinger, 1960). The extent of chloride donation varies; thus $HgCl_2$, BCl_3, $TiCl_4$, $SnCl_4$ and PCl_5 all react to give a solvated unipositive cation whereas $ZnCl_2$ and $AlCl_3$ react to give up two chloride ions and possibly three in the case of $AlCl_3$. Donor strength in this reaction follows the series

$$Et_4NCl \sim KCl \sim ZnCl_2 \sim AlCl_3 > TiCl_4 > PCl_5 \sim AlCl_3 \gg SbCl_5 \sim$$
$$HgCl_2 > BCl_3 \sim SnCl_4$$

(Baaz et al., 1961d). Only in certain instances can the reaction be considered to have gone to completion. However, although spectrophotometric measure-ments suggest this is so in the case of tetraethylammonium, aluminium and zinc chlorides (Baaz et al., 1960c), in the case of titanium(IV), and phos-phorus(V) chlorides the spectrum for the uncomplexed solvated iron(III) chloride is always present (Baaz et al., 1961d). Ebullioscopic measurements on the degree of dissociation of potassium tetrachloroferrate(III) (Gutmann and Mairinger, 1960) confirms results obtained by conductivity measurements (Gutmann and Baaz, 1959d). Only simple ion-pair association appears to be present, the dissociation constant of $KFeCl_4$ (Gutmann and Mairinger, 1961) is 3×10^{-4} compared with $KSbCl_6$, 9×10^{-4}; $K(Cl_5TiOPCl_3)$, 3×10^{-4}, and

$$[Al(OPCl_3)_6][FeCl_4]_3, \; 9 \times 10^{-5}.$$

Photometric studies of $0 \cdot 01$ M phosphoryl chloride solutions of iron(III) chloride when a suitable Lewis base, $\overline{B}$, is present show that chloride ion transfer occurs. For example, both pyridine and triethylamine react thus:

$$C_5H_5N + POCl_3 + FeCl_3 \rightleftharpoons C_5H_5N.POCl_2^+ + FeCl_4^-. \tag{40}$$

The Lewis base assists in the chloride ion transfer by the formation of the $\overline{B}.POCl_2^+$ cation by displacement of a chloride ion at the P—Cl bond. With tetraethylammonium permanganate and chlorate reaction occurs, e.g.

$$MnO_4^- + 4FeCl_3 \rightarrow Mn^{3+} \text{ (solv.)} + 4FeCl_4^- + 2Cl_2 \tag{41}$$

and with tetraethylammonium bromide, a bromotrichloroferrate(III) ion is formed (Baaz et al., 1961a).

The formation of conducting solutions of iron(III) chloride requires the formation of the tetrachloroferrate(III) ion. This can arise in a number of ways:

$$FeCl_3 + POCl_3 \rightleftharpoons POCl_2^+ + FeCl_4^- \tag{42a}$$

$$(x+1)FeCl_3 + yPOCl_3 \rightleftharpoons FeCl_{3-x}(OPCl_3)_y]^{x+} + xFeCl_4^- \tag{42b}$$

$$xFeCl_3 + MCl_n + yPOCl_3 \rightleftharpoons MCl_{n-x}(OPCl_3)_y]^{x+} + xFeCl_4^- \tag{42c}$$

$$FeCl_3 + \overline{B} + POCl_3 \rightleftharpoons \overline{B}.POCl_2^+ + FeCl_4^-. \tag{42d}$$

Reaction (a) has no evidence to substantiated it other than the fact that the tetrachloroferrate(III) ion appears on dilution of an iron(III) chloride solution. However, no compounds in which the $POCl_2^+$ has been recognized have yet been examined. Reaction (c) is well illustrated by the example given above, for example, aluminium chloride and iron(III) chloride react in this way. Likewise reaction(d) is simple and the reaction scheme is well substantiated. The interpretation of the behaviour of solutions of iron(III) chloride in terms of reaction(b) was first put forward by Meek and Drago (1961). Solutions of iron(III) chloride in triethylphosphate behave exactly as solutions in phosphoryl chloride. The solutions are red at $0 \cdot 1$ M and addition of further solvent causes a change in colour, whilst addition of lithium chloride does not appreciably change the absorption spectrum of the resulting yellow solution. It would thus appear that the solution contains the iron in the form of tetrachloroferrate(III) ion without the necessity of the chloride from the phosphoryl chloride. Similarly, it was possible to show breaks in the conductimetric titration curves similar to those reported earlier in this chapter for phosphoryl chloride solutions. The inference is that reaction(b) is one of the equilibria present in phosphoryl chloride solutions. The position of the equilibrium represented by this equation must depend upon a number of factors, notably the basicity, the dielectric constant and the solvating ability of the solvent. It would appear that the essential feature of phosphoryl chloride is not its ability to undergo self-ionization, which must be very slight indeed, but rather its capacity to act as an oxygen donor under certain conditions and a halide donor under others (Gutmann and Baaz, 1959a).

The effect on the solvent behaviour of the substitution of one of the chlorides in phosphoryl chloride by a phenyl group is not very great. A comparison of the properties is shown in Table VI:

TABLE VI

Comparison of Properties of Phenyl Phosphoryl Chloride and Phosphoryl Chloride

	$POCl_3$	$PhPOCl_2$
Density at 25°	1·648	1·197
M.p. (°C)	$+1$	$+3$
B.p.° (760 mm)	108	258
Viscosity at 25° (centipoise)	1·15	4·44
Dielectric constant at 25°	13·9	26·0
Molar volume	6·7	6·3
Specific conductivity at 25° (ohm^{-1} cm^{-1})	2×10^{-8}	9×10^{-8}
Λ_0 for Et_4NCl	53	14·5

Conductivity measurements of tetraethylammonium chloride in phenyl phosphoryl chloride ($PhPOCl_2$) are in accord with electrolyte theory. Iron(III) chloride gives conductivity values which do not vary regularly with concentration, behaviour similar to that found with this solute in phosphoryl chloride. Conductimetric titrations of tetraethylammonium chloride with a variety of chlorides, show breaks corresponding to the uptake of one chloride ion by boron(III), aluminium(III), iron(III), phosphorus(V) and antimony(V) chlorides. Zinc(II), titanium(IV) and tin(IV) take up either one or two chloride ions depending upon the conditions of the titration. Boron(III), titanium(IV) and phosphorus(V) chlorides donate one chloride ion to iron(III) and antimony(V) chlorides to form the corresponding tetrachloroferrate(III) and hexachloroantimonate(V) salts (Baaz et al., 1961h). Potentiometric methods have confirmed that mercury(II), boron(III), aluminium(III), iron(III), antimony(III), phosphorus(V) and antimony(V) and in addition mercury(II) chlorides each accept only one chloride ion from tetraethylammonium chloride. As with the conductivity data, potentiometric data suggests that zinc(II), titanium(IV) and tin(IV) chlorides accept one or two chloride ions depending upon the stoichiometry of the ions in solution. Aluminium(III) chloride donates two chloride ions to iron(III) and antimony(V) chlorides giving rise to a doubly charged solvated chloroaluminate ion (Baaz *et al.*, 1961i). Spectrophotometric studies show that iron(III) chloride dissolves in phenyl phosphoryl chloride to give a red solvated complex which is transformed into the yellow tetrachloroferrate(III) ion on the addition of a chloride donor, particularly the alkali or tetraethylammonium chlorides. The evidence for chloride ion transference follows the results described above and obtained from conductimetric and potentiometric studies. The donor strength to iron(III) chloride of the chlorides decreases in the order

$$KCl \sim Et_4NCl > AlCl_3^* \geqslant TiCl_4 > PCl_5 > ZnCl_2^* > BCl_3 \sim SnCl_4 \sim$$
$$AlCl_3^{**} > HgCl_2 > SbCl_3$$

* as monochlorodonors, ** as a dichlorodonor.

There appears to be little difference between iron(III) and antimony(V) chlorides as acceptors with this series of donors as measured photometrically (Baaz *et al.*, 1961c). The potentiometric measurements suggested the series of acceptors as

$$FeCl_3 > SbCl_5 \geqslant SnCl_4 > BCl_3 \geqslant HgCl_2 \sim PCl_5 > TiCl_4 > AlCl_3 > ZnCl_2.$$

Similarly the potentiometric data suggested that chloride ion activity in the solution decreased in the order

$$Et_4NCl > AlCl_3 > TiCl_4,\ BCl_3 > ZnCl_2 > PCl_5 > SbCl_5 > FeCl_3.$$

Triphenylmethyl chloride reacts with acceptors such as zinc(II), aluminium(III), iron(III), boron(III), titanium(IV), tin(IV) and antimony(V) chlorides in phosphoryl and phenylphosphoryl chloride to give a series of triphenyl carbonium salts, $Ph_3C^+MCl_{n+1}^-$. The acceptor strength towards chloride ion in this case diminishes in the order

$$FeCl_3 > SbCl_5 > SnCl_4 > BCl_3 > ZnCl_2 \sim TiCl_4 > AlCl_3 \sim HgCl_2 > SbCl_3 > PCl_5$$

for phenyl phosphoryl chloride (Baaz *et al.*, 1961e), and in the order

$$FeCl_3 > SbCl_5 \sim BCl_3 \sim SnCl_4 \geqslant TiCl_4 > AlCl_3 > ZnCl_2 > HgCl_2 > SbCl_3 > PCl_5$$

for phosphoryl chloride (Baaz *et al.*, 1961f). The order is different in detail from that observed with other chloride ion donors in phenylphosphoryl and phosphoryl chloride, but the essential features are the same, namely that iron(III) chloride and antimony(V) chloride are amongst the best acceptors, antimony(III) and phosphorus(V) chloride amongst the worst. The formation constants for the reaction

$$Ph_3C^+ Cl^- + MCl_n \rightleftharpoons Ph_3C^+ + MCl_{n+1}^- \tag{43}$$

shown in Table VII have been obtained using spectrophotometric methods. Phosphoryl chloride thus promotes the transfer of chloride ion more than phenylphosphoryl chloride, despite the difference in dielectric constant. The difference is a function of the ability of the phosphoryl group to solvate the anion and perhaps also the cation. This behaviour of chlorides as chloride ion acceptors or donors is not confined to the halide and oxyhalide solvents; recent work by Gutmann and his collaborators (Baaz *et al.*, 1962a,b,c; Gutmann *et al.*, 1963; Gutmann and Hampel, 1963; Hubacek *et al.*, 1963) in methyl cyanide, benzoyl chloride and other solvents has shown the occurrence of this type of solute behaviour in a widely differing range of solvents. The donor and acceptor strength series vary from solvent to solvent as might be expected.

TABLE VII

Formation Constants of the Complex $Ph_3C^+MCl_{n+1}^-$

| Solute | Solvent | |
	$POCl_3$	$PhPOCl_2$
$ZnCl_2$	12	5·3
BCl_3	100	10·8
$AlCl_3$	14	0·19
$FeCl_3$	290	130
$TiCl_4$	16	5·3
$SnCl_4$	85	15·5
$SbCl_5$	110	39·4

The ability of various sulphophthaleins to function as chloride ion indicators promises to be of value in studies of chloride transfer processes. The colour changes involved are close to those observed with aqueous solutions:

Chloride ion donors

A $\xrightarrow{\hspace{2cm}}$ B

(red)   Chloride ion acceptors   (yellow)

The changes involve ionization equilibria (Gutmann and Hubacek, 1963) analogous to those encountered with proton containing solvents. In certain cases, addition of $POCl_2$ groups has been shown to be involved in one of the coloured forms (Gutmann and Hubacek, 1963).

VI. Uses of Group V Halides and Oxyhalides as Solvents

So far little use has been made of the solvent properties of the halides and oxyhalides of Group V elements other than in the preparation of otherwise difficultly accessible chlorocomplexes. Arsenic(III) chloride is particularly suitable for reactions leading to complex chlorides and fluorides, similarly arsenic(III) bromide for complex bromides. Phosphoryl chloride is a convenient solvent for preparative use since it is always anhydrous, and is well suited to direct chlorination experiments. It is readily volatile so that any excess of solvent is removed easily. The application of the halide solvents for electrochemical studies has already been mentioned. Recently it has appeared that analytical applications of phenylphosphoryl chloride are possible particularly as solvents for electrochemical experiments, such as polarography (Gutmann and Schöber, 1962; Dehn et al., 1962, 1963; Dehn and Schöber, 1963).

Titanium(IV) and tin(IV) chlorides can be conveniently titrated in phosphoryl and arsenic(III) chloride solutions with various nitrogen bases using benzanthrone as indicator. The results show a considerable spread but may none the less find analytical application, as has been claimed (Paul et al., 1959a). A similar analytical result has been claimed using crystal violet as internal indicator (Paul et al., 1959b).

In conclusion it should be emphasized that the halides and oxyhalides do not appear to be particularly unusual in their solvent behaviour. The hydrogen bonding which largely determines the characteristics of water is, of course, absent in these solvents, but there is an ability to associate and to solvate other halides, which is similar in nature if different in magnitude. In particular, the acceptor character of phosphorus makes for the possibility of phosphoryl bridging $P=O \cdots\cdots P$ comparable with hydrogen bonding and the solvent characteristics of phosphoryl chloride can be seen in this light. The oxyhalides are good donors through the oxygen atom, giving rise to numerous complex solvated cations, and sometimes anions. The self-ionization of these solvents is not an essential feature of their behaviour, however, it is clear that by their very nature as chloride donors and acceptors, and by reason of their high dielectric constants, that a small amount of self-ionization is bound to occur. The importance of this self-ionization, and the associated ideas of acids and bases, would appear to have been greatly overstressed in many discussions in the past. It is now emerging that other solvents show similar behaviour although they do not necessarily contain chloride ions. The Group V halides and oxyhalides remain fruitful solvents for the ready study of chlorocomplex formation and undoubtedly there is a great deal still to be elucidated about the nature of the solutions.

The author would like to thank Professor V. Gutmann for discussion and useful criticism.

REFERENCES

Addison, C. C. and Hodge, N. (1961) *J. chem. Soc.* 240.

Addison, C. C. and Lewis, J. (1955) *Quart. Rev.* **9**, 115.

Adolfsson, G., Bryntse, R. and Lindquist, I. (1960) *Actachem. Scand.* **14**, 949.

Agerman, M., Andersson, L. H., Lindquist, I. and Zackrisson, M. (1958) *Acta chem. Scand.* **12**, 477.

Andersson, L. H. and Lindquist, I. (1955) *Acta chem. Scand.* **9**, 79.

Asmussen, R. W. (1939) *Z. anorg. Chem.* **243**, 127.

Baaz, M. and Gutmann, V. (1959a) *Mh. Chem.* **90**, 276.

Baaz, M. and Gutmann, V. (1959b) *Mh. Chem.* **90**, 256.

Baaz, M. and Gutmann, V. (1959c) *Mh. Chem.* **90**, 744.

Baaz, M. and Gutmann, V. (1959d) *Mh. Chem.* **90**, 426.

Baaz, M., Gutmann, V. and Hübner, L. (1960a) *Z. anorg. Chem.* **91**, 694.

Baaz, M., Gutmann, V. and Hübner, L. (1960b) *Mh. Chem.* **92**, 537.

Baaz, M., Gutmann, V. and Hübner, L. (1961a) *Mh. Chem.* **92**, 707.

Baaz, M., Gutmann, V. and Hübner, L. (1961b) *J. inorg. nucl. Chem.* **18**, 276.

Baaz, M., Gutmann, V. and Hübner, L. (1961c) *Mh. Chem.* **92**, 135.

Baaz, M., Gutmann, V. and Hübner, L. (1961d) *Mh. Chem.* **92**, 272.

Baaz, M., Gutmann, V. and Kunze, O. (1962a) *Mh. Chem.* **93**, 1142.

Baaz, M., Gutmann, V. and Kunze, O. (1962b) *Mh. Chem.* **93**, 1162.

Baaz, M., Gutmann, V. and Masaguer, J. R. (1961e) *Mh. Chem.* **92**, 582.

Baaz, M., Gutmann, V. and Masaguer, J. R. (1961f) *Mh. Chem.* **92**, 590.

Baaz, M., Gutmann, V. and Talaat, M. Y. A. (1960c) *Mh. Chem.* **91**, 548.

Baaz, M., Gutmann, V. and Talaat, M. Y. A. (1961g) *Mh. Chem.* **92**, 714.

Baaz, M., Gutmann, V. and West, T. S. (1961h) *Mh. Chem.* **92**, 164.

Baaz, M., Gutmann, V., Talaat, M. Y. A. and West, T. S. (1961i) *Mh. Chem.* **92**, 150.

Baaz, M., Gutmann, V., Hampel, G. and Masaguer, J. R. (1962c) *Mh. Chem.* **93**, 1416.

Baaz, M., Gutmann, V., Hübner, L., Mairinger, F. and West, T. S. (1960d) *Z. anorg. Chem.* **310**, 302.

Baughan, E. C., Jones, T. P. and Stoodley, L. G. (1963) *Proc. chem. Soc. Lond.* 274.

Beckham, L. J., Fessler, W. A. and Kise, M. A. (1951) *Chem. Rev.* **48**, 319.

Beckmann, E. (1906) *Z. anorg. Chem.* **51**, 111.

Boston, C. R. and Smith, G. P. (1958) *J. phys. Chem.* **62**, 409.

Boston, C. R. and Smith, G. P. (1962) *J. phys. Chem.* **66**, 1178.

Boston, C. R., Smith, G. P. and Howick, L. C. (1963) *J. phys. Chem.* **67**, 1849.

Bränden, C. I. and Lindquist, I. (1960) *Acta chem. Scand.* **14**, 726.

Bränden, C. I. and Lindquist, I. (1963) *Acta chem. Scand.* **17**, 353.

Bredig, M. A. (1959) *J. phys. Chem.* **63**, 978.

Bredig, M. A., Levy, H. A., Keneshea, F. J. and Cubicciotti, D. (1960) *J. phys. Chem.* **64**, 191.

Brühl, J. W. (1898) *Z. phys. Chem.* **27**, 319.

Burg, A. B. and Campbell, G. W. (1948) *J. Amer. chem. Soc.* **70**, 1964.

Burg, A. B. and McKenzie, D. E. (1952) *J. Amer. chem. Soc.* **74**, 3143.

Cady, H. P. (1897) *J. phys. Chem.* **1**, 707.

Casselmann, W. (1856) *Liebigs Ann.* **98**, 213.

Corbett, J. D. (1958a) *J. phys. Chem.* **62**, 1149.

Corbett, J. D. (1958b) *J. Amer. chem. Soc.* **80**, 4757.

Corbett, J. D. and Albers, F. C. (1960) *J. Amer. chem. Soc.* **82**, 533.

Craig, D. P., Maccoll, A., Nyholm, R. S., Orgel, L. E. and Sutton, L. E. (1954) *J. chem. Soc.* 332, 354.

Cronander, A. W. (1873a) *Bull. Soc. chim. Fr.* [2], **19**, 499.

Cronander, A. W. (1873b) *Ber. dtsch. chem. Ges.* **5**, 1466.

Cronander, A. W. (1873c) *Uppsala Univ. Årsskr.* 1.

Dadape, V. V. and Rao, M. R. A. (1955) *J. Amer. chem. Soc.* **77**, 6192.

Dafert, O. and Melinski, Z. A. (1926) *Ber. dtsch. chem. Ges.* **59**, 788.

Daure, P. (1929) *C.R. Acad. Sci., Paris* **188**, 1605.

Davies, A. G. and Baughan, E. C. (1961) *J. chem. Soc.* 1711.

Dehn, H., Gutmann, V. and Schöber, G. (1962) *Mh. Chem.* **93**, 1357.

Dehn, H., Gutmann, V. and Schöber, G. (1963) *Mh. Chem.* **94**, 312.

Dehn, H. and Schöber, G. (1963) *Mh. Chem.* **94**, 316.

Dess, H. M. and Parry, R. W. (1956) *J. Amer. chem. Soc.* **78**, 5735.

Dess, H. M., Parry, R. W. and Vidale, G. L. (1956) *J. Amer. chem. Soc.* **78**, 5730.

Ehrlich, P. and Dietz G. (1960) *Z. anorg. Chem.* **305**, 158.

Eïngorn, L. N. (1950) *Ukr. Khim. Zh.* **16**, No. 4, 404.

Fraser, M. J., Gerrard, W. and Patel, J. K. (1960) *J. chem. Soc.* 726.

Frycz, K. and Tolloczko, S. (1912) *Festschrift Univ. Lwow* 1912, **1**, 1.

Frycz, K. and Tolloczko, S. (1913) *Chem. Zbl.* **1**, 91.

Fuoss, R. M. (1935) *J. Amer. chem. Soc.* **57**, 488.

George, J. W. (1960) *Progr. inorg. Chem.* **2**, 33.

Gerding, H. and Houtgraaf, H. (1953) *Rec. Trav. chim. Pays-Bas* **72**, 21.

Gerding, H., Koningstein, J. A. and Van der Worm, E. R. (1960) *Spectrochim. Acta* **16**, 881.

Gerrard, W., Mooney, E. F. and Willis, H. A. (1961) *J. chem. Soc.* 4255.

Gibson, S., Johnson, J. B. A. and Vining, D. C. (1930) *J. chem. Soc.* 1710.

Gmelin (1949) "Handbuch der anorganischen Chemie", Part 18B.

Gorenbein, E. Y. (1945) *J. gen. Chem., Moscow* **15**, 729.

Greenwood, N. N. (1958) *J. inorg. nucl. Chem.* **8**, 234.

Greenwood, N. N. and Perkins, P. G. (1957) *J. inorg. nucl. Chem.* **4**, 291.

Greenwood, N. N. and Wade, K. (1957) *J. chem. Soc.* 1516.

Greenwood, N. N. and Worrall, I. J. (1958) *J. inorg. nucl. Chem.* **6**, 34.

Groeneveld, W. L. (1953) *Rec. Trav. chim. Pays-Bas* **72**, 617.

Groeneveld, W. L. and Zuur, A. P. (1957) *Rec. Trav. chim. Pays-Bas* **76**, 1005.

Groeneveld, W. L. and Zuur, A. P. (1958) *J. inorg. nucl. Chem.* **8**, 241.

Gustavson, G. (1871) *Z. Chem.* (2) **7**, 417.

Gutmann, V. (1951a) *Z. anorg. Chem.* **266**, 331.

Gutmann, V. (1951b) *Z. anorg. Chem.* **264**, 151.

Gutmann, V. (1951c) *Mh. Chem.* **82**, 473.

Gutmann, V. (1952a) *Mh. Chem.* **83**, 159.

Gutmann, V. (1952b) *Mh. Chem.* **83**, 279.

Gutmann, V. (1952c) *Mh. Chem.* **83**, 164.

Gutmann, V. (1952d) *Mh. Chem.* **83**, 583.

Gutmann, V. (1952e) *Z. anorg. Chem.* **269**, 279.

Gutmann, V. (1952f) *Z. anorg. Chem.* **270**, 179.

Gutmann, V. (1953) *Mh. Chem.* **54**, 1191.

Gutmann, V. (1954a) *Mh. Chem.* **85**, 491.

Gutmann, V. (1954b) *Mh. Chem.* **85**, 1077.

Gutmann, V. (1956) *Svensk kem. Tidskr.* **68**, 1.

Gutmann, V. (1959) *J. phys. Chem.* **63**, 378.

Gutmann, V. and Baaz, M. (1959a) *Z. anorg. Chem.* **298**, 121.

Gutmann, V. and Baaz, M. (1959b) *Angew. Chem.* **71**, 57.

Gutmann, V. and Baaz, M. (1959c) *Mh. Chem.* **90**, 239.

Gutmann, V. and Baaz, M. (1959d) *Mh. Chem.* **90**, 271.

Gutmann, V. and Baaz, M. (1959e) *Mh. Chem.* **90**, 729.

Gutmann, V. and Hampel, G. (1963) *Mh. Chem.* **94**, 830.

Gutmann, V. and Himml, R. (1955) *Z. phys. Chem.*, *Frankfurt* **4**, 157–64.

Gutmann, V. and Himml, R. (1956) *Z. anorg. Chem.* **287**, 199.

Gutmann, V. and Hubacek, H. (1963) *Mh. Chem.* **94**, 1019, 1098.

Gutmann, V. and Lindquist, I. (1954) *Z. phys. Chem.*, *Leipzig* **203**, 250.

Gutmann, V. and Mairinger, F. (1957) *Z. anorg. Chem.* **289**, 279.

Gutmann, V. and Mairinger, F. (1960) *Mh. Chem.* **92**, 529.

Gutmann, V. and Mairinger, F. (1961) *Mh. Chem.* **92**, 720.

Gutmann, V. and Schöber, G. (1962) *Mh. Chem.* **93**, 1353.

Gutmann, V., Hampel, G. and Masaguer, J. R. (1963) *Mh. Chem.* **94**, 822.

Herber, R. H. (1960) *J. Amer. chem. Soc.* **82**, 792.

Hetherington, G. and Robinson, P. L. (1957) *Chem. Soc. Special Publication* No. 11, p. 23.

Hewitt, F. and Holliday, A. K. (1953) *J. chem. Soc.* 530.

Holmes, R. R. (1960a) *J. Amer. chem. Soc.* **82**, 5285.

Holmes, R. R. (1960b) *J. inorg. nucl. Chem.* **12**, 266.

Holmes, R. R. and Bertaut, E. F. (1958) *J. Amer. chem. Soc.* **80**, 2980, 2983.

Hubacek, H., Stančie, B. and Gutmann, V. (1963) *Mh. Chem.* **94**, 1118.

Isbekow, W. and Plotnikow, W. (1911) *Z. anorg. Chem.* **71**, 332.

Jander, G. and Günther, K. (1958) *Z. anorg. Chem.* **297**, 81.

Jander, G. and Günther, K. (1959a) *Z. anorg. Chem.* **298**, 241.

Jander, G. and Günther, K. (1959b) *Z. anorg. Chem.* **302**, 155.

Jander, G. and Swart, K. H. (1959a) *Z. anorg. Chem.* **299**, 252.

Jander, G. and Swart, K. H. (1959b) *Z. anorg. Chem.* **301**, 54.

Jander, G. and Swart, K. H. (1959c) *Z. anorg. Chem.* **301**, 80.

Jander, G. and Weiss, J. (1957) *Z. Elektrochem.* **61**, 1275.

Jander, G. and Weiss, J. (1959) *Z. Elektrochem.* **63**, 1037.

Kendall, J., Crittenden, E. D. and Miller, H. K. (1923) *J. Amer. chem. Soc.* **45**, 963.

Keneshea, F. J. and Cubicciotti, D. (1959) *J. Phys. Chem.* **63**, 1472.

Klemensiewicz, Z. (1908) *Bull. int. Acad.*, *Cracovie*, **6**, 418.

Klemensiewicz, Z. (1924) *Z. phys. Chem.* **113**, 28.

Klemensiewicz, Z. and Balowna, Z. (1930) *Roczn. Chem.* **10**, 481.

Klemensiewicz, Z. and Balowna, Z. (1931) *Roczn. Chem.* **11**, 683.

Klemensiewicz, Z. and Zebrowska, A. (1934) *Roczn. Chem.* **14**, 14.

Köhler, H. (1880) *Ber. dtsch. chem. Ges.* **13**, 875.

Kolditz, L. (1955) *Z. anorg. Chem.* **280**, 313.

Kolditz, L. (1956) *Z. anorg. Chem.* **286**, 307.

Kolditz, L. (1957a) *Z. anorg. Chem.* **289**, 118.

Kolditz, L. (1957b) *Z. anorg. Chem.* **289**, 128.

Kolditz, L. and Engels, S. (1959) *Z. anorg. Chem.* **302**, 88.

Kolditz, L. and Feltz, A. (1957) *Z. anorg. Chem.* **293**, 286.

Kolditz, L. and Schmidt, W. (1958) *Z. anorg. Chem.* **296**, 188.

Kolthoff, I. M. and Laitinen, H. A. "pH and Electro Titrations", 2nd edition, 1941, John Wiley and Sons, Inc., New York.

Lacher, J. R., Campion, D. E. and Park, J. D. (1949) *Science* **110**, 300.

Lacher, J. R., Croy, V. D., Kianpour, A. and Park, J. D. (1954) *J. phys. Chem.* **58**, 206.

Leman, G. Tridot, G. (1959) *C.R. Acad. Sci.*, *Paris* **248**, 3439.

Lenher, V. (1908) *J. Amer. chem. Soc.* **30**, 740.

Lewis, J. and Sowerby, D. B. (1956) *J. chem. Soc.* 150.

Lewis, J. and Sowerby, D. B. (1957a) *J. chem. Soc.* 336.

Lewis, J. and Sowerby, D. B. (1957b) *J. chem. Soc.* 1617.

Lewis, J. and Sowerby, D. B. (1957c) *Chem. Soc. Special Publication*, No. 10, p. 123.

Lindquist, I. (1955) *Acta chem. Scand.* **9**, 73.

Lindquist, I. and Andersson, L. H. (1954) *Acta chem. Scand.* **8**, 128.

Lindquist, I. and Bränden, C. I. (1959) *Acta chem. Scand.* **12**, 642.

Meek, D. W. and Drago, R. S. (1961) *J. Amer. chem. Soc.* **83**, 4322.

Metzl, S. (1906) *Z. anorg. Chem.* **48**, 146.

Metzner, R. (1898) *Ann. Chim. (Phys.)* (7), **15**, 254.

Montignie, E. (1935) *Bull. Soc. chim. Fr.* [5], **2**, 1365.

Muetterties, E. L. and Phillips, W. D. (1957a) *J. Amer. chem. Soc.* **79**, 322.

Muetterties, E. L. and Phillips, W. D. (1957b) *J. Amer. chem. Soc.* **79**, 3686.

Oddo, G. (1905) *R.C. Accad. Lincei Sed. solen.* Classe Sci. fis. mat. nat., (5) **10**, 452.

Oddo, G. and Tealdi, M. (1903) *Gazz. chim. ital.* **33**, II, 427.

Olah, G. A. and Tolgyesi, W. S. (1961) *J. org. chem.* **26**, 2319.

Partington, J. R. and Whynes, A. L. (1948) *J. chem. Soc.* 1952.

Partington, J. R. and Whynes, A. L. (1949) *J. chem. Soc.* 3135.

Paul, R. C., Singh, J. and Sandhu, S. S. (1959a) *Analyt. Chem.* **31**, 1495.

Paul, R. C., Singh, J. and Sandhu, S. S. (1959b) *J. Indian chem. Soc.* **36**, 305.

Payne, D. S. (1961) *Quart. Rev.* **15**, 173.

Peach, M. E. and Waddington, T. C. (1962) *J. chem. Soc.* 3450.

Perrot, R. and Devin, C. (1958) *C.R. Acad. Sci., Paris* **246**, 772.

Petzold, W. (1933) *Z. anorg. Chem.* **214**, 355.

Porter, G. B. and Baughan, E. C. (1958) *J. chem. Soc.* 744.

Pusin, N. A. and Löwy, S. (1926) *Z. anorg. Chem.* **150**, 167.

Pusin, N. A. and Makuc, J. (1938) *Z. anorg. Chem.* **237**, 177.

Raman, K. N. V. and Murthy, A. R. V. (1960) *Proc. Indian Acad. Sci.* **51**A, 270–9.

Rettgers, J. W. (1893) *Z. phys. Chem.* **11**, 328.

Rheinbolt, H. and Wasserfuhr, R. (1927) *Ber. dtsch. chem. Ges.* **60**, 732.

Ruff, O. (1904) *Ber. dtsch. chem. Ges.* **37**, 4513.

Ruff, O. and Ipsen, R. (1903) *Ber. dtsch. chem. Ges.* **36**, 1783.

Schwarzmann, E. and van Wazer, J. R. (1959) *J. Amer. chem. Soc.* **81**, 6366.

Seel, F. (1943) *Z. anorg. Chem.* **252**, 24.

Seel, F. and Bauer, H. (1947) *Z. Natur.* **126**, 397.

Seel, F. Schmutzler, R. and Wasem, K. (1959) *Angew. Chem.* **71**, 340.

Sheldon, J. C. and Tyree, S. Y. (1959) *J. Amer. chem. Soc.* **81**, 2290.

Shirey, W. B. (1930) *J. Amer. chem. Soc.* **52**, 1720.

Sokol'skii, G. A., Knunyants, J. L. (1960) *Izv. Akad. Nauk S.S.S.R. otd. khim. Nauk*, 779–83.

Spandau, H., Beyer, A. and Preugschat, F. (1960) *Z. anorg. Chem.* **306**, 13.

Sudborough, J. J. (1891) *J. Chem. Soc.* **59**, 655.

Tolloczko, S. (1899) *Z. phys. Chem.* **30**, 705.

Tolloczko, S. (1901) *Bull. int. Acad. Cracovie* **1**, 1.

Troost, W. R. (1954) *Canad. J. Chem.* **32**, 356.

Van Heteren, W. J. (1899) *Z. anorg. Chem.* **22**, 277.

Vonk, C. G. and Wiebenga, E. H. (1959) *Rec. Trav. Chim. Pays-Bas* **78**, 913.

Waddington, T. C. and Klanberg, T. (1960a) *Z. anorg. Chem.* **304**, 185.

Waddington, T. C. and Klanberg, F. (1960b) *J. Chem. Soc.* 2339.

Walden, P. (1900) *Z. anorg. Chem.* **25**, 209.

Walden, P. (1902) *Z. anorg. Chem.* **29**, 371.

Walden P. (1903) *Z. phys. Chem.* **43**, 445.

Wertyporoch, E. and Firla, T. (1932) *Z. phys. Chem.* A**162**, 398.

Wheeler, H. L. (1893a) *Amer. J. Sci.* [3], **46**, 90.

Wheeler, H. L. (1893b) *Z. anorg. Chem.* [4] 452.

Woodward, R. A., Garton, G. and Roberts, H. L. (1956) *J. chem. Soc.* 3723.

Woolf, A. A. and Greenwood, N. N. (1950) *J. chem. Soc.* 2200.

CHAPTER 9

Molten Salts as Solvents

H. Bloom and J. W. Hastie

Chemistry Department, University of Tasmania, Hobart, Tasmania, Australia

I. Summary... 353
II. Introduction... 354
III. The Nature of Molten Salts.. 354
    A. Type of Entities Present... 355
    B. Holes and Free Volume in Ionic Melts.............................. 356
    C. Distribution Functions.. 357
    D. Nature of the Interionic Forces (Bonding) in Simple Melts.......... 357
IV. Solutions of Salt and Water... 357
V. Solutions of Salt and Organic Compounds................................ 358
    A. Solutions in an Organic Solvent................................... 358
    B. Solutions of Organic Compounds in Molten Salts.................... 360
VI. Solutions of Non-metallic Elements in Molten Salts..................... 361
    A. Sulphur... 361
    B. Iodine.. 361
VII. Solutions of Gases in Molten Salts...................................... 361
    A. Simple Solutions of Gas and Salt.................................. 362
    B. Complex Solutions of Gases in Molten Salts........................ 362
VIII. Solutions of Metals in Molten Salts.................................... 364
    A. Introduction.. 364
    B. Solutions Without Significant Interaction......................... 365
    C. Solutions With Strong Solute–Solvent Interaction (i.e. Non-metallic
       Solutions).. 369
    D. Solutions of Metals in Salts of Another Metal—Displacement Solubility.. 373
IX. Solutions of Salt in Molten Salt.. 374
    A. Molten Salt Systems with Incomplete Miscibility................... 375
    B. Molten Salt Systems with Complete Miscibility..................... 377
    C. The Structure of Molten Salt Solutions............................ 377
    D. Solvation and Complex Ion Formation in Molten Salt Mixtures....... 382
    E. Complex Ions and Reaction Kinetics................................ 382
X. Application of Molten Salts as Solvents................................. 383
    A. Reactions Involving Organic Substances or Volatile Inorganic Liquids in
       Molten Salt Solvents.. 383
    B. Other Reactions Involving Inorganic Substances in Molten Salt Solvents 385
    C. Future Developments... 387
References... 387

I. Summary

The chemical and physical properties and constitution of molten salts are discussed and also the need for such solvents. The main classes of solutions involving molten salts are systems involving salt and water, salt and organic substance, salt and non-metal, salt and gas, salt and metal, and salt with another salt. The properties of such systems are discussed. Where possible, tables of solubility are included and in certain cases the structure of the molten salt solutions are discussed. Examples of the application of molten salt solvents to chemical and industrial problems are given and the potential uses of such solvents are mentioned.

II. INTRODUCTION

In view of the growing importance and versatility of molten salts as solvents, the lack of solubility data, in general, is surprising. In fact molten salts are good solvents for a variety of materials, ranging from inorganic and organic vapours to high melting metals (even Pt) and oxides.

The considerable variety of salts and salt mixtures available leads to a potential class of solvents operative over a temperature range of more than one thousand degrees. For example, cryolite (Na_3AlF_6) melts at 1003°C, whilst the eutectic mixture, $AlCl_3 + NaCl + KCl$, melts at only 89°C. Molten halides form the most widely used molten salt system owing to their stability over a large temperature range, their effectiveness as solvents for a wide variety of materials, and their ready availability. Accordingly, in the following chapter we will deal mainly with molten halide salt systems.

Molten alkali-metal and alkaline-earth metal halides would be expected to be potentially useful solvents for carrying out chemical reactions owing to the large range of oxidation-reduction potentials available in such systems. For example, the range of stability in the $LiCl + KCl$ eutectic is about 3·5 V and in a $CsCl + MgCl_2$ eutectic, about 2·6 V at 700°C (Delimarskii, 1955). In aqueous solutions at room temperature the range of stability of xidizing and reducing agents is only approximately 1·2 V (Latimer, 1952).

III. THE NATURE OF MOLTEN SALTS

Bloom and Bockris (1959) showed that the following information is necessary in order to define the structure of a molten salt:

(a) the type of entities present, i.e. ions, molecules, complex ions, etc;
(b) the nature and effect of holes or vacancies present;
(c) distribution functions relating to the relative positions of structural entities and holes;
(d) the nature of the bonds or interionic forces between the various entities in the melt.

The availability of the above information would suffice to define the structures of both simple salts as well as salt mixtures and a discussion of the nature of molten salts may profitably be considered in such terms, e.g. the distribution of holes or other forms of free volume is of fundamental importance to transport properties since without any free space in the liquid, transport processes would be unlikely. Also, if distribution functions were available it would be possible to calculate thermodynamic properties of the melt.

A. TYPE OF ENTITIES PRESENT

A fundamental property of most salts is the sharp increase in conductivity on melting. This, together with the general applicability of Faraday's Laws of electrolysis, establishes the ionic nature of molten salts. The large range of stability of the liquids at ordinary pressure (e.g. 612°C for NaCl) further substantiates the presence of strongly interacting entities (ions) in molten salts. Although the melts are essentially ionic, there may be varying degrees of ionic association exhibited by different salts, depending largely on the position of the cation in the Periodic Table. For example, mercuric chloride has a liquidus range of only 26°C and also a relatively small equivalent conductance, suggesting that the melt consists predominantly of uncharged entities. Biltz and Klemm (1926), tabulated conductivities of various chlorides and the results clearly indicate an increase of covalency as the cationic position shifts from left to right, as well as from top to bottom, in the Periodic Table.

X-Ray and neutron diffraction investigations have established that in the melting of ionic solids, there occur only relatively small structural changes as far as the first and second co-ordination shells are concerned. The structural determinations by Harris *et al.* (1951), Danilov and Krasnitskii (1955), Zarzycki (1957a,b) and Levy *et al.* (1960b) show that during melting of the alkali-metal chlorides, the co-ordination number for nearest neighbours (unlike ions) usually decreases from 6 to about 4. The cation–anion average interionic distance also decreases slightly but in contrast, the cation–cation and anion–anion distances increase slightly. Hence the structure in ionic melts is a partly disordered version of that in the corresponding solid, the main difference between melt and solid being the complete loss of long range order on melting. Simultaneously, the molar volume increases by about 25% for alkali-metal chlorides (Landon and Ubbelohde, 1956).

It is necessary to account for the simultaneous loss of long range order on melting, decrease of average distance between unlike-ions, increase of average distance between like-ions and increase of molar volume on melting, while still basically preserving the short range order of the crystal lattice. To do so one can assume, that during melting, the "ionic atmospheres" due to unlike-ions become more random and that "holes" or vacant "lattice sites" are introduced into the structure.

Assuming the fundamentally ionic nature of molten salts, consideration may be given to the types of ions present. In alkali-metal halide melts, values of molar refractivity are comparable to those obtained for the salts in their aqueous solutions at infinite dilution (Bloom and Rhodes, 1956). This strongly suggests that the states of ionization in both cases are identical.

Hence such melts consist of simple cations and anions only. Cryoscopic determinations (Van Artsdalen, 1956) in molten $NaNO_3$ indicate that salts such as NaCl dissolve to form ideal solutions and it is therefore likely that the solute dissolves as simple ions only.

On the other hand, the lowering of the freezing points of such solvents as $NaNO_3$ by heavy metal, divalent halides, show deviations from ideality and such halides are therefore thought to exist partly as associated ionic species. The cryoscopic data can be explained by assuming the following relative order of association:

$$CdBr_2 > ZnCl_2 > CdCl_2 > CuCl_2 > PbCl_2.$$

Activity coefficients of some of these salts in molten halide mixtures also support the same relative order of association (H. Bloom and J. W. Hastie, unpublished results). It is possible that in these molten halides there exists, besides simple constituent ions, complex ions such as $CdCl^+$, $CdCl_3^-$, $CdCl_4^{2-}$ or even $CdCl_6^{4-}$.

Association constants for $CdCl^+$ and $PbCl^+$ in molten nitrate solvents have been determined (Braunstein et al., 1962), and the values are larger in each solvent for $CdCl^+$, than for $PbCl^+$. Similar values have been determined for $CdBr^+$ and CdI^+ (Braunstein and Lindgren, 1962). It is significant that the association follows the sequence

$$I > Br > Cl$$

which is the order of polarizability of the anion.

Magnetic susceptibility measurements (Farquharson and Heymann, 1935) preclude the possibility of singly-charged ions such as Cd^+ in melts of the heavy-metal dihalides. In these melts the ionization potentials make it clear that ions such as $CdCl^+$ and $CdCl_3^-$ are more energetically possible than Cd^{2+} and Cl^- and that the $CdCl^+$ ion is stereochemically more favoured than the $CdCl_3^-$ ion. The larger ion $CdCl_6^{4-}$ is also stereochemically possible in pure $CdCl_2$ melts in the region just above the melting point. A relatively small latent heat of fusion for $CdCl_2$, as compared to NaCl say, suggests that the solid structure does not break down completely into constituent Cd^{2+} and Cl^- ions, but into associated ions. Raman frequencies similar to those in the solid were observed in the melt by Bues (1955) and this also suggests correspondence between the structural units of the solid and the melt.

For salts such as nitrates that have complex anions in the solid, electronic and vibrational spectra clearly prove the existence of the same complex anions in the melt (e.g. NO_3^- exists as an entity in nitrate melts). In molten GaX_2 (where X = Cl, Br) the existence of the species GaX_4^- has also been well established spectroscopically (Wait and Janz, 1963).

B. HOLES AND FREE VOLUME IN IONIC MELTS

The volume increase on melting of ionic crystals such as the alkali-halides is in some cases greater than 25% (Landon and Ubbeholde, 1965). Cmo-pressibility experiments, however, indicate that the free volume per mole available for ionic vibration is only about 2% of the molar volume (Bockris and Richards, 1957). This suggests that the larger part of the volume increase is due to the formation of holes in the melt. Such holes may also provide the means for ionic transport through the molten medium. The formation of holes is also supported by the X-ray diffraction experiments referred to above.

Certain conductivity experiments (Campbell et al., 1962) also suggest the presence of holes in molten salts. For example, if molten $LiClO_3$ is used as a solvent for organic species, the addition of 0–0·4 weight % nitrobenzene causes a fairly rapid decrease of conductivity. Addition of methanol (0–1·25%), however, causes only a slow decrease of the conductivity. The addition of 0–6% of water increases the conductivity of the melt considerably and this may be attributed to an increase in the degree of ionization of $LiClO_3$ due to the strongly polar water molecule. The marked effect of nitrobenzene on the conductivity is most likely due to a reduction in the number of holes in the melt, thus making difficult the movement of ions necessary for conduction. The fact that the smaller molecules of methanol decrease the conductivity of $LiClO_3$ more slowly is in accordance with this view.

C. DISTRIBUTION FUNCTIONS

The determination of distribution functions, which are a description of order in molten salts, would enable the calculation of thermodynamic properties. It is possible to check postulated functions by comparing the calculated thermodynamic properties with experimental ones.

D. NATURE OF INTERIONIC FORCES (BONDING) IN SIMPLE MELTS

In the case of the molten alkali-halides, the forces between the ions will be largely coulombic and each ion will tend to attract an environment of oppositely charged ions. The latent heat of fusion of such salts is only a small fraction of the value of the lattice energy, hence the breakdown of the solid to form a melt does not involve a completely random distribution of cations and anions. On the contrary, each ion tends to attract an environment of oppositely charged ions. As indicated on p. 356, the heavy-metal dihalides form ionic melts in which there is a tendency towards covalent bonding, resulting in complex ions such as $CdCl^+$.

IV. SOLUTIONS OF SALT AND WATER

Usually water is considered to be the solvating species and this is physically more correct since the salts or the ionic components of the salts are usually solvated by a sphere of water molecules. However, one may formally consider the salt as the solvent species.

Much of the present day knowledge of salt and water solutions is connected with those solutions where water is present in excess. Discussion of such solutions is given in standard textbooks on electrolyte solutions. Investigations involving the solution of water vapour in molten salts are discussed in Section VII.

V. Solutions of Salt and Organic Compounds

Such solutions are unique in that the pure components differ markedly in their chemical bonding. Nevertheless there are surprisingly many examples of solutions of this type. Two types of solution arise, namely those that are formed by the addition of salt to an organic compound and those formed by addition of organic compound to the salt. The former type is the one which has received the most investigation.

A. SOLUTIONS IN AN ORGANIC SOLVENT

The existence of congruently melting compounds between solute and solvent, as indicated by phase diagrams, is a reasonable indication of chemical

TABLE I

Solutions of Salt in Organic Media
(Examples Involving Chemical Interaction)

System	Congruently melting compounds salt : org. ratio	Solubility of salt g : g org.	Temperature (°C)
$AsCl_3$ + aniline	1 : 3		[a]
$AsCl_3$ + 1,3,5-xylidine	1 : 3		[a]
$SnCl_4$ + o-nitroanisole	1 : 1		[a]
CaI_2 + acetone	1 : 3	1·129	50 [b1]
$Ca(NO_3)_2$ + acetone	1 : 1	0·184	50 [b]
$CaBr_2$ + acetone	1 : 2	0·0292	40 [b]
LiBr + acetone	1 : 2	0·346	50 [b]
$ZnBr_2$ + acetone	2 : 1	3·81	50 [b]
$SrBr_2$ + acetone	1 : 1/2 : 3	0·00274	50 [b]
$CoCl_2$ + acetone	1 : 1	0·0725	50 [b]
$PbCl_2$ + triazole	2	7·6	200 [c2]

[1] Represents compounds formed in the solid phase of the saturated solution.
[2] Forms a red melt of a much higher m.p. than pure triazole.
[a] Pushin (1948).
[b] Bell et al. (1930).
[c] J. W. Hastie (unpublished results).

interaction in solution. Table I summarizes the solubility properties of these systems. Those systems in which there is no compound formation on solidification, or in the saturated solid phase, may reasonably be considered to be "physical solutions" without any strong solute–solvent chemical interaction. The solubility properties of such systems are summarized in Table II.

TABLE II

Solutions of Salt in Organic Media
(Cases without Chemical Interaction)

System	Solubility	Temperature (°C)	Comments
Salt + acetone	g salt : g acetone		
LiCl + acetone	0·0061	50	Solubility Decreases with increasing temperature[a]
NiBr$_2$ + acetone			
NaI + acetone	0·309	50	
CaCl$_2$ + acetone	0·000213	50	
BaBr$_2$ + acetone	0·000246	50	
Salt + benzene	Wt % halide		
Al$_2$Br$_6$ + benzene	80·11	51·5	Solubility increases with increasing temperature[b]
Al$_2$Cl$_6$ + benzene	4·88	108·6	
Al$_2$I$_6$ + benzene	59·57	110·7	
PbCl$_2$ + triazole	11·6	140	Usually colourless or pale yellow melts, depending on concentration[c]
NaCl + triazole	2·9	132	
CsCl + triazole	>2·9		

[a] Bell et al. (1930).
[b] Eley and King (1951).
[c] J. W. Hastie (unpublished results).

1. *Solutions of Salt in Acetone* (Bell *et al.*, 1930)

The solubilities of salts in acetone form two fairly distinct classes. The class of relatively high solubility of salt in acetone is invariably associated with strong solute–solvent interaction and solid compounds can be prepared from such solutions.

2. *Solutions of Salt in Triazole and Other Organic Melts*

Molten triazole (m.p. 121°C) is a good solvent for a large number of salts (A. Easteal and G. Ruthven, unpublished results). In some cases, especially with transition metal salts, strong interaction between solute and solvent is apparent and solid complex co-ordination compounds separate out of solution on cooling. At temperatures not too far above the melting point of triazole (about 140°C), salts such as $PbCl_2$ and the alkali-metal chlorides form colourless or pale yellow melts. No compound formation is apparent on solidification of the melt. However, at higher temperatures the solutions of $PbCl_2$ in triazole assume a red colour and the solubility of salt increases more than one hundred-fold.

There are few other cases where solutions of salts in organic melts have been studied. Recently, solutions of $NiCl_2$ in molten pyridine hydrochloride have been used in a study of the Ni^{II} absorption spectrum (Smith, 1965). Similar studies have also been made on U^{IV} in molten pyridinium chloride (m.p. 144°C) (Gruen and McBeth, 1959).

3. *Solutions of Transition Metal Chlorides in Methanol* (De Maine and McAlonie, 1961)

Conductances at 20° and 45°C, for $CaCl_2$, $CaCl_2.2H_2O$, $CrCl_3.6H_2O$, $MnCl_2.4H_2O$, $FeCl_2.2H_2O$, $CuCl_2$, $CuCl_2.2H_2O$ and $ZnCl_2$ respectively, dissolved in methanol, have been determined.

B. SOLUTIONS OF ORGANIC COMPOUNDS IN MOLTEN SALTS

At the high temperatures normal to molten salt media, most organic molecules would be expected to decompose. It is not unnatural, therefore, that very little is known about solutions of organic compounds in molten salts. Methanol is known to dissolve in molten $LiClO_3$ without producing any significant change of the properties of the solvent, and it is probably stable in such a melt. Nitrobenzene also appears to be stable in this solvent (Campbell *et al.*, 1962). Sundermeyer and co-workers (1958, 1962, 1963) carried out a considerable number of organic and pseudo-organic reactions by passing the organic vapours through molten salt solvents. Solubilities are not known, but it is clear that the organic molecules must spend sufficient time in the melt to react, either amongst themselves or with the solvent species. The reasonably rapid flow rates and good reaction yields also suggest considerable solubility of the organic component in the melt. The solvents used by these workers are mainly chlorides and pseudo-halides of the alkali and alkaline-earth metals. Temperatures of operation range from 89°C to more than 600°C, depending on the choice of the solvent. Solutes include organo-silicones, carbon tetrachloride, ethane, acetylene, ethyl halides, alcohols, n-butyl chloride, etc. A list of the reactions occurring between these solutes and solvents will be given at the end of the chapter in the discussion of the applications of molten salt solvents.

VI. SOLUTIONS OF NON-METALLIC ELEMENTS IN MOLTEN SALTS

A. SULPHUR

The nature of sulphur dissolved in various solvents has been studied by only a few workers: Paterno and Muzzuchelli (1908), Gardner and Fraenkel (1956), Krebs (1957), Greenberg et al. (1958) have studied solutions of sulphur in molten salts by absorption spectra and paramagnetic susceptibility measurements.

In both LiCl+KCl and LiBr+KBr eutectics, addition of sulphur gives rise to blue solutions and the close similarity of the spectra of these solutions indicates that there is no specific interaction between sulphur and the halide ion. From the Gouy measurements of paramagnetic susceptibility it was con-cluded that the solution contains a paramagnetic species. It is possible that these species are diatomic sulphur molecules since higher polymers are reddish in colour (Gardner and Fraenkel, 1956).

B. IODINE

The absorption spectra of solid iodine in molten KI+LiI, at 400°C and in molten KCl+LiCl at 400°C have been determined (Greenberg and Sund-heim, 1958) and the results interpreted as indicating the presence of I_3^- in the former molten salt mixture and I_2Cl^- in the latter. The considerable solubilities ($10^{-3}-10^{-4}$ molar) at 400°C are probably due to the ions I_3^- or I_2Cl^-, being readily accommodated into the quasi-lattice of the salt mixture.

VII. SOLUTIONS OF GASES IN MOLTEN SALTS

Most of the work done on these solutions has been in connection with nuclear reactor technology. For the determination of small to moderate solubilities of non-reacting gases in molten salt systems, the melt is equili-brated with a known pressure of the gas. The solubility may be found by analysing the melt, or by measurement of the loss in weight or change of pressure in the gas reservoir. It is significant to note that dissolved gases are evolved on solidification of those systems where no solid compound exists between the components of the salt and the gas. Solutions of gases in molten salts may conveniently be grouped according to whether or not there is chemical interaction between solvent and solute.

A. SIMPLE SOLUTIONS OF GAS AND SALT

1. *Solubility of Carbon Dioxide in Molten Alkali-Metal Halides* (Grjotheim et al., 1962; Bratland et al., 1963)

The gas solubilities at different temperatures are approximately equal to the free volume of the melts and it is therefore likely that chemical reactions do not occur in the dissolution process. The solubility of gases in molten potassium chloride is greater than in molten sodium chloride at the same temperature. This is in accordance with the larger free volume in the former salt (Bockris and Richards, 1957). For example, the solubilities expressed as moles of CO_2 per ml of solvent (at 1 atm pressure) are 4.6×10^{-6} and 4.0×10^{-6} at $850°$ and $950°C$ respectively for NaCl, and 6.0×10^{-6} and 7.0×10^{-6} at $850°$ and $950°C$ respectively for KCl.

2. *Solutions of Noble Gases in Molten Halides* (Grimes et al., 1958)

The solubilities of He, Ne, Ar and Xe in the melts,

$$NaF \ (53 \ mole \ \%) + ZrF_4 \ (47 \ mole \ \%)$$

and

$$NaF \ (50 \ mole \ \%) + ZrF_4 \ (46 \ mole \ \%) + UF_4 \ (4 \ mole \ \%)$$

increase linearly with gas pressure, decrease with increasing atomic weight of the solute and increase with increasing temperature. The solubilities and heats of solution of He and Xe in both melts are very similar. Molten salts act therefore as normal liquids in dissolving such gases. The eutectic melts LiF (46.5%) + NaF (11.5%) + KF (42%) has similar solvent powers to the other fluoride melts mentioned (Blander et al., 1959). A model developed by Blander et al. (1959), which equates the free energy of formation of holes and the size of the gas molecules in a continuous fluid having the same surface tension as the solvent, yields solubility values which are in good agreement with those observed.

B. COMPLEX SOLUTIONS OF GASES IN MOLTEN SALTS

In cases where the gas reacts chemically with the solvent melt, large solubilities may be observed. For example, the solvent melt

$$CuCl_2 \ (25 \ mole \ \%) + KCl \ (75 \ mole \ \%)$$

is capable of taking up 0.75 moles of fluorine per mole of melt (Klemm and Huss, 1949). This is due to the chemical reaction,

$$CuCl_2 + 3KCl + 3F_2 = K_3(CuF_6) + 2\tfrac{1}{2}Cl_2. \qquad (1)$$

Another example of this type is indicated by solutions of titanium tetrachloride vapour in an equimolar NaCl + KCl melt. The solubility of $TiCl_4$ in such solutions has been determined by several workers (e.g. Kroll, 1955; Kreye and Kellogg, 1957), but the results of Flengas (1960) are probably the most reliable because his method involved direct observation of the increase of weight of the salt solution in contact with titanium tetrachloride vapour and was therefore free of the errors introduced by sampling and quenching techniques. The rate at which $TiCl_4$ was taken up in solution was determined both in the molten and finely powdered solid salt mixtures. Figure 1 summarizes the results. From these results, it is clear that the molten salt solvent

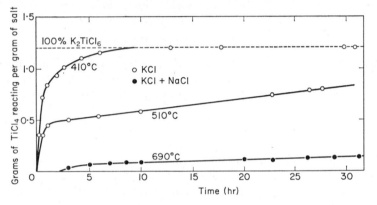

FIG. 1. Reaction rates between gaseous $TiCl_4$, and KCl or 1/1 mole KCl + NaCl at various temperatures (Flengas, 1960). (Reproduced by courtesy of the New York Academy of Sciences.)

mixture is capable of dissolving at least 14 mole % $TiCl_4$ while the solid salt mixture can dissolve 1 mole of $TiCl_4$ per 2 moles of KCl. X-Ray diffraction analysis of the solid indicates that a compound is formed, probably according to the reaction:

$$TiCl_4 + 2KCl = K_2TiCl_6. \qquad (2)$$

From the solubility results it is concluded that the optimum temperature range for the formation of this compound at a pressure of 1 atm of $TiCl_4$ is between 350° and 400°C. At temperatures above 800°C the solvation behaviour changes because of a reaction between $TiCl_4$ and NaCl probably forming Na_2TiCl_6.

Another example of chemical interaction between solvent and solute is given by solutions of hydrogen fluoride in molten NaF + ZrF_4 mixtures (Schaffer et al., 1959). In contrast with the behaviour of the noble gases in similar solvents, the solubility of hydrogen fluoride decreases as the temperature is increased. Also the dependence of its solubility on the nature of the solvent is far greater than that exhibited by noble gases in related solvents.

This is probably connected with the relatively high stability of compounds between NaF and HF. The solubility of hydrogen fluoride in molten alkali-metal fluorides increases with increase of atomic number of the metal. It is possible that this dependence of the solubility on the solvent may be related to the relative stabilities of some of the alkali-metal acid fluorides which have been noted at lower temperatures (Winsor and Cady, 1948).

The high solubility (Winsor and Cady, 1948) of hydrogen fluoride in caesium fluoride has a special use in that the solvent serves as an electrolyte for the electrolytic preparation of fluorine at room temperature (Mathers and Stroup, 1934). Considerable solvent–solute interaction is evident in solutions of hydrogen fluoride in caesium fluoride, and phase equilibrium studies indicate the formation of the following compounds:

$$CsF.HF, \quad CsF.2HF, \quad CsF.3HF \text{ and } CsF.6HF.$$

The LiCl + KCl eutectic is capable of dissolving water vapour (Burkhard and Corbett, 1957) and the solubilities follow Henry's Law to 18 mm Hg pressure of water vapour at 480°C and 14 mm Hg at 390°C. Beyond 18 mm at 480°C there exists a sharp break due to hydrolysis of the LiCl at the higher water pressures but at 390°C no such behaviour is observed. The unusual tenacity with which water is retained by the melt is probably connected with the high charge density of the Li^+ ion. In fact if the LiCl + KCl melt which was in equilibrium with H_2O vapour is evacuated for 1 h, up to 4 mm of H_2O per mole of LiCl are still retained. On the other hand, if a 62 mole % NaCl + 38 mole % KCl melt in equilibrium with water vapour at 700°C is evacuated for 15 min, no detectable amount of water is retained by the melt.

Water is also soluble in molten alkali-metal nitrates (Na, K, Cs), apparently accommodated in the interstices of the melt. Oxygen and nitrogen, on the other hand, are not appreciably soluble in these nitrate melts.

VIII. Solutions of Metals in Molten Salts

A. INTRODUCTION

Many molten salts act as solvents for metals; in particular molten halides often dissolve their parent metal. The ability of molten halides to dissolve their own parent metal was first suggested by the colouration produced in the melt by the electrolysis of molten rubidium and caesium chlorides (Bunsen and Kirchoff, 1861). Lorentz and Eitel (1915), from optical and X-ray studies on the solids, postulated that solutions of metals in molten salts were colloidal. However, Heymann and Friedlander (1930) showed this reasoning to be incorrect, since the solutions show none of the properties usually associated with colloids. It is now recognized that solutions of metals in molten salts fall into two categories.

(i) Those in which there is no appreciable chemical interaction between solvent (salt) and solute (metal). In these solutions the metal will impart some of its metallic character to the mixture.

(ii) Those in which considerable interaction between solute and solvent occurs.

There are also solutions that are not defined by either of these categories but are intermediate between the two. A discussion of the various theories of the nature of solutions of metals in molten salts is given by Delimarskii and Markov (1961) as well as by Bredig (1963).

B. SOLUTIONS WITHOUT SIGNIFICANT INTERACTION

Solutions of this type have also been referred to as "metallic". Metals of the first and second periods of the Periodic Table and the Lanthanides, mainly form this class of solutions, when dissolved in their own molten halides.

1. *Alkali-Metal Solutions in Molten Alkali-Metal Halides*

Bredig (1963) has summarized the physical properties of these systems. As shown in Table III for fluorides and chlorides, the consolute temperatures, i.e. temperatures at which there is complete miscibility between salt and metal in all proportions, decrease in the order:

$$Li > Na > K > Rb.$$

The temperatures range from about 1325° to 800°C for the fluorides.

The solubility of metals in their molten halides increases in the order:

$$Li < Na < K < Rb < Cs.$$

In each system involving caesium, there is complete miscibility and it is apparent that the size (or more specifically the charge density) of the alkali-metal cation is the most important feature involved in solubility relationships for these systems. The concentration of metal in the critical solution (namely that solution at the consolute temperature) increases from the fluoride to the iodide for the sodium, potassium and rubidium systems.

Supporting evidence for the non-existence of strong chemical interaction between solute and solvent in the above systems, is given by the activity coefficients (γ) of the salts (Bredig, 1963). These coefficients show increasing positive deviations from Raoult's Law with increasing metal concentration and these deviations are usually associated with systems having regions of immiscibility but with no strong chemical interaction. It is also probably significant that the plots of $RT \ln \gamma_{salt}$ versus ϕ^2_{metal} (where ϕ_{metal} is mole fraction of metal), for the KBr, RbBr and CsI systems, are only slightly curved. The approximate linearity of these curves is in accordance with the behaviour of regular solutions. Such solutions are characterized by an ideal entropy (in the

Raoult-Law sense) and only slight interaction between solute and solvent species.

Alternatively it has been suggested (Pitzer, 1962) that the excess free energy of mixing (i.e. $RT\ln\gamma_{salt}$) is due to the conversion of the metallic state of binding of the metal electrons to an ionic type of binding. This theory would predict a substantial positive excess entropy of mixing.

TABLE III

Alkali-Metal–Alkali-Metal Halide Systems

Metal-Salt System	Salt M.p. °K	Metal M.p. °K	Monotectic (for salt rich liquid only) Temp. °K	Mole % M	Eutectic (estimated by extrapolation) Mole % M	Consolute Temp. °K	Mole % M	Solubility in salt Temp. °K	Mole % M
Li+LiF	1121	452	1120	~1	—	1603	40	—a	
Li+LiCl	883	452	882	~0·5	—	—		—a	
Na+NaF	1268	370	1263	~3	10⁻⁹	1453	28	—ab	
								1273	7·6c
Na+NaCl	1073	370	1068	2·1	—	1353	50	—b	
								1084	2·8c
								1273	33·0c
K+KF	1131	337	1122	4·9	3×10⁻⁴	1177	20	—ad	
								1221	23·3
K+KCl	1043	337	1024	10·5	10⁻⁹	1063	39	—b	
								1073	7·6f
Rb+RbF	1068	312	1046	~9	—	1063	21	—ab	
Rb+RbCl	995	312	969	18	—	979	37	—b	
Cs+CsF	976	302	No miscibility gap		10⁻³	—		965	6·0a
Cs+CsCl	918	302	—		10⁻⁸	—		—e	
								899	9·0b

a Dworkin et al. (1962).
b Johnson and Bredig (1960).
c Bredig et al. (1955).
d Johnson and Bredig (1958).
e Bredig and Bronstein (1955).
f Belozerskii (1940).

For these systems, the specific conductivity increases markedly when metal is added to the molten salt and continues increasing with added amounts of metal. Hence Bronstein and Bredig (1958, 1961) concluded that a considerable part of the conduction is electronic. In the case of potassium iodide containing 42 mole % potassium, the electronic contribution to the conductivity is more than 99·5%. To explain the equivalent conductances of these systems, Bronstein and Bredig (1958, 1961) suggested that in these solutions:

(a) electron orbital overlap exists at relatively high metal concentrations;
(b) in sodium solutions of high metal content, electron pairs are trapped to form, for example, diatomic molecules of Na_2 (in lithium systems this electron pairing would be even more pronounced);

(c) the contribution to the specific conductivity by the metal solute increases greatly in going from the fluoride to the iodide systems, that is, with increase of atomic number or size of the halide ion.

(d) the metalic contribution to the specific conductivity decreases from sodium to potassium, i.e. with increasing size of metal ion.

2. Alkaline-Earth Metal Solutions in Molten Alkaline-Earth Halides

Only recently have accurate phase diagrams been determined for these systems. The phase diagram for the $Ba + BaCl_2$ system has been determined and is similar to those of the earlier alkali-metal+alkali-metal halide systems. Phase equilibria have also been reported for $Ca + CaF_2$ (Rogers et al., 1961), $Ca + CaCl_2$ (Peterson and Hinkebein, 1959), $Ca + CaBr_2$ and $Ca + CaI_2$ (Staffansson, 1959). Table IV gives the solubilities of the metal in

TABLE IV

Alkaline-Earth Metal + Alkaline-Earth Halide Systems

Metal-Salt System	Salt M.p. °K	Metal M.p. °K	Monotectic (for salt rich liquid only) Temp. °K	Monotectic Mole % M	Eutectic Temp. °K	Eutectic Mole % M	Consolute Temp. °K	Consolute Mole % M	Solubility in salt Temp. °K	Solubility in salt Mole % M
Mg+MgCl₂	987	923	~987	0.2	~923	100.0	—	—	—	—[a]
									1073	1.08[b]
									1323	1.57[b]
Ca+CaF₂	1691	1110	1563	25.5	1094	98.6	1595±5	45		—[c]
Ca+CaCl₂	1045	1110	1093	2.7	1033	2.0	1610±5	62		—[a]
									1273	5.4[d]
Ca+CaBr₂	1015	1110	1100	2.3	1000	3.0	1610±5	64		—[a]
Ca+CaI₂	1053	1110	1104	3.8	1033	2.0	1650±5	74		—[a]
									1273	9.66[d]
Sr+SrF₂									1273	19.9[d]
Sr+SrCl₂	1145	1044	1112	5.5	?	?	?	?		—[a]
									1273	24.6[d]
Sr+SrBr₂									1273	36.1[d]
Sr+SrI₂									1273	39.3[d]
Ba+BaF₂									1323	21.9[d]
Ba+BaCl₂	1235	1002	1163	15.0	985	99.0	1290	50		—[a]
									1323	30.6[d]
Ba+BaBr₂									1323	36.7[d]
Ba+BaI₂									1323	39.4[d]

[a] Bredig (1963).
[b] Zhurin (1935).
[c] Rogers et al. (1961).
[d] Guntz and Benoit (1924).

these systems. In general these systems resemble the alkali-metal halide systems, and exhibit a rapid increase in solubility with increase of atomic number of the metal. For example, the maximum solubility in mole % for the following systems near the melting point of each salt is given by:

$$Mg + MgCl_2 : 0.5$$
$$Ca + CaCl_2 : 2.7$$
$$Sr + SrCl_2 : 5.5$$
$$Ba + BaCl_2 : 20.$$

Various equilibria have been suggested to explain the properties of the solutions, e.g. from activity measurements on the $Mg + MgCl_2$ system the proposed solution mechanism was $Mg + Mg^{2+} = (Mg_2)^{2+}$. The conductivity behaviour is also similar to that in the alkali-metal + alkali-metal halide systems except that the rate of change of specific conductivity with added metal is not as great for the alkaline-earth systems.

TABLE V

Lanthanide-metal + Lanthanide-Metal Halide Systems
Solubility Data

Metal-Salt system	Salt M.p. °K	Metal M.p. °K	Eutectic Temp. °K	Mole % M	Solubility in MX_3 Temp. °K	Mole % M
La + LaCl$_3$	1131	1193	1099	9·0	1273	12·0[a]
La + LaBr$_3$	1061		1001	14·5	1173	15·5[ab]
La + LaI$_3$	1052		1007	8·2	1173	33[ac]
Ce + CeCl$_3$	1090	1068	1050	9·0	1171	9[a]
					1123	33[d]
Ce + CeBr$_3$	1005		960	12·0	1173	14[ab]
Ce + CeI$_3$	1034		988	8·8	1173	32[a]
Pr + PrCl$_3$	1059	1208	919	17·0	1073	19[ac]
Pr + PrBr$_3$	966		852	16·0	1023	18[ab]
Pr + PrI$_3$	1011		939	11·9	1073	29[a]
Nd + NdCl$_3$	1032	1297	913	14·0	1173	31[e]
Nd + NdBr$_3$	955		—	—	—	—[f]
Nd + NdI$_3$	1060		764	26·5	1073	37[e]
Gd + GdI$_3$	1204	1585	1098	14·0	1173	14[a]
Y + YI$_3$	1270	1782	1221	12·0	1423	15[f]

[a] Cubicciotti and Cleary (1952).
[b] Sallach and Corbett (1962).
[c] Druding and Corbett (1959).
[d] Cubicciotti (1949).
[e] Druding and Corbett (1959, 1961).
[f] Bredig (1963).

3. Lanthanide Metal Solutions in Molten Lanthanide Trihalides

These solutions are less "metallic" in character than those discussed in Section VIIIB, 1 and 2. Table V gives the solubilities of metal in the molten trihalide. A feature of these systems is that the phase diagrams indicate the existence of congruent and incongruently melting compounds. Stable solid compounds corresponding to the composition MX_2 were found in the $Nd + NdI_3$,

$Pr + PrI_3$, $Ce + CeI_3$ and $La + LaI_3$ systems. Also non-stoichiometric compounds such as $NdCl_{2.3}$, $NdCl_{2.2}$, $PrI_{2.5}$, $CeI_{2.4}$, $LaI_{2.4}$ appear to exist.

The specific conductivities of the metal + salt solutions increase in the order:

$$Nd < Pr < Ce < La \ll K.$$

C. SOLUTIONS WITH STRONG SOLUTE–SOLVENT INTERACTION (i.e. NON-METALLIC SOLUTIONS)

Non-metallic solutions of metals in their molten salts are defined as those which exhibit only a very slight change in conductivity of salt on addition of the metal. This indicates that the metallic electrons are in some way bound up in the melt and are not available for conduction. It is considered that this criterion outweighs, for example, the observable metallic lustre of solutions of bismuth in bismuth chloride (Cubicciotti, 1960).

A second criterion, distinguishing these systems from the "metallic" systems is the formation of stoichiometric solid halides of the metal in a lower valence state.

1. Transition Metal Systems

Little work has been done on metal solutions of this type. The $Ni + NiCl_2$ system has been studied by Johnson et al. (1958), the solubility of metal being 9 mole % Ni at the eutectic temperature of 980°C. The authors considered that Ni^+ ions were formed but alternative explanations are possible to explain the freezing point depression and heat fusion data. Solubility data are given in Table VI.

2. Post Transition Metal Systems

It has been suggested (Corbett et al., 1955, 1957, 1960) that the solubility of the metals in their molten halides depends on their ability to form a cationic species having a lower than normal oxidation state. Table VII indicates that this tendency increases with increasing atomic weight for each group. The solubility also increases in the order, $I < Br < Cl$, except that for cadmium and mercury the tendency is reversed.

(a) Subgroup I. The solubility of silver in molten silver chloride is 0·06 mole % at 700°C.

(b) Subgroup II. Mercury subhalides, Hg_2X_2 are well known and the chloride is stable to 525°C, where it decomposes into a salt-rich melt of almost the same composition and a small amount of liquid mercury phase containing 6·8 mole % $HgCl_2$ in solution (Yosim and Mayer, 1960). Hevesy and Löwenstein (1930) quote the solubility of Hg in $HgCl_2$ at 350°C as 50 mole % and in HgI_2 33·6 mole %.

The systems $Cd + CdX_2$ have been extensively studied (Aten, 1910; Lorentz and Eitel, 1926; Hevesy and Löwenstein, 1930; Farquharson and Heymann, 1935; Cubicciotti, 1953a,b).

TABLE VI

Transition Metal Systems—Solubility Data

System	Salt M.p. °C	Metal M.p. °C	Solubility	
			Temp. °C	Mole % M
$Ni + NiCl_2$			977	9.1^a
$Ag + AgCl$	455	960.8	490	0.03^b
			700	0.06^b
$Zn + ZnCl_2$	262	419.47	500	0.18^c
			500	8.9×10^{-5d}
$Zn + ZnI_2$	446	419.47	500	0.28^c
$Cd + CdCl_2$	568	40 (vac)	550	14.0^e
			600	15.2^e
			800	21.0^e
			1000	30.0^e
$Cd + CdBr_2$	567	40.0	550	14.0^d
			600	13.9^f
			700	20.0^f
			900	28.0^f
$Cd + CdI_2$	388	40.0	400	2.5^f
			600	6.07^f
			700	15.0^f
			950	25.0^f
$Hg + HgCl_2$	276	-38.87	280	7.0^d
			350	50.0^g
			400	18.0^g
			500	40.0^g
$Hg + HgI_2$	259	-38.87	230	25.0^d
			280	35.0^d
			350	33.6^d

[a] Johnson et al. (1958).
[b] Corbett and Winbush (1955).
[c] Corbett et al. (1957).
[d] Hevesy and Löwenstein (1930).
[e] Aten (1910); Hevesy and Löwenstein (1930); Topol and Laudis (1960).
[f] Topol and Laudis (1960).
[g] Yosim and Mayer (1960).

The solubility of Cd in $CdCl_2$ at 600°C has been given as 15.2 mole %. The diamagnetic nature of the solution indicates that the mechanism of metal solubility is either through the formation of Cd_2^{2+} or a true solution of molecules or atoms. Freezing point depression measurements indicate that the subchloride Cd_2Cl_2 may be formed (Grjotheim et al., 1955). This compound disproportionates on solidification, as is seen by the presence of crystalline

TABLE VII

Post Transition-Metal Systems—Solubility Data

System	Salt M.p. °C	Metal M.p. °C	Solubility Temp. °C	Solubility Mole % M
Al+AlI$_3$	191·0	659·7	423	0·3[a]
Ga+GaCl$_2$	170·5	29·78	180	1·92[a]
Ga+Ga$_2$Cl$_4$		29·78	180	3·7[a]
Ga+Ga$_2$Br$_4$		29·78	180	14·0[bc]
Tl+TlCl	430·0	302·0	550	0·09[a]
			650	0·09[a]
Sn+SnCl$_2$	246·0	231·9	500	0·0032[a]
Sn+SnBr$_2$	215·5		500	0·068[a]
Pb+PbCl$_2$	501·0	327·4	600	0·02[a]
			700	0·052[a]
			700	0·055[d]
			800	0·123[a]
Pb+PbI$_2$	402·0	327·4	440	0·024[e]
			600	0·15[e]
			700	0·41[e]
Sb+SbCl$_3$	73·4	630·5	270	0·18[b]
Sb+SbI$_3$	167·0	630·5	200	1·69[bf]
			300	3·5[f]
			400	5·8[f]
Bi+BiCl$_3$	230·2	271·3	202	28·0[g]
			320	46·0[g]
			450	47·5[h]
			550	28·0[i]
			780	100·0[g]
Bi+BiBr$_3$	218·0	271·3	205	21·0[j]
			294	57·0[j]
			440	45·0[j]
			538	100·0[j]
Bi+BiI$_3$	439·0	271·3	336	48·0[j]
			458	100·0[j]

[a] Corbett and Winbush (1955).
[b] Corbett et al. (1957).
[c] Corbett and Hershaft (1958).
[d] Karpachev et al. (1944).
[e] Bredig (1963).
[f] Bruner and Corbett (1961).
[g] Yosim et al. (1959).
[h] Cubicciotti and Cleary (1952).
[i] Levy et al. (1960a).
[j] Yosim et al. (1962).

cadmium metal in the solid. Activity data may be interpreted in terms of the presence of $(Cd_2)^{2+}$ and also in terms of the formation of complex anions such as $(CdCl_4)^{2-}$ (Bredig, 1962).

The weight of evidence seems to suggest that Cd most likely dissolves in $CdCl_2$ to form $(Cd_2)^{2+}$. Thus the amount of cadmium passing into solution would be dependent on the concentration of Cd^{2+} already present in the solution; hence a semi-quantitative estimate of the free Cd^{2+} ions in the molten salt mixtures such as $CdCl_2 + NaCl$ and $CdCl_2 + KCl$, may be obtained from the solubility of cadmium metal in these solutions. In fact, the presence of potassium chloride strongly suppresses the solubility of Cd in molten $CdCl_2$ over a wide composition range, thus suggesting the removal of Cd^{2+} from $CdCl_2$ solutions in the form of complex ions, such as $CdCl_4^{2-}$.

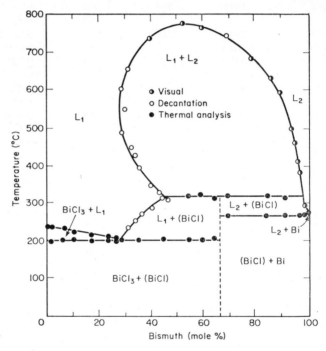

Fig. 2. Bismuth metal–bismuth trichloride system (Yosim et al., 1959). (Reproduced by courtesy of the American Chemical Society.)

The metal solubility in the $Zn + ZnX_2$ systems (Corbett et al., 1957) is only of the order of 1 mole %. By analogy with the cadmium systems we could attribute low solubility to the lack of free Zn^{2+} ions in molten $ZnCl_2$ which most probably exists in the form of complex ions. The smaller solubility of metal in this system relative to the Cd system is in accordance with the view that the smaller Zn^{2+} ion is more capable of forming stable complex ions than Cd^{2+}.

(c) *Subgroups III and IV*. In these subgroups the solubilities of metals in their molten halides are much smaller than under (a) and (b) above (Corbett and Winbush, 1955; Corbett et al., 1957).

(d) *Subgroup V* (Corbett and Albers, 1960). As, Sb, Bi all possess a stable trivalent oxidation state. The solubility of metals in their salts rises rapidly with increasing atomic number, the bismuth system forming sub-halides, BiX. The $Bi + BiCl_3$ phase diagram is shown in Fig. 2.

It should be noted that salts are themselves soluble in metals but usually to a much smaller extent than that of metal in salt, e.g. the solubility of $PbCl_2$ at 1000°C in Pb is approximately 1 mole % (Yosim and Luchsinger, 1960).

TABLE VIII

Equilibrium Constants for Displacement Solubility Reactions[1]

Equilibrium	Temperature °C	K
$Na + LiCl \rightleftharpoons NaCl + Li$	900	0·45
$K + NaCl \rightleftharpoons KCl + Na$	900	0·87
$K + NaI \rightleftharpoons KI + Na$	900	0·017
$3Na + AlCl_3 \rightleftharpoons 3NaCl + Al$	825	$\sim 5 \cdot 0 \times 10^{-10}$
$Mg + ZnCl_2 \rightleftharpoons MgCl_2 + Zn$	—	$1 \cdot 6 \times 10^{-5}$
$Cd + PbCl_2 \rightleftharpoons CdCl_2 + Pb$	600	$\sim 3 \cdot 0 \times 10^{-2}$

[1] Abstracted from Delimarskii and Markov (1961).

D. SOLUTIONS OF METALS IN SALTS OF ANOTHER METAL—DISPLACEMENT SOLUBILITY

In these systems there is the equilibrium:

$$M_I + M_{II}X \overset{K}{\rightleftharpoons} M_I X + M_{II}. \qquad (3)$$

It is possible to calculate the equilibrium constant K by determining the e.m.f. of the corresponding Jacobi-Daniell cell, assuming a negligible liquid junction potential between the two molten salts. For example, for the cell $Cd/CdCl_2/PbCl_2/Pb$ the reaction is,

$$Cd + PbCl_2 \rightleftharpoons CdCl_2 + Pb. \qquad (4)$$

The equilibrium constant K may be considered to summarize the solubility behaviour of metals in unlike salts and some values are given in Table VIII.

Delimarskii and Markov (1961) list tables of K values for a large number of metals in molten halides. It should be noted that for many metals the

13

equilibrium $M + xPbCl_2 \rightleftharpoons MCl_{2x} + xPb$ is displaced almost completely to the right and as molten metallic lead can be separated easily from the rest of the system, this is a convenient method of preparing heavy metal chlorides in the anhydrous state. Inman *et al.* (1960) used such a reaction at 650°C to prepare UCl₃,

$$2U + 3PbCl_2 = 2UCl_3 + 3Pb. \tag{5}$$

In industrial electrolysis it is very important to know the electrochemical series of metals in any desired solvent and Delimarskii and Markov (1961) have tabulated electrode potentials of metals in various molten electrolytes as well as listing a qualitatively determined electrochemical series of metals in molten salts. It should be pointed out that such a series is not necessarily the same for different molten salt solvents. There is also a change of electrode potential with temperature so that in the cell reaction $Cd + PbCl_2 = CdCl_2 + Pb$, cadmium will displace lead below 650°C and lead will displace cadmium at higher temperatures.

TABLE IX

Electrochemical Series of Metals in Molten Salts[1]

Solvent	Temperature °C	Electrochemical Series
$NaCl + AlCl_3$	500	Na, Be, Al, Mn, Tl, Zn, Cd, Sn^{II}, Pb, Co, Ag, Cu^I, Hg^{II}, Sb^{III}, Bi, Ni.
$NaCl + AlCl_3$	700	Na, Al, Mn, Tl^I, Zn, Cd, Pb, Ag, Cu^I, Co, Hg^{II}, Sb^{III}, Ni, Bi.
$NaBr + AlBr_3$	700	Na, Al, Zn, Cd, Pb, Sn^{II}, Cu^I, Ag, Co, Hg^{II}, Ni, Sb^{III}, Bi.
$NaI + AlI_3$	700	Na, Al, Cd, Ag, Sn^{II}, Pb, Cu^I, Bi, Hg^{II}, Co, Ni, Sb.

[1] Abstracted from Delimarskii and Markov (1961).

IX. SOLUTIONS OF SALT IN MOLTEN SALT

In general, molten salts are better solvents for salts than any other solvent and the majority of molten salt systems are completely miscible. The few systems that exhibit immiscibility, i.e. the formation of two liquid phases, are of growing interest from the point of view of extraction of some inorganic solutes from multiphase systems.

The molten halides are generally miscible with one another, especially for true binary systems. Molten reciprocal systems of halides with metal salts of a different anion can however exhibit immiscibility, e.g. sodium borate+ sodium halide (Boleslaw and Scheidt, 1961).

The solubility of salts in molten salts as such has received very little attention in the past. Phase diagrams are the most useful indication of their solubility properties. For a discussion of the interpretation of phase diagrams and their relation to solubility the reader should refer to standard texts. Phase diagrams have been collected and presented in Landolt-Börnstein (1956).

A. MOLTEN SALT SYSTEMS WITH INCOMPLETE MISCIBILITY

Molten salt systems in which there is incomplete miscibility are listed in Table X.

Many other binary systems exhibit mutual immiscibility—they generally consist of an aluminium salt with an ionic salt, e.g. $AlBr_3$ with NaBr, KBr, NH_4Br, $CaBr_2$ and TlBr; and $AlCl_3$ with NaCl, KCl, NH_4Cl, AgCl, $SnCl_2$ and $SnCl_4$ (Kendall et al., 1923).

The following molten reciprocal systems also have regions of immiscibility (Belyaev, 1960).

AgCl or AgBr with $LiNO_3$, $NaNO_3$, KNO_3, $TlNO_3$, $Ca(NO_3)_2$, Li_2WO_4, $LiVO_3$, $NaVO_3$, KVO_3, $NaCrO_4$, $NaMoO_4$, Na_2WO_4
AgI with NaCl, LiCl, $NaNO_3$, KNO_3, $TlNO_3$
TlBr with nitrates
TlCl with nitrates
$CdCl_2$ with some oxy-salts
$CdBr_2$ with some oxy-salts
LiF with CsCl, CsBr, PbO
PbO with NaF, KCl, NaCl, RbCl, NaBr, KF, KI
SiO_2 with MgF_2, CaF_2, SrF_2, BaF_2

Also, Li_2SO_4+$PbCl_2$, $PbCl_2$+Ag_2S, B_2O_3+NaCl and B_2O_3+KCl.

On the basis of these observations of partial miscibility, various classes of systems are distinguishable. Various workers, Kendall et al. (1923) and Belyaev (1958, 1960), have attempted to relate factors such as position of ions in periodic classification, temperature of mixture, internal pressure differences, molar and atomic volumes, etc., with the observed partial miscibility of certain molten salt systems.

The following types of systems display partial immiscibility:

$$AX+BY; \quad AX+BX; \quad AX+AY,$$

the first being a reciprocal system and the latter two being binary systems.

1. AX+BY Systems

In such systems it is apparent that for incomplete miscibility, one of the component salts must be a compound of comparatively low polarity, (i.e.

13*

TABLE X

Molten Salt Systems with Incomplete Miscibility (Binary Systems)

System	Region of immiscibility mole % second component	Congruently melting compounds
$AlCl_3 + PCl_5$	$74 - > 78 \cdot 9$	$1 : 1$
$AlCl_3 + NaCl$	2 phases near $AlCl_3$	$1 : 1$
$AlCl_3 + KCl$	2 phases near $AlCl_3$	$1 : 1$
$Hg_2Br_2 + AlBr_3$	$84 \cdot 6 - 99 \cdot 1$	$1 : 2$
$SnCl_2 + SbCl_3$	$8 \cdot 8 - 98 \cdot 6$	$x : y$
$PbBr_2 + AlBr_3$	$83 \cdot 8 - 99 \cdot 2$	$1 : 2$
$AlCl_3 + NH_4Cl$	$0 \cdot 2 - 20 \cdot 5$	$x : y$
		$1 : 1$
$AlBr_3 + NaBr$	$2 \cdot 6 - 16 \cdot 3$	$x : y^a$
		$7 : 2^a$
		$2 : 1^a$
		$1 : 1^a$
$AlBr_3 + KBr$	$0 \cdot 4 - 22 \cdot 1$	$x : y^a$
		$2 : 1^a$
		$1 : 1^a$
$AlBr_3 + NH_4Br$	$0 \cdot 5 - 20 \cdot 8$	$x : y^a$
		$3 : 1^a$
		$2 : 1^a$
		$1 : 1^a$
$AlBr_3 + CaBr_2$	$0 \cdot 8 - 14 \cdot 0$	$x : y^a$
		$2 : 1^a$
$AgCl + AlCl_3$	$82 \cdot 4 - 99 \cdot 3$	$x : y^a$
		$1 : 1^a$
$AgBr + AlBr_3$	$83 \cdot 0 - 97 \cdot 8$	2 compounds[a]
$TlCl + AlCl_3$	$85 \cdot 3 - 98 \cdot 8$	3 compounds[a]
$TlBr + AlBr_3$	$77 \cdot 2 - 99 \cdot 4$	[a]
$SnBr_2 + AlBr_3$	$85 \cdot 8 - 98 \cdot 2$	[a]

[a] Kendall *et al.* (1923). All other systems: Landolt-Börnstein (1956).

covalent) or a halide, oxide or sulphide of a transition or post-transition element, while the other component is a typical salt—usually of an alkali-metal. Exceptions to this rule are known, e.g. $LiF + CsCl$ and $LiF + CsBr$ systems have incomplete miscibility in the molten state.

2. *AX + BX Systems*

One of the component salts must be of low polarity, containing a multi-valent cation such as Al^{3+}, Bi^{3+}, Sb^{3+} etc., while the other is a typically polar salt. The formation of complex compounds is also favoured by these conditions although the compounds formed are usually not well characterized.

3. $AX + AY$ Systems

In such systems the anions are usually very different in size and charge density, e.g. salts such as silicates, titanates or borates together with simple alkali-metal halides.

B. MOLTEN SALT SYSTEMS WITH COMPLETE MISCIBILITY

Systems having complete miscibility are too numerous to list and the reader should refer to the phase diagrams for information on the equilibrium states of the systems.

The solubility of metal oxides in molten salts is of some interest in connection with the general problem of metal oxidation in these media. Thus Stern (1961) carried out a study of oxide solubility in molten NaCl at 900° for metals of the first transition series from Ti to Cu. The following regularities in the solubility data are noticed.

(a) Only oxides of metals having an odd atomic number, i.e. an odd number of $3d$ electrons, show any appreciable interaction with NaCl. Of the remainder, Cr_2O_3 is an exception only in the presence of oxygen.

(b) With the exception of V_2O_5 which oxidizes Cl^-, soluble oxides have possibly more than one oxide stable at 900°. All the insoluble oxides have only one stable oxide (NiO, Fe_2O_3 are included since their solubilities are very low).

(c) The metal to oxide ratio found in the melts for the soluble oxides is much greater than can be accounted for on the basis of a simple solubility, also the stoichiometry does not correspond to any known oxide stable in the solid state.

(d) In spite of the considerable scatter of solubilities, all the soluble oxides with the exception of copper dissolve to the extent 0·001–0·01 mole fraction of metal in the melt.

C. THE STRUCTURE OF MOLTEN SALT SOLUTIONS

There have been many reviews on the structure of molten salt mixtures (e.g. see Bloom, 1959; Blomgren and Van Artsdalen, 1960). As in the case for aqueous solutions, the physical and chemical nature of molten salt mixtures is better understood than for the individual molten salts. Most of the thermodynamic and structural methods of physical chemistry have been applied to molten salts for the elucidation of structure but, unfortunately, the number of systems that have received detailed attention by several methods are few. The heavy-metal dihalide + alkali-metal halide systems appear to have received the most attention and these will be discussed as examples of molten salt solutions.

The molten heavy-metal dihalide + alkali-metal halide systems have a wide range of thermodynamic properties from which the nature of solute–solvent interaction can be ascertained. Thermodynamic activity determinations have been particularly useful in this respect. It is thermodynamically possible to describe systems as "ideal", "regular" (for which there are varying degrees of entropy assumptions), or "complex". Ideal mixtures by definition do not involve any significant interaction between solute and

TABLE XI

Immiscibility in Reciprocal Molten Salt Systems

System	Region of immiscibility mole % second component
$FeO + NaF$	3·0–94·0
$AgCl + Li_2SO_4$	1·5–98·0
$AgCl + LiNO_3$	
$CdCl_2 + Li_2SO_4$	6·0–80·0
$AgNO_3 + NaCl$	29·0–76·0
$HgBr_2 + AlCl_3$	50·0–99·0
$TlBr + KNO_3$	14·0–92·5
$TlI + KNO_3$	0·0–97·0
$Tl_2SO_4 + AgI$	11·0–86·0
$TlNO_3 + KBr$	
$TlNO_3 + AgI$	1·5–93·0
$AlBr_3 + NaI$	2·0–13·0
$AlBr_3 + KI$	2·0–13·0
$Na_2B_4O_7 + NaCl$	66·0–99·8
$BaCl_2 + Na_2CO_3$	39·0–62·0
$Ag_2SO_4 + LiCl$	41·0–87·0
$AgNO_3 + KCl$	32·0–64·0
$CdSO_4 + LiCl$	
$TlNO_3 + KI$	24·0–72·0
$AgNO_3 + LiCl$	
$TlI + AgNO_3$	45·0—53·0

solvent and the distribution of the species may be completely random (if Raoult Law ideality is assumed) or may involve a quasi-lattice arrangement with interlocking cation and anion semi-lattices, for Temkin ideality (Temkin, 1945). The ionic nature of the melts favours the latter ideality criterion. It should be noted that for binary systems of the type $MX_2 + AX$, activity determinations make no distinction between the ideality models.

Systems containing LiCl appear to be very nearly ideal (e.g. $LiCl + CdCl_2$ and $LiCl + PbCl_2$). Systems containing NaX exhibit slightly negative activity deviations from the Temkin model. Other data, such as partial molar volumes, conductivities, surface tension and phase diagrams suggest that there is little or no tendency to produce ion-associated species and accordingly ideal entropy conditions should prevail (Bloom, 1959). The activity values found in these systems may then be explained in terms of a non-zero heat of mixing of solute and solvent, arising from coulombic interaction between the constituent ions. This is in fact the zeroth approximation of the familiar regular solution model. The high temperatures of molten salt systems would appear to favour the zeroth rather than the first or higher approximations.

On the other hand, molten systems of the type $MX_2 + KX$ show thermo-dynamic properties that are too different from those in an ideal or regular situation to be explainable by these models. The small activities of the component salts imply that they are partly bound up in solution in the form of complex ions. Other measurements such as conductivity, molar volume, cryoscopy and the more direct Raman spectra, are in agreement with this view. Systems such as $MX_2 + RbX$ and $MX_2 + CsX$ are even more pronounced in their non-ideal thermodynamic behaviour. This is interpreted in terms of an increasing stability of complex ions with decreasing charge density, or ionic potential, of the alkali-metal cation.

Bloom (1963) has discussed the factors influencing the formation of complex ions in molten salt mixtures. The tendency of certain ions such as Cd^{2+}, Zn^{2+} and Pb^{2+} to form complex ions leads to the formation of minima in the isotherms of equivalent conductance against composition as well as positive deviations in the molar volume isotherms. Gruen et al. (1958) and Wait and Janz (1963) have shown that in such molten salt solutions the applied properties such as ultra-violet, Raman and infra-red spectra show the formation of new species on mixing the component molten salts. These new species are termed complex ions and in the $KCl + CdCl_2$ system have been postulated as $CdCl_3^-$, $CdCl_4^{2-}$ or $CdCl_6^{4-}$ resulting from the reactions:

$$KCl + CdCl_2 = KCdCl_3 \qquad (6a)$$

$$2KCl + CdCl_2 = K_2CdCl_4 \qquad (6b)$$

$$4KCl + CdCl_2 = K_4CdCl_6. \qquad (6c)$$

The addition of chloride ions to the system in order to form complex ions, leads also to the addition of cations (in order to maintain electrical neutrality). The charge density and therefore polarizing power of the added alkali-metal cation is inversely related to its ionic radius, hence the addition of a highly polarizing ion such as Li^+ is sufficient to disrupt the tendency to form complexes. Alternatively it may be assumed that Li^+ competes strongly with Cd^{2+} for the available Cl^- ions. The tendency to destroy the efforts of ions such as Cd^{2+} to build up complex ions, will decrease with increase of ionic radius of the added alkali-metal cation, hence the addition of $NaCl$ to molten $CdCl_2$ has less disrupting effect on the tendency of cadmium to build up complex ions. Similar considerations apply to the addition of LiCl and NaCl to molten $PbCl_2$. K^+, Rb^+ and Cs^+ will have increasingly less tendency to prevent the formation of the complex ions containing cadmium or lead; the progressively increasing conductance minima in these systems as the alkali-metal cation radius increases, support this view. The conductance isotherms for $PbCl_2 + MCl$ systems are shown in Fig. 3. Hence if complex

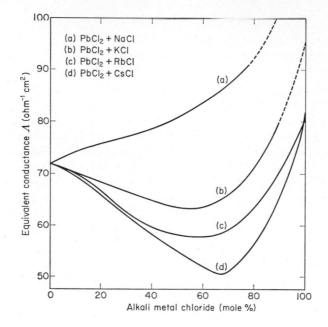

(a) $PbCl_2 + NaCl$
(b) $PbCl_2 + KCl$
(c) $PbCl_2 + RbCl$
(d) $PbCl_2 + CsCl$

FIG. 3. Isotherms of equivalent conductance at 720°C (Bloom, 1963). (Reproduced by courtesy of the International Union of Pure and Applied Chemistry.)

ions tend to be produced, they will most likely be most stable in the presence of Cs^+ and least stable in the presence of Li^+.

On the basis of the foregoing considerations, the following classification of some salt mixtures may be made and are summarized in Table XII (Bloom, 1963).

From the systems so far studied it is possible to list the following factors which appear to determine the existence and stability of complex ions, resulting from strong solute–solvent interaction.

(a) Systems that form compounds in the solid state, as indicated by phase equilibrium studies, appear to favour the formation of complex species in the melt. This is not unreasonable since the melt may structurally be considered to be a disordered solid and it is likely that solid-like species exist on melting.

(b) Any factors that increase the covalent nature of the bonding in the complexes favour the stability of these species in the melt, e.g. the increased polarizability of the halide ligands in going from chloride to bromide favours covalent bonding.

(c) Since the complexes formed are of the type MX_n, any factors that enhance the central cation's ability to attract anions will promote complex formation. It is not surprising, therefore, that the tendency of M to form complex anions increases in the order,

$$Pb^{2+} < Cd^{2+} < Zn^{2+} < Mg^{2+}.$$

TABLE XII

Systems in which Complex Ions are Formed (Bloom, 1963)

System	Method of investigation	Complex ions postulated
$KCl + CdCl_2$	Conductivity, molar volume, Raman spectra, e.m.f., vapour pressure, cryoscopy	$CdCl_3^-$ $CdCl_4^{2-}$ $CdCl_6^{4-}$
$KCl + ZnCl_2$	Conductivity, Raman spectra, e.m.f.	$ZnCl_3^-$
$KCl + PbCl_2$	Conductivity, molar volume, transport number, surface tension, e.m.f., vapour pressure	$PbCl_3^-$ $PbCl_4^{2-}$ $PbCl_6^{4-}$
$KCl + MgCl_2$	Conductivity, molar volume	$MgCl_3^-$
$KCl + CuCl$	Conductivity	$CuCl_3^{2-}$
$KF + ZrF_4$	Vapour pressure	ZrF_5^-
$KI + CdI_2$	Conductivity, molar volume	CdI_4^{2-}
$RbCl + PbCl_2$	e.m.f. surface tension, conductivity, molar volume	$PbCl_3^-$ $PbCl_4^{2-}$ $PbCl_6^{4-}$
$CsCl + CoCl_2$	U.V. absorption spectra	$CoCl_4^{2-}$
$CsCl + NiCl_2$	U.V. absorption spectra	$NiCl_4^{2-}$
$CsCl + CuCl_2$	U.V. absorption spectra	$CuCl_4^{2-}$
$CsCl + NpCl_4$	U.V. absorption spectra	$NpCl_6^{2-}$
$CsCl + PbCl_2$	Conductivity, molar volume	$PbCl_3^-$ $PbCl_4^{2-}$ $PbCl_6^{4-}$
$NaF + AlF_3$	Conductivity, surface tension, cryoscopy	AlF_6^{3-} AlF_4^-

This is also the order of increasing charge density.

It should be pointed out that it is not always possible to deduce the existence of solid phase compounds from phase diagrams since many phase equilibria studies may not be sufficiently accurate. This is well borne out in the $FeCl_3 + NaCl$ system. In this system the phase diagram was originally interpreted (Cook and Dunn, 1961) to involve only a simple eutectic and it was expected that no complex ions would be formed in the melt. However, activity determinations seemed to indicate otherwise. Recent determinations of the phase diagram indicate the existence of the solid compound $NaFeCl_4$, the two eutectics being close to the melting point of the compound, hence complex ions are very likely in this molten system. The disrupting tendency of the Na^+ ion (which prevents complex formation in the similar Pb and Cd systems) appears to be outweighed by the opposing fact of a highly charged, relatively small, complexing cation (Fe^{3+}).

D. SOLVATION AND COMPLEX ION FORMATION IN MOLTEN SALT MIXTURES

Solvation effects, in ionic melts, may vary in intensity from slight tendency toward clustering, which may be observed as a non-ideal entropy of mixing, to the formation of covalent complex ions, resulting in non-ideal heats of solution. The formation of complex ions is therefore a special case of solvation. Complex ions such as $PbX_n^{(n-2)-}$ and $CdX_n^{(n-2)-}$ (where $n>2$) are partly ionic and the ligands will certainly undergo exchange reactions with other ligands of the same type in the solution.

Generally, mixtures that allow the formation of complex ions by solute-solvent interaction will be miscible in all proportions, although there are exceptions. The tendency for two components of a mixture to be immiscible, exhibits itself in the form of positive deviations in thermodynamic activities from the ideal values. This is clearly indicated in the Bi-Cd system. On the other hand, if there is any solvent–solute interaction, even with the retention of ideal entropy, the thermodynamic activities follow regular solution curves. These curves generally exhibit negative deviations from ideality as in the case with molten $AgBr+KBr$ mixtures (Hildebrand and Salstrom, 1932). If the solvent–solute interaction is strong enough for chemical bonding to occur, resulting for example in the formation of complex ions, then the activity deviations from ideality will necessarily be substantially negative as in the $CdCl_2+CsCl$ system.

E. COMPLEX IONS AND REACTION KINETICS

The ability to complex a cation may be used to control the concentration of reactive species in oxidation–reduction equilibria (Van Artsdalen, 1959). This is important at high temperatures where molten salts are likely to corrode their metal containers; e.g. if corrosion occurs by the reaction:

$$2M^{3+}+A = 2M^{2+}+A^{2+}, \tag{7}$$

this may be reduced by the addition of X^- to the system provided complex ions such as MX_4^- are formed. The large complex ions produced will be of low mobility and will necessarily have lower rates of reaction than smaller and more mobile ions.

X. APPLICATION OF MOLTEN SALTS AS SOLVENTS

Molten salts have been used as reaction media for both inorganic and organic synthesis. The electrolytic uses of molten salts have received the most attention in the past, especially in connection with the deposition of metals. More recently, separation and extraction processes have been carried out in molten salt solvents.

For practical applications eutectic mixtures of salts have been preferred, mainly because of the advantage of lower operating temperatures. The KCl + LiCl eutectic especially has been widely used, as have the lower melting alkali-metal nitrate mixtures. Because of the importance of this mixture, its method of preparation will be briefly discussed here.

Preparation of an LiCl + KCl Eutectic

The hygroscopic nature of LiCl necessitates the use of special precautions in preparing the solvent. Inman *et al.* (1960) prepared the melt by mixing molten LiCl (pure grade) and molten KCl (Analytical Reagent) in a glass tube and filtering through glass wool into a Pyrex beaker. This eutectic was transferred to an electrolytic cell where it was remelted and pumped out until the pressure in the system fell to approximately 10^{-4} mm Hg. Anhydrous HCl was then bubbled through the molten eutectic in a stream of purified argon. The final traces of impurities, including dissolved HCl, were removed by pre-electrolysing the melt in vacuo with tungsten or molybdenum cathodes and carbon anodes, at a potential below the decomposition potential of the melt. The progress of the purification was followed either by the steadily falling residual current at constant potential or the steadily rising voltage at constant current.

A. REACTIONS INVOLVING ORGANIC SUBSTANCES OR VOLATILE INORGANIC LIQUIDS IN MOLTEN SALT SOLVENTS

Many organic compounds when bubbled through molten salt solvents undergo exchange reactions. For example, fluorination may take place when chlorine-containing compounds are allowed to come into contact with molten fluorides.

1. *Fluorination Reactions* (Sundermeyer, 1962b; Sundermeyer and Meise, 1962)

KF (45%) + NaF (45%) + LiF (10%) melt was found to be a suitable medium for fluorination of some organic compounds in the range 500°–600°C. Alternatively, if lower temperatures were necessary, the melts KF + ZnCl$_2$ + KCl or CaF$_2$ + ZnCl$_2$ + KCl were used. In the latter case a temperature as low as 250°C could be employed. The following reactions were found to occur readily in the molten salt solvents and the products were formed in good yield. It was often sufficient to bubble the compounds through the melt once only, using efficient stirring, e.g.

$$(CH_3)_3SiCl + NaF = (CH_3)_3SiF + NaCl \tag{8}$$
$$SOCl_2 + 2NaF = SOF_2 + 2NaCl. \tag{9}$$

2. *Pseudohalide Reactions* (Sundermeyer, 1962a)

Exchange reactions of pseudohalides such as cyanides, cyanates, and thiocyanates with halogens are possible because of the ready solubility of the pseudohalides of the alkali-metals in mixed alkali and alkaline-earth metal halide melts. For example using a $LiCl + KCl$ melt as solvent the reaction,

$$SiCl_4 + cyanates \rightarrow Si(NCO)_4 \tag{10}$$

could be carried out with 55% yield.

3. *Organo-Azido Silane Reactions* (Sundermeyer, 1963)

Using a 54% $ZnCl_2 + 46\%$ KCl eutectic (m.p. 228°C) organo-azido silanes can be prepared at temperatures ranging from 230°–250°C. NaN_3 (10 to 20%) was suspended and partly dissolved in the eutectic solvent. The following reactions were carried out,

$$(CH_3)_3SiCl + NaN_3 = (CH_3)_3SiN_3 + NaCl \; (43\%) \tag{11a}$$
$$(CH_3)_2SiCl_2 + 2NaN_3 = (CH_3)_2Si(N_3)_2 + 2NaCl \; (69 \cdot 5\%) \tag{11b}$$
$$CH_3SiCl_3 + 3NaN_3 = CH_3Si(N_3)_3 + 3NaCl \tag{11c}$$

$(CH_3Si(N_3)Cl_2$, $CH_3Si(N_3)_2Cl$ and $(CH_3)_2Si(N_3)Cl$ are also produced).

4. *Dehydration of Alcohols* (Glemser and Kleine-Weischede, 1962)

Using a $58 \cdot 5\%$ $ZnCl_2 + 41 \cdot 5\%$ NaCl melt at 340°C it was possible to carry out dehydration of alcohols by bubbling the alcohol vapour, with nitrogen as a carrier gas, through the melt. Olefins, together with some unaltered alcohol, were obtained.

5. *Hydrochlorination Reactions* (Glemser and Kleine-Weischede, 1962)

Using a $ZnCl_2$ (85%) + CuCl (15%) melt, dehydrochlorination of alkyl halides may be carried out, e.g. n-butyl chloride gave butene (95%) at 400°C, the optimum temperature, and $77 \cdot 5\%$ of the starting material reacted, whereas at 240°C only 24% reacted. The advantage of the high temperatures involved in molten salt media is indicated clearly by this example. However, if the temperature was too high, some of the product decomposed on the glass walls. It should be noted that an equimolar melt of $AlCl_3 + NaCl$ was found to be unsatisfactory because of the partial polymerization of the butene.

Using an $AlCl_3$ melt the reverse reaction is also possible, e.g. in $AlCl_3 + NaCl + CuCl_2$ at 400°C, ethane and chlorine react to form 45% ethyl chloride. If a eutectic melt of $AlCl_3 + NaCl + KCl$ (89°C) is used, ethylene and hydrogen chloride give ethyl chloride in 82% yield.

The remaining 18% of ethylene polymerizes or cracks in the melt and this undesirable reaction increases with increasing temperature. Thus there is need, in some cases, for molten salt mixtures of low melting points. Ternary eutectic mixtures would appear to be the most suitable low temperature solvents.

6. Other Preparations Involving Reactions in Molten Salt Solvents

Sundermeyer *et al.* (1962) have prepared vinyl chloride in 97% yield by passing 1,1-dichloroethane vapour into molten $ZnCl_2 + KCl$ or $ZnCl_2 + CuCl$ respectively at 330°C. Alternatively, an equimolar mixture of acetylene and chlorine can be used with a melt containing a mercury salt. A melt containing $NaCl + AlCl_3$ at 175°C was found excellent for Friedel-Crafts reactions (Glemser and Kleine-Weischede, 1962).

7. The Preparation of Silane (Sundermeyer and Glemser, 1958)

A commercially important application of reactions involving molten salt solvents is in the preparation of silane. $SiCl_4$ vapour was passed into LiH dissolved in a $LiCl + KCl$ eutectic melt at 400°C and mono-silane was obtained in almost 100% yield. The LiH was regenerated by electrolysis, followed by the passage of hydrogen through the melt.

B. OTHER REACTIONS INVOLVING INORGANIC SUBSTANCES IN MOLTEN SALT SOLVENTS

Molten salt solvents are generally better solvents for certain substances than the conventional solvents, hence greater concentrations of reacting species can be used. Whilst the nature of a molten salt solvent differs from that of the usual room temperature solvents, concepts such as acid-base dissociation and "pH" are still valid in considering reactions in molten salts.

Molten alkali-metal nitrates may be considered to be analogous to the solvent water in that they both exhibit the property of acid–base dissociation, e.g.

$$NO_3^- \rightleftharpoons NO_2^+ + O^{2-} \tag{12}$$

which is analogous to the dissociation,

$$H_2O \rightleftharpoons H^+ + OH^-. \tag{13}$$

The dissociation constant of the first reaction is much smaller than that of the second. By bubbling NO_2 over platinum an electrode reaction,

$$NO_2 \rightleftharpoons NO_2^+ + e \tag{14}$$

may take place and this is analogous to the hydrogen electrode reaction,

$$\tfrac{1}{2}H_2 \rightleftharpoons H^+ + e. \tag{15}$$

The familiar acid–base, dichromate–chromate reaction, also occurs in molten salts (Blomgren and Van Artsdalen, 1960). Potassium dichromate dissolves in molten $NaNO_3$ to give the characteristic colour of the dichromate ion. The addition to this solution of a little solid sodium carbonate causes an acid–base reaction in which CO_2 is given off from the solution and its colour changes to that of the chromate ion:

$$Cr_2O_7^{2-} + CO_3^{2-} = 2CrO_4^{2-} + CO_2. \tag{16}$$

Oxidation reactions also frequently take place,

$$\text{e.g. } BrO_3^- + 5Br^- = 3Br_2 + 3O^{2-}. \tag{17}$$

If bromide ion is dissolved in molten sodium nitrate and a trace of sodium bromate added, bromine is then formed according to the above equation.

1. *Metal Production in Molten Salt Solvents*

(a) *Commercial extraction of aluminium.* In the extraction of aluminium from its bauxite ore, purified alumina is electrolysed in molten cryolite (Na_3AlF_6) as solvent. The nature of the solvent is considered to be completely ionic, the dissociation process of melting being,

$$Na_3AlF_6 = 3Na^+ + AlF_6^{3-}. \tag{18}$$

The AlF_6^{3-} is thought partly to dissociate as follows:

$$AlF_6^{3-} \rightleftharpoons AlF_4^- + 2F^- \text{ (Foster, 1960)}. \tag{19}$$

(b) *Extraction of actinides.* Gruen *et al.* (1958) listed laboratory experiments for the preparation of Zr, Tl, U and Np from solutions of the tetravalent chlorides in a molten $LiCl + KCl$ eutectic by reaction with Mg metal. Uranium metal has also been prepared by reaction of the double salt Cs_2UCl_6 with Mg metal in an equimolar $CsCl + MgCl_2$ melt at 550°C,

$$Cs_2UCl_6 + 2Mg = U + 2MgCl_2 + 2CsCl. \tag{20}$$

The uranium precipitate was separated from the molten salt by filtration and subsequent washing. Spectroscopic analysis showed the metal to be free of caesium and magnesium. Uranium metal may also be electrolytically deposited in a molten $LiCl + KCl$ solvent with metallic uranium anodes.

(c) *Separation of similar metals.* Mixtures of similar metals dissolved as salts in molten salt-solvents may be separated readily by electrolysis. Molybdenum and tungsten have been extracted directly from the ore, scheelite in a molten salt-solvent (Zadra and Gomes, 1963). Different current densities were used to extract the metals separately.

(d) *Extraction of magnesium from silicate minerals.* Magnesium also can be extracted from its silicate minerals such as alinine and serpentine, by electrolysis (Labounski, 1963).

(e) *Extraction of lead from galena.* Lead may be extracted from the mineral galena in an equimolar mixture of sodium and potassium chlorides at 700°C. On passing a current through the mixture, lead is deposited at the cathode and chlorine and elementary sulphur are liberated on the anode (Gul'din and Buzhinskaya, 1961).

The refining of pig lead may be carried out by electrolysis in a molten KCl + LiCl solvent. $PbCl_2$ is dissolved in the solvent such that the relative proportions give a eutectic mixture (Delimarskii et al., 1961). Counter-current multi-stage molten salt-molten metal extraction has also recently been investigated for various metals (Josephson Jr., 1962).

2. Chromatographic Separations of Molten Salts (Gruen et al., 1958)

Approximately 0·01 M (with respect to the transition metal ions) solutions of the chlorides of Fe^{III}, Co^{II}, Ni^{II}, Cu^{II}, and UO_2^{II} in a molten $LiNO_3 +$ KNO_3 eutectic give well-defined coloured bands of the transition metal ions on a chromatographic column of γ–Al_2O_3. The absorbed ions may then be selectively eluted from the oxide column using a molten nitrate eutectic containing ammonium chloride (approx. 3 M). The success of the elution process depends markedly on the chloride concentration in the eluent.

3. Solvent Extraction of Molten Salts (Gruen et al., 1958)

Nitrates are particularly effective as salting out agents in aqueous systems. It is not surprising, therefore, that molten nitrates are also very effective. Transition metal ions such as Fe^{III}, Co^{II}, Ni^{II}, U^{VI}, Pr^{III}, and Nd^{III} dissolved in a $LiNO_3 + KNO_3$ eutectic have been quantitatively extracted by tributyl phosphate at 150°C.

It is also possible to use inorganic extractants. Molten B_2O_3, which forms an immiscible phase with molten LiCl + KCl eutectic is capable of extracting transition metal ions from the chloride solvent.

C. FUTURE DEVELOPMENTS

The uses of molten salts as solvents will increase as the research continues to show added applications. The most important future developments appear to be in the field of fuel cells, extraction and purification of metals, chemical reactions involving organic and inorganic substances, and nuclear reactors.

REFERENCES

Aten, A. H. W. (1910) Z. phys. Chem. **73**, 578.
Bell, W. R. G., Rowlands, C. B., Bamford, I. J., Thomas, W. G. and Jones, W. J. (1930) J. chem. Soc. 1927, 31.
Belozerskii, N. A. (1940) "Collected Works on the Electrochemistry of Fused Salts" (Russian), St. Inst. appl. Chem., issue 35, 50.

Belyaev, I. N. (1958) *Zh. neorg. Khim.* **3**, 2805.

Belyaev, I. N. (1960) *Russian chem. Rev.* **29**, 899.

Blander, M., Grimes, W. R., Smith, N. V. and Watson, G. M. (1959) *J. phys. Chem.* **63**, 1164.

Biltz, W. and Klemm, W. (1926) *Z. anorg. Chem.* **152**, 267.

Blomgren, G. E. and Van Artsdalen, E. R. (1960) *Annu. Rev. phys. Chem.* **11**, 273.

Bloom, H. (1959) *Rev. pure appl. Chem.* **9**, 139.

Bloom, H. (1963) *Pure appl. Chem.* **7**, 389.

Bloom, H. and Bockris, J. O'M. (1959) "Modern Aspects of Electrochemistry Vol. II", pp. 160–261. Butterworths Scientific Publications, London.

Bloom, H. and Rhodes, D. C. (1956) *J. phys. Chem.* **60**, 791.

Bockris, J. O'M. and Richards, N. E. (1957) *Proc. roy. Soc. A***241**, 44.

Boleslaw, L. D. and Scheidt, R. C. (1961) *XVIII Con. Pure Appl. Chem.* 170.

Bratland, D., Grjotheim, K. and Krohn, C. (1963) *XIX Con. Pure and Appl. Chem.* (Proceedings not yet published).

Braunstein, J., Blander, M. and Lindgren, R. M. (1962) *J. Amer. chem. Soc.* **84**, 1529.

Braunstein, J. and Lindgren, R. M. (1962) *J. Amer. chem. Soc.* **84**, 1534.

Bredig, M. A. (1962) *J. chem. Phys.* **37**, 451.

Bredig, M. A. (1963) "Mixtures of Metals with Molten Salts", ORNL–3391 UC–4–Chem.

Bredig, M. A. and Bronstein, H. R. (1955) *J. Amer. chem. Soc.* **77**, 1454.

Bredig, M. A. and Johnson, J. W. (1960) *J. phys. Chem.* **64**, 1899.

Bredig, M. A., Johnson, G. and Smith, W. (1955) *J. Amer. chem. Soc.* **77**, 307.

Bronstein, H. R. and Bredig, M. A. (1958) *J. Amer. chem. Soc.* **80**, 2077.

Bronstein, H. R. and Bredig, M. A. (1961) *J. phys. Chem.* **65**, 1220.

Bruner, B. L. and Corbett, J. D. (1961) *J. inorg. nucl. Chem.* **20**, 62.

Bues, W. (1955) *Z. anorg. Chem.* **279**, 104.

Bunsen, N. and Kirchoff, R. (1861) *Pogg. Ann.* **113**, p. 345 (now *Ann. Phys., Lpz.*).

Burkhard, W. J. and Corbett, J. D. (1957) *J. Amer. chem. Soc.* **79**, 6361.

Campbell, A. N., Kartzmark, E. M. and Williams, D. F. (1962) *Canad. J. Chem.* **40**, 890.

Cook, C. M. Jr. and Dunn, W. E. Jr. (1961) *XVIII Con. Pure Appl. Chem.* 110.

Corbett, J. D. and Albers, F. C. (1960) *J. Amer. chem. Soc.* **82**, 533.

Corbett, J. D. and Hershaft, A. (1958) *J. Amer. chem. Soc.* **80**, 1530.

Corbett, J. D. and Winbush, S. V. (1955) *J. Amer. chem. Soc.* **77**, 3964.

Corbett, J. D., Winbush, S. V. and Albers, F. C. (1957) *J. Amer. chem. Soc.* **79**, 3020.

Cubicciotti, D. (1949) *J. Amer. chem. Soc.* **71**, 4119.

Cubicciotti, D. and Cleary, G. (1952) *J. Amer. chem. Soc.* **74**, 557.

Cubicciotti, D. (1953a) *J. Metals. N.Y.* **5**.

Cubicciotti, D. (1953b) *Trans. Amer. Inst. mech. Engrs* **197**, 1106.

Cubicciotti, D. (1960) *J. chem. Educ.* **37**, 540.

Danilov, V. I. and Krasnitskii, S. Ya. (1955) *Dokl. Akad. Nauk S.S.S.R.* **101**, 661.

Delimarskii, Yu. K. (1955) *Zh. fiz. khim.* **29**, 28.

Delimarskii, Yu. K. and Markov, B. F. (1961) "Electrochemistry of Fused Salts", pp. 336. Sigma Press.

Delimarskii, Yu. K., Markov, B. F., Panchenko, I. D., Gutmann, E. B. and Kolotii, A. A. (1961) "Soviet Electrochemistry", Vol. III, p. 96. Consultants Bureau, New York.

De Maine, P. A. D. and McAlonie, G. E. (1961) *J. inorg. nucl. Chem.* **18**, 286.

Druding, L. F. and Corbett, J. D. (1959) *J. Amer. chem. Soc.* **81**, 5512.

Druding, L. F. and Corbett, J. D. (1961) *J. Amer. chem. Soc.* **83**, 2462.

Dworkin, A. S., Bronstein, H. R. and Bredig, M. A. (1962) *J. phys. Chem.* **66**, 572.

Eley, D. D. and King, P. J. (1951) *Trans. Faraday Soc.* **47**, 1287.

Farquharson, J. and Heymann, E. (1935) *Trans. Faraday Soc.* **31**, 1004.

Flengas, S. N. (1960) *Ann. N.Y. Acad. Sci.* **79**, 853.

Foster, L. M. (1960) *Ann. N.Y. Acad. Sci.* **79**, 919.

Gardner, D. M. and Fraenkel, G. K. (1956) *J. Amer. chem. Soc.* **78**, 3279.

Glemser, O. and Kleine-Weischede, K. (1962) *Liebigs Ann.* **659**, 17.

Greenberg, J. and Sundheim, B. R. (1958) *J. chem. Phys.* **29**, 1029.

Greenberg, J., Sundheim, B. R. and Gruen, D. M. (1958) *J. chem. Phys.* **29**, 461.

Grimes, W. R., Smith, N. V. and Watson, G. M. (1958) *J. phys. Chem.* **62**, 862.

Grjotheim, K., Gronvold, F. and Krogh-Moe, J. (1955) *J. Amer. chem. Soc.* **77**, 5824.

Grjotheim, K., Heggelund, P., Krohn, C. and Motzfeldt, K. (1962) *Acta chem. Scand.* **16**, 689.

Gruen, D. M., Fried, S., Graf, P. and McBeth, R. L. (1958) "Chemistry of Fused Salts", pp. 26. A/CONF. 15/P/940 U.S.A.

Gruen, D. M. and McBeth, R. L. (1959) *J. inorg. nucl. chem.* **9**, 290.

Gul'din, I. T. and Buzhinskaya, A. V. (1961) "Soviet Electrochemistry", vol. III, pp. 100–109. Consultants Bureau, New York.

Guntz, A. and Benoit, F. (1924) *Bull. Soc. chim. Fr.* **35**, 709.

Harris, R. L., Wood, R. E. and Ritter, H. L. (1951) *J. Amer. chem. Soc.* **73**, 3151.

Hevesy, G. and Löwenstein, E. (1930) *Z. anorg. Chem.* **187**, 266.

Heymann, E. and Friedlander, E. (1930) *Z. phys. Chem.* **148**, 177.

Hildebrand, J. H. and Salstrom, E. J. (1932) *J. Amer. chem. Soc.* **54**, 4257.

Inman, D., Hills, G. J., Young, L. and Bockris, J. O'M. (1960) *Ann. N.Y. Acad. Sci.* **79**, 803.

Johnson, J. W. and Bredig, M. A. (1958) *J. phys. Chem.* **62**, 604.

Johnson, J. W. and Bredig, M. A. (1960) *J. phys. Chem.* **64**, 64.

Johnson, J. W., Cubicciotti, D. and Kelley, C. M. (1958) *J. phys. Chem.* **62**, 1107.

Josephson, P. R. Jr. (1962) *Dissertation Abstr.* **22**, 2322.

Karpachev, S. V., Stromberg, A. G. and Iordan, E. (1944) *Zh. fiz. khim.* **18**, 43.

Kendall, J., Crittenden, E. D. and Miller, H. K. (1923) *J. Amer. chem. Soc.* **45**, 963.

Klemm, W. and Huss, E. (1949) *Z. anorg. Chem.* **258**, 221.

Krebs, H. (1957) *Z. Naturf.* **12***b*, 795.

Kreye, W. C. and Kellogg, H. H. (1957) *Trans. electrochem. Soc.* **104**, 504.

Kroll, W. J. (1955) *Metallurgy* **9**, 366.

Labounski (1963) U.S. Patent 3,093,558.

"Landolt-Börnstein Zahlenwerte und Funktionen," Vol. II, Part 3 (1956). Springer-Verlag, Berlin.

Landon, G. J. and Ubbelohde, A. R. (1956) *Trans. Faraday Soc.* **52**, 647.

Latimer, W. M. (1952) "Oxidation Potentials", 2nd edition, 392 pp. Prentice Hall, Inc., New York.

Levy, H. A., Bredig, M. A., Danford, M. D. and Agron, P. A. (1960a) *J. phys. Chem.* **64**, 1959.

Levy, H. A., Agron, P. A., Bredig, M. A. and Danford, M. D. (1960b) *Ann. N.Y. Acad. Sci.* **79**, Art. 11, 762.

Lorentz, R. and Eitel, E. (1915) *Z. anorg. Chem.* **91**, 46.

Lorentz, R. and Eitel, W. (1926) "Pyrosole" Akademische Verlagsgesellschafte, M.B.H., Leipzig.

Mathers, F. C. and Stroup, P. T. (1934) *J. electrochem. Soc.* **66**, 245.

Paterno, E. and Muzzuchelli, A. (1908) *Gazz. chim. ital.* **38**, 137.

Peterson, D. and Hinkebein, J. A. (1959) *J. phys. Chem.* **63**, 1360.

Pitzer, K. (1962) *J. Amer. chem. Soc.* **84**, 2025.

Pushin, N. (1958) *J. gen. Chem., Moscow* **18**, 1599.

Rogers, P. S., Tomlinson, J. W. and Richardson, F. D. (1961) *Met. Soc. Conf.* **8**, 909.

Sallach, R. A. and Corbett, J. D. (1962) *Inorg. Chem.* **2**, 457.

Schaffer, J. H., Grimes, W. R. and Watson, G. M. (1959) *J. phys. Chem.* **63**, 1999.

Smith, G. P. (1965) "Electronic Absorption Spectra of Molten Salts", *in* "Molten Salt Chemistry" (M. Blander, ed.). Interscience, New York (in the press).

Staffansson, L. I. (1959) "The Physical Chemistry of Metals in their Molten Halides." Ph.D. Thesis, London.

Stern, K. H. (1961) *XVIII Con. Pure Appl. Chem. 177.*

Sundermeyer, Von W. (1962a) *Z. anorg. Chem.* **313**, 290.

Sundermeyer, Von. W. (1962b) *Z. anorg. Chem.* **314**, 100.

Sundermeyer, Von W. (1963) *Chem. Ber.* **96**, 1293.

Sundermeyer, Von. W. and Glemser, O. (1958) *Angew Chem.* **70, Nr. 20**, 625.

Sundermeyer, Von W., Glemser, O. and Kleine-Weischede, K. (1962) *Chem. Ber.* **95**, 1829.

Sundermeyer, Von W. and Meise, W. (1962) *Z. anorg. Chem.* **317**, 334.

Temkin, M. (1945) *Acta phys.-chim. U.R.S.S.* **20**, 411.

Topol, L. E. and Laudis, A. L. (1960) *J. Amer. chem. Soc.* **82**, 6291.

Van Artsdalen, E. R. (1956) *J. phys. Chem.* **60**, 172.

Van Artsdalen, E. R. (1959) "The Structure of Electrolytic Solutions", (W. J. Hamer, ed.) p. 411–421. Wiley, New York.

Wait, S. C. and Janz, G. J. (1963) *Quart. Rev.* **17**, 225.

Winsor, V. R. and Cady, G. H. (1948) *J. Amer. chem. Soc.* **70**, 1500.

Yosim, S. J. and Luchsinger, E. B. (1960) *Ann. N.Y. Acad. Sci.* **79**, 1079.

Yosim, S. J. and Mayer, S. W. (1960) *J. phys. Chem.* **64**, 909.

Yosim, S. J., Darnell, A. J., Gehman, W. G. and Mayer, S. W. (1959) *J. phys. Chem.* **63**, 230.

Yosim, S. J., Ransom, L. D., Sallach, R. A. and Topol, L. E. (1962) *J. phys. Chem.* **66**, 28.

Zadra and Gomes (1963) U.S. Patent 3,075,900, 204.

Zarzycki, G. (1957a) *C.R. Acad. Sci., Paris* **224**, 758.

Zarzycki, G. (1957b) *J. Phys. Radium* **18**, 65A.

Zhurin, A. I. (1935) *Metallurgy* **10** Nr. 4, 87.

Author Index

(Numbers in italics refer to pages in the References at the end of each Chapter.)

A

Accascina, F., 9, 10, *43*
Acrivos, J. V., 17, *41*
Adams, R. M., 51, 57, 57, 67, 72, *79*
Addison, C. C., 307, 332, *349*
Adie, R. H., 176, *205*
Adler, J. H., 142, *208*
Adolfsson, G., 342, *349*
Aellig, C., 257, 258, *283*
Agerman, M., 312, *349*
Agron, P. A., 355, 371, *389*
Albers, F. C., 327, *349*, 369, 370, 371, 372, 373, *388*
Alder, B. J., 18, *42*
Anderson, H. H., 187, *205*
Andersson, L. H., 309, 311, 312, 316, *349*, *352*
Andre, S., 259, *282*
Andrews, L. J., 215, *249*, 259, *282*, 286, *298*
Aoyama, S., 286, *298*
Archibald, E. H., 83, 85, 88, 89, 90, 96, 97, 100, *115*
Argument, C., 182, *209*
Armstrong, G. T., 2, 3, *41*
Arnold, E., 18, *42*
Arotsky, J., 180, 182, *205*, 289, *298*
Asher, D. R., 274, *284*
Asmussen, R. W., 329, *349*
Asprey, L. B., 294, *298*
Atoji, M., 60, *79*
Aten, A. H. W., 369, 370, *387*
Audrieth, L. F., 2, 20, 25, 34, *42*, 242, *249*, 253, 260, *282*
Aynsley, E. E., 257, *282*, 289, 296, 297, *298*

B

Baaz, M., 212, 213, *249*, *250*, 309, 318, 333, 335, 336, 337, 338, 341, 342, 343, 344, 345, 346, 347, *349*, *350*, *351*
Baenziger, N. C., 291, *299*
Bagster, L. S., 264, *282*
Baker, W., 186, *205*

Balog, G., 50, 53, 59, *80*, 85, *115*
Balowna, Z., 321, 323, *351*
Bamford, I. J., 358, 359, 360, *387*
Banks, A. A., 292, *298*
Barabonova, A. S., 219, *251*
Bar-Eli, K., 33, *42*
Barnes, J. C., 244, *249*
Barr, J., 180, 205, *205*
Barraclough, C. G., 187, *205*
Bass, S. J., 125, 126, 127, 132, 133, 136, 137, 138, 139, 142, 162, *205*
Bateman, L. C., 259, *282*
Baude, E., 257, *282*
Bauer, H., 272, 273, *284*, 329, 330, *352*
Baughan, E. C., 190, *210*, 302, 323, 325, 326, *349*, *350*, *352*
Beach, H. T., 255, *282*
Beachell, H. C., 72, *79*
Beattie, I. R., 244, *249*
Becker, E., 18, *42*
Beckham, L. J., 328, *349*
Beckman, T. A., 18, *42*
Beckmann, E., 96, *114*, 321, *349*
Beilstein, 226, *249*
Bekier, E., 264, *282*
Belcher, R. L., 238, *249*
Bell, W. R. G., 358, 359, 360, *387*
Belozerskii, N. A., 366, *387*
Belton, W. E., 255, 257, *282*
Belyaev, I. N., 375, *388*
Benesi, H. A., 215, *249*
Benoit, F., 367, *389*
Bent, H. A., 217, *249*
Berger, A., 191, *205*
Bergin, M. J., 30, *43*
Bergius, F., 142, *205*
Bergstrom, F. W., 2, 23, 31, *42*, *44*
Berns, D. S., 244, *249*
Bernstein, H. J., 156, *210*
Bernstein, R. B., 276, *283*
Bertaut, E. F., 311, *351*
Berthoud, A., 5, *42*
Betz, H. F., 162, *207*
Beyer, A., 307, 333, *352*
Bickerton, J. H., 257, *282*

Biltz, W., 61, *80*, 287, 288, *298*, 355, *388*
Bingle, J., 295, *298*
Birch, A. J., 2, 13, 34, 36, 41, *42*
Birchall, T., 156, 190, 191, 192, 198, *205*, 207
Bjerrum, N., 261, *282*
Blander, M., 356, 362, *388*
Blennemann, D., 34, *43*
Blois, M. S., 180, 199, *208*
Blomgren, C. E., 377, 386, *388*
Bloom, H., 354, 355, 356, 377, 379, 380, 381, *388*
Bockris, J. O'M., 354, 357, 362, 374, 383, *388*, *389*
Boez, A. K., 271, *284*
Boleslaw, L. D., 375, *388*
Bolton, J. R., 198, *205*
Bond, P. A., 255, 257, *282*
Booth, H. S., 257, *282*
Boston, C. R., 327, *349*
Boswijk, K. H., 292, *298*
Bouknight, J. W., 53, *81*
Bourke, P. J., 34, *42*
Bowman, G. B., 2, *43*
Bradley, A., 192, *205*
Brand, J. C. D., 128, 131, 139, 157, 159, 188, 204, *205*, *206*
Bränden, C. I., 212, *249*, 337, 338, 342, *349*, 352
Bratland, D., 362, *388*
Brauner, B., 172, 180, *206*
Braunstein, J., 356, *388*
Brayford, J. R., 122, 134, 139, 161, *206*
Bredig, M. A., 327, *349*, 355, 365, 366, 367, 368, 371, 372, *388*, *389*
Briegleb, G., 60, *79*, *81*
Bright, J. R., 259, *282*
Brivati, J. A., 198, *206*
Brockmann, R., 34, *43*
Bronstein, H. R., 366, *388*
Brost, G. A., 169, *210*
Brown, J., 34, *42*
Brown, T. H., 76, *79*
Browne, A. W., 95, *115*, 287, 288, *299*
Brubaker, C. H., 170, *206*
Brühl, J. W., 301, *349*
Bruner, B. L., 371, *388*
Bruner, L., 264, *282*
Bryntse, R., 342, *349*
Buckley, H., 178, *207*
Bues, W., 356, *388*
Buffagni, S., 229, 231, 232, 234, 236, *249*

Bull, W. E., 217, *249*, 251
Bunsen, N., 364, *388*
Bunton, C. A., 191, *206*
Burg, A. B., 257, 259, *282*, 328, 329, 330, 331, *349*
Burge, D. E., 273, 274, 277, 278, *282*
Burkhard, W. J., 364, *388*
Burwell, R. L., 246, 247, *249*
Busby, R. E., 240, *249*
Buzhinskaya, A. V., 387, *389*
Byrd, W. E., 259, *283*

C

Cadenbach, G., 53, 58, 74, 77, *79*
Cady, G. H., 65, *80*, 297, *298*, 364, *390*
Cady, H. P., 10, *43*, 264, 280, *283*, 301, *349*
Campbell, A. N., 357, 360, *388*
Campbell, G. W., 328, 329, *349*
Campion, D. E., 322, 326, *351*
Cannizzaro, S., von, 200, *206*
Carlson, R. L., 216, 224, 226, 228, 230, 231, 232, 234, 239, 243, 244, 246, *249*, *250*
Carpenter, G. B., 95, *115*
Carrington, A., 198, *205*, *206*
Carson, T., 179, *209*
Carter, R. P. Jr., 241, *250*
Casalino, A., 193, 196, 197, *209*
Casselmann, W., 334, *349*
Centnerszwer, M., 253, 255, 264, 273, *283*, 284
Chalandon, P., 223, 239, *251*
Chang, S., 87, *114*
Chatt, J., 41, *42*
Chedin, J., 173, *206*
Chittum, J. F., 5, *43*
Chou, D. Y. P., 37, *42*
Chretien, P., 181, *206*
Clark, H. C., 171, *206*
Clark, H. O., 18, *42*
Cleary, G., 368, 371, *388*
Clifford, A. F., 65, 72, 75, *79*
Clusius, K., 276, *283*
Coates, G. E., 170, 171, *206*
Cole, A. G., 30, *42*
Cole, R. H., 128, *207*
Conley, R. F., 10, *45*
Connick, R. E., 218, *249*
Conradi, J. J., 198, *210*
Cook, C. M. Jr., 382, *388*
Cook, D., 96, *114*
Cooling, G., 264, *282*

Corbett, J. D., 327, *349*, 364, 368, 369, 370, 371, 372, 373, *388*, *390*
Cornides, I., 6, *42*
Corwin, A. H., 192, *208*
Cotton, F. A., 217, 237, *249*
Coulter, L. V., 15, 30, *42*, *45*
Couture, A. M., 8, *42*, 140, *206*
Crage, C., 4, *42*
Craig, D. P., 302, *349*
Craig, R. A., 132, 167, 203, *206*, *209*
Cram, D. J., 24, 31, 41, *42*
Crittenden, E. D., 319, *351*, 375, 376, *389*
Cronander, A. W., 314, *350*
Crone, E. B., 255, *282*
Croy, V. D., 326, *351*
Cruse, K., 245, *250*, 265, *283*
Cseko, G., 6, *42*
Cubicciotti, D., 327, *349*, *351*, 368, 369, 370, 371, *388*, *389*
Curran, C., 259, *284*
Cuthrell, R. E., 30, *42*
Cutler, D., 17, *42*
Czapski, G., 35, *42*

D

Dacre, B., 125, 154, *206*
Dadape, V. V., 343, *350*
Dafert, O., 316, *350*
Daggett, H. M., 261, *283*
Dahmlos, J., 53, *79*
Dallinga, G., 198, *206*
Danford, M. D., 355, 371, *389*
Danilov, V. I., 355, *388*
Danyluk, S. S., 96, 101, *115*
d'Arcy, R. H., 164, *206*
Darnell, A. J., 371, 372, *390*
Dasent, W. E., 181, *206*
Daure, P., 311, *350*
Davidson, A. W., 142, *208*
Davies, A., 292, *298*
Davies, A. G., 323, 325, 326, *350*
Davis, S., 87, *114*
Davis, W. Jr., 76, *80*
Davis, W. J., 52, 53, 54, 60, *80*
Davison, A., 184, 185, *206*
Dawson, K. R., 238, *249*
Dawson, L. R., 230, 231, 232, 237, 240, 242, *249*, *251*
Dayton, J. C., 33, *45*

Deans, F. B., 169, *206*
de Boer, E., 198, 204, *206*, *210*
de Boer, J. L., 293, *298*
De Grotthuss, C. J. T., 29, *42*
Dehn, H., 348, *350*
Del Fresno, C., 86, *114*
Del Greco, F. P., 75, *79*
Delimarskii, Yu. K., 354, 365, 373, 374, 387, *388*
de Maine, P. A. D., 219, 235, *250*, 259, *283*, 360, *388*
Denison, W. A., 6, *45*
Deno, N. C., 160, 190, 196, 198, 199, 200, 201, 202, 203, 204, *206*, *209*
de Right, R. E., 197, *206*
Dess, H. M., 318, *350*
Detmar, O., 294, 297, *299*
Devin, C., 329, *352*
Devlin, O. M., 169, *210*
Dewald, J. F., 37, *42*
Deyrup, A. J., 63, *79*, 132, 133, 157, 159, 190, *208*
Dickerson, R. T., 86, *114*
Dietz, G., 327, *350*
Dingwall, A., 190, *206*
Dirian, G., 34, *42*
Dittmar, H. R., 197, *206*
Dodd, D. M., 130, 131, 162, *210*
Dodgen, H. W., 28, *43*
Dodger, H. W., 27, *44*
Dole, M., 141, *208*
Dolezalek, F., 172, *206*
Donoghue, J. T., 235, *249*
Dorfman, L. M., 35, 38, *42*
Down, J. L., 41, *42*
Drago, R. S., 213, 214, *216*, 217, 218, 222, 223, 224, 226, 228, 230, 231, 232, 234, 235, 236, 239, 241, 242, 243, 244, 246, *249*, *250*, *251*, 306, 344, *352*
Dravieko, F., 198, *206*
Dresdner, R. D., 53, *81*
Druce, J. G. F., 170, *206*
Drucker, J., 264, *283*
Druding, L. F., 368, *388*
Dullenkopf, W., 31, *45*
Dunn, T. M., 216, 229, 231, 233, 234, 236, *249*, *250*
Dunn, W. E. Jr., 382, *388*
Dutoit, P., 262, *283*
Dworkin, A. S., 366, *388*
Dye, J. L., 16, *42*
Dykhno, N., 6, *42*

E

Eaborn, C., 169, *206*
Easteal, A., 360
Eastham, J. F., 39, 40, *44*
Edwards, J. O., 166, *206*
Ehrlich, P., 327, *350*
Eigen, M., 136, *210*
Einarsson, P., 272, *284*
Eingorn, L. N., 314, *350*
Eitel, E., 364, *389*
Eitel, W., 369, *389*
Elbs, K., 172, *206*
Eley, D. D., 359, *388*
Ellendt, G., 245, *250*
Elliott, W. W., 197, *206*
Elma, R. J., 293, *298*
Elsey, H. M., 4, *42*, 280, *283*
Elving, P. J., 253, 260, *283*
Eméleus, H. J., 294, 295, *298, 299*
Engels, S., 315, *351*
Ephraim, F., 257, 258, *283*
Esch, W., 172, *206*
Evans, R. V. G., 187, *206*

F

Fackler, J. P. Jr., 216, 242, *250*
Farquharson, J., 356, 369, *388*
Feder, H. M., 52, *79*
Fedorova, G. K., 99, *115*
Fellinger, L. L., 34, *42*
Feltz, A., 314, *351*
Fenske, M. R., 6, *42, 43*
Fernelius, W. C., 2, 23, *42, 43, 44*, 259, *282*
Ferraro, J. R., 238, *250*
Fessler, W. A., 328, *349*
Fiat, D. N., 218, *249*
Fichter, F., 180, *206*
Field, F. B., 186, *205*
Figgis, B. N., 191, *206*
Fine, D. A., 216, 231, 237, *250*
Finkelstein, W., 288, *298*
Finkh, K., 172, *206*
Firla, T., 341, *352*
Fischer, F., 172, *206*
Fischer, J., 295, *298*
Fischer, W., 61, *80*
Fish, R. W., 101, *114*, 202, *208*
Fitzgerald, T. B., 259, *283*
Fleischer, J., 257, 258, 259, *283*

Flengas, S. N., 363, *389*
Fletcher, H. G., Jr., 77, *80*
Flexser, L. A., 190, *206*
Flowers, R. H., 125, 127, 129, 132, 133, 137, 138, 139, 142, 145, 146, 152, 162, 163, 164, 165, 167, 168, 169, 179, 180, 188, 193, 194, 205, *205, 207*
Fluck, E., 99, *114*
Fohn, E. C., 30, *42*
Foote, H. W., 257, 258, 259, *283*
Foster, L. M., 386, *389*
Fowles, G. W. A., 2, 34, *43*
Fraenkel, G. K., 361, *389*
Francis, R., 217, *249*
Franck, E. U., 53, 54, 60, *79, 81*
Franklin, E. C., 2, 5, 10, 25, 30, *43*, 254, *283*
Fraser, M. J., 102, *114*, 338, *350*
Fredenhagen, H., 74, *79*
Fredenhagen, K., 53, 58, 74, 77, *79*
Freed, S., 17, 18, *43*
French, C. M., 231, *250*
Fresco, J. M., 173, *209*
Freund, H., 273, *282*
Fried, S., 379, 386, 387, *389*
Friedlander, E., 364, *389*
Friedman, N. J., 238, *250*
Frost, A. A., 39, *43*
Frycz, K., 321, 324, *350*
Fujita, J., 187, *209*
Fuoss, R. M., 9, 10, *43*, 90, *114, 115*, 234, 240, 244, *249, 251*, 260, 261, *283*, 336, *350*

G

Gable, C. M., 162, *207*
Gagnaux, P., 236, 239, *250*
Gallagher, W. P., 110, *115*, 241, *250*
Gardner, D. M., 361, *389*
Garnet, C. S., 28, *45*
Garrett, A. B., 132, 167, 196, 203, *206, 209*
Garton, G., 340, *352*
Garver, E. E., 292, 295, *299*
Gauldie, J., 192
Gebert, E., 216, 238, *250*
Gehman, W. G., 371, 372, *390*
Geier, R. G., 6, *42, 43*
Geisel, E., 13, *45*
George, J. W., 311, 315, 327, *350*
Gerding, H., 212, *250*, 310, 328, 330, 340, *350*

Gerrard, W., 102, *114*, 338, *350*
Gerson, F., 102, *114*
Gianque, W. F., 3, *44*, 126, 129, 130, 154, 162, *207*, *208*, 254, *283*, 286, *298*
Gibson, C. S., 187, *206*
Gibson, S., 316, *350*
Giguère, P. A., 58, *79*, 130, 131, 155, 162, 163, *207*
Gilbert, L. F., 178, *207*
Gill, N. S., 235, *250*
Gillespie, R. J., 76, *79*, 88, 99, 112, *114*, 118, 122, 123, 125, 126, 127, 128, 129, 130, 131, 132, 133, 134, 135, 136, 137, 138, 139, 142, 145, 146, 148, 150, 152, 153, 154, 156, 157, 159, 161, 162, 163, 164, 165, 166, 167, 168, 169, 170, 171, 172, 173, 174, 177, 179, 180, 182, 187, 188, 189, 190, 191, 192, 193, 194, 196, 197, 198, 202, 203, 205, *205*, *207*, *208*
Glasstone, S., 85, *114*
Glazer, H., 254, *283*
Glebocka, M., 259, *283*
Glemser, O., 360, 384, 385, *389*, *390*
Glockler, G., 85, *114*
Glover, K. H., 231, *250*
Gluekauf, E., 137, 138, *208*
Gmelin, 255, 256, 276, *283*, 321, 322, *350*
Goddard, D. R., 173, *208*
Golben, M., 240, *249*
Gold, M., 13, 17, 18, 19, *43*, *44*
Gold, V., 100, *114*, 155, 179, 198, 199, 200, *208*
Gomes, 386, *390*
Goodgame, D. M. L., 237, *249*
Goodgame, M., 237, *249*
Gordon, S., 56, *80*
Gore, G., 83, 97, *114*
Gorenbein, E. Y., 327, *350*
Goubeau, J., 31, *45*
Gover, T. A., 226, 227, *250*
Grace, J. A., 201, *208*
Graf, P., 379, 386, 387, *389*
Graff, W., 95, 107, *114*
Graham, J., 122, 132, 135, 173, 174, 192, *207*, *208*
Grandcollot, P., 34, *42*
Grange, P., 85, *114*
Green, L. R., 6, 7, 8, 14, 15, *43*
Greenberg, J., 361, *389*
Greenwood, N. N., 127, 129, 145, 166, *208*, 210, 289, 290, 292, 297, *298*, 310, 317, 318, 340, *350*, *352*

Griffiths, U. S., 240, *249*
Grigg, E. C. M., 274, *283*
Grimes, W. R., 362, 363, *388*, *389*, *390*
Grisard, J. W., 292, *298*
Grjotheim, K., 362, 370, *388*, *389*
Groeneveld, W. L., 315, 339, *350*
Gronvold, F., 370, *389*
Grossweiner, L. I., 38, *45*
Groves, P. T., 198, 201, 204, *206*
Grubb, H. M., 5, *43*
Gruen, D. M., 360, 361, 379, 386, 387, *389*
Gryder, J. W., 75, *79*
Gul'din, I. T., 387, *389*
Gunn, S. R., 6, 7, 8, 14, 15, *43*
Günther, K., 319, *351*
Guntz, A., 367, *389*
Gurney, R. W., 141, 142, *208*
Gur'yanova, E. N., 24, *43*
Gustavson, G., 334, *350*
Gutmann, E. B., 387, *388*
Gutmann, V., 88, *114*, 212, 213, *249*, *250*, 290, 294, *298*, 305, 308, 309, 310, 312, 314, 315, 316, 317, 318, 329, 333, 334, 335, 336, 337, 338, 339, 340, 341, 342, 343, 344, 345, 346, 347, 348, *349*, *350*, *351*
Gyr, E., 262, *283*

H

Hall, S. K., 122, 143, 150, 188, 205, *208*
Hallada, C. J., 13, 17, *43*, *44*
Hammett, L. P., 63, 71, *79*, 132, 133, 135, 157, 159, 190, 193, 196, 198, *206*, *208*, 210
Hammick, D. L., 197, *206*
Hampel, G., 347, *349*, *351*
Hanby, W. E., 181, *209*
"Handbook of Chemistry and Physics" 39th Edition, 1957–8, 85, *114*
Hansley, V. L., 41, *45*
Hantzsch, A., 86, *114*, 142, 164, 192, 193, 195, 196, 199, 203, *208*
Hardy, M. L., 189, *210*
Hardy, W. B., 259, *283*
Hargreaves, G. B., 295, 296, 297, *298*
Harmon, K. M., 87, *114*
Harned, H. S., 7, *43*
Harper, D., 4, *42*
Harris, R. L., 355, *389*
Harrter, D. R., 158, 160, *208*

Hart, D., 216, 226, 228, 230, 231, 239, 241, 246, *249*
Hart, H., 101, *114*, 201, 202, *208*
Hasing, J., 15, *43*
Hastie, J. W., 356, 358, 359
Hathaway, B. J., 171, *208*, *209*
Haul, R., 34, *43*
Hawes, B. M. W., 199, *208*
Hawes, W. W., 9, 28, *43*
Hecht, H., 268, 270, *283*
Heggelund, P., 362, *389*
Heilbronner, E., 102, *114*
Hepler, L. G., 8, *43*
Hepworth, M. A., 294, *298*
Herber, R. H., 274, 276, *283*, 310, 339, *351*
Herbrandson, H. F., 86, *114*
Hermodsson, Y., 272, *283*
Hershaft, A., 371, *388*
Herzberg, G., 55, *79*, 85, *114*
Herzenstein, A., 264, *284*
Hess, G. P., 78, *80*
Hetherington, G., 332, *351*
Heubal, J., *115*
Hevesy, G., 369, 370, *389*
Hewitt, F., 328, *351*
Heymann, E., 356, 364, 369, *388*, *389*
Heyn, A. H. A., 30, *43*
Heyns, K., 34, *43*
Higler, W. S., 73, *80*
Hildebrand, J. H., 19, 21, *43*, 59, 60, *80*, *81*, 215, *249*, 287, *299*, 382, *389*
Hill, A. E., 259, *283*
Hill, M. E., 192, *205*
Hillesund, S., 5, *45*
Hills, G. J., 374, 383, *389*
Himml, R., 308, 329, 338, 341, *351*
Hindman, J. C., 76, *79*
Hinkebein, J. A., 367, *389*
Hitchcock, C. S., 85, 102, *115*
Hnizda, V. F., 5, 9, *43*
Hodge, J. D., 202, 203, *206*
Hodge, N., *349*
Hodgins, J. W., 13, *43*
Hofstra, A., 69, *80*, 198, *209*
Holliday, A. K., 96, 107, *115*, 328, *351*
Holm, C. H., 17, *44*
Holmes, L. H., *251*
Holmes, R. R., 110, *115*, 230, 231, 240, 241, *249*, *250*, *251*, 311, *351*
Holstead, C., 191, *208*
Hood, G. C., 157, *208*

Hornig, D. F., 58, 60, *80*
Horning, E. E., 162, *207*
Horning, W. C., 139, 157, 159, 188, 204, *206*
Horsfield, A., 18, *42*
Houser, J. J., 202, 203, *206*
Houtgraaf, H., 310, 328, 330, *350*
Howick, L. C., 327, *349*
Hu, J. H., 53, 54, *79*, 286, *298*
Hubacek, H., 309, 347, *351*
Hubbard, W. N., 52, *79*
Hübner, L., 212, *249*, 309, 338, 341, 343, 344, 346, *349*
Huggins, C. M., 218, *251*
Hughes, E. D., 122, 132, 135, 173, 174, *207*, *208*, 259, *282*
Hulme, R., 198, *206*
Hume, D. N., 216, 244, *249*, *250*
Hunt, H., 4, 5, *43*, *45*
Hunt, J. P., 28, *43*
Huss, E., 362, *389*
Huster, E., 18, *43*
Huston, J. L., 274, 275, 276, *283*
Hutchison, C. A. Jr., 14, 17, *43*
Hyman, H. H., 50, 51, 53, 56, 59, 64, 71, 72, 76, *79*, *80*, 86, 94, *115*, 292, *298*

I

Ihle, H., 34, *43*
Imhof, V., 239
Immig, H., 259, 268, 269, 270, 271, 272, *283*
Ingold, C. K., 122, 132, 135, 155, 173, 174, 176, 204, *207*, *208*, 259, *282*
Inman, D., 374, 383, *389*
Iordan, E., 371, *389*
Ipat'ev, V. V., 6, *43*
Ipsen, R., 334, *352*
Isbekow, W., 319, *351*
Ishida, K., 6, 21, *43*
Izrailevich, E. A., 4, *45*

J

Jache, A. W., 65, *80*
Jack, W. M., 72, *79*
Jackman, D. C., 37, *42*
Jackson, J. H., 218, *250*
Jaffe, H., 14, *43*
Jaffée, H. H., 102, *115*

Jakubson, S., 288, *298*
James, J. C., 128, *206*
Jander, G., 2, 20, *43*, 253, 255, 256, 257, 258, 259, 260, 263, 266, 267, 268, 269, 270, 271, 272, 273, 275, 280, *283*, *284*, 286, 288, *298*, 319, 322, 323, 326, *351*
Janjic, D., 236, 239, *250*
Janz, G. J., 96, 101, *115*, 356, 379, *390*
Jaques, C., 194, 195, *208*
Jarry, R. L., 52, 53, 54, 60, 76, *80*
Jarvie, A. W. P., 204, *206*
Jarvzelski, J. J., 201, *206*
Jasper, J. J., 259, *282*
Jeep, K., 288, *298*
Job, P., 216, *250*
Joesten, M. D., 217, 223, 224, 226, 230, 234, 236, 241, 243, *250*
Johnson, G., 366, *388*
Johnson, J. B. A., 316, *350*
Johnson, J. W., 366, 369, 370, *388*, *389*
Johnson, L. F., Jnr., 274, *283*
Johnson, R. E., 274, *283*
Johnson, W. C., 7, 13, 14, *43*, *44*
Johnston, H. L., 53, 54, *79*, 286, *298*
Jolly, W. L., 2, 8, 12, 13, 14, 15, 16, 17, 18, 19, 22, 25, 26, 27, *43*, *44*
Jones, G., 141, *208*
Jones, T. P., 323, 325, *349*
Jones, W. H., 28, *45*
Jones, W. J., 358, 359, 360, *387*
Jørgensen, C. K., 237, *250*
Jorgenson, M. J., 158, 160, *208*
Jortner, J., 15, *44*
Josephson, P. R. Jr., 387, *389*
Josien, M. L., 85, *114*
Jouber, J. M., 203, *209*

K

Kahovec, L., 95, *115*
Kanda, E., 286, *298*
Kaplan, J., 17, *44*
Karpachev, S. V., 371, *389*
Kartzmark, E. M., 357, 360, *388*
Kashtanov, L. I., 259, *283*
Katriskey, A. R., 158, *210*
Katz, J. J., 50, 51, 56, 57, 64, 67, 72, 77, 78, *79*, *80*, *81*, 86, 94, *115*, 292, 295, *298*, *299*
Katzin, L. I., 216, 238, 240, 242, *250*
Kay, R. L., 9, 10, *44*
Keefer, R. M., 215, *249*, 259, *282*, 286, *298*

Keenan, C. W., 37, 39, 40, *42*, *44*
Kelley, C. M., 369, 370, *389*
Kellogg, H. H., 363, *389*
Kelly, E. J., 39, 40, *44*
Kendall, J., 142, *208*, 319, *351*, 375, 376, *389*
Keneshea, F. J., 327, *349*, *351*
Kerr, G. T., 168, *210*
Kershaw, D. N., 193, *208*
Kianpour, A., 326, *351*
Kibbel, H. U., 166, *210*
Kikuchi, S., 7, *44*
Kilpatrick, M., 50, 51, 53, 56, 59, 64, 67, 69, 71, 72, 73, *79*, *80*, 85, 86, 94, *115*
King, P. J., 359, *388*
Kirchoff, R., 364, *388*
Kirkbride, B. J., 125, 130, 139, 154, *208*
Kirsanov, O. V., 99, *115*
Kise, M. A., 328, *349*
Kittel, C., 17, *44*
Kivelson, H. D., 254, *283*
Klanberg, F., 28, *43*, 84, 89, 92, 95, 96, 98, 99, 100, 104, 106, 107, 108, 109, 110, 111, 112, *115*, 281, *284*, 338, *352*
Klanberg, T., 328, 329, *352*
Klein, F. S., 33, *42*
Kleinberg, J., 2, 20, 25, 34, *42*, 242, *249*, 253, 260, *282*
Kleine-Weischede, K., 360, 384, 385, *389*, *390*
Klemenc, A., 86, *115*
Klemensiewicz, Z., 321, 323, *351*
Klemm, W., 355, 362, *388*, *389*
Kliman, H., 260, *284*
Knight, W. D., 17, *44*
Knöll, H., 259, *283*
Knollmüller, K., 95, *115*
Knunyants, J. L., 332, *352*
Kobayashi, M., 187, *209*
Koch, A. L., 77, *80*
Koch, F. K. V., 238, *250*
Kohl, O., 86, *115*
Köhler, H., 334, *351*
Kohlschütter, H. W., 84, 89, 98, 99, 112, *115*
Kolditz, L., 314, 315, 316, 318, 323, *351*
Kolotii, A. A., 387, *388*
Kolthoff, I. M., 308, *351*
Kon, H., 180, 199, *208*
Kongpricha, S., 75, *79*
Königstein, J. A., 212, *250*, 328, 340, *350*
Kopple, K. D., 77, 78, *80*

Korezynski, A., 259, *283*
Korinek, G. J., 218, *250*
Kornblum, J., 257, 258, *283*
Kosanovic, Dj., 188, 195, 196, *209*
Kosower, E. M., 225, 232, 236, 239, 241, 243, *250*
Kothner, von P., 192, *208*
Koubek, E., 219, 235, *250*
Krasnitskii, S. Ya., 355, *388*
Krauss, C. A., 2, 5, 9, 13, 15, 16, 30, *43*, *44*, 90, *114*, *115*, 260, *283*, 288, *298*
Krebs, H., 361, *389*
Kreye, W. C., 363, *389*
Krogh-Moe, J., 370, *389*
Krohn, C., 362, *388*, *389*
Kroll, W. J., 363, *389*
Kudo, S., 7, *44*
Kuhl, H., 170, *210*
Kuhn, L. P., 192, 204, *208*
Kuipers, G. A., 55, *80*
Kuivila, H., 196, *209*
Kunze, O., 347, *349*
Kunzler, J. E., 126, 129, 130, 131, 154, 162, *207*, *208*

L

Labounski, 386, *389*
Lacher, J. R., 322, 326, *351*
Ladyshnikova, N. I., 4, *45*
Lagowski, J. J., 30, *42*
Laidler, K. J., 8, *42*, 140, *206*
Laitinen, H. A., 10, 11, 28, *44*, 308, *351*
Lamberton, A. H., 191, *208*
Lamont, W. A., 77, *80*
Landesman, H., 218, *250*, *251*
Landolt-Börnstein, 375, 376, *389*
Landon, G. J., 355, 356, *389*
Lane, T. I., 53, 59, 64, 72, *79*
Lang, R., 239, 241, *251*
Langer, M., 179, *209*
Langford, C. H., 246, 247, *249*, *250*
Langford, P. O., 246, *250*
Lappert, M. F., 102, *114*
LaRoche, L., 217, 223, 224, 226, 230, 236, 250
Lascombe, J., 85, *114*
Latimer, W. M., 25, *44*, 354, *389*
Laubicht, I., 274, 275, *284*
Lauder, I., 274, *283*
Laudis, A. L., 370, *390*
Lawroski, H., 6, *42*, *43*

Le Boucher, L., 61, *80*
Lecher, H. Z., 259, *283*
Lee, J. C., 34, *42*
Leech, H. R., 294, *298*
Le Fevre, R. J. W., 254, *283*
Lefrancois, B., 6, *44*
Leftin, H. P., 254, 260, 261, *284*
Lehmann, H. A., 162, *208*
Leighton, P. A., 31, *44*
Leisten, J. A., 88, 99, 112, *114*, 118, 134, 187, 188, 191, 192, 193, 194, 195, 196, 197, 198, 203, 204, *207*, *208*, *209*
Leman, G., 338, *351*
Lemons, J. F., 218, *250*
Lenard, J. I., 78, *80*
Lenher, V., 334, *351*
Lepoutre, G., 2, 16, 37, *42*, *44*
Lester, G. R., 226, 227, 228, 237, 242, *250*, 251
Levine, R., 2, *44*
Levy, H. A., 327, *349*, 355, 371, *389*
Levy, R. A., 17, *44*
Lewis, J., 41, *42*, 307, 310, 329, 332, *349*, 351
Lewis, J. I., 59, 67, *80*
Lia, J. S., 202, 203, *206*
Lichtin, N. N., 253, 254, 259, 260, 261, 266, 274, 275, 277, 281, 282, *283*, *284*
Lichty, D. M., 197, *209*
Lien, A. P., 73, *80*
Lier, A. P., 198, *209*
Liimatainen, R., 295, *298*
Liler, M., 150, 188, 195, 196, 197, *209*
Lindgren, R. M., 356, *388*
Lindquist, I., 212, 213, *249*, *250*, 272, *284*, 305, 309, 311, 312, 316, 317, 337, 338, 342, *349*, *351*, *352*
Lindquist, R. H., 18, *42*
Lippincott, E. R., 257, 281, 282, *284*
Lipscomb, W. N., 60, *79*
Loewenstein, A., 29, *44*
Long, F. A., 64, *80*, 157, *209*
Long, R. W., 60, *80*
Lorentz, R., 364, 369, *389*
Lowenstein, A., 191, *205*
Löwenstein, E., 369, 370, *389*
Löwy, S., 319, *352*
Luborsky, F., 69, 73, *80*
Lucasse, W. W., 13, 15, 16, *44*
Luchsinger, E. B., 373, *390*
Luchinskii, G. P., 254, *284*
Lugash, M. N., 201, *206*

Lupien, Y., 96, *114*
Lynch, M. A., 297, *299*

M

Maas, O., 95, 100, *115*
McAlonie, G. E., 360, *388*
McBeth, R. L., 360, 379, 386, 387, *389*
McBride, W. R., 31, *45*
McCaulay, D. A., 73, *80*, 198, *209*
MacClean, C., 198, *209*
Maccoll, A., 302, *349*
McConnell, H. M., 17, *44*
McCormick, R. H., 6, *42*, *43*
McDaniel, D. H., 86, 87, *115*
MacDonald, D. K. C., 13, *42*
McElroy, A. D., 11, *44*
McFarlane, W., 184, 185, *206*
MacInnes, D. A., 28, *44*
McIntosh, D., 83, 85, 88, 89, 90, 95, 96, 97, 100, *115*, 286, 287, *298*, *299*
McIntosh, R., 254, *284*
McKenzie, D. E., 328, 329, 330, 331, *349*
Mackor, E. L., 69, *80*, 198, *206*, *209*, 240, *250*
MacLean, C., 69, *80*
McNeer, R. L., 240, *251*
Madan, S. K., 217, *249*
Mahler, J. E., 198, *210*
Mairinger, F., 309, 310, 341, 342, 343, 344, *349*, *351*
Maki, A. G., 86, *115*
Makuc, J., 319, *352*
Marcinkowski, A. E., 244, *250*
Marcus, R. A., 173, *209*
Margrave, J. L., 52, *79*, 294, *298*
Markov, B. F., 365, 373, 374, 387, *388*
Markowitz, J. M., 253, 260, *283*
Marron, S. H., 162, *207*
Marsh, R. E., 295, *299*
Martens, R. D., 14, *44*
Martens, R. I., 7, *43*
Martin, D. R., 257, *282*, *284*
Masaguer, J. R., 346, 347, *349*, *351*
Masson, I., 178, 181, 182, *207*, *209*
Masters, B. J., 274, 276, 277, *284*
Mathers, F. C., 364, *389*
Maybury, R. H., 56, *80*
Mayer, S. W., 369, 370, 371, 372, *390*
Meek, D. W., 213, 214, 217, 223, 224, 226, 230, 232, 233, 236, *249*, *250*, 306, 344, *352*

Meinecke, E., 287, *298*
Meirboum, S., 191, *205*
Meise, W., 360, 383, *390*
Melinski, Z. A., 316, *350*
Mellor, J. W., 85, *115*, 176, 177, 180, *209*
Mellor's Comprehensive Treatise on Inorganic and Theoretical Chemistry (1956), 50, 54, 63, 69, *80*
Mesech, H., 257, 258, 259, 263, *283*, *284*
Metzl, S., 323, *352*
Metzner, R., 315, *352*
Meyer, A. W., 13, 14, *43*, *44*
Meyer, F., 60, *79*
Meyer, J., 179, *209*
Michaelis, A., 259, *284*
Middaugh, R. L., 222, 223, *250*
Mikhailowskaya, V. I., 288, *298*
Miles, F. D., 179, *209*
Millen, D. J., 155, 163, 172, 173, 174, 176, *207*, *208*, *209*
Miller, H. K., 319, *351*, 375, 376, *389*
Minc, S., 244, *250*
Mishra, H. C., 177, 178, 180, 182, *205*, *209*
Moede, J. A., 259, *284*
Moessen, G. W., 288, *298*
Monchick, L., 15, *42*
Monozson, A. M., 9, 29, *44*, *45*
Montignie, E., 316, *352*
Mooney, E. F., 338, *350*
Moore, B., 41, *42*
Morell, W. E., 60, *80*
Morris, A. G., 75, *79*
Morrison, G. C., 166, *206*
Motzfeldt, K., 362, *389*
Mountford, G. A., 154, *209*
Muetterties, E. L., 76, *80*, 294, 295, 296, *298*, 318, 319, *352*
Mulder, H. D., 30, *44*
Murray, F. E., 96, *115*
Murthy, A. R. V., 340, *352*
Muxart, R., 274, *284*
Muzzuchelli, A., 361, *389*

N

Nakata, S., 274, 275, *284*
Nakomoto, K., 187, *209*
Nayak, B., 191, *206*
Neilson, A. H., 55, *80*
Neumayr, S., 30, *45*
Newman, L., 216, *250*

Newman, M. S., 132, 167, 190, 193, 196, 199, 200, 203, *206*, *209*
Nicholls, D., 2, 34, *43*
Nichols, R., 296, 297, *298*
Nickerson, J. D., 254, *284*
Niedzielski, R. J., 222, 223, *250*
Nogradi, J., 271, 273, *284*
Norris, J. F., 203, *209*
Norris, T. H., 273, 274, 276, 277, 278, *282*, *283*, *284*
Nyholm, R. S., 235, *250*, 302, *349*
Nyman, C. J., 11, 27, *44*

O

O'Brien, R. J., 171, *206*
Oddo, G., 142, 190, 192, 193, 194, 196, 197, 199, 203, *209*, 334, *352*
O'Donnell, T. A., 53, 59, 64, 72, *79*
Ogg, R. A., 173, *209*
Ogg, R. A. Jr., 27, 31, *44*
Okawara, R., 171, *209*
Olah, G. A., 328, *352*
Oliver, G. D., 292, *298*
Onak, T. P., 218, *251*
O'Reilly, D. E., 14, 17, *43*
Orgel, L. E., 217, *251*, 302, *349*
Oubridge, J. V., 122, 125, 126, 127, 129, 132, 133, 137, 138, 139, 142, 162, 164, 165, 194, 205, *205*, *207*
Overstreet, R., 3, *44*
Owen, B. B., 7, *43*

P

Paddock, N., 174, *209*
Palm, V. A., 161, *209*
Panchenko, I. D., 387, *388*
Panish, M. B., 67, *80*, 292, 295, *299*
Pappas, P., 260, 261, *284*
Park, J. D., 322, 326, *351*
Parry, R. W., 318, *350*
Partington, J. R., 328, 329, *352*
Pascard, R., 123, *209*
Pastor, R. C., 17, *43*
Patel, J. K., 338, *350*
Paterno, E., 361, *389*
Patterson, A. Jr., 16, 18, *42*, *44*
Paul, M. A., 64, *80*, 157, *209*
Paul, R. C., 348, *352*
Pauling, L., 24, *44*, 62, *80*
Payne, D. S., 311, 315, *352*

Peach, M. E., 89, 90, 92, 93, 94, 96, 97, 98, 99, 100, 101, 102, 103, 104, 105, 106, 107, 109, 110, 111, 112, *115*, 338, *352*
Peacock, R. D., 257, *282*, 294, 295, 296, 297, *298*
Pearson, R. G., 39, *43*
Peck, R. E., 85, *114*
Pedersen, C., 77, *80*
Peeling, E. R. A., 122, 132, 135, 173, 174, *208*
Perkins, A. J., 53, *80*
Perkins, P. G., 340, *350*
Perrot, R., 329, *352*
Peterson, D., 367, *389*
Petruska, E. W., 168, *210*
Pettit, R., 198, *210*
Petzold, W., 312, *352*
Phillips, W. D., 76, *80*, 294, 295, 296, *298*, 318, 319, *352*
Pimentel, G. C., 218, *251*
Pincher, S., 274, 275, *284*
Pinevich, G., 4, *45*
Piper, T. S., 223, 232, *250*
Piskur, M. M., 13, *44*
Pitzer, K., 366, *389*
Pitzer, K. S., 17, 18, 19, *41*, *42*, *43*
Plane, R. A., 238, *250*
Plank, C. J., 4, *45*
Pleskov, V. A., 9, 24, 29, *43*, *44*, *45*
Plotnikov, W. A., 288, *298*
Plotnikow, W., 319, *351*
Pollak, V. L., 17, *45*
Poole, H. G., 155, 173, 176, *208*
Pople, J. A., 156, *210*
Popov, A. I., 244, *251*
Porter, G. B., 302, 323, *352*
Potter, N. D., 274, 277, 278, *284*
Powell, T. M., 286, *298*
Powles, J. G., 17, *42*
Pratt, L., 184, 185, *206*
Preugschat, F., 307, 333, *352*
Pribble, M. J., 37, *42*
Price, F. P., 167, 168, 169, *210*
Proskauer, E. S., 234, 236, 239, 241, 243, *251*
Pruett, R. D., 295, *299*
Purcell, K. F., 216, 228, 230, 231, 239, *249*
Pushin, N., 358, *389*
Pusin, N. A., 319, *352*

Q

Quarterman, L. A., 50, 51, 72, 76, 78, *79*, *80*, 86, 94, *115*, 292, *298*

R

Rabinowitsch, M., 286, *298*
Rafos, R. R., 201, *208*
Raman, K. N. V., 340, *352*
Ransom, L. D., 371, *390*
Rao, K. N., 260, 261, *284*
Rao, M. R. A., 343, *350*
Ray, J. D., 173, *209*
Reavill, R. E., 168, *210*
Rebora, P. L., 34, *45*
Reeves, L. W., 218, *251*
Reid, C., 198, *210*
Reilly, C. A., 157, *208*
Rettgers, J. W., 319, *352*
Rheinbolt, H., 329, *352*
Rhodes, D. C., 355, *388*
Rice, 167
Richards, N. E., 357, 362, *388*
Richardson, F. D., 367, *389*
Richey, H. G., 202, 203, *206*
Riddich, J. A., 234, 236, 239, 241, 243, *251*
Riehl, L., 258, *284*
Ritter, H. L., 355, *389*
Roberts, H. L., 340, *352*
Roberts, J. E., 297, *298*
Roberts, N. W., 34, *42*
Robinson, E. A., 88, *114*, 118, 122, 123, 125, 126, 127, 130, 131, 132, 133, 134, 137, 138, 139, 142, 143, 145, 146, 148, 150, 152, 153, 154, 159, 161, 162, 163, 164, 165, 166, 167, 168, 169, 170, 171, 172, 174, 177, 179, 180, 188, 196, 202, 205, *205, 207, 208, 210*
Robinson, P. L., 257, *282*, 294, 296, 297, *298*, 332, *351*
Rogers, M. T., 67, *80*, 292, 295, *299*
Rogers, P. S., 367, *389*
Roggenbuck, A., 34, *43*
Roper, G. C., 30, *42*
Rose, N. J., 226, *250*
Rosenbaum, J., 204, *210*
Rosenthal, M., 241, 242, *251*
Ross, V. F., 166, *206*
Rosse, R., 273, *284*
Rossini, F. D., 4, 8, *45*
Roth, W. A., 63, *80*
Rothschild, W. G., 55, *80*
Rowlands, C. B., 358, 359, 360, *387*
Royer, J. L., 178, *210*
Rubin, T. R., 162, *207*

Rudge, A. J., 292, *298*
Ruff, O., 13, *45*, 334, 343, *352*
Runner, M. E., 50, 53, 59, *80*, 85, *115*
Rupert, E. F., 95, *115*
Russell, H. Jr., 2, *45*
Rutherford, A., 128, *206*
Ruthven, G., 360
Rutledge, G. P., 76, *80*
Ryss, I. G., 294, *299*

S

Saires, G., 198, 201, 204, *206*
Sakakibara, S., 78, *80*
Sallach, R. A., 368, 371, *390*
Salstrom, E. J., 382, *389*
Salthouse, J. A., 87, 93, *115*
Sanderson, R. T., 25, *45*
Sandhu, S. S., 348, *352*
Sankuer, R. F., 16, *42*
Sargent, J., 65, *79*
Sastri, M. L. N., 58, 60, *80*
Satenstejn, A. I., 257, *284*
Savoie, R., 130, 131, 155, 162, 163, *207*
Scandola, E., 142, 190, 192, 194, 199, 203, *209*
Schaffer, J. H., 363, *390*
Schaap, W. B., 10, *45*
Schally, A. V., 78, *80*
Scharf, E., 292, *299*
Scheidt, R. C., 375, *388*
Schierholz, H., 34, *43*
Schilt, A. A., 185, *210*
Schleich, K., 276, *283*
Schlenk, W., 264, *284*
Schmeisser, M., 292, *299*
Schmidt, F. C., 6, 10, 15, 30, *44, 45*
Schmidt, W., 316, *351*
Schmulbach, C. D., 217, *251*
Schmutzler, R., 331, 332, *352*
Schneider, W., 78, *80*
Schneider, W. G., 96, *114, 115*, 156, *210*, 218, *250, 251*
Schöber, G., 348, *350, 351*
Schott, G., 166, *210*
Schultz, J. W., 166, *206*
Schumb, W. C., 297, *299*
Schwarz, H. A., 35, *42*
Schwarzmann, E., 327, *352*
Scmid, M., 180, *206*
Scott, N. D., 41, *45*
Scott, R. L., 21, *43*

Sears, P. G., 226, 227, 228, 230, 231, 232, 237, 240, 242, *249*, *250*, *251*
Secor, H. Y., 39, 40, *44*
Seel, F., 258, 271, 272, 273, *284*, 294, 297, *299*, 329, 330, 331, 332, *352*
Selbin, J., *251*
Selig, H., 294, *299*
Senior, J. B., 180, 182, *207*
Shamir, J., 294, *299*
Shapiro, I., 218, *251*
Sharp, D. W. A., 86, 87, *115*
Sharpe, A. G., 294, 295, *298*, *299*
Shatenshtein, A., 6, *42*
Shatenshtein, A. I., 4, 30, 31, 32, 33, *45*
Shedlovsky, T., 261, *283*
Sheldon, J. C., 213, *251*, 310, 342, *352*
Shier, G. D., 218, *251*
Shin, K. H., 78, *80*
Shirey, W. B., 316, *352*
Shoemaker, C. E., 10, 11, 28, *44*
Shoolery, J. N., 218, *251*
Si Chang Fung, 27, *44*
Siegel, S., 295, *299*
Sienko, M. J., 2, 5, 12, *44*, *45*
Silberrad, O., 257, *284*
Silverthorn, M. E., 294, *298*
Simons, J. H., 50, 53, 59, 62, 66, 68, *80*, *81*
Sinclair, J. R., 30, *42*
Singer, S. J., 78, *81*
Singh, J., 348, *352*
Sisler, H. H., 2, *45*
Skelly, N. E., 244, *251*
Sly, W. G., 295, *299*
Smith, D. F., 55, 59, 76, *80*, *81*, 295, *299*
Smith, G. E., 16, *42*
Smith, G. P., 327, *349*, 360, *390*
Smith, H., 2, 34, 36, 41, *42*
Smith, H. A., 197, 200, *210*
Smith, N. V., 362, *388*, *389*
Smith, W., 366, *388*
Smyth, C. P., 85, 102, *115*
Sodek, H., 234, 240, *251*
Sokolova, L. N., 259, *283*
Sokol'skii, G. A., 332, *352*
Solomons, C., 122, 126, 129, 139, 145, 146, 150, 162, 163, 188, *207*
Solomons, S., 125, 127, 132, 133, 137, 138, 139, 142, 162, 205, *205*, *207*
Somiya, T., 131, *210*
Sommer, L. H., 168, *210*
Sottysiak, J., 6, 15, *45*

Sowards, D. M., 31, *45*
Sowerby, D. B., 310, 329, 332, *351*
Spalthoff, W., 53, 54, 60, *79*, *81*
Spandau, H., 307, 333, *352*
Speirs, J. L., 67, *80*, 292, 295, *299*
Staffansson, L. I., 367, *390*
Stairs, R. A., 5, *45*
Stančie, B., 347, *351*
Stavenhagen, A., 176, *210*
Steele, B. D., 83, 85, 88, 89, 90, 96, 97, *115*
Steele, B. O., 264, *282*, *284*
Stephens, W. R., 255, 257, *282*
Stephenson, C. C., 254, *283*
Stern, K. H., 377, *390*
Stevens, J. B., 158, *210*
Stewart, R., 190, *210*
Stokes, R. H., 138, *210*
Stoodley, L. G., 323, 325, *349*
Straub, D. K., 217, *250*
Strohmeier, W., 60, *79*, *81*
Stromberg, A. G., 371, *389*
Stroup, P. T., 364, *389*
Studer, F. J., 15, *45*
Sudborough, J. J., 329, *352*
Sugarman, N., 17, 18, *43*
Sulzberg, J., 201, *208*
Sundheim, B. R., 361, *389*
Susz, B. P., 223, 236, 239, *250*, *251*
Sutton, L. E., 302, *349*
Svirmickas, A., 76, *79*
Swart, K. H., 322, 323, 326, *351*
Swenson, G. W., 38, *45*
Swinehart, J. H., 219, *251*
Symons, M. C. R., 2, 18, *42*, *45*, 177, 178, 180, 182, 183, 198, 201, 204, *205*, *206*, *208*, *209*, *210*, 289, *298*
Szmant, H. H., 169, *210*
Szöke, A., 29, *44*

T

Taft, R. W., 160, *206*
Tajkowski, E., 6, *45*
Talaat, M. Y. A., 342, 343, 346, *349*
Tanaka, S., 187, *209*
Taub, I. A., 38, *42*
Taube, H., 218, 219, *250*, *251*
Taylor, N. W., 287, *299*
Taylor, R. C., 95, *115*
Tealdi, M., 334, *352*
Temkin, M., 378, *390*

Teodorovich, V. P., 6, *43*
Thomas, W. G., 358, 359, 360, *387*
Thompson, A., 127, 129, 145, 166, *208, 210*
Thompson, H. B., 67, *80*, 292, 295, *299*
Thompson, R. C., 205, *205*
Thornley, M. B., 139, 157, 159, 188, *206*
Tobe, M. L., 187, *205*
Toft, R., 264, *283*
Tolgyesi, W. S., 328, *352*
Tolloczko, S., 301, 321, 324, *350, 352*
Tomlinson, J. W., 367, *389*
Toops, E. E. Jr., 234, 236, 239, 241, 243, *251*
Topol, L. E., 370, 371, *390*
Treffers, H. P., 135, 193, 196, *210*
Tremearne, T. H., 6, *45*
Tridot, G., 338, *351*
Troost, W. R., 311, *352*
Trotter, J., 171, *206*
Tsubomura, H., 239, 241, *251*
Tye, F. L., 100, *114*, 155, 179, 198, 200, *208*
Tyree, S. Y., 213, *251*, 310, 342, *352*

U

Ubbelohde, A. R., 355, 356, *389*
Ullman, D., 267, *283*
Ullstern, R. E. Jnr., 259, *284*

V

Valleé, R. E., 86, 87, *115*
Van Artsdalen, E. R., 356, 377, 382, 386, *388, 390*
van der Meij, P. H., 204, *206*
Van Der Voorn, P., 231
van der Worm, E. R., 212, *250*, 328, 340, *350*
Van der Waals, J. H., 69, *80*, 198, *209*
Van Heteren, W. J., 329, *352*
Vaniscotte, C., 6, *44*
van Wazer, J. R., 327, *352*
Vaughan, J. W., 228, *250*
Vegard, L., 5, *45*
Veis, A., 77, *81*
Verdier, P. H., 76, *79*
Verrigin Stuart, A. A., 198, *206*
Vidale, G. L., 95, *115*, 318, *350*
Vierk, A. L., 254, *284*
Viktorov, M. M., 257, *284*
Vining, D. C., 316, *350*

Voitovich, B. A., 219, *251*
Vonk, C. G., 293, *299*, 327, *352*
von Rosenberg, J. L., 198, *210*
Von Sundermeyer, W., 360, 383, 384, 385, *390*
Vos, A., 293, *298*

W

Waddington, T. C., 84, 85, 86, 87, 89, 90, 92, 93, 94, 95, 96, 97, 98, 99, 100, 101, 102, 103, 104, 105, 106, 107, 108, 109, 110, 111, 112, *115*, 181, *206*, 281, *284*, 328, 329, 338, *352*
Wade, K., 310, 340, *350*
Waentig, G., 287, *299*
Waentig, P., 96, *114*
Wait, S. C., 356, 379, *390*
Walden, P., 253, 255, 263, 273, *284*, 301, 312, 316, 319, 321, 333, *352*
Walker, J. F., 41, *45*
Walker, J. W., 100, *115*
Walrafen, G. E., 130, 131, 162, 163, *210*
Walton, P. R., 204, *209*
Warshawsky, I., 37, *45*
Wasem, K., 331, 332, *352*
Wasif, S., 139, 142, 146, 173, 189, 193, 196, 203, *207*
Wasserfuhr, R., 329, *352*
Watson, G. M., 362, 363, *388, 389, 390*
Watson, H. R., 41, *42*
Watt, G. W., 2, 31, 34, *45*
Wayland, B., 224, 232, 234, 243, 246, *249*
Webster, D. E., 171, *208, 209*
Webster, M., 244, *249*
Weickel, T., 264, *284*
Weinland, R. F., 170, *240*
Weinstein, J., 86, *114*
Weiss, J., 326, *351*
Weissman, S. I., 198, *210*
Welch, C. M., 197, 200, *210*
Welch, F. E., 257, 281, 282, *284*
Wendt, H., 268, *283*
Wenz, D. A., 226, *250*
Werblan, L., 244, *250*
Wertyporoch, E., 341, *352*
West, R., 86, *115*
West, T. S., 341, 343, 345, 346, *349*
Westrum, E. F. Jr., 87, *114*
Weyl, W., 10, *45*
Weissberger, A., 234, 236, 239, 241, 243, *251*

Wharmby, D. H. W., 289, 297, 298
Wheat, J. A., 95, 115, 287, 288, 299
Wheeler, H. L., 312, 352
Whipple, E. B., 76, 79
White, D., 53, 54, 79, 286, 298
White, J. A., 84, 85, 87, 89, 90, 96, 98, 99, 106, 107, 108, 109, 112, 115
White, J. D., 259, 284
White, R. F. M., 128, 156, 157, 207
Whitford, E. L., 197, 210
Whitmore, F. C., 168, 210
Whynes, A. L., 328, 329, 352
Wicke, Von E., 136, 210
Wickert, K., 256, 259, 265, 266, 267, 269, 280, 283, 284
Wiebe, R., 6, 45
Wiebenga, E. H., 292, 293, 298, 299, 327, 352
Wiesendanger, H. U. D., 28, 45
Williams, D. F., 357, 360, 388
Willis, H. A., 338, 350
Winbush, S. V., 369, 370, 371, 372, 373, 388
Winsor, V. R., 364, 390
Wood, R. E., 355, 389
Woodward, R. A., 340, 352
Woolf, A. A., 294, 295, 299, 317, 318, 352
Worrall, I. J., 310, 350
Wiig, E. O., 197, 210
Wiles, L. A., 190, 197, 210
Wilhoit, E. D., 230, 231, 232, 237, 249, 251
Wilkinson, G., 41, 42, 184, 185, 206
Williams, G., 189, 210
Williams, J. F. A., 201, 210
Williams, R. E., 218, 250, 251

Willis, J. E., 217, 249
Wilmarth, W. K., 33, 45
Winterstein, A., 204, 208
Wise, S. S., 52, 79
Wisotsky, M. J., 202, 203, 206
Woldbye, F., 216, 251
Wolsky, S. P., 15, 45
Wyatt, P. A. H., 122, 125, 130, 131, 134, 139, 147, 154, 161, 162, 191, 206, 208, 209, 210

Y

Yates, K., 158, 190, 210
Yeh, S. J., 102, 115
Yoon, Y. K., 95, 115
Yosim, S. J., 369, 370, 371, 372, 373, 390
Yost, D. M., 2, 45
Young, J., 374, 383, 389
Young, T. F., 157, 163, 210

Z

Zackrisson, M., 312, 349
Zadra, 386, 390
Zarzycki, G., 355, 390
Zdanuk, E. J., 15, 45
Zebrowska, A., 321, 323, 351
Zelezny, W. F., 291, 299
Zengin, N., 58, 79
Zhurin, A. I., 367, 390
Zintl, E., 30, 31, 45
Zuur, A. P., 339, 350
Zwicker, E. F., 38, 45

Subject Index

(Numbers in bold type indicate the page on which a subject is treated most fully.)

A

Acetone, **237**, 247
Acetonitrile, **243**, 247
Acid–base reactions
  in hydrogen fluoride, 62, 75
  in liquid ammonia, 28
  in sulphuric acid, 152
  halides and oxyhalides, 331
Acidity
  ammonia, liquid, 23
  halide–oxyhalide solvents, 305
  hydrogen fluoride, 62
  hydrogen fluoride, liquid, solutes in, 72
  hydrogen halides, solutions in, 97
  iodine monohalides, 289
  sulphuric acid and its solutions, 121, 124, 157
  nitrosonium salts, 331
Alkaline-earth halides, 354, 367
Aluminium halides, 339
Amines, solutions of metals in, 41
Ammonia, liquid, physical properties of, 1
  crystal structure, 5
  density, 4
  dielectric constant, **5**, 19
  derived constants, 5
  electrical conductivity, 5
  heat capacity, 3
  heat of fusion, 3
  heat of vapourization, **3**, 25
  refractive index, 5
  surface tension, 5
  thermodynamic functions for gas at 25°, 4
  vapour pressure, 2, 3
  viscosity, **4**, 25
Ammonia, liquid, physical properties of solutions, 6
  electrolytes, 6
  metals, 10, 34
  non-electrolytes, 6
Ammonia, liquid, reactions in
  acid–base reactions, 28
  comparison with other solvents, 19
  ionic solvation, 26
  oxidation potential range, 22
  reactions of metal solutions, 34
Antimony
  bromide, 326
  chloride, 311, **321**
Arsenic
  bromide, 319
  chloride, **311**, 348
  fluoride, 317

B

Barium nitrate, 7
Basicity
  alkali metal iodides, 289
  ammonia, 20, 23
  halide–oxyhalide solvents, 305
  metal hydrogen sulphates, 118
  nitrosonium chlorides, 331
  solutions in hydrogen fluoride, 68, 69
  solutions in hydrogen halides, 97, 99–104
  solutions in sulphuric acid, 119, 174, 187–196
  sulphuric acid, 124
Bismuth chloride, 327
Bromine, 287
  pentafluoride, 295
  trifluoride, 292, 294

C

Caesium fluoride, 364, 365
Carbohydrates, 76
Cellulose, 77
Chlorine, 287
  pentafluoride, 295
  trifluoride, 292, 293
Co-ordinating solvents, 211
Co-ordinating solvents, criteria for establishing, 215
  conductivity, 219
  cryoscopy, 219
  infra-red spectroscopy, 216

Co-ordinating solvents (*contd.*)—
nuclear-magnetic resonance, 217
ultra-violet and visible spectroscopy, 215
Co-ordinating solvents, energetics, 200
Co-ordinating solvents, solute behaviour, 226
acetone, **237**, 247
acetonitrile, **243**, 247
dimethylsulphoxide, **230**, 248
methanol and ethanol, **239**, 248
nitromethane and nitrobenzene, **234**, 247
NN-dimethylacetamide (DMA), **228**, 247, 248
N-methylacetamide (NMA), **230**, 247
pyridine, **241**, 248
tetramethylene sulphone, **245**, 247

D

NN-Dimethylacetamide (DMA), **228**, 247, 248
Dimethylsulphoxide, **230**, 248

E

Electrochemistry
ammonia, liquid, 5, 9, 15
co-ordinating solvents, 220
halides and oxyhalides, 302, 321, 322, 327, 348
halogens and interhalogens, 285, 296
higher hydrogen halides, 88, 100 *et seq.*
hydrogen fluoride, liquid, 49, 66–73
molten salts, 353 *et seq.*
sulphur dioxide, liquid, 253, 264
sulphuric acid, 128, 135, 142, 179
Enzymes, 77
Ethanol, 239
Ethanol–sodium reaction, 39

F

Fluorides, 47, 65, 290, 292, 295, 296, 297, 317, 364
Fluorine, liquid, 286

H

Halides
alkaline-earth, 354, 367
ammonium, 7

hydrogen, 7, 83
metal, **7**, **354**, 364, 369, 373
molten salts, 354
of Group V elements, 301
potassium, 10
silver, 20
Halides and oxyhalides of Group V Elements, 301
acidity and basicity, 305, 311
alkaline-earth halides, 354, 367
aluminium halides, 339
experimental methods, 306
halides, **311**, 348
oxyhalides, **327**, 348
phosphoryl chloride, 306, 328, **332**, 348
solutes, 312–332, 334–348
conductivity measurements, 307
cryoscopic measurements, 310
ebullioscopic measurements, 310
examination of solid phases, 307
isotopic exchange reaction, 310
physical properties, 303, 304
potentiometric measurements, 308
products of electron transfer, 307
qualitative solubility considerations, 306
spectrophotometric measurements, 309
thermodynamic measurements, 310
titrations using indicators, 309
transport number measurements, **308**
viscosity measurements, 810
Halogens, 286, *see also* Interhalogens
bromine, 287
chlorine, 287
fluorine, liquid, 286
iodine, 288
physical properties, 286
reactions of, 286
solutes, 287–289
Henry's Law, 6
Hydrogen chloride, liquid, 83, *see also* Hydrogen halides
Hydrogen fluoride, liquid, 47
equipment for studying, 47
physical properties of, 52
solutes in, 64
solutions of compounds of biological importance, 76
Hydrogen fluoride, liquid, properties of
acidity, 62
physical properties, 52
polymerization, 59
self-ionization, 57

Hydrogen fluoride (*contd.*)—
structure of the liquid, 57
vibronic absorption spectra, 55
Hydrogen fluoride, liquid, solutes in
acid solutes : fluoride ion acceptors, 72
compounds of biological importance, 76
metal fluorides, 65
non-metallic, non-acidic, ionizing fluorides, 67
proton acceptors, 68
salts in the system as solutes, 74
solution without ionization, 75
Hydrogen halides, higher, as ionizing
solvents, 83
experimental methods, 88
physical properties, 84
self-ionization, 86
solutions, 97
Hydrogen halides, higher, solutions in
acids and bases, 97
protonation of Groups IV and V
elements, 99
protonation of π-bond systems, 100
protonation of doubly-bonded oxygen,
102
Redox rections, 112
solvolysis reactions, 111
Hydrogen sulphates, 118, 122

I

Insulin, 77
Interhalogens 290, *see also* Halogens
compounds of formula AB, 290
compounds of formula AB_3, 292
compounds of formula AB_5, 295
compounds of formula AB_7, 297
solutes, 290, 294, 296
Iodine, 288
bromide, 290
heptafluoride, 297
in molten salt, 361
monochloride, 290
monohalides, 289
pentafluoride, 295
trichloride, 292
trifluoride, 292
Isotopic exchange reactions, 273, 310, 332

K

Kinetics, 27, 279, 382

L

London forces, 21

M

Metal co-ordination compounds, 79
Metal fluorides, 65
Metal production in molten salt solvents,
386
Methanol, **239**, 248, 360
N-Methylacetamide (NMA), **230**, 247
Molten salts
applications as solvents, 383
nature of, 354
solutions of gases in, 361
solutions of metals in, 364
solutions of non-metallic elements in,
361
solutions of salt and organic compounds,
358
solutions of salt and water, 357
solutions of salt in molten salt, 374

N

Nitrobenzene, **234**, 247
Nitromethane, **234**, 247
Nitrosyl chloride, 327
Nitrosyl fluoride, 332

O

Oxidation potential range in ammonia, 22
Oxidation–reduction reactions in liquid
hydrogen chloride, 112
Oxidation–reduction reactions in liquid
sulphur dioxide, 271

P

Peptides, 78
Phenylphosphoryl chloride, 348
Phosphoryl chloride, 306, 328, **332**, 348
Physical properties
acetone, 237
acetonitrile, 243
ammonia, liquid, 2
ammonia, liquid, solutions in, 6
dimethyl sulphoxide, 230
halides and oxyhalides of Group V
elements, 303, 304
halogens, 286

Physical properties (*contd.*)—
hydrogen fluoride, liquid, 52
hydrogen halides, higher, 84
interhalogens, 292, 296
iodine bromide, 290
iodine monochloride, 290
methanol and ethanol, 239
N-methylacetamide, 230
NN-dimethylacetamide, 226
nitromethane and nitrobenzene, 234
pyridine, 241
sulphur dioxide, liquid, 254
sulphuric acid, 123
sulphuric acid solutions, 131
tetramethylene sulphone, 245
Proteins, 76, 322
Pyridine, **241**, 248
Pyridine hydrochloride, 360
Pyridinium chloride, 360

R

Redox reactions, 112

S

Salt solutions, 354, *see also* Molten salts
chemical interaction, 358
gases, 361
metals, 364
non-metallic elements, 361
organic compounds, 358
salt in molten salt, 374
water, 357
Salts in a system as solutes, 74
Salts, molten, *see* Molten salts
Sodium–ethanol reaction, 39
Solvent systems
ammonia, liquid, 1
co-ordinating solvents, 211
halides and oxyhalides of group V
elements, 301
higher hydrogen halides, 83
halogens and interhalogens, 285
hydrogen fluoride, 47
molten salts, 353
sulphur dioxide, liquid, 253
sulphuric acid, 117
Solvent Systems Concept, 212
Sugars, 77
Sulphur dioxide, liquid
electrical conductivity and ionization in, 253

electrochemical studies, 264
isotopic exchange reactions, 273
physical properties, of, 254
solubilities, 254
solvate formation, 256
Sulphur dioxide, liquid, chemical reactions in, 266
amphoteric reactions, 268
complex formation, 272
metathetical reactions, 267
oxidation–reduction reactions, 271
solvolysis, 266
Sulphuric acid, 117
Sulphuric acid, inorganic solutes, 162
arsenic, antimony and bismuth, 174
boron, 164
chelation by the sulphate group, 186
halogens, 180
H_2O and SO_3, 162
nitrogen and phosphorus, 172
silicon, 167
sulphur, selenium and tellurium, 179
tin and lead, 170
transition metal complexes, 184
vanadium, 177
Sulphuric acid, organic solutes, 187
amides and ureas, 190
carbonium ions, 198
carboxylic acids, 196
carboxylic anhydrides, 193
esters, 192
ethers, 194
nitriles, 195
polybasic compounds, 188
simple bases, 187
Sulphuric acid, physical properties of, **123**, 131
Sulphuric acid, self-dissociation, **124**, 132

T

Tetramethylene sulphone, **245**, 247
Thermochemistry, 3, 6, 8, 15, 26, 52, 69, 87, 130, 154, 310
Triazole, 360

V

Van der Waals forces, 21